Natural Resources

UNIVERSITY OF CALIFORNIA
ENGINEERING EXTENSION SERIES

Beckenbach · Modern Mathematics for the Engineer

Huberty and Flock · Natural Resources

Puckett and Ramo · Guided Missile Engineering

Ridenour · Modern Physics for the Engineer

Robertson · Modern Chemistry for the Engineer and Scientist

Sines and Waisman · Metal Fatigue

Varden Fuller

Martin R. Huberty

Everett D. Howe

Milner B. Schaefer

Roger Revelle

Morris Neiburger

Albert F. Bush

Robert M. Glendinning

Richard F. Logan

Hans Jenny

Arthur F. Pillsbury

F. W. Went

Walter P. Taylor

John A. Zivnuska

Maynard A. Joslyn

Harold S. Olcott

Donald Carlisle

Louis B. Slichter

Charles A. Scarlott

Frederick A. Brooks

Chauncey Starr

S. V. Ciriacy-Wantrup

Joseph L. Fisher

Glacier Peak from Image Lake,
Glacier Peak Wilderness, Washington.
(*Photograph by Philip Hyde.*)

Natural Resources

Edited by

Martin R. Huberty

PROFESSOR OF
IRRIGATION AND ENGINEERING
DIRECTOR
WATER RESOURCES CENTER
UNIVERSITY OF CALIFORNIA
LOS ANGELES

and

Warren L. Flock

ASSOCIATE ENGINEER
AND LECTURER
UNIVERSITY OF CALIFORNIA
LOS ANGELES

1959

McGraw-Hill Book Company, Inc.

NEW YORK   TORONTO   LONDON

THE MAPLE PRESS COMPANY, YORK, PA.

The Authors

Varden Fuller, Professor of Agricultural Economics, University of California, Berkeley

Martin R. Huberty, Professor of Irrigation and Engineering, University of California, Los Angeles

Everett D. Howe, Professor of Mechanical Engineering, University of California, Berkeley

Milner B. Schaefer, Director of Investigations, Inter-American Tropical Tuna Commission, Scripps Institution of Oceanography, University of California, La Jolla

Roger Revelle, Director, Scripps Institution of Oceanography, University of California, La Jolla

Morris Neiburger, Professor of Meteorology, University of California, Los Angeles

Albert F. Bush, Associate Professor of Engineering, University of California, Los Angeles

Robert M. Glendinning, Professor of Geography, University of California, Los Angeles

Richard F. Logan, Associate Professor of Geography, University of California, Los Angeles

Hans Jenny, Professor of Soil Chemistry and Morphology, University of California, Berkeley

Arthur F. Pillsbury, Professor of Irrigation and Engineering, University of California, Los Angeles

vii

F. W. Went, Director, Missouri Botanical Garden

Walter P. Taylor, Senior Biologist, Fish and Wildlife Service, U.S. Department of the Interior (Retired); Visiting Lecturer, Claremont Graduate School

John A. Zivnuska, Associate Professor of Forestry, University of California, Berkeley

Maynard A. Joslyn, Professor of Food Technology, University of California, Berkeley

Harold S. Olcott, Professor of Marine Food Technology, University of California, Berkeley

Donald Carlisle, Associate Professor of Geology, University of California, Los Angeles

Louis B. Slichter, Director, Institute of Geophysics, University of California, Los Angeles

Charles A. Scarlott, Manager, Technical Information Services, Stanford Research Institute

Frederick A. Brooks, Professor of Agricultural Engineering, University of California, Davis

Chauncey Starr, Vice President, North American Aviation, Inc.; General Manager, Atomics International Division

S. V. Ciriacy-Wantrup, Professor of Agricultural Economics, University of California, Berkeley

Joseph L. Fisher, Associate Director, Resources for the Future, Inc.

Foreword

Engineering achievement within a country is dependent to a large extent on the available resources of that country. As new resources are discovered and known resources are developed, a parallel refinement in technology may be observed.

Engineers and scientists must be continually aware of both natural and man-made resources, recognizing the impact on their community, state, and nation, as well as on their own specific areas of technical interest.

With this need in mind the departments of engineering at the University of California arranged a series of lectures in natural resources for the staffs, students, and graduates in industry in order to familiarize them with recent developments and thought in the subject. These invitational lectures were presented by distinguished scientists, prominent in their fields, from the University of California, other universities, and governmental organizations. The series was offered under the sponsorship of University Extension.

We are pleased to share the stimulating experience of the natural-resources lecture series with you, the reader, through the pages of this book.

PAUL H. SHEATS
Professor of Education
Director, University Extension
University of California
Los Angeles

L. M. K. BOELTER
Professor of Engineering
Dean, College of Engineering
University of California
Los Angeles

MORROUGH P. O'BRIEN
Professor of Engineering
Dean, College of Engineering
University of California
Berkeley

Preface

Natural Resources is an outgrowth of a lecture series given on the campus of the University of California, Los Angeles, by Engineering Extension in the fall of 1955. Chapters in this volume correspond to lectures in the series, although changes have taken place in the roster of persons making contributions.

The chapters are written by authorities in the field. All the major natural resources are considered. Yet in a subject as vast as natural resources, it cannot be claimed that all interesting or important aspects have been covered. A prominent feature is the consideration of technological developments and problems, including obtaining fresh water from saline sources, air pollution, geophysical exploration, solar energy, and nuclear energy.

The book is intended for the general public and for students in all fields as well as for those engaged in business or resource management, engineers, scientists, and educators.

Uses and potential uses for natural resources are increasing because of population growth, higher per-capita consumption, and the efforts of underdeveloped regions to achieve industrialization and higher standards of living. In addition, the present race for world military and scientific leadership applies extra demands upon resources. The potential needs are in many cases large with respect to known supplies. In view of the growing demands, the attitudes developed toward natural resources take on vital significance. The supplies and demands and the attitudes of men are discussed in the various chapters of this volume.

Much of the text is devoted to resources generally necessary for man's existence—water, air, soil, food, forests, minerals, and energy sources. Several chapters are given, however, to basic concepts and considerations. Chapters 1 and 20 deal with population, natural-resource consumption, attitudes toward natural resources, and natural-resource research themes. Chapter 19 treats of economics and policies of resource management. Chapter 10 describes the process of photosynthesis, while particular attention is given to wilderness in Chapter 11. Recreational resources, and recreational aspects of resources, are discussed in several chapters. Human resources are considered, but a comprehensive treatment of this subject is beyond the scope of this volume.

Some other investigations of resources have been largely restricted to the question of meeting man's requirements for survival. Surely, however, quality of life is important, and those resources, and aspects of resources, which contribute to quality may be as important as those which merely make life in the modern world possible. As used here the term *quality of life* does not refer to being supplied in an ever-increasing degree of lavishness with entertainment, gadgets, or necessities, such as food, clothing, housing, and transportation. The term quality is used instead to indicate such things as desirable human relationships, freedom, knowledge, the arts, and with particular reference to natural resources, attractive, healthful, and inspiring surroundings. In this respect increasingly large numbers of people feel the need for maintaining sufficiently large and varied areas of natural beauty for inspiration and recreation. Such factors are given consideration in this treatment.

Energy is a key factor in resource considerations because of its wide and varied uses. Therefore energy is given a prominent role in this volume. Solutions of the world's material and food problems would be greatly facilitated by new, large sources of low-cost energy. Thus successful development of nuclear-fusion potentialities, for example, would be of great importance. It must be remembered, however, that the cost of energy is the crucial factor. The energy problem is not only one of technical availability but to a large extent one of economics. Furthermore, even with vast new sources of low-priced energy, all natural-resource problems would not be automatically solved. Space itself would be a prime consideration and might well be in short supply. Disposal of wastes may be a serious problem. Scenic and recreational areas are at present under strongly increasing pressures and may be entirely inadequate in the future unless vigorous measures are taken for their protection. Indeed there appears to be reason for being even more concerned about certain resources and aspects of resources which are primarily important to quality of life than for being concerned about the supply of energy, food, water, metals, or other materials. Some industries, as well as individuals, located in metropolitan areas have already come to realize that while they may not be immediately concerned about energy or material shortages they are very much beset by such factors as air pollution, congestion, lack of space for parking, air fields, and testing facilities, lack of pleasant surroundings, and lack of ready access to scenic and wild areas.

A confusing factor with relation to natural resources has been the apparent disparity between expressions of concern about resources and predictions of extremely high levels of prosperity with short-work weeks and remarkable technological developments including wide applications of automation. Ordway* has discussed these matters and pointed out that the prosperity of the present and the immediate future provides time to obtain the solutions to resource problems. It might be added that the present world political and military situation is hardly conducive to thoughts of a leisurely, luxurious future. In addition, Ordway has raised questions concerning the desirability, for the present, of the devotion to growth which has in the past characterized much of the thinking of the nation. The latter topic is also discussed by Professor Fuller in this volume's initial chapter, which presents some of the most crucial considerations regarding natural resources, including the necessity for the assumption of responsibility by individuals.

No effort has been made to eliminate the inevitable differences in attitude and emphasis which can be detected among the contributors. It has been the intention in all cases, however, to present discussions which look forward to solutions to natural-resource problems.

The lecture series, on which this volume is based, and the preparation of the volume have been due to the direction and inspiration of Dean L. M. K. Boelter of the College of Engineering of the University of California, Los Angeles. The organization and presentation of the lecture series were coordinated by W. L. Flock, with the cooperation and advice of M. R. Huberty, the late S. T. Yuster, and the Engineering Extension staff, particularly J. C. Dillon, Head, R. R. O'Neill, and Mrs. Bernice Park. The editors wish to express their appreciation to the above persons for their part in the program and to the lecturers in the series, the authors of the chapters, and colleagues who have made helpful suggestions. They are also grateful to Mrs. Derfla Guthrie and Mrs. Marjorie Keller for secretarial assistance in the preparation of the manuscript.

Martin R. Huberty
Warren L. Flock

---

* Ordway, Samuel, *Prosperity Beyond Tomorrow*, The Ronald Press Company, New York, 1955.

Contents

Prologue

L. M. K. BOELTER

Natural resources are the bulwark of the nation. The range of resources and the quantities and location of resources at its disposal are measures of the nation's potential.

Engineering has been defined as "transforming the resources of nature for the benefit of mankind." Thus knowledge of the status and condition of resources is essential to the practice of engineering. The professional engineer should be familiar with the availability and consumption of resources, their cost, and the state of the art of beneficiation and transportation.

The utilization of resources is of earnest significance to every citizen as well as to the engineer. Every effort should be made to harbor our resources and at the same time to use them to yield significant positive influence on the economy. Great emphasis should be placed on the development of the use of renewable resources.

A new concept has been introduced in the measurement of the quantities of natural resources. Putnam (Palmer Putnam, *Energy in the Future*, Van Nostrand, 1953) has replaced the concept of use to extinction with use to a multiple of present cost. On the basis of such a concept, a second look at estimates of resources is here recommended.

Man has introduced synthetic materials, such as plastics, and has made available intermediate resources, such as transportation. Practically all these man-supplied resources rest on the bedrock of nonrenewable resources, such as the fossil fuels, and renewable resources, such as water. The designer utilizes either the original natural resources or a transformed state of those resources. A sound knowledge of natural resources has thus become of even greater importance.

Greater costs to the economy have been caused by human habits. Peoples from water-plentiful regions, for example, bring their water-profligate habits with them when they migrate to the desert. Another look at the resource picture, however, would suggest that strenuous efforts be made to accommodate to the new conditions.

xvii

The economy of the United States depends on bringing certain resources and products to groups of people in given locations and taking certain resources and products from these sites to other locations. The successful optimization of this complex transport problem will yield a rational and successful economic structure.

The greatest resource of all, man, is considered in this volume in a context which will allow conclusions on the shift of emphasis from man as a source of energy to perform tasks to man as a thinker, a planner, and a source of control. It is hoped that the volume will prove stimulating to the reader and that it will generate thought and action.

1

Natural and Human Resources

VARDEN FULLER

PROFESSOR OF AGRICULTURAL ECONOMICS
UNIVERSITY OF CALIFORNIA, BERKELEY

1.1 Perspective

Civilized man is simultaneously a consumer of resources, a producer of resources, a manager of the yield and stock of resources, and himself a productive resource. He is both creator and creature of his culture. Over the centuries, thoughtful men have striven to discover a "law" or a general principle that would explain the complexly multisided relation between man and his physical universe. To make such inquiries at all manageable, it is convenient if not actually necessary to approach the inquiry from one or the other of two alternative perspectives: assume that man is the producer, the active agent, the determiner; or assume that man is the product, the creature, the determined. From the latter perspective, the search becomes that of a natural law or a biotic or ecological principle that explains man's numbers and his welfare condition. From the perspective that man is the producer and, hence, the determiner of his numbers and his state of welfare, the search becomes that of a concept of an optimum population and the identification of the forces and influences that could be expected to produce it.

In spite of their great efforts, neither the searchers for a natural law nor those seeking a concept of a controllable optimum have succeeded. The ingenuity of man's intellect defies his being analyzed as the counterpart of the lower-life biotic forms. Yet, on the other hand, man's ingenuity has not sufficiently developed to give him more than a partial, and at that possibly only temporary, dominance over the forces and endowments of his physical world. So long as the fabric of civilized life is woven of some strands that man determines and of others that are determined for him, it would appear unlikely that the search for an all-inclusive explanation of population-resource relations is soon to be rewarded.

1

For the purpose of this chapter, it is assumed that the foremost concern is whether man is overusing the endowments of his habitable world. "Overuse" in the sense here employed implies nothing more than that the current and prospective rate of population growth combined with the current and prospective rate of improvement in the standard of living may not be sustainable. If all societies of the world understood and were able to accommodate to the prospect that, at some stage, either the numbers of people or the standard of living might have to be reduced, then rapid current use would not be *overuse* in the sense indicated above. But if human beings individually and collectively do not have the capacity to accommodate themselves realistically to such a prospect or persist in assuming that its burdens can be passed to some other part of the world, then any current rate of population growth or rate of improvement in the standard of living that is not sustainable involves an overuse of resources.

If the relation of man to his resources were a direct biotic one, it would seem possible to detect present or approaching overuse of resources. However, for modern-day man, such a detection is difficult or impossible because of the intricacies of the political, economic, and technological systems through which he approaches resource utilization. Rapid depletion of a national stock of mineral or petroleum may not actually be overuse if there is assurance of international trade; but reversion from international trade to a system of closed national economies may change the situation completely and clearly reveal an unwise overuse. Similarly, unrewarded confidence in the prospect of technological advance may ultimately reveal that rapid depletion of nonrenewable stocks was actually an irrational overuse.

The complexity of the economic-political-technological systems through which modern man approaches resource use involves a number of paradoxes. In undeveloped countries where a low rate of resource exploitation usually prevails, economic development (and accelerated resource use) may be obstructed by actual or latent high rates of population growth which prevent the accumulation of capital. Conversely, in the advanced industrial economies, maintenance of high rates of growth (and of resource use) may depend heavily upon high rates of population growth. Thus, to facilitate the initiation of economic development, the undeveloped country needs to restrain population growth; to guarantee its further development, the already developed country may need to encourage population growth.

Unadvanced countries are more than ever committed to improvement and economic development. Advanced countries are committed to a philosophy of progress, prosperity, and full employment. Can the goals of all countries be simultaneously attained? Whether they can depends first of all on the extent to which free world trade as against economic nationalism prevails. Intermediately, there is the question of whether the rates of population growth will be appropriate to each type of situation; and, ultimately, there is the question of the sufficiency of the world's stock of nonrenewable resources and of man's technological ability to manipulate their use. In the past, the totality of the world's resources has probably never been more than a very remote question. But today it is much more immediate. The maintenance of progress and prosperity in industrially advanced countries requires a prodigious and accelerating consumption of resources and raw materials, including such critical ones as metals and fuels. As the less-developed countries become more advanced, they similarly will have mounting resource and raw-material needs. Given the prospects that now exist in the world, the likelihood of critical situations in the world's stock of resources is hardly debatable; the only real uncertainty is the timetable.

Modern studies in the field of population-resource relations commenced in controversy and with a name—Malthus—that has popularly become a synonym of pessimism and dismay. In this tradition, and unfortunately, discussions of population-resource relations are likely to be exercises in controversy in which the participants usually feel obligated to declare themselves as to whether they are pessimists or optimists, Malthusians or anti-Malthusians. In a similar way, the bulk of the current publications in this field tend toward extremes of position and toward shrill argumentation. Implicitly if not explicitly, writers are impelled to prove something, and most often it is whether Malthus was right or wrong.

The propensities to preconception and to the taking of positions are unquestionably obstructive to clear thinking and to orderly development of knowledge. One often hears reference to the race between population and food supply. If, by more thorough mastery and exploitation of his universe, man is able to subsist ever larger populations, is he then triumphant? Surely the substance of civilization is more profound and fundamental. If man is in any sort of race with the endowments of his physical world, attaining the maximum population that can survive seems hardly a goal worth trying to win. And even if the goal is optimum level of living rather than maximum numbers, the conception of a race is still inappropriate for it is doubtful if the optimum quality of life is to be attained by the maximum consumption of physical goods. Surely the societies of advancing economies will reach a point where woods and streams will be preferred to more superhighways, and where additional leisure time will contribute more than the latest model household appliances or ever more powerful automobiles.

Notwithstanding whatever there may be of argumentation for the sake of the argument and of shrillness for the sake of egocentric satisfaction, it is true that there is much serious concern about population-resource questions and ample reason for even greater concern. The world's population is presently growing at a rate that, if maintained, will approximately double the total by the end of the century. With a present population of some 2.6 billion, the world already has more tormenting problems of poverty than it is capable of solving; and if the world's population were to double, is it realistically possible to expect other than aggravation and intensification of poverty and hardship?

The person who seeks an answer to this question or any counterpart of it will find he can take his choice of opinions—yes or no. Among many other possibilities—all published since World War II—one may pursue a course of pessimism with such titles as *Our Plundered Planet*,[1] *Standing Room Only*,[2] *Prophesy of Famine*.[3] Or he may elect an optimistic course with such titles as *Let There Be Bread*,[4] *Food Enough for All*,[5] *The Road to Abundance*.[6] Where the first category would exhort on behalf of change from present trends in population growth or in resource consumption or in both, the second category of books offers a soothing justification of these trends or at least undertakes to offer reassurance against concern about them.

In a parallel way, both the assurances and the exhortations are deficient. They both fail to be realistic by taking into account the organizational structures and institutions upon which civilized man relies to achieve most of the management that exists in population-resource relations. Those who would soothe and allay concern add up the many and various potentialities for expanding output, with emphasis on food. Their inventories of potentialities include the land in the tropical jungles, the arctic, the arid deserts that conceivably could be drained, cleared, irrigated, or otherwise prepared for cultivation; the minerals, chemicals, desalinated water, and managed fisheries of the seas; the pests and diseases of plants and animals to be eradicated; the genetic possibilities of improving plants and animals; and so on through a long list around which a great halo of faith in science and technology is drawn.

There may be considerable truth in these optimistic assessments. Nevertheless, in realism, and irrespective of however glowing the possi-

---

[1] Fairfield Osborn, *Our Plundered Planet*, Little, Brown & Company, Boston, 1948.

[2] Karl Sax, *Standing Room Only*, The Beacon Press, Boston, 1955.

[3] Harold John Massingham and Edward Hyams, *Prophesy of Famine*, Thames and Hudson, London, 1953.

[4] Robert Edward Brittain, *Let There Be Bread*, Simon and Schuster, Inc., New York, 1952.

[5] Constantin Paul Lent, *Food Enough for All*, Pen-Ink Publishing Co., New York, 1947.

[6] Jacob Rosin and Max Eastman, *The Road to Abundance*, McGraw-Hill Book Company, Inc., New York, 1953.

bilities may be, they need to be assessed in terms of some persistent facts:

1. The world is not a single political and economic entity in which resource supplies and needs may be advantageously matched; rather, it is a collection of national states having competitive objectives and conflicts of interest.

2. Within the national entities, forms of government and economic systems are the major determining factors in whether and to what extent the potentialities are realized. There is little of the Robinson Crusoe in any modern economy, regardless of how undeveloped. Large-scale and complex organizations are required for the initiation of most of the important developments left to be undertaken; capital has to be accumulated from within or provided from without; internal conflicts of interest must be resolved; and methods of decision making and modes of communication between governments and electors have to be perfected.

3. Past accomplishments of the majority of individual nations and of the world at large offer little evidence to justify assuming the future perfectability of man.

Hence, even if the optimists' accounting of resource and production potentials were conceded to be unchallengeable on technical grounds, it is highly vulnerable on political and organizational grounds.

Nor are the exhortative appeals of the pessimists free of unrealism. Some would apparently expect that individuals upon learning the "facts" will respond appropriately; others would rely upon invoking the power of the state to restrain either the rate of population growth or the rate of resource use or both. In actuality, the power of the state to control population growth—essentially the power to control conceptions and births—is surely extremely limited. Likewise, in respect to controlling the rate of resource use, the state may have certain powers of acceleration, but the power of positive restraint is apparently very limited.

The foregoing comments should not be taken as implying the view that it is hopeless to be concerned about population-resource relations. Completely the opposite is intended—it is a fundamental and profound matter about which all hopeful men must be concerned. But to be useful, inquiries and hypotheses need to become more humble and more sophisticated. Humility is necessary to prevent overassessment of man's capabilities to control both his physical world and his own institutions; sophistication plus humility is necessary to understanding how man's institutions and his natural endowments may be employed toward the reduction of strife and uncertainty and toward attainment of the welfare status he seeks.

A major purpose of this chapter is to examine the capabilities of state power in respect to controlling population growth and rate of resource use.

Before doing that it will be helpful to sketch briefly the most salient features of contemporary population growth and resource use.

1.2   Trends and Potentials in Population Growth

The contemporary world-population prospect is a wholly new creature whose attributes and powers are not yet fully comprehended. Western nations (the United States in particular) were surprised at the postwar upturn in births and were happy with the boost to prosperity from this unexpected source. Many observers have taken great satisfaction—at what they believe was the demographer's expense—in pointing out the wrongness of the 1920–1940 projections of stable or even declining populations by 1965–1975.

But the birth-rate surprises of the industrialized Western world are no match for the death-rate surprises in the less-developed portions of the world. In the decade 1945–1955, the annual birth rates of North America and Western Europe increased by almost 5 per thousand of population. Meanwhile, there were counterpart decreases of approximately 10 in the death rates of many countries of the underdeveloped world. These comparative changes in birth and death rates are depicted in Figure 1.1.

Rising birth rates against stable death rates have increased the net growth rates of Western countries. Virtually all countries of Western Europe and North America participated in this phenomenon, commencing about 1940. However, in the pattern shown in Figure 1.1 for Sweden and the United Kingdom, the upward turn in the birth-rate trend in Europe was only temporary. With the notable exception of the United States in which the high birth rate persists, the rates of other countries have all turned down again and will apparently resume their consistent prewar downward directions. Even though the United States birth rate continues at its high postwar level, its indefinite persistence at such a level would amount to a sharp break of cultural patterns associated with Western Europe. It is probably more an extended lag than a new and permanent difference.

The United States rate of growth is presently 1.5 per cent per year (the rate of growth at which the population doubles in 47 years) and some of the European rates are still relatively high—in the vicinity of 1 per cent per year (the rate of growth at which a population doubles in 70 years). Nevertheless, it is not unrealistic to expect that by 1960 the growth rate for Western Europe and North America combined may not far exceed $\frac{1}{2}$ of 1 per cent per year (the rate at which a population grows by 28 per cent in 50 years and by 65 per cent in 100 years). Hence, even though the evidence is not conclusive, the prospect is strong that this segment of the world faces a conservative future in population growth.

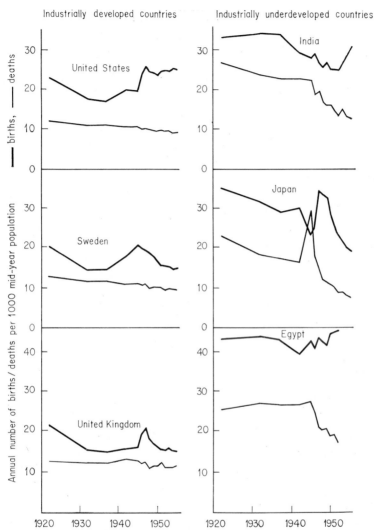

Fig. 1.1 Birth and death rates of six countries. (*United Nations Statistical Office, Demographic Yearbook* and *Monthly Bulletin of Statistics.*)

The population future of the less-advanced part of the world is a more significant question. Here, there is under way an astonishing revolution in medicine and sanitation. Within little more than 10 years, many of these countries have achieved the same decrease in death rates as previously required a half century in western nations. A simplified yet generally representative comparison of eastern and western experience may be summarized as follows:

Death rate per year per 1000 of population	Time required	
	Western countries	Eastern countries
From 30 to 20...............	1750–1900 (150 years)	1900–1945 (45 years)
From 20 to 10...............	1900–1950 (50 years)	1945–1960 (15 years)

The sharp contrasts in timing are significant. As the Western world pioneered advances in medicine and sanitation, the results came uncertainly and slowly; this gave the time needed for a gradual downward adjustment from high birth rates. In contrast, less-developed parts of the world now have only to adopt sanitation and medical practices that are already discovered and perfected. Adoption has been much more rapid than original discovery. Hence, the heretofore underdeveloped

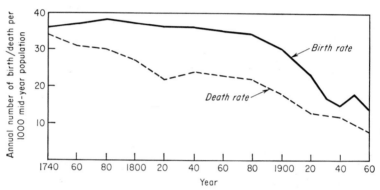

Fig. 1.2a The pattern of the demographic gap associated with the Industrial Revolution in Western Europe and North America. The dynamics of this pattern raised the total population of these regions from 140 million to 725 million.

world is now in the process of compressing centuries into decades as regards the prolonging of life.

This is important because it in effect deprives these later developing countries of an equal opportunity in which to accommodate birth rates to the revolutionary changes in death rates. Though it is characteristic of all cultures that changes in birth and death rates tend in the long run to be correlated, these adjustments take time. Even though the Western world had two centuries of time to adjust to a higher rate of survival, the reduction in birth rates lagged far behind the down trend in the death rate. This left a substantial gap—a high net natural increase. From this difference, which demographers call the *demographic gap*, a very considerable population explosion resulted. From 1750 to 1950 the population of Europe and North America jumped from 140 million to 725 million—a fivefold increase in two centuries. Within the same two centuries, the world population is estimated to have grown from 728 million to 2400 million. Thus, the western population segment, which constituted only one-fifth of the world's total as of 1750, and notwithstanding its declining birth rates, contributed nearly two-fifths of the increase that occurred in the following two centuries.

Figure 1.2a depicts the evolutionary changes in the pattern of population determinants as they were associated with the years of the Industrial Revolution in Western Europe and North America.[1] It is noteworthy

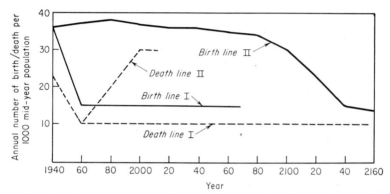

Fig. 1.2b Possible alternatives in demographic dynamics that confront nations in prospect of industrialization.

that, in the earliest stages of declining death rates, the downward revision of birth rates was very slight. Actually, the initial change was upward, as is also presently the case in Egypt and India. Most of the total downward change occurred after 1880.

The introduction of modern medicine, sanitation, and other public-health measures into the less-advanced parts of the world is being accelerated in numerous ways. United Nations' agencies, private foundations, and other technical-assistance programs are all performing roles. The saving of lives, particularly through the reduction of infant mortality, is accepted as humanitarianism in the best tradition. If not for this

[1] Figure 1.2a is a generalized and somewhat hypothetical pattern typical of most countries of Western Europe and North America. Vital statistics for the early years are very sketchy; going back to 1740, those for England and Wales are the most adequate. Numerous sources were consulted in connection with this section of the chapter, including principally: W. S. Woztinsky and E. S. Woztinsky, *World Population and Production*, The Twentieth Century Fund, Inc., New York, 1953; U.S. Department of Commerce, Bureau of the Census, *Current Population Reports*, Series P-25; A. M. Carr-Saunders, *World Population*, Oxford University Press, New York, 1936; United Nations Statistical Office, *Demographic Yearbook* and *Monthly Bulletin of Statistics;* United Nations, Department of Social Affairs, *The Determinants and Consequences of Population Trends*, New York, 1953.

reason only, then out of international political competition, it may be accepted as a virtual certainty that these efforts will continue.

In consequence, it may be assumed with assurance that there will be sufficient medical and sanitary improvements and facilities to limit the typical death rate for now underdeveloped countries to 10 per thousand by 1960 and thereafter. Against a typical current birth-rate level of 36, the demographic gap this fact poses is one of incomprehensible explosive power. If it were actually possible to maintain a death rate of no higher than 10 (as depicted by death line I in Figure 1.2b) and if birth rates in the now underdeveloped countries were to follow the same evolutionary pattern as those in the industrial west (i.e., the path of birth line II in Figure 1.2b), the present 1.6 billion population of these underdeveloped countries would by 2060 have exploded to 26 billion [estimated by taking the interval rates of growth, i.e., the distances between birth line II and death line I in Figure 1.2b, and applying the "compound-interest" formula $Pe = Pc(1 + r)^n$]. This is inconceivable. The question is whether the restriction will be the rationalized preventative, or will it have to be the Malthusian positive? If the check is preventive, the prospective low death rate (death line I) would be protected by a sharply accommodated downward revision in the birth rate (birth line I); if the check is Malthusian, the too high birth rate will be offset by an upward revision in the death rate (death line II).

The present rate of world-population growth is nearly 1½ per cent per year—approximately the same as the United States. The explosive possibility outlined above, in the absence of preventive checks, could raise the world growth rate to 2 per cent and higher for a limited period of time (at 2 per cent rate of growth a population doubles in 35 years). But even if the average rate were not to rise above the present 1½ per cent, the population of year 2000 would increase to at least 5 billion. Some authorities do not believe that the world's resources are sufficient to support so large a population.

To see the magnitude of the preventive obligation that rests on birth-rate adjustments in order to avoid the possibility of imposing Malthusian checks, let us assume that the world could handle a 50 per cent increase over 1950—a population of 3.6 billion—to be achieved by the year 2000. To stay within this limit, the growth rate could not be higher than 0.8 of 1 per cent per year. This would mean immediately reducing current world birth rates by one-third to one-half. It is a revolutionary change. Even so it is not enough, for the possibility of supporting 3.6 billion in 2000 is only an assumption. At this rate of growth, it might be possible to avoid serious deterioration in the standard of living, but there is no basis of realistic hope for improvement in standards.

To reduce uncertainty and the stress and strife associated with it,

½ of 1 per cent per year is possibly a conservative rate of growth at which there would be some prospect of raising living standards and improving the quality of life. This rate would yield a world population of approximately 3.1 billion by 2000. To stay within this limit, an immediate reduction to a world average birth rate of approximately 14 per thousand of population is needed. For Western Europe, North America, and Oceania (but excluding the United States), this result could be attained by trends now under way. The United States would have to reduce its present birth-rate level by approximately 40 per cent. The revolutionary obligation rests mainly on the underdeveloped countries where birth rates would need to be reduced by an average of approximately 60 per cent, as indicated in birth line I.

1.3   Rationalized Population Policies

All natural species are equipped with a high reproductive capacity. When hazards to life are everywhere present, a high reproductive rate is a necessary condition of survival. In fact, the differences in reproductive capacities among the species are generally calibrated to the level of prospective hazards, the less the likelihood of survival, the greater the reproductive capacity. Man shares in this attribute, for his reproductive capacity is adequate to offset the imposing combination of natural hazards that his primeval environment has presented to him. But even though man shares with other species in the attribute of high reproductive capacity, he uniquely differs in being the only one that has been able to reconstitute its environment, including the elimination or curbing of predators, and thereby to achieve a great reduction of the hazards to extended survival. Hence, the survival and expansion of modern man have depended not so much on his high reproductive potential as on his ability to reduce the predators and the adverse forces that would challenge his life.

Herein enters a paradox. Civilized communities accept it as a moral obligation to save and extend life—avoiding death has become unreservedly a matter of public concern. In contrast, the decisions as to reproduction are accepted as a private matter in which the community does not take an active role. This in effect means that, while the community asserts its right to control one of the determinants of population size, its position in respect to the other determinant is, with some exceptions, a "hands-off" policy.

But the role of the community in respect to the birth rate is not completely neutral. There are differing degrees of neutrality among cultures; also, there are conflicting influences within cultures. The philosophical foundations of most contemporary religions are still solidly anchored in the ancient past—in the conditions that predated the emergence of man's abilities to reconstruct his physical environment. The Biblical injunctive to "be fruitful, and multiply, and replenish the earth" (Genesis 9:1) is still read as though no reductions in life's hazards had been achieved. Furthermore, in today's reading of this admonition, little attention is paid to the word *replenish* which was indeed appropriate to the world of floods, famines, and pestilences.

It is factually justifiable, though perhaps not very generous, to say that man appears far more ingenious in the reconstruction of his physical environment than he is in the reconstruction of his philosophical and moral foundations, or even of avoiding the tyranny of those moralisms which were once purposeful but are now obsolete. Largely because of the rigidity of men's minds, the compulsions of ancient exhortations hang on. In consequence, most contemporary cultures are willing to undertake influencing rates of birth on the expansionist side, but few are prepared to assume or even sanction a role on the restrictionist side. In fact, some communities and cultural groups undertake to obstruct individual and private choice by outlawing birth-control literature and materials.

The survival of obsolete moralistic compulsions does not stand alone in obstructing rationality as regards births. Political nationalism, in both passive and active forms, also shares the stage. Prior to World War II, the German, Italian, and Japanese states undertook expansionist programs deliberately with the objective of advancing nationalistic power position. In other instances, among them notably France, the state adopted population expansionist measures not to advance nationalistic power but rather to offset its prospective decline. Almost all Western nations have social-welfare programs which, whether it be their deliberate objective or not, tend to promote conditions that are favorable to increased births.

In undertaking deliberate state restrictionist action in any form, Japan and India now stand alone. And even here the actions are restrictionist largely in the sense of removing some of the obstructions to freedom of individual choice.

To the extent that nations hold cultural goals, whether passively or deliberately formulated, it would seem a truism that size and change in the national population will be major forces in the achievement of such goals. The process of forming deliberate, rational perspectives on population and of logical consideration of the ways to give effect to such perspectives is implied in the term *population policy*. It is a term used with some frequency. Yet, there are a mere handful of nations that have ever achieved a stage of civilization where the essential questions affecting population could be given dispassionate consideration. And, significantly, these nations achieved such a cultural stature when the outlook was that of prospective population decline. The nations referred to are England,

Denmark, and particularly Sweden—all of which have had government commissions on population policy.

Denmark and Sweden appointed commissions in 1935. Notwithstanding that their immediate obligation was to cope with population decline, the perspectives adopted were fundamental and flexible. The Danish commission was instructed by its government as follows:[1]

> Any population policy in Denmark, which can unite the nation and overcome the distrust towards population policy which still exists, must accord with the general outlook in democratic society and with the cultural and social development of the country, and therefore has to be *an integral part of social welfare policy*. This means that, in forming a policy for Denmark, the measures must not only counteract the tendency towards depopulation but must also constitute a further step in the development of social welfare towards *better, healthier and more secure conditions of living for the whole population*.

Though the Swedish commission was clearly charged with the responsibility of proposing policies to offset the threat of depopulation, it nevertheless took a comprehensive view of its charge as indicated by such statements in its report as this:[2]

> Taking the long view, the solution of the population problem must be sought in the birth of normally large numbers of children by couples in all social classes. If it is desired to apply any scheme of public education to more positive family attitudes and at the same time afford space to important social improvements for children . . . it is necessary that *the starting point be the principle of voluntary parenthood, conscious of responsibility for one's own and others' welfare*.

The British commission was appointed in 1944. While proposing welfare measures designed to encourage increased births, it did so in terms of the conclusion that "a replacement size of family is desirable in Great Britain at the present time."[3]

These are beginnings. For Sweden and Britain, permanent arrangements were proposed which would continuously observe population changes and formulate appropriate policy recommendations. Neither country has yet acted. Meanwhile, Japan and India, within the limited powers and sanctions available to them, have endeavored to include deliberate population policy within the framework of national economic programs.

---

[1] Hope T. Eldridge, *Population Policies: A Survey of Recent Developments*, The International Union for the Scientific Study of Population, American University, Washington, D.C., 1954, pp. 13–14.

[2] Quoted in Alva Myrdal, *Nation and Family*, Harper & Brothers, New York, 1941, p. 170.

[3] Eldridge, *op. cit.*, p. 13.

Outside these meager efforts, population anarchy reigns. Nations do intervene in international migration, mainly on the restrictionist side, and migration has become a relatively insignificant factor in determining the size of national populations. In accordance with accepted concepts of welfare and purpose, national governments are in the business of supplying orderly administration. But it is impossible to expect that much administrative orderliness can be achieved when uncertainty and indeterminateness characterize the population magnitude. There has been little progress since Alva Myrdal wrote in 1941:[1] "Population has been studied far less as a problem for political action than as a problem for fact-finding research."

For many quite apparent reasons, there is a justified sense of defeatism in the endeavor of any one nation to adopt a rationalistic population policy so long as others do not. Yet, no reason exists for a more hopeful conclusion than that of Hope T. Eldridge in 1954:[2] "It will probably be a long time before a truly international approach to population policy will be possible." Consequently, the urgently needed and indeed indispensable policy formulations will have to be created within individual states—later to be employed in evolving whatever world rationalization can be brought to exist.

Most writers who are convinced of the importance of removing obstacles to rational population growth lay foremost stress upon the availability of birth-control knowledge and technique. They call for more physiological and medical research in these matters. It is doubtless true that research in these areas is being tragically neglected. However, it is also true that a coordinate and transcendent problem is being just as tragically neglected in the social sciences. This is the problem of understanding and of the humility to seek understanding of the significance of individual action in respect to the aggregate of individual actions. The Swedish spoke of it as being *"conscious of responsibility for one's own and others' welfare."*

This consciousness, with the sense of power and also of humility that are part of it, must surely be the key to any system of population rationality that can succeed against nationalistic totalitarianism. The social sciences could well devote more efforts to finding out how such keys might be designed.

1.4 Raw Materials and Growth

In 1951–1952 the United States intensively reviewed its resource position. This was not its first review, but it was the most comprehensive. The President's Materials Policy Commission reported its findings in

[1] Myrdal, *op. cit.*, p. 100.
[2] Eldridge, *op. cit.*, p. 17.

Resources for Freedom, popularly known also as the Paley Report.[1] It is a well-prepared set of five volumes which, though not expensive as books go, unfortunately weighs close to 10 pounds. It is unfortunate because the report is so significant that it ought to be passed from hand to hand until every American having concern for himself and his children as well as his nation has the chance to read it.

Regardless of what else its readers may learn, one outstanding point should not be missed: at the inception of World War II, the United States passed into a new era in its resource situation; pre-1940 concepts of the nation's resource strength are obsolete; we are in absolutely no position to sustain isolationist, self-sufficiency, or go-it-alone philosophies.

A few quotations from the first five chapters will hopefully do justice in reflecting the general outlines of the resource picture as seen by the Commission:

The United States appetite for materials is gargantuan—and so far insatiable.

Indeed, there is scarcely a metal or a mineral fuel of which the quantity used in the United States since the outbreak of the First World War did not exceed the total used throughout the world in all the centuries preceding.

The decade of the 1940's marked a crucial turning point in the long-range materials position of the United States. Historical trends long in the making finally came to a climax when the national economy moved just prior to the depression into a period, still continuing, of high employment and production. By the mid-point of the twentieth century we had entered an era of new relationships between our needs and resources; our national economy had not merely grown up to its resource base, but in many respects had outgrown it. We had completed our slow transition from a raw materials surplus Nation to a raw materials deficit Nation.

As a Nation we have lived long and prospered mightily without serious concern for our material resources. Our sensational progress in production and consumption has been attributable not only to the freedom of our institutions and the enterprise of our people, but also to our spendthrift use of our rich heritage of natural resources. We have become the supreme advocates of the idea that man and his labor are the most valuable of all, and that inanimate materials are to be used as fully as possible to give men the greatest amount of return for the effort they put forth.

Most Americans have been nurtured on the romantic notion that technology will always come to the rescue with a new miracle whenever the need arises; after all, it gave us synthetic rubber and the atomic bomb in a hurry when the

---

[1] *Resources for Freedom,* A Report to the President by the President's Materials Policy Commission, vols. I to V, U.S. Government Printing Office, Washington, D.C., June, 1952. Other recent publications concerned with the same subjects are: J. Frederick Dewhurst and Associates, *America's Needs and Resources,* The Twentieth Century Fund, Inc., New York, 1955; *The Nation Looks at Its Resources,* Report of the Mid-Century Conference on Resources for the Future, Washington, D.C., Dec. 2–4, 1953, Resources for the Future, Inc., Washington, D.C., 1954.

need was urgent. But isolated solutions of problems relating to individual materials, no matter how dramatic, are no substitute for the broad frontal attack which technology needs to make on the materials problem as a whole.

The plain fact seems to be that we have skimmed the cream of our resources as we now understand them; there must not be, at this decisive point in history, too long a pause before our understanding catches up with our needs. We are much more supple today in the use of materials than our ancestors were in the past; but when we consider the number of materials our ancestors did not use, it will become us to remember that frequently they left much unused not because it was undiscovered, but because they did not know what to do with what they knew to exist.

Growth of demand is at the core of the materials problem we face; it is the probability of continued growth, even more than the incursions of past growth and two world wars, that present us now with our long-range problems. It is mainly our unwillingness to stand still, to accept the status of a "mature economy" that challenges the adequacy of our resources.

Notwithstanding that it encountered these sobering characteristics in the nation's resource picture, the Commission did not recommend a policy of restraint in growth or in resource use. Rather, its recommendations took the general form of a systematic and coordinated development in science and technology that would enable greater resource yield from domestic sources and the promotion of trade policies with other nations in order to obtain raw materials from abroad. Though the Commission spoke of conserving for the future and of prudence in the face of uncertainty, the emphasis of its attention was how to supply the materials for expanse. Given the time focus the Commission adopted, which was until 1975, the tone of the report is one of reassurance. If one avoids reflection, 1975 may seem soothingly distant. But as this is written, 1975 is closer than 1935, which more than 50 million present-day Americans should recall quite clearly. If things go tolerably well, more than 100 million present-day Americans, to say nothing of their descendants, will have a considerable interest in 1976 and thereafter.

As noted above, the Commission found that "growth of demand is at the core of the materials problem we face." The validity of this demand was not questioned. Indeed, the Commission dismissed the raising of any such question by the formulation of a "fundamental concept" that:

We share the belief of the American people in the principle of Growth. [The capital G was bestowed by the Commission.] Granting that we cannot find any absolute reason for this belief we admit that to our Western minds it seems preferable to any opposite, which to us implies stagnation and decay.

This declaration of principle raises several important questions that have profound implications in resource use. What really is the principle of growth to which the American people are said to be dedicated? By whom and by what means are its pace and its acceleration determined? Are stagnation and decay the only alternatives to growth? Is it prudent to push further into the depths of resource uncertainty in order to maximize the certainty of contemporary prosperity?

The classical political economists anticipated the ultimate emergence of the stationary state, and they did not believe that it would be so bad. Now, in contrast, we are virtually moved to a state of frenzy if business trends begin to level off. What has brought the change? Many things, of course, have contributed; but basically it is because we dread having depressions, and the best insurance against the possibility of a depression that present-day economists and business leaders can prescribe is to maintain a boom. Though sustained booms may be quite pleasurable in many respects, they do unfortunately depend upon a prodigious rate of resource consumption.

Let us consider an example of the implications of growth. From 1946 through 1953 the United States per capita annual increase in steel averaged approximately 2.5 per cent. Our population grew at an average annual rate of 1.5 per cent. Combined, these two elements of growth yield an expansion in steel use of 3.75 per cent per year. In 1950, we used 130 million short tons of iron ore. If these rates of growth were to be sustained for 50 years, we would by the year 2000 need over 800 million short tons of iron ore of the same grade. We would then be using about the same amount of iron in 3 years as were used in the entire 80 years from 1870 to 1950.

This is incredible. But it is only a 25-year further mathematical extension of the principle of growth in which the Materials Policy Commission concurred, but extended to 2000 instead of only to 1975.

Being committed, as we say we are, to the principle of growth indeed implies gargantuan obligations in raw materials of some sort, if not ultimately to be met in steel or other materials now in use, then in their substitutes. It is an obligation that plunges us continuously deeper into the vulnerabilities of the unknown and the uncertain. It pledges us to dependence on other peoples' resources and to yields from technologies as yet undiscovered.

In our frontier days, we were impelled to rapid growth for reasons that are not obscure. Our immigrant people needed sources of livelihood. The high value that was placed on human labor could be realized only by heavy capital investment. As our economy achieved a degree of maturity at the end of the nineteenth century, much poverty still remained which, in current social and political thought, was in need of alleviation. At this stage the nation could have elected to solve its poverty problems by undertaking a more equalitarian distribution of income. But in place of redistribution, we chose rather to place our emphasis in a goal of general productivity enhancement, one effect of which is to achieve a more satisfactory living standard for the lowest income segment. This philosophy has endured, evidence of it still being in the practice of labor unions to offer increasing productivity as their favorite argument in support of a wage increase.

But this nation has now arrived at a state of economic development at which most of the urgent problems of poverty have been solved. Our leisure time is unprecedented for the total of any society, and we could well afford more. If people, as individuals, could elect their choice of work week—20, 30, 40, 50 hours—it is not impossible to believe that considerable numbers would choose more leisure time, at the sacrifice of income, than they now have—at least a proportion of those who are not over their heads in installment payments. However, job and work-week standardization are not very flexible. Moreover, financial obligations resulting from submission to the incessant propaganda of sales promotion further decrease the opportunity for choice.

One would surmise from reports of advertising, trade, and installment-finance associations that the American consumer is becoming a troublesomely reluctant performer in the modern cult of growth. Some of the statements from these sources come perilously near saying that the person is unpatriotic who buys only what he needs and waits until he can pay cash. Consider the roles to which advertising and merchandizing agencies bespeak themselves:[1,2]

National Appliance and Radio-TV Association. The whims and desires of consumers are now more important than purchasing power in building sales. Let's motivate people to do what we want them to.

Retailing Daily. It is not only our privilege to obsolete the minimum home and many home furnishings. It is our obligation. We are obliged to work on obsolescence as our contribution to a healthy, growing society. There is nothing more obsolete than the status quo.

In many ways, the evidence mounts that, to sustain the current level of growth and output, consumers are being propelled into satisfying wants they did not know they had, into abhorring still useful articles merely because they are becoming old, into replacing equipment deliberately "obsoleted" by controlled inferiority in manufacture, and into doing all this with money they do not have.

It seems possible that we shall fairly soon want to reexamine the principle of growth and to question at the same time whether it is worth while to decimate our natural-resource strength in its service.

[1] *Consumer Reports*, Consumers Union of U.S., Inc., Mount Vernon, N.Y., February, 1956, p. 86.

[2] *Ibid.*, June, 1956, p. 317.

1.5 Decelerating the Rate of Resource Use

As individual producers and consumers, the citizens of advanced industrial nations are astonishingly unaware of the raw materials that are required to produce their high standard of living. They are even more ignorant of the national inventories of present and prospective non-renewable-resource stocks. One of the apparent reasons for this state of affairs is the alienation that is imposed by massive organization and minute job and industry specialization. The average person is simply too far away, organizationally if not geographically, from raw-materials sources to know or to be sensitive of their stock and rate of use. Moreover, the momentum of the system is to produce and not to be precautionary. There is a disposition to understand the significance of industrial expansion and resource development. But proposals to restrict development and to retard resource use create confusion and doubt whether they are initiated by government or by private industry.

California oil provides an example. In November, 1956, the state's electors were confronted with a legislative measure affecting oil conservation, which was initiated by a part of the petroleum industry. The proposition was resoundingly defeated. The conservation merits of the measure, whatever they may have been, are not here under assessment. Under the barrage of argumentation of collateral issues, it is doubtful if a majority of electors were ever able to get an unobstructed view of the central problem. And in any event, individual electors can hardly be expected to take petroleum conservation seriously while being at the same moment implored and beguiled to buy ever more powerful new model automobiles and also being able to fill their tanks at "gas-war" prices.

Even if the United States economy were overusing its mineral resources to build automobiles and overusing its petroleum resources to propel them, there is little reason to expect that the respective markets would supply warning signals very far in advance. A free-enterprise economy relies upon rising market prices to reflect relative scarcities. However, for nonrenewable resources whose usable extent can only be estimated, market price may fail to be a sensitive indicator. It could very well be that only with sudden and abruptly rising supply prices will the general populace come to know that past use has been profligate.

Advanced industrial economies are deeply committed to progress and prosperity—to profits, dividends, and full employment. Even if industrial scientists were to become greatly concerned about the prospects of raw-materials supplies, say, 25 years hence, there seem to be only limited ways for them to translate their concern into conservative action. Managements of individual corporations would not find it possible to adopt retrenchment plans for conservation reasons. In the lack of an industry-wide or general program, the individual firm would only be throwing away profits to competitors. Neither stockholders nor employees would concur in this.

Nor is it realistic to expect the leadership of an industry to undertake a concerted resource-use restriction program. Not the least of the reasons for this is that it would be difficult, if not actually impossible, to distinguish such an action from illegal monopolistic collusion.

When industrial leadership becomes apprehensive of future raw-materials supplies from domestic sources, it seeks alternative ways of sustaining consumption rather than taking the lead in adjusting to a more conservative rate of consumption. This may mean developing access to foreign supplies or accelerated research and technological development of substitutes. The shift from domestic coal to overseas oil in Western Europe and the United States is an example of both of these. But the future of this arrangement has for several years looked anything but certain.

If, as seems inescapably true, industrial enterprise and consumers' markets cannot adopt a program of conservative use, short of its being imposed by sharply rising supply prices (with the prospect of immediate rationing), then the inquiry must turn to the power of the state. What is the capability of democratic government to adopt conservative policies for raw-materials use and to make them effective?

Recent decades of experience in the United States show that government can have a material role in sustaining the capabilities of continuously yielding resources such as soils, forests, and water. Here, the role is not primarily a rationing function as it would have to be in respect to a nonrenewable stock. Rather, the governmental role has been directed to promotion of management practices that, while maintaining the delivery of product, prevent the concurrent loss of the capital resource. Significantly, while the United States has national conservation programs for soils, forests, and water, it has none for minerals and petroleum. On the contrary, its tax laws, by undertaking to protect owners of mineral and petroleum deposits against the day of depletion, actually reward accelerated removal.

To become conservative in the use of a nonrenewable resource, government would have to impose some sort of rationing either at the raw-materials source or at the consumer-product level. Democratic governments have had to do this as a wartime emergency measure, but there is no evidence to suggest willingness or ability to do so outside the emergency situation.

On the contrary, the governments of advanced industrial economies have become deeply committed to maintaining prosperity, full employment, and sustained economic improvement. In free-enterprise economies, voluntary private saving and investment are the principal mechanisms relied upon to achieve these objectives. Not many years ago, any failure to maintain prosperity would have been accepted as an inevitable maladjustment in the functioning of economic forces, from which relief

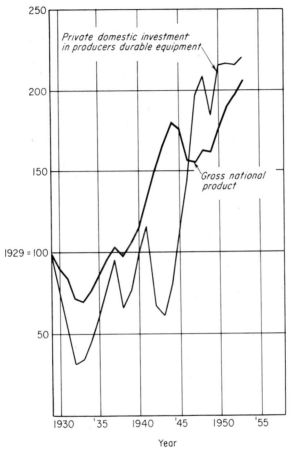

Fig. 1.3 Gross national product and private domestic investment in producers' durable equipment, United States (in constant 1947 dollars, index numbers based on 1929 = 100). (*U.S. Bureau of the Census, Historical Statistics of the U.S. and Statistical Abstract.*)

would be attained only through internal self-correction. Now, it is scarcely debatable that a government of any major political party in America or Western Europe would persistently subscribe to a laissez-faire policy at the onset of recession. Instead, every effort would be made to encourage acceleration of private investment; and if this failed, then a program of public investment would be invoked.

Savings and investment materialize only through construction and manufacture of productive equipment and facilities. Savings and investment take resources. Figure 1.3 indicates the close relationship that has prevailed in the United States between investment in producers' durable equipment and total economic activity as measured by gross national product. The further relationship between investment in producers' equipment and the use of steel and energy are seen in Figure 1.4.

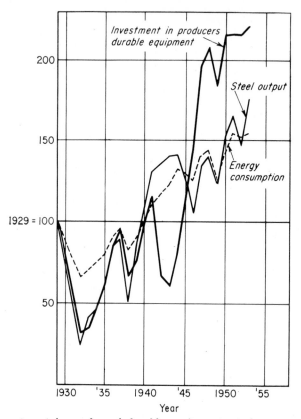

Fig. 1.4 Investment in producers' durable equipment, steel output, and energy consumption, United States (index numbers based on 1929 = 100). (*U.S. Bureau of the Census, Historical Sta istics of the U.S. and Statistical Abstract.*)

It is readily observable that depression in the past has been a way of rationing the consumption of resources. It is equally apparent that, if in the future depressions are successfully avoided, sustained acceleration in the consumption of resources is a necessary condition.

One of the attributes of the more highly developed economies is that increasing proportions of total production are in the so-called tertiary industries, the services that, in contrast to manufacturing, do not depend so heavily on raw materials. This is a characteristic of the United States economy. Nevertheless, it does not necessarily follow that per capita consumption of raw materials will cease to rise. Contrarily, as the standard of living measured in per capita gross national product has continued to rise, so also have per capita uses of steel and energy (see Figure 1.5). (In this figure, energy consumption refers to total energy consumption rather than useful energy, which equals energy consumption times

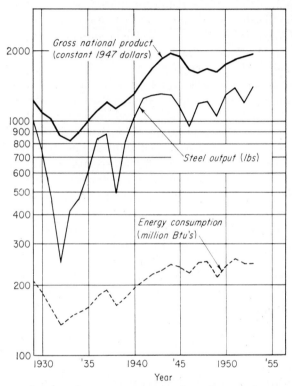

Fig. 1.5   Per capita annual rates: gross national product, steel output, and energy consumption, United States. (Multiply number of Btu by 2.93 × 10⁻⁴ to obtain number of kilowatthours.) (*U.S. Bureau of the Census, Historical Statistics of the U.S. and Statistical Abstract.*)

efficiency.) The reason for this is that, although manufacturing industries are declining proportionally, they are not declining in total and the amount of capital equipment per worker is constantly increasing.

Economists and business leaders share the conviction that sustained new investment is critical in avoiding depression and economic stagnation. In the lack of sufficient new investment, unemployment will occur with a consequent weakening of consumer demand, thus raising the prospect of further retrenchment as markets become unprofitable.

To achieve the necessary level of investment, it is not essential that the proportion of aggregate output going into new investment should increase, but neither should it decrease. Hence, as the magnitude of the economy becomes ever larger, total investment must be correspondingly greater. It thus becomes an unrelenting upward spiral, with ever greater resource needs.

It is possible that the minimum level of new investment for prosperity could be maintained with a rising population and a stable standard of living. Or it might be maintained with a stable population but with a rising standard of living. As free industrial economies are now constituted, one or the other is essential, and a combination of both offers the greatest assurance against the uncertainty of threatening stagnation.

Thus, any substantial attempt by government authorities to extend the yield period of nonrenewable-resource stock by restraining or rationing current use holds the hazard, if not in actuality then certainly in allegation of political competitors, of obstructing the maintenance of prosperity and full employment. Politicians and political parties, of which governments are composed, interpret prosperity as one of the keenest devotions of the electorate. Quite understandably, success or failure to maintain prosperity is a matter on which they are zealously alert to take credit or to assess blame.

Consequently, governments are in no better position than are managements of firms and industries to impose deceleration in the rate of resource use. Actually, the commitment of government is to guarantee the continuance of resource use—first, by promoting private investment, then, if necessary, by direct public works (which would also consume resources) should private industry fail to maintain a satisfactory level. Rather than restrain resource use, democratic governments presently put their confidence in the prospect of scientific and technological advances which may develop substitutes for the depleting resources.

1.6   Restraints on Population Growth and Resource Consumption

The foregoing considerations have indicated certain conclusions:

1. In the less-advanced segments of the world, there presently exists the virtual certainty of a disabling population explosion, which can be avoided only by a revolutionary downward adjustment of birth rates.

2. Advanced industrial countries, in some of which present population growth rates are also very high, have a prodigious and relentlessly expanding demand for resources and raw materials.

3. The ambitions of underdeveloped countries to industrialize and to improve their economies are in prospect of being frustrated if population growth within these countries is not restrained. But if they are able to

meet the conditions necessary to moderately rapid industrialization and meanwhile the already industrialized economies continue further growth along present resource-consuming trends, the pressure on the world's stocks of nonrenewable resources will rapidly intensify until sooner or later the aggregate demand will reach a point where further growth is not likely to be sustained.

4. While communities and national states hold considerable power to change one determinant of population growth (deaths), they hold little power to change the other (births).

5. Advanced industrial economies, committed as they are to full employment and continued economic growth, presently possess little power, either in the mechanisms of free-enterprise markets or in those of democratic government, to restrain or decelerate the rate of resource use.

6. Nevertheless, the pathway of wisdom prescribes a sharp restraint of birth rates for one segment of the world and concurrently a restraint in the rise of the material-goods standard of living in another.

7. Neither of these restraints can be successfully achieved by government authority, at least not without the sacrifice of precious individual liberties to harsh totalitarianism.

8. Within systems of democratic individual liberties, achieving these essential restraints will depend ultimately on the degree of humility and conservatism that can be engendered within electorates by better understanding and consciousness of one's own and others' welfare.

Many writers in population-resource relations use an entirely different reasoning process than has been employed here, and they arrive at virtually opposite conclusions. These writers look upon population growth and the standard of living as being autonomous forces, which therefore are not to be restrained or otherwise interfered with. These writers undertake to project the future populations and the demands for production and for resources. From such projections, they then undertake to assess the responsibilities that must be assumed in science, technology, or government. A few of those who follow this line of reasoning come to a substantially laissez-faire conclusion, i.e., that normal scientific, industrial, and economic processes will suffice and that no extraordinary effort is called for. But the majority of those who believe that resources and resource utilization must adapt to prospective needs do see the solution in terms of some form of extraordinary effort. Generally speaking, the emphasis of such extraordinary effort is seen either as more effective governmental organization to expand output from current production technique or as new and revolutionary technique. For convenience, these might be thought of as organizational as against scientific revolutions. As an example of the former, Constantin Paul Lent in *Food Enough for All* would establish a national public utility to produce and distribute food and would also create a world pooling arrangement by means of which all the world's peoples are assured of an adequate food supply at lowest possible cost. An example of a proposed scientific revolution is that of Jacob Rosin and Max Eastman in *The Road to Abundance*, which calls for a chemistic society in which foods and manufacturing materials would be synthetically produced, without dependence on biological plants and geologic mines.

Either of such proposed solutions would indeed be abruptly revolutionary. They both tax the ordinary imagination. It is perhaps unwise to declare them impractical; yet, the need of precaution is scarcely met by saying merely that they are uncertain.

We noted in beginning this chapter that a common defect of most inventories and projections of "possibilities" that allegedly would avoid a Malthusian outcome to an explosive population growth is that their advocators fail to take into account the fact that man approaches resource use through intricate governmental, economic, and technological systems. Even if personal, individual motivations were fully coordinate with the effort required, which they are not, there remain the questions of organizational and institutional effectiveness. The state, regional, or international system that is capable of yielding more than a fraction of the apparent "possibilities" is highly exceptional.

Widely different levels of effectiveness may be observed in the utilization of already known resources and in the application of already developed industrial and organizational technique. This being true, the basis for expecting equal or greater effectiveness in respect to resources not yet known and technique not yet invented becomes most suspect. Actually, optimistic scientific and technological expectations cannot be based on much more than confidence that the future will unfold in much the same pattern as the past. For optimism in expectations of revolutionary improvements in governmental and economic organization, one must rely mainly on confidence only and without regard for the pattern of the past.

The very most that can be said for these proposals of ways to meet the needs of an exploding population is that they are uncertain. Given a century or so of time for these possibilities to be achieved, one could develop a degree of confidence that persistent poverty in a world population of the present size might be satisfactorily eradicated. More than two centuries of brilliant progress has failed to relieve want in more than a small fraction of the world; hence nothing of the past or of the realistic future gives authority or certainty to the supposition that poverty could be conquered in a population of 5 billion or more.

Technological and scientific potentialities do not become certainties merely by affirmation of people who talk like authorities. Nor can it be guaranteed that possibilities will become certainties in consequence of a vast network of billion-dollar research projects, even though the probabilities may be improved. Even after laboratory discovery—and many have been accidents—it is still a long way in time and organization to application in field and factory.

Thus, to assure political leaders that solutions are at hand which make it unnecessary to be concerned about burgeoning population is to perpetrate a cruel hoax on mankind.

This does not imply that man must strive for complete certainty, for this is manifestly impossible. The best that can be hoped for is a degree of serenity and assurance to be achieved through minimizing uncertainties. Surely, some degree of uncertainty minimization should in itself be a worthwhile objective. Minimization of uncertainty as against maximization of profits is recognized and practiced in the management of individual business firms. It is considered sound business judgment to forego the possibility of large profits if the venture is too uncertain. Why is it not equally sound that civilized man in the aggregate should follow a parallel path of conservatism? The most advanced of the industrial economies have fairly well succeeded in providing the goods and services for healthy physiological life; their record in providing the conditions of sound mental health is, in contrast, appallingly bad.

If serenity could be bought in a department store at 10 per cent down and 24 months to pay, it seems plausible to believe that sometime, though doubtless very slowly, it would come to compete fairly well with such commodities as pink refrigerators, jeweled dog collars, and electronic exercisers. But, except to the extent that it can be built into pills or potable fluids or dispensed by psychiatrists, the providing of serenity is not well adapted to private enterprise and the profit motive.

The proposition is herewith advanced that reduction of uncertainty is an important component of a high standard of living and that it is a component that has been tragically neglected. It is a type of service that must be supplied through government. Yet, even though the need for it becomes increasingly intense, democratic governments are not prepared to assume such a responsibility until their electors attain a greater consciousness of individual and collective roles, and the interrelations between them, in determining the state of welfare of modern societies.

In many ways, there is less uncertainty in the unadvanced sectors of the world. However, with rising ambitions for the future and with decline of passive acceptance of perpetual poverty, the foundations are being laid for increasing uncertainty and frustration. To achieve the economic advance these peoples desire, they must increase their per capita resource use. Aside from the indicated restraints on population growth, the desired economic advance implies the ultimate necessity of retaining more of their own raw materials for local use, thereby diminishing the supply available to the advanced industrial segment. Concurrently, the market outlets within these countries for exported manufactures is likely to decline.

The objectives of the developed and of the underdeveloped segments of the world are thus to a considerable degree in conflict. To achieve the population-resource relationships that would minimize conflict of interest and uncertainty of outcome requires immediate and dramatic pioneering upon which neither world segment now shows much readiness to embark. For the underdeveloped world, the unpioneered frontier is how to avoid a frustrating population explosion; for the more developed world, the unpioneered frontier is how to maintain prosperity without depending so heavily upon a relentless upward spiral in resource consumption. For both, the basic need is for social innovations that will create a profound awareness of the interrelations between personal behavior and aggregate consequences. This is the basic responsibility of civilized man. Technological innovations, that seemingly prove Malthus was wrong, are no substitute. Technological innovation can play a splendid supplementary role to conscious social responsibility, and it should never be more than supplementary. But there is always the danger that, as in the past, man's technological genius will be adopted as license for arrogance and social irresponsibility.

2

Fresh-water Resources

MARTIN R. HUBERTY

PROFESSOR OF IRRIGATION AND ENGINEERING

UNIVERSITY OF CALIFORNIA, LOS ANGELES

2.1 Introduction

The important role water plays in our lives is largely dependent upon its abundance and its physical and chemical characteristics. It is the most widely distributed inorganic liquid. It exists in nature as a liquid, a gas, and a solid. Except for mercury, it has the highest specific heat of all liquids.

The water molecule is composed of two hydrogen atoms and one oxygen atom, with each hydrogen atom having one electron and the oxygen atom having eight electrons. The arrangement of the atoms in the water molecule is the basis of its various properties. In the solid state, the molecules are less densely packed than in the liquid phase, causing ice to have a density of about 90 per cent that of water. This fact is responsible for ice forming at the surface of water bodies. It is indeed a fortunate condition for otherwise many of our lakes would become completely frozen.

The high heat of vaporization (540 calories per g) results in a relatively slow rate of water loss through evaporation. Its strong cohesion, its solvent action, and its latent heat of fusion (86 calories per g) are all important characteristics of water.

Standards for Fresh Water. Fresh water, in contrast to saline and sea waters, is low in dissolved solids. There is a lack of agreement, however, as to the upper limit of salts that water can contain and still be classed as fresh. Some have placed this limit at 500 parts per million (ppm), while to others waters with as much as 2500 ppm are considered to be fresh. The U.S. Public Health Service has established standards for satisfactory drinking water, as shown in Table 2.1. These standards are much higher than many communities can provide. In some areas, such as in Libya and parts of the southwestern United States, people

29

Fig. 2.1 Eildon Dam and Reservoir in the state of Victoria, Australia. A multi-purpose project. (*Photograph by State Rivers and Water Supply Commission.*)

have become accustomed to drinking water containing as much as five times the amount of total solids set as the upper limit in the Public Health Standards.

It is clearly evident from Table 2.1 that the quality of a water is determined not alone by the total amount of salts present, but by the chemical composition as well.

Table 2.1   U.S. Public Health Standards for Domestic Water Supplies

	Ppm		*Ppm*
Turbidity (silica scale)	10	Iron + manganese	0.3
Color (platinum-cobalt scale)	20	Magnesium	125
Lead	0.1	Zinc	15
Fluoride	1.5	Chloride	250
Arsenic	0.05	Sulfate	250
Selenium	0.05	Phenolic compound	0.001
Hexavalent chromium	0.05	Total solids	500
Copper	3.0		

The Hydrologic Cycle.   The earth's water supply is largely in a state of flux. *Hydrologic cycle* is the term normally applied to this natural system of water movement, illustrated in Figure 2.2.

The oceans, which cover approximately 70 per cent of the earth's surface, are the great reservoirs from which our fresh-water supplies come. Energy provided by the sun evaporates water from the oceans, and the atmosphere transports it over the land, where it may be deposited in the form of rain, snow, etc. Having reached the land, the water is disposed of by evaporation, transpiration (loss through plants), runoff, and infiltration to the soil, where it may be stored and where some of it may contribute to the ground-water supplies. Movement of ground water can create springs and maintain stream flow.

The amount of water annually evaporated from the oceans and the continents is not known. It has been estimated to equal a volume of 80,000 cu miles over the oceans and 15,000 cu miles over the continents.

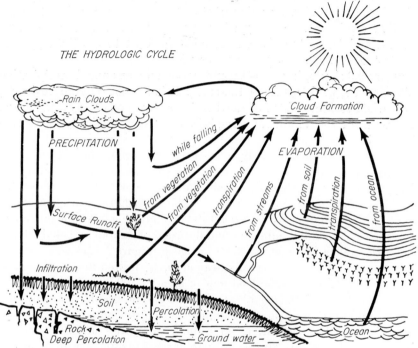

THE HYDROLOGIC CYCLE

Fig. 2.2   The Hydrologic cycle. (*After Water, Yearbook of Agriculture, U.S. Department of Agriculture, Washington, D.C., 1955.*)

Sverdrup has made computations of the evaporation from the Atlantic Ocean based on the assumption that there is a boundary layer immediately adjacent to the water surface in which the transport of water vapor takes place by ordinary diffusion; above the boundary layer the transport takes place by eddy conductivity. The results indicate a wide range in evaporation, from as high as $6\frac{1}{4}$ ft per annum in the range 30 to 8°N to as low as $2\frac{1}{4}$ ft between 8 to 3°N. These figures are in close agreement with the direct observations made by Wust. McEwin extended the computations to include the North Pacific and obtained lower values than Sverdrup did for the Atlantic. These values were of the order of 4.3 ft per annum in latitude 20°N to as low as 1.85 ft at 50°N.

2.2   Extent and Characteristics of Supply

Moisture reaching the land surface varies in form (snow, hail, rain, dew, etc.) and in total amount, intensity, and time of deposition. The solid-phase state is usually deposited in greatest amounts in the steep upper levels of the river basins where it is stored until melted during the warm season of the year. It can be the main source of dry-season flow. The amount of water stored in the snow pack greatly exceeds the capacity of artificial reservoirs. Duration of storage is influenced mainly by local weather conditions. In many areas systematic snow surveys are conducted, and forecasts of runoff are made in order to use the supply to greatest advantage.

Figure 2.3 shows, in a broad manner, the average annual precipitation falling on the land surface of the earth. It is at best only approximate, for marked variations in precipitation occur within relatively small areas. The general range in annual precipitation is from practically nil to over 500 in. in limited areas. It has been estimated that the total annual precipitation, if spread evenly over the earth surface, would be about 1 lb for every square inch of surface. Average annual precipitation for the United States is shown generally in Figure 2.4. Mreinzer places the average annual loss by evaporation over the United States at about 20 in. Runoff is dependent not alone upon total precipitation but upon numerous other factors, including intensity and duration of rainfall and characteristics of the soil and rock of the drainage basin. Figure 2.5 presents graphically the general picture regarding runoff in the United States. The total flow is equivalent to a sustained flow of about 1,800,000 cfs.

The circulation of the earth's atmosphere and orographic features play a very important role in determining the nature and distribution of precipitation. Wide variations in rainfall intensities are to be found throughout the world. Storms of high intensity often occur in desert areas. Among examples of high-intensity precipitation in the United States is that at Opids Camp, California, where 1.03 in. of rain fell in 1 min. In St. Louis, Missouri, 5.05 in. fell in 15 min, 10.0 in. of precipitation occurred in 1 hr at Catskill, New York, and at D'Hanis, Texas, there was 21.84 in. in 3 hr. Examples of storms of even higher intensities can probably be found in other parts of the world. When they do occur, the capacity of the soil to absorb the water is apt to be exceeded, and the ratio of runoff to precipitation is high. An extreme example of high runoff occurred on Sheepskin Creek in New Zealand, where in February, 1952, measurements of peak runoff from 2.7 sq miles showed a flow of 14,500 cfs per sq mile. In this instance, previous storms had charged the watershed.

Distribution of precipitation throughout the year greatly influences the use of water and man's attitude toward its conservation. Under arid

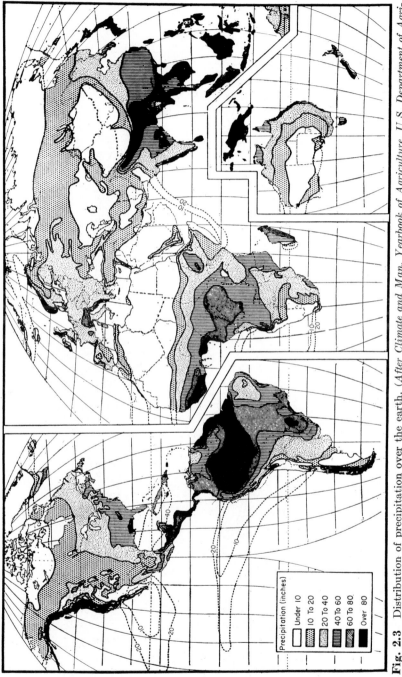

Fig. 2.3 Distribution of precipitation over the earth. (*After Climate and Man, Yearbook of Agriculture, U.S. Department of Agriculture, Washington, D.C., 1941.*)

Precipitation (inches)

	Under 10
	10 To 20
	20 To 40
	40 To 60
	60 To 80
	Over 80

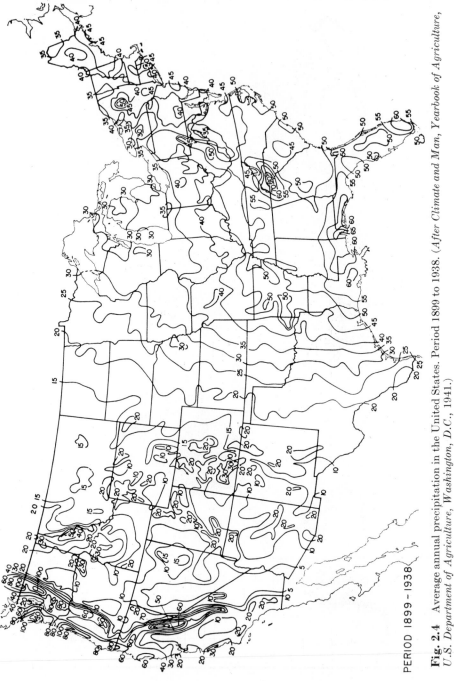

PERIOD 1899–1938

Fig. 2.4 Average annual precipitation in the United States. Period 1899 to 1938. (*After Climate and Man, Yearbook of Agriculture, U.S. Department of Agriculture, Washington, D.C., 1941.*)

34

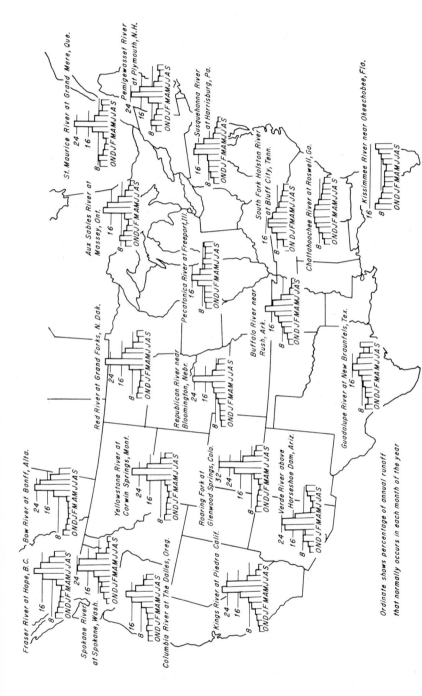

Fig. 2.5 Normal distributions of runoff throughout the United States. Months are designated by their initial letters, beginning with October (ONDJFMAMJJAS). (*After Water, Yearbook of Agriculture, U.S. Department of Agriculture, Washington, D.C., 1955.*)

35

and Mediterranean climates, irrigation has been developed to increase agricultural production, and the people are generally conscious of the need to conserve water.

The total average amount of moisture in the air is not necessarily an indication of the average precipitation. The western coast of Peru is a good example of an area of extremely low precipitation; yet the average volume of water in the atmosphere is great. In this particular instance, conditions favorable to the condensation of moisture are not present in the region influenced by the cold Humboldt Current.

Some evaluations have been made of the direct contribution of dew to water supply. Under some conditions, relatively large amounts of water are condensed on plant foliage and drop to the ground. Regardless of the magnitude of these direct contributions, the reduction in transpirational losses are great, for other things being equal, transpiration will be proportional to the water deficit of the air.

Surface Supplies.   Surface-water supplies are manifested in lakes, streams, and springs; but spring flows, and much of the low-stage stream flows, are derived from ground water. Although the two types are treated separately in this chapter, the fact must not be overlooked that they are interrelated.

Of the world's land surface, some 56,250,000 sq miles, approximately 10 per cent, is covered by perpetual snow and ice. While accurate data on the amount of water stored in the solid phase are not available, it is known that the volume is tremendous and that if it were to melt great changes in ocean levels would occur. Soundings in the antarctic have indicated that in places the ice cap is about 1½ miles thick. One of the objectives of the International Geophysical Year was to obtain better information on the amount of water stored in polar regions.

Thorarinson, in 1940, estimated the area covered by glacial ice to be as shown in Table 2.2.

Table 2.2

Land Area	Square Miles
Continental Europe	3,880
Continental Asia	43,270
Continental North America	30,900
Continental South America	9,600
South polar regions	5,020,450
North polar regions	721,150
Africa	8
New Zealand	386
New Guinea	6
Total	5,829,650

At present, the great bulk of the polar ice fields does not constitute a usable water supply.

The world's total runoff has been estimated to be of the order of 20 billion acre-ft annually, of which some 12 billion is from 80 major rivers. Although man has long been interested in stream flow, much of the early information obtained concerns high-water marks, which are not necessarily a true index of discharge because of possible variations in the stream channel during the period of record. Flood-height readings were made on the Tiber as early as 413 B.C. These data indicate that the flood of A.D. 1589 was the greatest of record for that stream. Measurements of high-water levels have been kept continuously at the Roda gauge on the Nile River since A.D. 622 and on the Danube for more than a thousand years. Daily discharge records of the Rhine River at Basel, Switzerland, were started as early as 1809. In the United States, incomplete but authentic records of flood flow have been kept for about three-fourths of a century.

A characteristic of flow in many streams is the wide variability in discharge during various parts of the year. In semiarid and arid climates a great part of the total runoff occurs within a relatively short period. Figure 2.6 illustrates the normal seasonal flow of 17 streams in western United States. Those streams which have their major flow during the growing season are especially well suited to irrigation. Hydropower development is best served by streams with rather uniform flows. Fortunately, in certain areas, through regulation of stream flow by storage, many purposes can be served.

The following selected list of important streams of the world names them by continents. Others could be enumerated.

Africa   Nile, Zambezi, Congo, Niger
Asia   Yangtze, Hwang Ho, Lena, Ob, Amur, Amu Darya, Aldan, Syr Darya, Tigris, Euphrates, Indus, Ganges, Brahmaputra, Irrawaddy, Mekong
Europe   Volga, Dnieper, Danube, Elbe, Po, Rhine, Rhone, Seine
Oceania   Murray
South America   Amazon, Plate, Orinoco, São Francisco
North America   Mississippi, Yukon, Columbia, St. Lawrence, Fraser, Sacramento–San Joaquin, Mackenzie, Colorado, Rio Grande

Africa. The four rivers listed for Africa are all major streams. The Nile, which has played a very important role in history, is the longest in the world, some 4100 miles. It has a drainage basin of about 1,100,000 sq miles and an average annual discharge of approximately 75 million acre-ft.

The Zambezi, draining the east-central portion of the continent and flowing into the Indian Ocean, is a major stream that has been largely undeveloped. At present, a major multipurpose project (Kariba) is under way. The storage capacity of the reservoir is of such magnitude (about 130 million acre-ft) that it will impound about four times as much water as Lake Mead on the Colorado River, which at present is the largest artificial reservoir. The Congo River is a stream with great power potentialities. The Belgian government has a plan to harness the river at Inga,

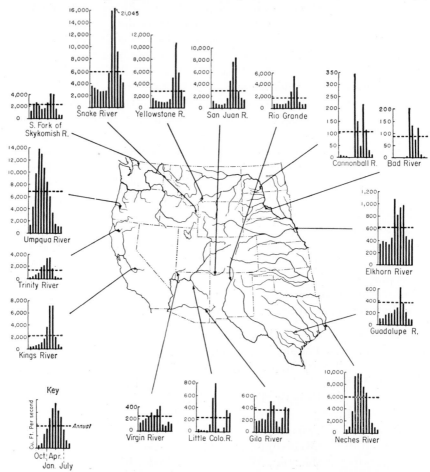

Fig. 2.6 Normal seasonal flow of selected streams in western United States. Median monthly and annual flow of representative streams at points indicated, in terms of cubic feet per second, periods of 10 or more water years, October to September. (*After U.S. Dept. Agr., Misc. Pub.* 670.)

which would provide more power than the Kariba project. The Niger is the fourth largest stream of the continent.

Asia. The Yangtze and the Hwang Ho are the two main rivers in China. The former drains an area of 750,000 sq miles and for the first 1500 miles has an average gradient of 100 ft per mile. Both streams carry large amounts of silt, especially the latter. While extensive use is made of the streams for navigation and irrigation, lack of flood control is a serious problem, as fluctuations of as much as 100 ft in water levels are not uncommon on parts of the Yangtze.

Many of the Asian streams that flow to the north are ice bound for as much as a third of the year. In the interior portion of the continent the rivers discharge mainly into seas. The Syr Darya, with an average annual discharge of 17 million acre-ft, and the Amu Darya, with 52 million, discharge into Lake Aral. Both streams are undergoing extensive development.

In the Near East, the Tigris and Euphrates are the principal streams. They are important not only for their present potentialities but also because of the high degree of use in ancient times. The combined average annual flow is about 55 million acre-ft.

The Indus, draining parts of India and most of Pakistan, is a major stream, with peak flows approaching 750,000 cfs. The stream was extensively developed during the past 100 years and now serves a large irrigated area.

Khosla, using a formula in which he assumes that temperature can be taken to be a complete index of all the various factors which are responsible for loss of rainfall to runoff, has estimated the average annual runoff of India to be 1,356,000,000 acre-ft. Of this amount 397,090,000 acre-ft is provided by the Ganges system and 308,950,000 by the Brahmaputra. As of 1951, only 5.6 per cent of the total amount was being used for irrigation and power. Plans for a marked increase are under way, and the great multipurpose Bhraka-Nangal project on a tributary of the Indus is nearing completion.

Southeast Asia is an area of high average rainfall, and the combined flow of the numerous minor streams is great.

Europe. The Danube River, which drains part of eight countries, has an average annual discharge of about 228 million acre-ft. Because the danger of flood is great, a careful patrol is maintained. The upper reaches of the European rivers are highly developed for power, and in the lowlands the streams are important means of transportation. The Dnieper River flows into the Black Sea and the Volga into the Caspian. Both streams are being developed for multipurpose use by the Soviet Union.

Oceania. Of all the continents, Australia has the lowest runoff. The principal river is the Murray, with a natural annual flow of about 11 million acre-ft from a drainage basin of about 414,000 sq miles. The flow of the Murray is to be augmented by diverting flows from the southeastern drainage. The runoff for the entire area of Australia, approximately 3 million sq miles, is estimated at about 210 million acre-ft, 40 per cent of which is from minor short streams on the eastern slope.

New Zealand, which is a part of Oceania, has a more favorable water supply and rainfall distribution than does Australia. The short high-gradient streams present serious flood hazards. The longest stream, the Waikato, is only about 200 miles in length. The power potentialities of the north island are largely developed.

South America. The world's largest river, the Amazon, is on this continent. The river drains some 2,722,000 sq miles of area which has an average annual rainfall of 60 to 80 in. (The estimated annual discharge is $3\frac{1}{2}$ billion acre-ft.) Its principal present use is for navigation.

The Plata River, with the Paraná and other tributaries, is an important drainage system in the southeastern part of the continent.

The Orinoco and the São Francisco, although dwarfed in magnitude by the Amazon and Plata, are important streams of South America.

North America. In North America the major stream is the Mississippi. It has an average annual flow of nearly a half billion acre-feet and drains about a million and a quarter square miles in central United States. Included among its tributaries are the Missouri, Ohio, and Tennessee Rivers. The main stream has a relatively flat gradient. The Yukon River, the second largest stream on the continent, drains a large part of Alaska and discharges into the Bering Sea. The Columbia, with an average annual discharge of 180 million acre-ft, is the third largest stream. Approximately 40 per cent of its flow originates in Canada. Multipurpose projects have been developed on this stream, and others have been planned. The St. Lawrence is also an international stream and is fourth in size on the continent, with approximately 150 million acre-ft annually. The Great Lakes, which are in part associated with this river system, have a storage approximately equal to the amount of rainfall on the whole United States during a $2\frac{1}{2}$-year period.

Over 6 per cent of Canada's surface area is composed of fresh water. The Fraser River, the most important stream in British Columbia, and the Mackenzie are other important streams in the northern part of the continent.

The Sacramento–San Joaquin river system drains the central valley of California. In this area, where the mean annual runoff under natural conditions is estimated to have been of the order of 32 million acre-ft, a high degree of multiuse projects has been developed. It is also an area where extensive use of ground water has been made in conjunction with surface water.

The Colorado River drainage basin represents about one-twelfth the area of the United States. As the average precipitation over the drainage basin is low, the runoff is correspondingly low, being about 16 million acre-ft annually. The stream is important in that it is the principal fresh-water source in a vast arid country. Extensive developments have been made on the stream, and others will follow.

The Rio Grande, while not a large river, plays an important international role in an area of low fresh-water supply. The average annual discharge is slightly in excess of 5 million acre-ft.

The major drainage basins of the United States are shown in Figure 2.7. For additional information on streams of the United States, the reader

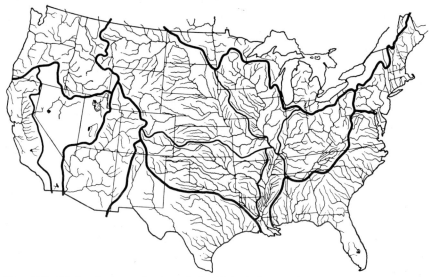

Fig. 2.7 Major drainage basins of the United States. (*After National Resources Board, Report of the Water Planning Committee, Part* III.)

is referred to Volume II of the President's Water Commission, *Ten Great Rivers.*

Soviet Union. Average long-time characteristics of three sections of the Soviet Union have been studied. One area is near the western frontier, a second in the middle Volga drainage, and a third in the southeast in the Nukus area. The results obtained are given in Table 2.3.

Table 2.3

Area	Average annual precipitation, mm	Average annual evaporation, mm	Average annual runoff, mm
Minsk................	600	500	300
Kuibyshev............	400 ±	700	80
Nukus................	100 ±	2000 ±	0

Ground Waters. Although on a world-wide basis, at least 90 per cent of the water used comes from surface sources, we must not overlook the great quantities of fresh water stored underground. For the United States,

Thomas has estimated these quantities to be in excess of all the nation's surface reservoirs and lakes, including the Great Lakes. This volume would be equal to 35 years of runoff.

In 1950 the aggregate withdrawal from United States ground-water basins was 30 to 35 billion gal per day, or about 18 per cent of the total use. Some 60 per cent of this supply was used for irrigation. In Germany, about 85 per cent of the water used is obtained from wells.

While ground water has no direct use for navigation, recreation, hydro-power, or waste disposal, it is important in maintaining stream flow, and it is the source of springs. A characteristic of ground water is its relative constancy of composition and temperature. Losses from evaporation are of no consequence.

Where bountiful surface supplies are available, ground waters are not normally developed. On the other hand where surface supplies are marginal, conjunctional use of ground-water aquifers makes it possible to store water from years of excess runoff for use during dry periods.

In the southwestern part of the United States, extensive uses of ground water have been made. The amount of water being pumped from ground-water basins in California, Texas, Arizona, and New Mexico is estimated to be about 14 billion gal per day. In fact there are excessive overdrafts in some areas. For example, in the high plains of Texas the rate of with-drawal is at least twenty-five times as great as the recharge. In certain areas in California, pumping has decreased the water levels to such a point that sea water is invading the fresh-water basin. In some cases the lowering in the water table has resulted in considerable ground subsidence. Besides being a threat to the supply of water, overdraft may increase the danger of pollution.

The development of highly efficient deep well pumps and the wide-spread use of relatively cheap power have made it possible in many cases for the farmer and small towns and cities to develop adequate and safe water supplies. Large cities use ground-water supplies, but seldom depend upon them for the entire supply.

While ground water may be found in a wide range of formations, the principal occurrence is in the loose, or only slightly consolidated, sands and gravels. In limestone formations, solution channels may be present and serve for the storage or transmission of water. Such waters are apt to be hard, that is, they contain relatively large amounts of calcium. Cracks and joints in otherwise solid rock can also store ground water.

The rate of ground-water movement is usually very slow, often of the order of only a few feet per year. In coarse gravel the rate can be relatively rapid. The quantity of water moving through the aquifer is dependent upon the hydraulic gradient, the cross-sectional area of the medium, and the permeability of the medium.

Figure 2.8 presents a general picture of the ground-water basins of the United States. The Atlantic and Gulf Coastal Plains have the country's greatest reserve of fresh ground water, while the Great Plains region is generally deficient. Scattered throughout the country are areas of saline ground water. The development of a low-cost method of saline-water reclamation would prove a boon to many localities.

Watercourses in which ground water can be replenished by perennial streams

Buried valleys not now occupied by perennial streams

Unconsolidated and semiconsolidated aquifers

Consolidated-rock aquifers

Both unconsolidated and consolidated-rock aquifers

Not known to be underlain by aquifers that will generally yield as much as 50 g.p.m. to wells

Fig. 2.8 Ground water areas of the United States. Patterns show areas underlain by aquifers generally capable of yielding to individual wells 50 gpm or more of water containing not more than 2000 ppm of dissolved solids (includes some areas where more highly mineralized water is actually used). (*After Water, Yearbook of Agriculture,* 1955.)

Augmentation of Natural Supplies. *Reclamation of Saline Waters.* The augmentation of our fresh-water supplies with reclaimed saline waters is a subject much discussed, even by the layman. Chapter 3 deals with this topic; so no further mention of the subject will be made in this chapter.

Artificial Nucleation. Over a long period of time man has been interested in inducing rain, especially in arid regions. Aborigines have resorted to various rituals, and others have prayed for rain. Explosives have been detonated in the atmosphere. About a dozen years ago, experiments involving the sprinkling of dry ice from airplanes were tried. Later it was found that silver iodide caused ice crystals to form in the temperature range of 5 to 25°F, a much higher temperature than under natural conditions. One approach has been to locate thermal generators which release iodide crystals at strategic locations on the ground so that the crystals are carried upward to the storm clouds. Special physiographic features must be present for this method to be effective. Bowen, using airplanes to carry the nucleating agent, has obtained good results in the Snowy Mountain area of Australia.

Although the practice of cloud seeding is used in various parts of the world, a great difference of opinion exists regarding its potential for increasing total precipitation. In time the real value of the practice will be determined.

2.3   Uses and Development

Water can be considered a resource if it serves, or can be made to perform, a useful purpose. This usefulness of a stream is not necessarily dependent upon the total discharge. Many of the streams that serve the greatest needs are relatively small in comparison to the major rivers of the world.

The time sequence in man's use of water is unknown, but it probably developed somewhat as follows: drinking, cleansing, transportation, irrigation, power, and industry. Just where recreational use fits into the sequence is not clear, but some of the older civilizations recognized it and made wide use of baths and fountains.

Extensive uses of water were first made for irrigation. The Tigris and Euphrates valley in Mesopotamia, the Nile valley, and the Indus River valley have all been considered as the site of the earliest development. In any event, it has been at least 5000 years since this practice began. Some of the old systems and structures were of monumental proportions, requiring a high degree of technical skills to build. The Nahrwan Canal in Mesopotamia is estimated to have been 400 ft wide and 40 ft deep. As early as 2000 B.C., a 12-mile canal was built which diverted the Nile River into Lake Moeris. The 700-mile-long Imperial Canal in China, which served both for irrigation and transportation, was built in A.D. 700. Extensive domestic and municipal water-supply systems, in the form of wells, cisterns, reservoirs, and aqueducts, were built by the early civilizations. The Romans were especially effective in developing municipal water-supply and sewage systems. As early as 312 B.C., an 11-mile-long aqueduct was built into Rome, and by A.D. 52 there were nine aqueducts delivering water to that city. The aqueduct at Segovia, built in A.D. 109, is still in use.

As man develops new uses for water the demand increases, and as water demand per capita as well as the population increase our problems of water supplies become more acute. Associated with the increase in use is the deterioration in water quality.

Trends in Use. As a country changes from a rural to an urban economy, the pattern of water use changes. In the United States, municipal and industrial demands for water have changed greatly during the present century. The U.S. Geological Survey estimated water use in the United States in 1955 to have been 63 billion gal, or approximately 13 per cent of the country's runoff. Of this amount, 83 per cent came from surface sources and 17 per cent was ground water. Irrigation accounted for about half the use, although industry was a heavy user also.

Irrigation use is largely a consumptive use, as water transpired by the plants and evaporated from the soil is lost to the atmosphere. Much of the water used in industry, however, is used for cooling or cleansing and

Table 2.4   Water Withdrawals in 1950 and Estimates of United States Water Needs in 1975

Use	Estimated withdrawals, 1950		Estimated requirement, 1975	
	Gal per day, billions	Per cent of total	Gal per day, billions	Per cent of total
Municipal and rural............	17*	9	25	7
Industrial.....................	80†	43	215	62
Irrigation.....................	88	48	110	31

* About one-half the municipal supplies are used industrially.
† Includes about 15 billion gal per day of salt water for cooling.
Figures denote use and not total consumption.

is therefore available at a lower quality for reuse. The water requirements of some industrial processes are extremely high. Some 250 tons of water is required to process 1 ton of wood pulp, and for every ton of coal burned about 800 tons of water is used. On the other hand, the generation of hydropower does not affect the quantity or quality of the water, except for the losses that might accrue from storage.

Table 2.4 presents The President's Materials Policy Commission estimates of the United States total water withdrawals for 1950 and the expected water requirements for 1975. As that Commission saw the future, the industrial fresh-water use in the United States will be more than twice the irrigation use by 1975. It is doubtful if this will prove to be the case as irrigation is extending into the more humid areas at a rapid rate, while industry is tending to reuse fresh water and make wider use of saline waters.

Domestic and Industrial Uses. A moderately active average individual in a temperate-zone climate requires about 3 qt of water per day to exist. Part of this supply would come from liquid and part from the oxidation of the food eaten. Under desert conditions the requirement would be much greater, even as high as several gallons per hour. In the moist, warm climate of the tropics, the water demand is not great. Here, a high rate of activity cannot long be maintained as the body cannot adequately dissipate heat and clear itself of wastes.

Although the daily per capita water requirements of people under primitive conditions is very low (5 to 6 gal), the average daily per capita

Fig. 2.9   An irrigated orchard. (*Photograph by U.S. Department of Agriculture.*)

use in the United States is about 140 gal. In some countries, the use is less than 10.

Estimates of present-day uses of water by United States industry, and forecast for 1975, have been given. Of the amount used in 1950, industry provided much of its own supply, largely from ground-water sources. So long as it is cheaper to pump water on a once-through operation than it is to provide and maintain a recirculation system, industry in general will continue to operate on a once-through basis. While the actual amount of water consumed by municipalities and industry is not great in proportion to total use, the resultant deterioration in water quality can be very great.

Irrigation. N. D. Gulhati, formerly Secretary General of the International Commission on Irrigation and Drainage, has compiled the most complete census on world irrigation available. In 1955 he published his findings for 60 countries under the title "Irrigation in the World: A Global Review." His survey indicates that approximately 300 million acres are presently irrigated annually and that the development of additional acreages is taking place at a rapid rate.

Table 2.5 contains information on the 12 countries with the greatest acreages under irrigation. China, the leading country from an acreage point of view, has approximately one-fourth of the cultivable area under irrigation. Egypt, on the other hand, is dependent entirely upon irrigation for crop production. China and India together make up about 45 per cent of the world's irrigated acreage. In both countries the practice of irrigation is very old. Extensive use is made of small surface reservoirs (tanks).

Table 2.5 Irrigated Acreages and Land Areas in the 12 Countries with the Greatest Irrigated Area*

Country	Area, thousands of acres			Percentage of irrigated area to total area	Percentage of irrigated area to cultivated area
	Total	Cultivated annually	Irrigated		
China........	2,405,837	335,000	77,275	3.2	23.0
India.........	810,777	296,400	59,057	7.3	19.9
United States..	1,934,256	340,998	26,233	1.4	7.7
Pakistan.......	230,000	45,000	21,310	9.1	47.4
Soviet Union...	5,502,917	....	16,062	0.3	
Indonesia......	470,565	....	10,665	2.3	
Japan.........	91,051	12,479	9,430	1.0	75.6
Iraq..........	109,821	....	8,150	7.4	
Egypt........	247,100	7,000	7,000	2.8	100
France........	136,360	78,219	6,178	4.5	7.9
Mexico........	486,787	57,700	5,330	1.1	9.2
Italy..........	76,370	54,856	5,190	6.8	9.5

* Information from N. D. Gulhati, "Irrigation in the World: A Global Review," International Commission on Irrigation and Drainage, Delhi, India, 1955.

Although more than 90 per cent of the irrigated acreage of the United States is to be found in the 17 Western states, irrigation is expanding rapidly in other parts of the country. Indications are that the United States census for 1960 will find a total irrigated acreage in excess of 32 million. The 10 leading states in descending order of irrigated acreages are: California, Texas, Idaho, Colorado, Montana, Nebraska, Oregon, Wyoming, Arizona, and Utah. Arizona has the highest percentage of its farm land irrigated. Much of the irrigation development of the future will be part of great multipurpose projects in major river-basin development.

The Soviet Deputy Minister of Agriculture N. A. Askochensky

reported to the Training Center on Irrigation and Drainage held in the Soviet Union during the fall of 1956 that the Soviet Union had 10.3 million hectares (26 million acres) of irrigated crops in 1955, with systems capable of irrigating an additional 1.1 million hectares. This represented an increase of 1.9 million hectares in the interval from 1950 to 1955. In the Central Asian and Transcaucasian Republics about three-fourths of the cultivated land is irrigated. In fact in a part of this region, as in Kazak, agriculture is not feasible without irrigation. All arable land of the country is held by some 86,000 collective farms and 5100 state farms.

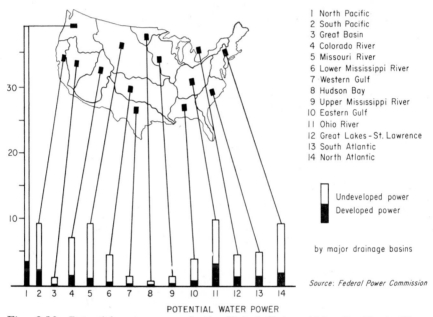

1 North Pacific
2 South Pacific
3 Great Basin
4 Colorado River
5 Missouri River
6 Lower Mississippi River
7 Western Gulf
8 Hudson Bay
9 Upper Mississippi River
10 Eastern Gulf
11 Ohio River
12 Great Lakes - St. Lawrence
13 South Atlantic
14 North Atlantic

Undeveloped power
Developed power

by major drainage basins

Source: Federal Power Commission

POTENTIAL WATER POWER

Fig. 2.10 Potential water power in the United States. (*After President's Water Policy Commission, A Water Policy for the American People, vol.* 1, 1950.) (*Federal Power Commission.*)

The Amu Darya, Sir Darya, Chu, Murghab, Ural Rivers in Asia, and the Dnieper and Don Rivers in Eastern Europe provide the main source of irrigation water. Because of the large supplies of surface water extensive development of ground water has not been necessary.

In the fall of 1956, Russia had 18 major design and survey institutes which employed some 6000 engineers and technicians. Plans provide for a marked increase in irrigation in central Asia and in the European area north and west of the Caspian Sea. The sixth Five-Year Plan provides for the irrigation of 80 million hectares.

While attention has been directed to irrigation projects, they are actually multipurpose in nature. The Don-Volga project is a multipurpose one combining irrigation, flood control, hydropower generation, and navigation. In fact in the Kuibyshev, Stalingrad, and Tsymlyansky projects, a large percentage of the capital invested is for power, with transportation second and irrigation third.

Hydropower. Power from water is derived from a renewable natural resource and therefore should be considered in the plans for the multiuse development of fresh-water resources.

Various estimates of the fresh-water resources have been made. Young has estimated the hydropower potential of the world at 20×10^{12} kwhr. The U.S. Geological Survey estimated, in 1955, that the world's potential hydropower, based on ordinary minimum stream flow, to be of the order shown in Table 2.6.

Table 2.6

Continent	Horsepower, millions	Per cent developed
Africa	274	0.5
Asia	151	9.6
Europe	58	86.0
North America	84	57.0
South America	67	6.6
Oceania	20	8.3
Total	664	20

Nearly half the world's potential hydropower is in Africa. A vast project is now being developed on the Zambezi River in Rhodesia, while a much larger project is under consideration for the Congo.

The figures presented do not represent the full power potential, for with storage the amount of firm power developed could be very much greater. For example, Germany, with a power potential based on minimum stream flow of 2 million hp, has doubled the output through the storage of peak flow.

On a unit-area basis, Switzerland has the highest hydropower potential, with Formosa second.

Recreational Use. In areas of abundant streams and lakes, adequate recreational features can be provided; but in arid and semiarid areas, fresh-water recreation is associated with storage facilities. This often leads to a conflict in point of view, as suppliers of domestic water fear contamination of their supplies. Power and irrigation reservoirs, however, are widely used by the public. A disadvantage of some of the reservoirs used for this purpose is the wide fluctuation in water-surface elevation.

Table 2.7   Developed and Potential Water Power in Thousands of Horsepower, as of January, 1955

Continent	Country	Developed	Potential	Per cent
North America..........	....	52,628	92,000	57.2
	Canada	16,684	36,000	45.6
	United States	34,700	36,500	91.1
	Mexico	900	8,490	10.6
South America..........	....	4,148	62,700	6.6
	Argentina	140	5,400	2.6
	Brazil	2,585	20,000	13.9
	Chile	550	7,000	7.8
	Peru	325	6,400	5.1
Europe................	....	54,793	63,780	85.9
	France	9,400	6,000	156.6
	Germany	4,000	2,000	200.0
	Italy	9,500	6,000	158.3
	Spain	3,000	3,500	85.7
	Sweden	5,800	4,000	145.0
	Switzerland	4,550	3,000	151.6
	United Kingdom	1,100	750	146.6
	Soviet Union	6,000	14,000	42.9
Africa................	....	1,249	250,990	0.49
	Algeria	278	300	92.7
	Belgian Congo	355	130,000	0.27
	Rhodesia	41	3,500	1.2
	Tanganyika	29	4,000	0.71
	Uganda	126	4,000	3.15
Asia..................	....	14,949	155,700	9.6
	China	4	22,000	0.19
	Formosa	470	1,000	47.0
	India	1,000	27,000	3.7
	Japan	10,000	12,000	83.3
	Korea	1,800	3,000	60.6
	Soviet Union	1,125	64,000	1.76
Oceania................	....	1,952	23,350	8.3
	Australia	440	1,000	44.0
	Java	140	1,100	12.8
	New Zealand	1,193	5,000	23.4
	Philippine Islands	110	2,000	5.5
Total................	....	129,718	648,620	20.3

Information from *U.S. Geol. Survey Circ.* 367.

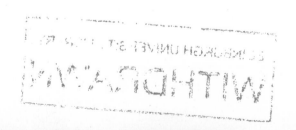

Table 2.8   Potential Hydroelectric Power in the United States
(Summary of developed and potential power)

Area	Developed power, Jan. 1, 1950			Potential power		
	Number of projects	Capacity, kw*	Average annual amount generated, 1000 kwhr	Number of projects	Capacity, kw	Average annual amount generated, 1000 kwhr
United States total..........	552	16,500,271	87,111,350	2,363	104,570,396	478,209,855
North Atlantic..............	89	1,734,960	7,407,400	237	9,181,960	27,879,200
South Atlantic..............	49	1,172,135	3,420,000	143	4,877,635	15,133,500
Eastern Gulf...............	17	576,823	2,781,000	77	3,730,813	15,580,600
Ohio River................	46	2,996,405	15,131,500	142	9,849,505	42,219,400
Great Lakes–St. Lawrence...	103	1,192,233	7,817,400	228	4,435,933	25,561,400
Hudson Bay...............	1	4,000	19,000	11	24,200	110,300
Upper Mississippi River.....	28	385,330	1,944,000	131	1,178,030	5,604,300
Missouri River.............	26	608,648	3,406,800	172	9,219,108	44,424,300
Lower Mississippi River.....	8	301,300	964,000	99	4,656,800	13,806,700
Western Gulf...............	9	178,800	628,000	61	1,078,375	3,607,005
Colorado River.............	17	1,296,400	6,814,650	99	7,029,000	35,838,350
Great Basin................	23	315,000	934,000	59	986,300	3,810,100
South Pacific..............	70	2,195,920	12,411,000	259	9,508,520	50,716,000
North Pacific..............	66	3,542,317	23,432,600	645	38,814,217	193,918,700

* Plants of 2500 kw capacity and over.
SOURCE: Federal Power Commission. (After President's Water Resources Policy Commission, vol. I.)

Major Water-storage Facilities.   Present-day water-storage projects are normally of such magnitude that it is necessary that they serve more than one purpose. Table 2.9 gives information on some very large water-storage projects, all multipurpose projects.

Table 2.9   Selected List of Major Water-storage Facilities

Dam	Country	River	Height, ft	Reservoir capacity, acre-ft
Hoover...................	United States	Colorado	726	32,000,000
Grand Coulee.............	United States	Columbia	550	9,645,000
Bhakra*..................	India	Sutlej	680	7,200,000
President Alémán.........	Mexico	Balsas	230	6,500,000
Shasta...................	United States	Sacramento	602	4,500,000
Falcon...................	Mexico	Rio Grande	160	4,000,000
Eildon...................	Australia	Goulburn	260	2,750,000

* Nearing completion. The Kariba Dam on the Zambezi River in Southern Rhodesia is now under construction. When completed, it will impound 130 million acre-ft of water.

2.4 Water Pollution

Associated with the increased use of water is the increased potential for artificial water pollution. Fortunately the danger is being recognized in many countries, and action is being taken to minimize the hazard. Natural pollution occurs from silt and salines. The former is most prevalent during flood flows, while the latter is usually associated with low stream flows, not so much from the total amount of salt but because of the low quality of the water resulting from the high salt concentrations. Flood waters can overflow highly saline areas, causing the initial flood flows to be high in salt.

Fig. 2.11   Moccasin Power Plant, a unit in the San Francisco municipal water system.

In well-aerated waters the rate of organic-matter breakdown can be rapid, but there is always danger that the safe limit will be exceeded. The pollution load man has imposed on the water system is exceedingly great. Packing-house wastes have an oxygen demand about ten times as great as domestic waste.

Some 10 years ago the U.S. Public Health Service made a study of 11 major river valleys in the United States, covering 4409 municipalities and 3413 industrial plants. Of the cities, 43 per cent were discharging raw untreated waste into the streams, while 57 per cent of the factories were doing likewise. In some streams over half the low flows were composed of sewage water. Of 9000 sewer systems, serving about 75 million people, one-third were discharging untreated sewage into streams.

Many of the major waste-disposal systems include processing plants, which make the organic matter in waste available for use and also utilize the by-product gas. The next major step in areas of water shortage will be to make the discharge water available for use.

2.5 Conservation

Conservation of our water resource should not mean nonuse, but rather the most effective use. Some uses are consumptive in that they deplete the supply; others have little effect on total volume but may naturally degrade quality. All aspects of use and value should be considered in the development of water supplies.

While we may be hopeful of artificially increasing our natural supply of fresh water, we should strive to increase materially the efficiency of use. Some of these steps are briefly discussed.

An important consideration in water conservation is the development of adequate legal and administrative procedures governing the use and control of water. This must be true not only locally but at the state, interstate, and international levels. On large international streams in humid climates flood control is usually the dominant problem, while in arid climates water conservation is of major interest.

Another social approach to the water problem would be to attempt to impress upon the people coming from humid climates to arid regions the need to conserve water. Under their native habitat, they have been profligate in the use of water. There is need to consider the water resource beyond the water tap.

Cost is usually the factor determining what actions will be taken to conserve water. So long as a city can obtain another supply cheaper than it can reclaim the waste water dumped into the seas, or so long as industry can operate cheaper on a once-through use than by installing a reuse system, they will do so. For the nation as a whole, water costs average about 5 cents per 1000 gal. Reclamation of waste water lost to the sea will some day be widely employed to conserve water.

The greatest savings of water will come from eliminating wasteful practices and by reducing evaporation losses from free water surfaces and from plants. In addition, better management of watersheds will yield more and higher-quality water.

One of the great sources of loss is seepage from unlined canals passing through highly permeable soils. The damage done lies not alone in the loss of water, but there is also the possibility of creating drainage and salinity difficulties. The problem can be met through the use of proper lining or the use of closed systems.

The amount of water loss in irrigation is very great. Much can be done to improve the systems and practices of irrigation. The improvements will result in less loss to runoff and deep percolation and in more efficient placement of the water, so that the plants can better utilize the water. Through proper fertilizer practices more efficient water uses will also be obtained, and through selection and breeding plants will be developed that are better suited to irrigated areas.

Weeds generally and phreatophytes in particular are large consumers of water. The latter are plants, usually of little or no economic value, which obtain their water mainly from ground water. The most prominent plants in this group in the southwestern United States include willows (*Salix*), salt cedar (*Tamarix gallica*), cotton wood (*Populus*), and salt grass (*Distichlis spicata*).

Control lies either in the removal of the vegetation or in the lowering of the ground-water level below the principal rooting depths. Both are considered expensive at the present time. Robinson of the U.S. Geological Survey in 1953 estimated that the use of water by phreatophytes in the 14 Western states to be about 17 million acre-ft. This is an amount equal to the natural flow of the Colorado River.

The rate of recharge of ground-water basins can often be increased through the practice of water spreading, i.e., diverting water from natural channels and causing it to spread over adjacent porous lands or into pits and shafts which tap highly permeable formations. Although not a widely used practice, it is extensively employed in certain areas where ground-water withdrawals exceed natural recharge, such as is the case in the south coastal basin of Southern California. Here, the highly permeable upper portions of the alluvial fans make ideal spreading grounds. If the spreading area is vegetatively covered, the drop in infiltration rates with time will be much less than if the area were bare. This is especially true if the water contains silt.

Shafts are not effective where the water is ladened with silt or where the temperature of the water is conducive to the growth of microorganisms which can readily reduce the permeability of the strata which the shaft penetrates.

The danger of contaminating the ground water in an alluvium through water spreading is nil if the pumped wells are not located immediately adjacent to the spreading grounds. This would not be true for ground-water aquifers in formations where the water enters through cracks, fissures, or solution channels.

Although the heat of vaporization of water is high, large amounts of water are lost from reservoirs and natural water bodies by evaporation. As structural coverings for large water-surface areas are not economical, considerable attention has been given to the use of evaporation-suppression agents which form a very thin layer (monomolecular layer) on the surface of the water. Cetyl alcohol is an example of one of the materials being tested. Results of tests have varied from little or no benefits to large reductions in evaporation. Laboratory studies at the East Africa Meteorological Station at Nairobi showed normal reductions of 50 per cent to as high as 70 per cent on hot sunny days.

While reductions in loss from large bodies of water have not been so great as those reported above, the Commonwealth Scientific and Industrial Research Council of Australia has had some very encouraging results with these trials on large reservoirs.

A successful evaporation-suppression agent should be low in cost, have a long life, spread easily, re-form readily after being disturbed, and be nontoxic to fish life. For use on domestic supplies it should have the additional characteristics of being odorless and colorless. It should present no taste problem, nor be toxic to humans, and it should not interfere with normal water treatment. The development of a satisfactory evaporation-suppression agent would be a great boon to areas where water costs are high.

While means will undoubtedly be found at reasonable costs to augment the fresh-water supplies in some areas through sea-water reclamation and precipitation nucleation, water conservation will remain the most important approach to the maintenance of fresh-water supplies.

3

Fresh Water from Saline Sources

EVERETT D. HOWE

PROFESSOR OF MECHANICAL ENGINEERING
UNIVERSITY OF CALIFORNIA, BERKELEY

3.1 Introduction

Considered as a resource, water is probably the most essential of all natural resources. This follows from the fact that men have perished at sea and in desert areas when food was still available and water was the only lack. Likewise, water is as essential to the making of steel as to the growing of vegetables. Thus, as the world population increases, requiring more and more land to be placed under cultivation, and producing a demand for more manufactured goods, the demand for high-quality water has increased beyond the quantity which can be supplied from readily available sources of the normal type, i.e., from stream diversion, from surface reservoirs arranged to collect precipitation, and from underground pools. The expense accompanying the long-distance transportation of water, for example, from the San Joaquin delta to San Diego, is so great as to lead one to question whether suitable water could be obtained from nearby saline sources by some process of demineralization.

The quality of water for potable supplies and for irrigation is nearly the same. The U.S. Public Health Service regards potable water as completely satisfactory if it contains not more than 500 ppm of total dissolved minerals, including not more than 125 ppm of magnesium ions, not more than 250 ppm of chloride ions, and not more than 250 ppm of sulfate ions. This specification also states that potable supplies must not contain over 1000 ppm of dissolved salts. Although there is no equally specific criterion for irrigation supplies, the use of water containing more than 500 ppm of dissolved minerals has proved quite unsatisfactory in semi-arid California. While there are some parts of California where irrigation water has become quite brackish, the major source of large quantities of additional water which might be made useful through demineralization is the Pacific Ocean. This water, like all sea water, contains about

56

35,000 ppm of total dissolved solids, of which nearly 30,000 ppm is sodium chloride, one of the most soluble of materials. Whether or not sea water can be demineralized cheaply enough to compete with natural supplies requires a thorough analysis of the economics of the many possible processes as well as an investigation of schemes not presently utilized commercially.

Price Trends.   Fresh water for domestic, municipal, and irrigation uses is in demand throughout the world today. The prices paid for it vary widely, known values being as low as $1 per acre-foot for irrigation water and as high as about $1000 per acre-foot for distilled municipal water on certain islands. Maximum present prices in the United States range from $40 per acre-foot for irrigation water to $125 per acre-foot for municipal supplies. Water recovered from the ocean or other saline sources would be competitive with fresh water from "natural" sources only if the costs of production were equal to or less than the above figures. The price trend of "natural" waters in the United States is rising since it is necessary to utilize waters from sources increasingly distant from the point of use. Likewise, the trend of costs of demineralized water is downward because of the influence of the extensive research programs currently in progress.

Existing Plants.   Present-day plants for demineralizing water are relatively numerous but are limited to comparatively small sizes and to distillation using the multieffect and compression-distillation processes. Small plants are to be found in many of the larger cities of the United States and are used for the production of the distilled water preferred by some people for potable supply and required for maintaining storage batteries. Plants producing up to 40,000 gal per day are found on board ships in most of the oceans of the world. The largest multieffect plants are those under construction at Kuwait (Persian Gulf) and at Aruba in the Netherlands West Indies, both scheduled for completion in 1958. The Kuwait plant consists of four four-stage flash-type distiller units and will yield 2.5 million gal per day. The Aruba plant consists of five six-effect submerged-coil-type units and will produce 2.7 million gal per day. Costs of fuel for the Aruba plant are charged in part to a steam turbo-generator unit which is placed between the boiler and distiller plant and generates power at the rate of 10,000 kw.

Also under construction in South Africa is a large electrodialysis plant for desalting the water pumped from mines. This plant will handle 3.0 million gal of water per day and will reduce the mineral concentration from 3000 ppm to 1000 ppm.

Separation Processes.   Schemes for separating potable water from saline brines may be broadly classified as physical processes, chemical processes, and electrical processes. Physical processes would include distillation, freezing, adsorption, diffusion effects, and osmosis. Chemical processes would include precipitation, ion exchange, and hydration; electrical processes would include various applications of electrolysis and any other electrical or magnetic phenomena utilized. While relatively few phenomena have been utilized in demineralizing water commercially, experimental work is being carried on in many areas. It is the intent of this chapter to review the basic particulars of several of the existing and potential separation schemes.

3.2 Distillation Processes

Multieffect Distillation. Distillation is the process of separating pure water from brine by evaporating the water, removing the vapor from the evaporator, and then condensing it. This separation process is possible because the salts dissolved in sea water are practically non-volatile as compared with the pure water solvent. Economy in the use of heat is possible by designing the plant for reuse of the heat several times. This can be done with multieffect equipment in which steam produced in one effect is condensed in the next effect and, in so doing, furnishes heat for evaporating more water from the latter effect. Each effect is operated at a lower pressure than the previous one, the pressure changes corresponding to the temperature differences needed to produce the flow of heat required in reasonably sized units. Conventional plants may be found with various numbers of effects, the most common being three effects. British practice prefers the use of six effects, which gives nearly twice the fuel economy of three effects and requires the use of twice as much equipment as the latter. Figure 3.1 shows schematically a double-effect plant with representative pressures and temperatures.

Since the costs of water produced by highly efficient six-effect plants are of the order of $1000 per acre-foot and are predominantly fuel costs, one may well inquire whether or not even more stages could be economically added to reduce the over-all costs. Gilliland[1] has made such a study and concluded that, under certain conditions, plants with between 13 and 17 effects should produce water at $100 to $160 per acre-foot. Plants with these numbers of effects have not been built as yet and would presumably be far different in design and arrangement from existing three- and six-effect plants.

Flash Distillation. The foregoing remarks apply to equipment in which the heat is transferred directly from condensing steam to evaporating water through a heat-transfer surface. Multieffect flash distillation is a scheme in which the condensing steam is used to heat water. The water so heated is passed through a nozzle to reduce its pressure. Vapor

[1] E. R. Gilliland, "Fresh Water for the Future," *Ind. Eng. Chem.*, vol. 47, no. 12, pp. 2410–2422, 1955.

is formed at the low-pressure end of the nozzle, the latent heat of evaporation being supplied by the cooling without phase change of the bulk of the water which passed through the nozzle. The temperature drop of the warm water in each effect is kept to a small amount. The use of the multieffect principle in this case is practiced with five to eight effects.

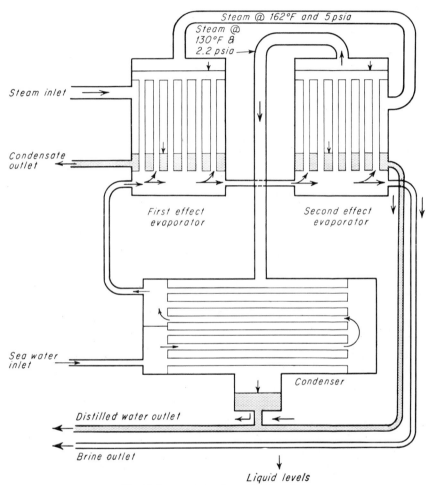

Fig. 3.1 Double-effect distiller plant.

Costs of water produced by this scheme are uncertain because of the small number of existing installations. However, estimates indicate the economy to be greater than in the case of the conventional multieffect plants.

Combined Power-generating Plant and Multieffect Distilling Plants. Many suggestions have been made to the general effect that the use of bled steam from power-generating turbines would make for very low fuel costs. The general argument is that the amount of steam to be charged against the distilling plant is not the actual flow rate through the plant but rather the steam flow rate which must be added at the throttle of the turbine to yield the same power output from the turbine as would have been the case if the distilling plant steam had been left in the turbine to expand all the way to condenser conditions. On this basis the steam charged against the distilling plant may be as low as 43 per cent of the steam used by the plant. Thus, the fuel costs to the distiller plant would be proportionately lowered. To be complete, the analysis would, of course, require the addition of the special costs associated with the use of the bleeder-type turbine as contrasted with a nonbleeder turbine.

The above argument is valid where the amount of water needed is relatively small. However, the figures on daily per capita consumptions of electric power and water for domestic and industrial supplies alone are such as to indicate that, if *all* power-generating units were back-pressure steam turbines delivering steam to distiller plants, the total water produced would be less than one-fifth of the domestic and industrial demand in the United States. Hence, while the use of the combined power and distiller plant is highly desirable in special cases, this scheme alone cannot solve the water problem of cities in the United States.

Vapor-compression Distillation. The central feature of this system is the vapor compressor by which the temperature of vapor coming from sea water is increased. The general scheme is that sea water contained in a pressure vessel discharges steam to the compressor. The compressor discharges the high-pressure steam to the shell around the heating tubes contained in the pressure vessel noted above. Here the high-pressure steam condenses and transfers its latent heat through the tube walls to the sea water inside the tubes and causes some of it to evaporate. Figure 3.2 shows a schematic layout of the plant, and Figure 3.3 shows an actual plant. Thus, except for heat losses from the system as a whole, *all* the heat absorbed in evaporation is recovered from the condensation of the purified water. This very economical system was evolved by von Kleinschmidt for service on diesel-driven ships of the United States Navy during World War II. Commercial units as large as 50,000 gal per day have been constructed and yield distilled water at a cost of slightly less than $500 per acre-foot. The capacity of large units seems to be limited by compressor design. The conventional plant of this type operates at evaporating temperatures of about 212°F and, hence, is subject to serious scaling on the sea-water side of the heat-transfer surface. While extensive studies of the prevention and control of scale are under way, the present plant design calls for a compressor

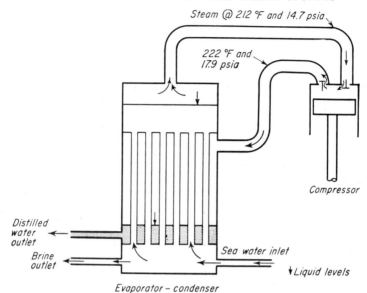

Fig. 3.2 Vapor-compression distiller.

Fig. 3.3 50,000 gal per day vapor-compression distiller plant at Port Etienne, French West Africa. (*Photograph by Cleaver-Brooks Co.*)

which will provide the same quantity of steam at increasingly high pressures as scale accumulates, in order that the higher temperatures accompanying the higher pressures will overcome the heat-flow resistance of the scale and maintain the unit output near the output before scale accumulation. This severe specification for the compressor limits the choice of types to the Roots-Blower unit or other direct-displacement pumps, all of which are of limited size.

Recent experimental work by Hickman[1,2] gives some promise that considerably increased efficiencies may be obtained from the vapor-compression system. Hickman's invention includes as its primary contribution a rotating heat-transfer surface. The rotating heat-transfer surface decreases liquid film resistance to heat flow and makes possible the use of temperature differentials across the heat-transfer surface of about 3°F rather than the 10°F required by conventional units. This smaller temperature rise demanded of the compressor not only reduces the compressor power requirement but also makes for a much simpler mechanism. If, in addition to the above features, the system is operated at temperatures so low that scale will not form on the sea-water side of the heat-transfer surface, the limitation to direct-displacement machinery is eliminated and, instead, the centrifugal type of machine may be used. These features are the most essential ones of the Hickman experiments. It is thought to be possible for development of these units to yield water at less than half the cost of that produced in the previous type of vapor-compression unit.

Supercritical-pressures Distillation.   This scheme was proposed by von Platen[3] and makes use of the fact that the latent heat of vaporization is zero at the critical pressure and is very small at pressures just below the critical. The term *supercritical* is applied since the pressures used are above the critical pressure of pure water. It should be noted that the critical pressure and temperature both increase with the salinity of the solution. For example, the critical values for pure water are 706°F and 3224 psia, while those for a 5 per cent solution of sodium chloride are 795°F and 5020 psia.

In this scheme, sea water is pumped through a heat exchanger at the supercritical pressure selected. The distillate produced runs through the same heat exchanger, in a counterflow direction, as does also the waste brine. Leaving this heat exchanger, the heated sea water is passed into a separately heated vessel where only a small amount of heat is needed to cause partial vaporization. Here the vapor is separated from the brine and fed back into one of the channels in the counterflow heat exchanger mentioned previously, while the brine is fed into another return passage in the same heat exchanger. Von Platen reports operation of such a

[1] Anonymous, *Third Annual Report on Saline Water Conversion*, U.S. Department of the Interior, Washington, D.C., January, 1955.

[2] Anonymous, "Saline Water Conversion," *Annual Report of the Secretary of the Interior for 1955*, U.S. Department of the Interior, Washington, D.C., 1956.

[3] B. C. von Platen, Process for Removing Dissolved Salts from the Liquid Solvent, U.S. Patent 2,520,168, 1950.

system using as little as 12 Btu per pound of water distilled. Problems of design and operation not yet solved include:

1. Selection of materials for the heat-transfer surface which will resist the extremely corrosive properties of the hot sea water
2. Means for preventing or controlling the rapid deposition of scale at the low-temperature end of the heat exchanger
3. Design of efficient hydraulic turbines and pumps to handle sea water and brine at the temperatures and pressures involved
4. Elimination of the salts which contaminate the vapor phase at these high pressures and temperatures (200 ppm at 716°F and 3500 psi for sodium chloride)

These problems and other associated items have been investigated by Nuclear Development Associates[1] under a contract with the U.S. Department of the Interior. If these problems could be solved, NDA estimated a production cost of water by this process of something less than $200 per acre-foot. However, NDA was unable to solve the problems of salt deposition and corrosion, so that work on this process was halted.

Vacuum Flash Distillation. This scheme is considered separately from multieffect flash distillation since it does not make use of the multieffect principle and does not require the use of fuel for heat. It consists in the exploitation of two sources of sea water at different temperatures, one of them being 17 to 35°F warmer than the other. The warmer water is passed into a vacuum chamber, where part of it evaporates, the latent heat being supplied by the cooling of the balance of the water by a few degrees. The vapor so produced is discharged to a surface condenser where it is condensed by the circulation of the colder water supply on the other side of the heat-transfer surface. See Figure 3.4 for a schematic layout of the equipment. Power must be supplied for removing the brine from the vacuum chamber, eliminating the air from the system, removing the condensate from the condenser, and circulating the cold water. If the temperature difference available is 35°F or more, it appears practicable to interpose a turbine wheel in the vapor path between the evaporator and condenser. For such plants producing 100,000 gal per day or more, a turbine wheel so installed would produce sufficient power to operate all the pumping machinery. Experiments to determine design criteria for the rather unusual equipment involved have been under way for several years at the University of California[2] at Berkeley. Figure 3.5 shows the University of California plant at Richmond, California. Gen-

---

[1] Anonymous, "Saline Water Conversion," *Annual Report of the Secretary of the Interior for 1955, op. cit.*

[2] E. D. Howe, "Progress Report for the California State Legislature, 1955," Institute of Engineering Research, University of California, pub. 2, ser. 75.

eral indications at the present time are that water could be produced by this process for about $100 per acre-foot where adjacent sea-water supplies are available with the stipulated temperature difference of 35°F.

It will be recognized that the above scheme including the turbine is that proposed by Claude[1] in 1928 for the generation of power using the

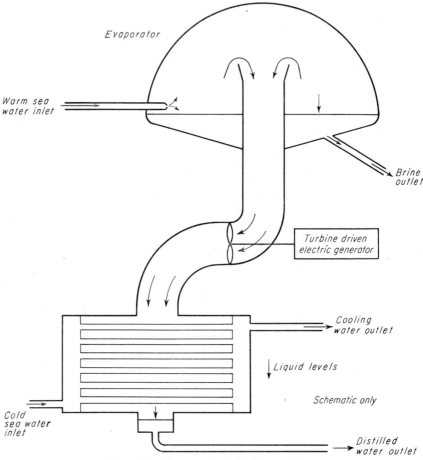

Fig. 3.4 Vacuum-flash-distillation plant.

heat of the ocean. Claude proposed that warm water be obtained from the surface of the ocean and cold water from deep (about 1500 ft down) in the ocean. At a few locations in the world, temperature differences in excess of the 35°F can be obtained. Nizery[2] has proposed a plant of this

[1] G. Claude, "Power from the Tropical Seas," *Mech. Eng.*, vol. 52, no. 12, p. 1039, 1930.

[2] A. Nizery, "Utilization of the Thermal Potential of the Sea for the Production of Power and Fresh Water, 1954," Institute of Engineering Research Publication, University of California, Berkeley, Calif.

type for construction at Abidjan in French West Africa. Energie des Mers, a French corporation, has conducted certain tests on the techniques of laying the deep-sea pipeline at Abidjan, but as yet construction on the 10,000-kw plant has not been started.

The California tests referred to above were undertaken with the purpose of utilizing waste heat and low-temperature heat from nonfuel sources. The reason for this lay in the fact that the fuel (or power) cost was one of the major components of the cost of any water-demineralizing process, and further that, even if fuel costs could be held down, the sheer quantities of fuel involved would be prohibitive. For example, Aultman[1]

Fig. 3.5 Vacuum-flash-distillation plant under construction. (*A*) Vacuum evaporator, (*B*) condenser.

pointed out that, if the entire water supply for Los Angeles were to be produced by vapor-compression distillation, the annual fuel requirement would be nearly one-fourth of the annual petroleum production of California. The vacuum-flash-distillation equipment could be used for waste heat from diesel engines, condenser circulating water from some power plants, and cooling water from oil-refinery units, chemical plants, and various other manufacturing plants. It should be noted that the Abidjan plant of the French is designed to utilize solar heat for a 5°C reheat of the warm water. While these sources of warm water are limited, their exploitation should serve to pave the way for future ocean-type plants similar to the unit proposed for Abidjan.

[1] W. W. Aultman, "Fresh Water from Salt," *Eng. and Sci. Monthly*, vol. 12, no. 2, pp. 3–7, 1949.

Solar Distillation.   Solar distillation, like the vacuum-flash system previously discussed, is characterized by the use of heat from nonfuel sources. Solar energy is collected by a glass-covered blackened tray which has water standing in it at a shallow depth. The water is heated by contact with the tray so that some of it evaporates and rises as humidity of the air above the tray. The glass cover is made in the form of a sloping hood and, being exposed to radiant and convective cooling on its outer surface, is generally cooler than the air inside and, hence, serves as the condenser for part of the humidity. Distillate is collected from a trough along the base of the sloping glass panes and removed from the enclosure.

Extensive tests of different variations of the above arrangement have been conducted at the University of California at Berkeley during the

Fig. 3.6   Solar-distillation plant, University of California.

past several years, the experimental plant being shown in Figure 3.6. Test work under U.S. Department of the Interior contracts has also been carried on at New York University and at the Bjorksten Laboratories in Madison, Wisconsin. Tests have also been conducted on similar units by researchers in Algeria, Australia, Cyprus, French Morocco, Italy, and the Virgin Islands. So far, no large prototype installation has resulted, and the only semicommercial ventures seem to be those in Algeria and Australia. In both cases, small trays, about 4 by 8 ft, are molded from asbestos cement (similar to Transite) and covered with low-angle sloping glass in metal frames.

The test work so far indicates that, on a year-round basis, about 50 per cent of the solar energy incident on a horizontal surface can be accounted for by the latent heat of the distillate produced in these simple stills. This gives a production intensity in California latitudes of about one gallon for each 8 to 10 sq ft of horizontal collector surface. The first cost of simple distillers is of the order of $10 per gallon per day of capacity so that the production costs are high. Löf,[1] on a U.S. Department of the Interior contract, estimated that ultimate development of this type of apparatus should yield costs of the order of $250 per acre-foot.

Proposals have been made for more efficient use of the solar heat, since the above units are equivalent to single-effect stills. Landry[2] studied the application of steam produced by solar energy to a conventional triple-effect plant. Solar concentrators of the parabolic cylindrical-mirror type were considered in various configurations, the heat in all cases being collected in water circulating under pressure through blackened pipes along the focus of the mirror. Steam was to be produced by flashing part of the water into vapor in a flash evaporator. No tests of this scheme were carried out since Landry concluded that the costs of water so produced would be of the order of $1000 per acre-foot. Coanda[3] also proposed the use of a concentrating collector, the heat being collected by air, which was used as the driving fluid in a vapor-compression system. Although some test work has apparently been done by Coanda, no overall performance data or costs are presently available.

Freezing or Cold Distillation.   The use of freezing as a means of water demineralizing has been proposed since, when sea water is frozen, only the pure water crystallizes, the dissolved salts remaining in solution as brine. The energy relationships also seem attractive, since the latent heat of fusion is only one-seventh that for vaporization. The two major problems connected with exploiting this process seem to be the separation of the brine from the ice crystals and the regenerative use of the heat effects. Schemes for separating the ice and brine involve one of the following:

1. Compression of the ice so that the brine is squeezed out, much like the wringing of water from a sponge
2. Centrifuging and washing of flake ice or chipped ice
3. The migration of brine pockets to the ends of solid ice cylinders caused by the movement of a heated zone along the cylinder

Moulton and Hendrickson[4] conducted experiments on the use of compression and reported that pressures of 1000 to 2000 psi reduced the

[1] G. O. G. Löf, "Demineralization of Saline Water with Solar Energy," *Saline Water Research and Development Progress Report, No. 4*, U.S. Department of the Interior, Washington, D.C., 1954.

[2] B. A. Landry, and Others, "An Investigation of Multiple-effect Evaporation of Saline Waters from Solar Radiation," *Saline Water Research and Development Progress Report, No. 2*, U.S. Department of the Interior, Washington, D.C., 1953.

[3] Henri Coanda, "Sea Water Changed to Fresh Water," *Science et vie*, vol. 86, no. 443, pp. 146–151, 1954.

[4] R. F. Moulton and H. M. Hendrickson in "Saline Water Conversion," *Annual Report of the Secretary of the Interior for 1955*, U.S. Department of the Interior, Washington, D.C., 1956.

salinity of sea-water ice to 500 ppm, with the recovery of 90 per cent of the ice contained in the original slush. The tests are continuing, with the general objective of developing a compression machine suited to continuous rather than batch operation.

Efforts to separate the ice and brine by centrifuging have been carried on by several experimenters. So far, results have not been encouraging, since only about 20 per cent of the sea water has been recovered as distillate, the balance of the water being used for washing. Rose and Hoover[1] experimented with the washing process alone. It was noted that the concentration of the brine in a slush resulting from freezing a salt solution was roughly proportional to the salt concentration in the original solution. They also found that if a slush of sea-water ice crystals and brine is drained and the ice contacted with a more dilute brine, the salinity of the brine clinging to the ice crystals will be reduced. By successively draining and washing with more and more dilute brines, it should therefore be possible to arrive at an acceptably dilute brine. The Rose and Hoover tests involved 15 cycles of contacting drained ice and dilute brines and showed that the ice melted at the purified end of the system contained only 22 ppm of salt. The successively more dilute brines were obtained by melting and refreezing the drained ice crystals. This interesting process may lead to a practical application.

The other problem, that of using the heat effect regeneratively, has been considered by a few writers. Ellis[2] suggested that the heat removed in the freezing process should be transferred to the melting tank by a refrigerating system and that there should be a counterflow heat exchanger to cool the incoming sea water by warming the outgoing brine and condensate. Zarchin[3] suggested that the freezing be accomplished by forming the ice under a high vacuum and removing the vapor formed. This vapor was then to be compressed to a temperature high enough to melt the drained ice crystals.

The Carrier Engineering Company, on a U.S. Department of the Interior contract, has constructed and tested a small unit using the freeze-evaporation process proposed by Zarchin. A suspension of ice in brine is formed when cold sea water is sprayed into the vacuum chamber. This suspension is pumped out of this chamber and into the bottom of a washing column. Fresh water is fed into the top of the washing column and flows downward against the ice particles which are rising because of buoyant forces. Brine diluted with the wash water is removed from the

[1] A. Rose and T. B. Hoover, "Research on Salt Water Purification by Freezing," *Saline Water Research and Development Progress Report No. 7*, U.S. Department of the Interior, Washington, D.C., 1955.

[2] Cecil B. Ellis, *Fresh Water from the Ocean*, The Ronald Press Company, New York, 1953.

[3] A. Zarchin, Demineralizing of Sea Water by Freezing, Israeli Patent 7764, 1953.

bottom of the washing column. Results from the first tests indicated possible over-all costs as low as $100 per acre-foot.

It is generally conceded that freezing should be economical because of the low latent heat of fusion and the small specific volume of ice as compared to vapor. Gilliland[1] estimates an ultimate cost of water produced by the use of freezing to be between $80 and $160 per acre-foot, one of his lowest figures.

3.3 Chemical Methods

The demineralizing of sea water by chemical processes could be accomplished by adding chemicals which would precipitate the unwanted materials from solution or by an exchange process in which the exchange material could be regenerated. For small quantities of water the precipitation method is satisfactory, but for large quantities it is much too expensive. For example, the drinking-water kits used on life rafts during World War II contained a combination of silver zeolite, barium hydroxide, and silver oxide. The cost of these kits was more than justified by the saving of lives, but the application of these chemicals to large-scale water development would have lead to chemical costs of thousands of dollars per acre-foot of water obtained.

Exchange materials, generally typified by the zeolites, have been used in water purification for some years and are economical for water in which the original dissolved mineral content is 2000 ppm or less. The exchange process may be explained through its application to the softening of water. Natural exchange materials, such as the double salt sodium aluminum silicate, are coated on the surface of the medium filling a vertical tank some 6 ft in height. The water to be softened, i.e., water containing unwanted calcium and magnesium ions, is caused to flow through the coated medium. As it goes through the bed, the sodium ions in the zeolite coating go into solution and the calcium and magnesium ions attach themselves to the coating in place of the sodium ions. After sufficient water has passed through, the supply of sodium ions will become used up and the bed is ready for regeneration. This is accomplished by interrupting the flow of product water through the bed and circulating through it a solution of sodium chloride. The surplus of sodium ions in this salt solution causes the zeolite exchange to be reversed, and the sodium ions "plate out" into the medium coating. These displace the calcium and magnesium ions which then go into solution and are discharged with the waste brine. After the regeneration is completed, the flow of supply and product water is resumed.

The use of the exchange materials with sea water begins with the exchange of hydrogen ions for sodium and magnesium, using a synthetic

[1] Gilliland, *loc. cit.*

hydrogen cation exchanger of the sulfonated-coal or sulfonated-resin type. The acidified effluent is then passed through an anion exchanger in which a complex amino resin of weakly basic character exchanges hydroxide ions for the sulfate and chloride ions. Finally, the water is passed into a degasifier unit for the removal of the carbonate ions as CO_2 gas. Since hydrogen and hydroxide ions must be replaced in the regeneration process, it will be seen that expensive chemicals such as sulfuric acid and sodium hydroxide must be used. The costs of purifying water by the use of these materials is estimated to be nearly $1000 per acre foot. Gilliland[1] has suggested another scheme in which the exchanger materials contain the ions of gases such as NH_4 and CO_3 rather than hydrogen and hydroxide ions. The product water could then be heated to drive off these ions as NH_3 (gas) and CO_2 (gas) and these gases dissolved in water and used for regeneration of the spent exchanger materials. Thus, the regeneration would not require fresh chemicals but only heat. Spiegler and Coryell[2] suggested an electrical scheme for regeneration. However, as yet neither of the above schemes has been demonstrated on a large enough scale so that reliable cost estimates could be made.

Other related methods such as adsorption and solvent extraction have been studied briefly. In general, it may be concluded that the most attractive of present proposals for the use of chemical effects is the ion-exchange process with regeneration by the use of heat.

3.4 Electrical Methods

Sea water is a solution containing many ionized materials and, as such, is capable of carrying electric currents. It is known that electric currents are carried through ionized solutions by the ions themselves, which migrate toward the electrodes, and under certain conditions are there plated out of solution. Based on this phenomenon a number of schemes for demineralizing water have been tried. The three-compartment cell is one in which two semipermeable membranes separate the end compartments from the center one. These membranes will, in effect, transmit ions but not water. An electrical potential imposed between electrodes in the end compartment then causes the ions to migrate out of the center compartment and into the end compartments, so that the water in the center compartment is demineralized. This type of unit works satisfactorily and with sufficient economy for the softening of fresh water but requires too much power when used with sea water. The fact that most of the potential drop occurs in the electrode compartments suggests that economy could be increased by having many compartments in series

[1] *Ibid.*

[2] K. S. Spiegler and C. D. Coryell, "Electromigration in a Cation Exchange Resin," *J. Phys. Chem.*, vol. 56, no. 1, pp. 106–113, 1952.

between the two electrode compartments. This became possible very recently when electrically positive and negative membranes were developed.

Selective membranes made of synthetic materials are now available from several sources and are being used in several pilot plants for demineralizing water. The new membranes utilize exchange materials as the source of the "built-in" electric charge and may be made entirely of these materials (homogeneous membranes) or coated with these materials over a sheet plastic base (heterogeneous membranes). The demineralizing unit is made up of 41 to over 201 compartments in series, the membranes bounding the compartments being alternately electrically positive and negative. The spacing of the membranes is small, of the order of $\frac{1}{16}$ to $\frac{1}{8}$ in., and the general arrangement is much the same as a plate and frame filter press. The flow of water through the thin compartments is continuous, and demineralized water is obtained from alternate compartments, brines coming from the other compartments. Experiments with equipments of this kind are being carried out by Juda and others[1] in the United States, by Wegelin and others[2] in the Netherlands, and by Rapson[3] in South Africa. So far, these equipments have been found economical for demineralizing brackish water (up to 5000 ppm initial salinity), but they consume more power than the vapor-compression system when used with sea water.

The inherent advantage of any electrical system lies in the fact that the power requirement is proportional to the amount of ions to be removed, whereas, by contrast, the power or fuel requirement for distillation or freezing is proportional to the amount of water produced and is completely independent of the initial salinity of the water source. Whether or not the electrical scheme with selective membranes can be made to demand less power than the vapor-compression scheme when used to demineralize sea water is not yet known. However, it does appear economical with brackish water and is probably capable of producing acceptable irrigation water now from supplies at 3500 ppm initial salinity at a cost of less than $50 per acre-foot.

3.5 Summary

In the preceding discussion an attempt has been made to review the salient points of the methods under experimental investigation. Another phase of the investigations has been an analytical study, using the princi-

[1] W. Juda and W. A. McRae, "Coherent Ion-exchange Gels and Membranes," *J. Am. Chem. Soc.*, vol. 72, no. 2, p. 1044, 1950.

[2] E. Wegelin, "Demineralization d'eau salée par électrodialyse," *Bull. centre belge étude et document. eaux (Liége)*, vol. 3, no. 21, pp. 182–186, 1953.

[3] W. S. Rapson, "Purification of Mine Water," *Optima (Johannesburg)*, vol. 5, no. 2, pp. 43–46, 1955.

ples of thermodynamics to determine the minimum power requirements for idealized processes. Computations by Sherwood,[1] Murphy,[2] Tribus,[3] and Gilliland[4] agree rather well on a value of slightly less than 3 kwhr per thousand gallons for sea water. The closest approach to date is that of the vapor-compression system, with a power requirement of over 70 kwhr per thousand gallons. The small theoretical value noted above gives hope that the fuel requirement for some process may eventually be reduced to 20 kwhr per thousand gallons or less.

The lowest reliable cost estimate for demineralizing sea water was about $470 per acre-foot for vapor compression in 1952. The intensive investigations of the past five years have led several authorities in the field to suggest figures of $100 to $125 per acre-foot as quite possible in the next few years. These prices could be interesting for certain domestic and industrial applications. Further reduction to the $40 figure could possibly come either from very radical modification of existing processes or, more likely, from the development of some new process. It is highly important that both possibilities be investigated with much vigor in the next few years.

In January, 1959, a proposal was made by Teller,[5] Kennedy,[6] and others to discharge a hydrogen bomb some 6000 feet below ground surface to produce a subterranean heat source. Sea water would be introduced through a well which would tap the bomb cavity. The condensate would be removed via another well. The proposal makes use of the principle described on page 62, under the heading "Supercritical-pressures Distillation."

[1] T. K. Sherwood, "Fresh Water from the Sea," *Tech. Rev.*, vol. 57, no. 1, pp. 15–20, 1954.

[2] Murphy in *Third Annual Report on Saline Water Conversion*, U.S. Department of the Interior, Washington, D.C., January, 1955.

[3] M. Tribus, "The Thermodynamics of Separating Fresh Water from the Sea," unpublished paper, Los Angeles, Calif., 1955.

[4] Gilliland, *loc. cit.*

[5] Edward Teller, Professor of Physics, University of California, Berkeley.

[6] George C. Kennedy, Professor of Geophysics, University of California, Los Angeles.

4

Marine Resources[1]

MILNER B. SCHAEFER

INTER-AMERICAN TROPICAL TUNA COMMISSION
SCRIPPS INSTITUTION OF OCEANOGRAPHY
UNIVERSITY OF CALIFORNIA, LA JOLLA

and

ROGER REVELLE

DIRECTOR
SCRIPPS INSTITUTION OF OCEANOGRAPHY
UNIVERSITY OF CALIFORNIA, LA JOLLA

4.1 Introduction

The oceans of the world, covering about 71 per cent of its surface, profoundly influence human life. Few nations are not affected by their relationships to the sea, and for many nations their maritime heritage has been perhaps the most important determinant of economic and political development. It is not accidental that modern civilization had its origin along the shores of the Mediterranean and that the powerful industrial nations, until very recent times at least, have been, in major part, those with a seafaring population.

The existence of great natural harbors, control of important routes of sea transportation, or location near lucrative fishing grounds have been important factors in the development of many of the world's major cities, and these factors continue to form the basis of much industry and to determine the location of many major centers of population.

The existing and latent resources of the sea are many and varied; their rational development and utilization offer a technical, economic, and social challenge. We shall consider, in the following pages, some of these resources and some of the problems that need to be solved to make full use of them.

[1] Contribution from Scripps Institution of Oceanography, New Series.

73

4.2   Nature of Marine Resources

Man's economic activity consists in combining the agents of production (natural resources, labor, and capital) to create utilities. In general, he neither creates nor destroys matter (although there are exceptions involving nuclear reactions); he simply rearranges it for his own benefit. He normally accomplishes this only when the application of labor and capital to the naturally occurring arrangement of matter is "profitable"; that is, more utilities are created than are consumed. We may, then, consider that a natural resource consists of an arrangement of matter to which man can apply his activities to increase his net welfare.

As man's knowledge advances, he is able to develop new techniques, new ways of creating utilities, so that what was formerly not a resource, because it could not be used profitably, becomes one. It can often be foreseen that certain arrangements of matter, though not resources today, will be so tomorrow; these we might call *latent resources*. Many components of the sea are of this type, they are not usable at the present stage of knowledge, but a moderate and reasonably certain advance in technology would make them valuable. One familiar example is food from the sea. At the present time, only a small fraction of the many kinds of marine organisms constitute resources—those which occur in especially dense aggregations. A far greater mass of potential protein food exists in other organisms, which are less densely aggregated. Although these cannot now be harvested profitably, they will almost certainly become important food resources in the future.

In considering the utilization of resources we must think not only of immediate benefits but also of the maintenance of these benefits for future generations. We shall discuss some conservation problems in more detail subsequently, but it is pertinent here to note that natural resources can be divided into two classes. In one class are those which are nonrenewable, e.g., fossil fuels and mineral deposits, or for which the rate of renewal is so slow as to be negligible. Man can use these *nonrenewable resources* rapidly or slowly, efficiently or inefficiently, but their total quantity, particularly the quantity in high-grade deposits, is limited.

For some nonrenewable resources, e.g., petroleum under the sea floor, the amount recovered will depend to some extent on the rate of use, because the efficiency of recovery varies approximately inversely with the number of wells and the pumping rates. Under the best circumstances, however, there remains a limit to the total production, whether it is spaced over 20 years or 200. Conservation consists (1) of employing the technical methods that will result in optimum recovery and (2) in spreading the production over time in the manner most beneficial to man; this involves complex economic and social considerations.

In the second class are those resources which are constantly renewed by natural processes; they are provided by nature in an unending stream and thus are capable of sustained use indefinitely. Among these *renewable resources* are the living resources of the sea, the dissolved salts, and the water itself.

The renewable resources are, however, of two types: those for which the rate of renewal depends on the amount left unused to perpetuate itself, and those where such dependence does not exist, or is negligible. The latter, or *non-self-regulating resources*, are composed of nonliving elements in the sea, such as the water, dissolved minerals, waves, tides, and currents. Sea water is constantly replaced by runoff and precipitation; the dissolved minerals are renewed by return from the land; the power of the waves and tides and the ocean currents and diffusivity, so useful for waste disposal, are continuously generated by winds and gravitational forces and by heat from the sun. For this type of renewable resources, there is no conservation problem. Since the quantity used in any year will not affect the quantity available for subsequent use, we have no need to take heed for the future.

The other type of renewable resources encompasses the living resources of the sea, the populations of plants and animals; these have the peculiar property that the rate of renewal is dependent both on the physical environment and on the magnitude of the propagating stock, which is diminished by harvesting; for these *self-regulating resources* there exists some optimum rate of use that will provide maximum harvest indefinitely.[1]

4.3   Kinds of Marine Resources

Living Resources.   The seas are so alien to us as land mammals that it is difficult to conceive of the ways of life in the ocean. On land the cycle of life is relatively simple; we may describe it in four figurative stages. First is the grass, which by a subtle and complex chemistry captures the energy of sunlight and builds organic matter. Herbivorous animals live on the grass; carnivores and men eat them. Finally there are the bacterial microorganisms, which decompose the dead bodies and the excreta of all living creatures, making their constituent substances again available as building materials for the plants. In the sea, the cycle is longer. Instead of grass there are the tiny floating plants called phytoplankton; in place of cows, the zooplankton animals that eat the plants are small crustacea, no bigger than the head of a pin. Many kinds of carnivores eat the foragers, but they are mostly also zooplankton, only a fraction of an inch in length. Other intermediate flesh eaters exist between them and the

---

[1] Milner B. Schaefer, "Some Considerations of Population Dynamics and Economics in Relation to the Management of the Commercial Marine Fisheries," *J. Fisheries Research Board Can.*, vol. 14, no. 5, pp. 669–681, 1957.

fishes of our ocean harvest. Because every link in this long food chain is inefficient, we reap from the sea only a small fraction of its organic production.

Two other characteristics of the ocean tend to limit the harvest as compared with that from the land. One is its giant size; more than 70 per cent of all the sunlight that penetrates the atmosphere falls on the sea; moreover, this sunlight can act throughout the top 20 to 100 m of water, thus the living space for plants and animals is far greater than on land. This great areal extent and volume, combined with the fluidity of the oceans, results in a low concentration of organisms per unit volume and therefore inefficiency in harvesting.

On land, the standing crop of plants and animals is of the same order of magnitude as the amount of organic production per year, while in the ocean the crop is very small, compared to the production, because of rapid turnover. The average rate of organic production per unit area is probably about the same on land and in the sea, but the efficiency of harvesting depends more on the size of the crop than on the total amount of organic matter produced.

The plants of the sea, on which all other living things depend, grow only in the waters near the surface, where bright sunlight penetrates. These waters differ widely in fertility. Like the land, the ocean has its green pastures where life flourishes in abundance and its deserts where a few poor plants and animals barely survive.

The fertility of the land depends on four things: temperature, intensity of sunlight, water, and available plant nutrients—substances that usually occur in very small amounts but are essential for plant growth. In the sea, water is, of course, always abundant; the plants are well adapted to the narrow range of temperature; the intensity of sunlight determines the length of the growing season and the depth of growth, but usually not the differences in fertility. These fertility levels depend only on the plant nutrients in the waters near the surface. As in any well-worked soil on land, the nutrients in the waters must be replenished each year. They are continually depleted by the slow sinking of plant and animal remains from the brightly lighted near-surface layers into the dark waters of the depths. The fertility of the sea is restored when nutrient-rich deeper waters are brought up near the surface. As Sverdrup[1] has said, the ocean plows itself. The regions where the ocean plowing is most effective are the green pastures of the sea.

This plowing is accomplished in three ways: In some regions the wind drives the surface waters away from the coast or away from an internal boundary, and nutrient-rich waters well up from mid-depths. In other

[1] H. U. Sverdrup, "Some Aspects of the Primary Productivity of the Sea," *FAO Fish. Bull.*, vol. 5, no. 6, pp. 215–223, 1952.

areas, the surface waters are cooled to nearly freezing in the winter, become heavy and sink, and mix with the deep waters. Elsewhere, violent mixing occurs along the boundaries between ocean currents, and deeper waters are thereby brought into the brightly lighted zone.

Many of the great fisheries of the world depend for their existence on one or another of these three ways in which the ocean plows itself. The sardines, anchovies, and mackerel of California, the sardines of South Africa, the tuna off the west coast of North and South America, the bonitos, albacore, and hake off Chile and Peru, the apparently abundant deep tuna in the equatorial zone of the Pacific all live in regions of upwelling, where the deep water is brought to the surface by wind action. The cod, herring, and haddock of Newfoundland, Labrador, Iceland, Greenland, and Bear Island live in the regions of winter cooling. The sardines of Maine and the flatfishes of the Grand Banks live where the Gulf Stream and the Labrador Current clash in turbulent mixing; the sardines and herring of Japan and Kamchatka similarly depend on turbulence between the Oyashio and Kuroshio Currents, the west Pacific equivalents of the Labrador Current and the Gulf Stream. All three processes are important around Antarctica, where the giant whales live in abundance. The guano industry of Peru depends on intense upwelling on the shoreward side of the Peru Current. There the guano birds carry out what is probably the world's largest fishery, amounting to several million tons of anchovies and related fish each year.

The above-described variations in fertility of the world oceans are illustrated in Figure 4.1, which shows the annual production of organic matter (in grams of organic carbon per square meter) as recently estimated by Fleming and Laevastu.[1]

Many of the commercially important marine organisms are harvested in coastal waters. Several factors may be involved: (1) Profitable fisheries can be conducted more easily near ports and harbors. (2) The coastal waters are of high fertility, because of greater upwelling and turbulent mixing and the ease of replenishment of plant nutrients from the shallow sea floor, and perhaps also because of the supply of nutrients and organic detritus from land. (3) The standing crop of plants and animals attached to or living on the bottom in coastal areas is large relative to the total organic production.

Owing to the importance of the coastal zone and the shallow bottom, the living resources of the sea are usually divided into two groups, based on the habits of the organisms: demersal and pelagic. The demersal group consists of those fishes and other marine animals which live on or near the bottom and are more or less sedentary in the adult stage (some demersal

[1] R. H. Fleming and T. Laevastu, "The Influence of Hydrographic Conditions on the Behavior of Fish," *FAO Fish. Bull.*, vol. 9, no. 4, pp. 181–196, 1956.

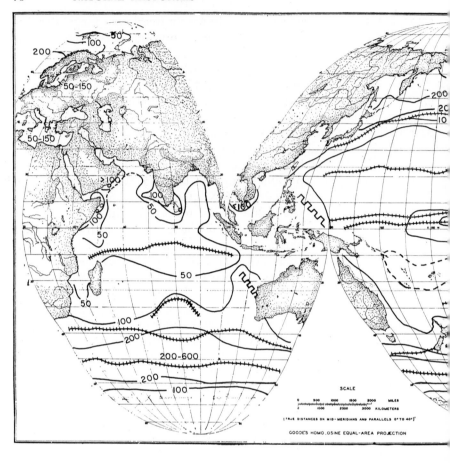

○ ○ ○ ○ Upwelling   ⊔⊔⊔⊔ Divergence

Fig. 4.1 Estimated production of organic matter in the oceans (grams of carbon per square meter of sea surface per year). (*After R. H. Fleming and T. Laevastu,*

species migrate over considerable distances, however). The pelagic group lives in or near the surface waters, often far from shore and from the bottom, and is commonly migratory over considerable distances.

In describing the living resources, we may, of course, also use the biological classifications based on morphology and genetic relationships. Almost all the phyla and most of the classes of marine animals are utilized, to a greater or less extent, by man.

Fishes and Marine Invertebrates. The sea fisheries are not only one of the oldest human industries, but up to the present they are by far the largest extractive industry based on the resources of the sea. The most recent data on their production have been compiled by the Food and

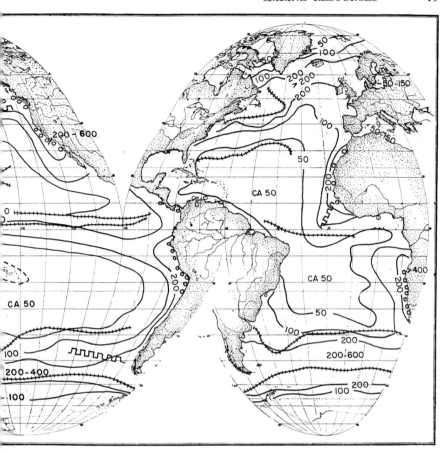

↦ Convergence and other boundaries

"The Influence of Hydrographic Conditions on the Behavior of Fish," FAO Fish. Bull., vol. 9, no. 4, pp. 181–196.)

Agriculture Organization of the United Nations (FAO) for the year 1954.[1] These data indicate a total harvest of 24.2 million metric tons, in addition to some 2.2 million tons produced by fisheries of lakes and streams. The recent trend of the production is shown in Figure 4.2, which indicates an increase of about 40 per cent since 1948.

Table 4.1 shows the production of the oceans by zones.

It may be seen that the great bulk of the harvest of the sea fisheries is taken from the waters of the Northern Hemisphere, despite the fact that the southern oceans constitute 57 per cent of the world's sea area. The

[1] Food and Agriculture Organization of the United Nations, *Yearbook of Fishery Statistics*, vol. V (1954–1955), Rome, 1957.

disproportionately large yield in the Northern Hemisphere is related to three factors: (1) Human populations are heavily concentrated there. (2) The major fishing nations are the industrialized maritime nations,

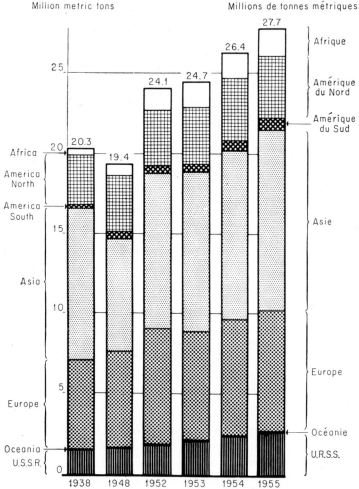

WORLD CATCH:
By continents 1938,1948,1952–55

Million metric tons

QUANTITÉS PÊCHÉES DANS LE MONDE:
Par continents 1938,1948,1952–55

Millions de tonnes métriques

Fig. 4.2 World catch of fishes and marine invertebrates by continents, 1938, 1948, 1952–1955 (million metric tons). (*From FAO Yearbook of Fishery Statistics, vol. V* (1954–1955), *Rome,* 1957.)

which are mostly located in the north. (3) Except for some of the tuna, salmon, and herring fisheries, the important sea fisheries are located in the relatively shallow areas along the continents, and the extent of these shallow areas is much greater in the Northern than in the Southern

Table 4.1 Harvest of Fishes and Marine Invertebrates in 1954, by Latitude Zones

Zone	Metric tons, millions	Per cent
Arctic region.....................................	1.2	5
Northern Hemisphere, temperate zone...........	17.5	72
Tropical zone.....................................	4.1	17
Southern Hemisphere, temperate zone...........	1.4	6
Antarctic regions................................	0*	0*

* About 4 million tons of whales were taken in the antarctic, but few fish or marine invertebrates.

Hemisphere. In Table 4.2 are tabulated the harvests made by the six leading fishing nations, which account for 15,189,000 metric tons, or nearly 60 per cent of the world production. These are all nations of the Northern Hemisphere and, except for the United States and Japan, fish

Table 4.2 Production of Six Leading Countries in 1954, by Types of Fish
(In thousands of metric tons)

Type of fish	Japan	United States	United Kingdom	Norway	China (main-land)	Soviet Union
Freshwater fishes........	31.2	67.4	....	0.3		
Salmons, trouts, smelts, etc...................	54.4	154.3	2.0	31.7		
Flounders, halibuts, soles, etc...................	116.7	77.6	63.7	11.5		
Cod, hakes, haddocks, etc.	265.8	153.4	702.3	420.7		
Herrings, sardines, anchovies, etc...........	752.6	974.1	208.2	1,470.4	Not available	Not available
Tunas, bonitos, mackerel, etc...................	612.7	164.4	5.0	22.4		
Misc. marine teleosts....	1,256.8	276.6	32.8	14.4		
Sharks, rays, etc........	101.5	2.0	31.3	53.1		
Crustaceans............	101.0	199.5	8.5	9.5		
Mollusks...............	799.6	636.0	15.9	0		
Not specified...........	354.4	1.1	....	34.2		
Total................	4,446.7	2,706.4	1,069.7	2,068.2	2,400.0*	2,498.0

* For 1955.

exclusively in the seas of the Northern Hemisphere. A small share of the catch of tunas and related species by Japanese and United States fishermen comes from the Southern Hemisphere, north of about 15 or 20 deg south latitude, however.

The location of most of the established fisheries of the world is shown in Figure 4.3 from a recent article by the staff of the FAO Fisheries Division.[1] While this chart could be brought up to date by including newly established tuna fisheries in the tropical Pacific, tropical Atlantic, and Indian Oceans, this would not change the main features, which show that the principal fisheries are largely within 100 or 200 miles of land.

An additional notable feature of the sea fisheries is that the bulk of the harvest consists of relatively few species, despite the fact that (as shown by Table 4.2) there are a large number of kinds of fish represented in the catches. In the United States, for example, over 125 kinds of fish were listed by the U.S. Fish and Wildlife Service[2] as comprising the 1954 fish catch of 1.9 million metric tons (excluding crustacea and mollusks), but 13 of these accounted for 1.4 million metric tons, or over 70 per cent. These are shown in Table 4.3.

Table 4.3

Fish	Thousand metric tons
Menhaden	789
Salmon (5 kinds)	147
Sea herring	75
Skipjack tuna	70
Yellowfin tuna	54
Pacific sardine	62
Atlantic Ocean perch	82
Flounder	50
Total	1329

Of the list (Table 4.3) of the principal kinds of fish contributing to the United States catch, it is probable that the salmon, haddock, yellowfin tuna, and Pacific sardine are being exploited at or near the maximum productive capacity of the stocks. For the herring (at least of the Atlantic), skipjack tuna, ocean perch, and flounder stocks, it is quite certain that the harvests can be expanded on a sustainable yield basis. In addition, there are known to be present very large numbers of fish of species little utilized, or not utilized at all, such as the hake, saury, and pollock off the United States Pacific Coast.

The picture of a few kinds of fish being heavily exploited, some being fished but underexploited, and others known to be abundant but remaining essentially unharvested applies to other parts of the world as well. In the United Kingdom, for example, 76 per cent of the total landings in 1954 was composed of six demersal species and one pelagic species (her-

[1] Staff, Fisheries Division of Food and Agriculture Organization of the United Nations, "Improving the Fisheries Contribution to World Food Supplies," *FAO Fish. Bull.*, vol. 6, no. 5, pp. 159–196, 1953.

[2] A. W. Anderson and E. A. Power, "Fishery Statistics of the United States: 1954," U.S. Fish and Wildlife Service, Statistical Digest No. 39, 1956.

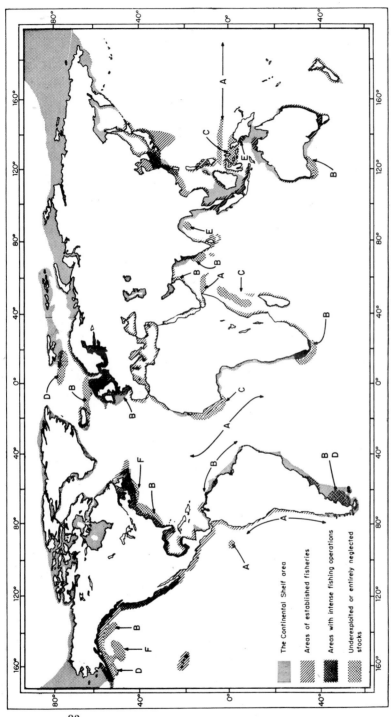

Fig. 4.3 Locations of the important marine fisheries of the world and of some underexploited or entirely neglected stocks: (a) tuna; (b) clupeoids; (c) percomorphs, as reef stocks; (d) gadoids; (e) crustacea; (f) redfish. (*From the staff of the Food and Agriculture Organization, Fisheries Division.*)

The Continental Shelf area

Areas of established fisheries

Areas with intense fishing operations

Underexploited or entirely neglected stocks

ring). The data, from the FAO summaries for 1954,[1] are shown in Table 4.4.

According to Wood,[2] many of the demersal stocks are being nearly fully utilized, although Parrish[3] and Graham[4] believe that the cod fishery could almost certainly yield a greater harvest. The pelagic species, both the herring and other kinds now little utilized, including sprat, pilchard, and mackerel, could, on the other hand, provide much greater catches.

At a meeting of fishery experts at the United Nations Scientific Conference on the Conservation and Utilization of Resources (UNSCCUR) in 1949,[5] a map was prepared to show the location of known large stocks of

Table 4.4

Fish	Thousand Metric Tons
Plaice	33
Cod	361
Haddock	127
Hake	18
Coalfish	32
Whiting	46
Herring	199
Total	816

fish that are underexploited or entirely neglected. These are shown in Figure 4.3, prepared by the fisheries division of the FAO[6] after the map drawn at the UNSCURR Conference. It is evident that in every part of the world there are known to exist large fish stocks which are not being utilized to any appreciable extent. We may be confident that other stocks will be discovered in the future.

A sizable share of the fish harvest of the sea is used for other purposes than human food. The menhaden of the United States, for example, which is landed in greater quantity than any other kind of fish (*vide supra*) is converted entirely into fish meal and solubles (used primarily as feed for

[1] Food and Agricultural Organization of the United Nations, *loc. cit.*

[2] Henry Wood, "Fisheries of the United Kingdom," in *Sea Fisheries, Their Investigation in the United Kingdom*, Edward Arnold & Co., London, 1956, chap. 2, pp. 10–79.

[3] B. B. Parrish, "The Cod, Haddock, and Hake," in *Sea Fisheries, Their Investigation in the United Kingdom*, Edward Arnold & Co., London, 1956, Chap. 7, pp. 251–331.

[4] M. Graham, "The State of the Northern Stocks of Cod," *Cons. Perm. Int. Explor. Mer. Rapp. et Proc. Verb.*, vol. 136, pp. 48–50, 1954.

[5] "Developing Fishery Resources: Summary Discussion," *Proc. United Nations Sci. Conf. on Conservation and Utilization of Resources*, Aug. 17–Sept. 6, 1949, Lake Success, New York, vol. 7, *Wildlife and Fish Resources*, pp. 60–66, United Nations, New York, 1951.

[6] Staff, Fisheries Division of Food and Agriculture Organization of the United Nations, *loc. cit.*

chickens, cattle, and other animals) and fish oil, which has numerous industrial uses. The herring catch of Norway, constituting about 70 per cent of the total fish catch of that nation, is also used in large part for these purposes. The production of fish meal has doubled since 1948, according to the FAO tabulations,[1] because of the expansion of existing fisheries and of the development of new fisheries off South Africa, South America, and elsewhere. Considering the evident consumer preference for meat products in many countries, and the technical difficulties of distributing and marketing edible fish products in others, it may be expected that in the immediate future the use of fish products as food for domestic animals will grow more rapidly than their use for direct human consumption, despite the fact that it is manifestly nutritionally inefficient to recycle fish protein through chickens and cows to provide human food protein.

Whales. Unlike the fishes and marine invertebrates, nearly all the major whale stocks are either being overfished at present or are rapidly approaching that condition.[2] These huge animals, averaging over 50 tons, are largely used for domestic fats and oils and animal feed, although much of the meat is consumed directly as food by humans.

Table 4.5 Catch of Whales (Numbers) by Species, 1947–1955

Species	1947–1948	1950–1951	1951–1952	1952–1953	1953–1954	1954–1955
Blue whales	7,157	7,278	5,436	4,218	3,009	2,495
Fin whales	24,028	22,819	25,605	25,581	31,335	32,185
Humpback whales	515	4,352	4,023	3,328	3,155	2,713
Sei whales	1,573	3,033	3,123	2,208	2,491	1,940
Sperm whales	9,850	18,264	11,557	9,577	13,543	15,593
Others	308	49	88	97	109	148
Total	43,431	55,795	49,832	45,009	53,642	55,074

The catch of blue whales is declining quite rapidly, despite an increasingly intense fishery,[3] and the whaling fleets are turning increasingly to fin whales. According to Ruud, however, these are also showing signs of depletion, and he does not provide grounds for optimism respecting an increased catch of other species.

With careful conservation management by the International Whaling Commission, the present harvest of whales could probably be maintained and perhaps slightly increased, but certainly no large increase in the harvests of these marine mammals is possible. Indeed, under the present regulations of the Whaling Commission, which provide little in the way of

[1] Food and Agriculture Organization of the United Nations, *loc. cit.*

[2] Johan T. Ruud, "Modern Whaling and Its Prospects," *FAO Fish. Bull.*, vol. 5, no. 5, pp. 2–21, 1952.

[3] *Ibid.*

differential protection for the several antarctic species,[1] even lower harvests may be in prospect.

Marine Plants. Whereas the harvesting of the drifting microscopic plants of the sea (the phytoplankton) is not, at present, economically practical, use is made in some parts of the world of the attached plants, the "seaweeds," which grow in shallow waters. Since these plants live in a restricted zone along the margins of the seas, their total biomass is much less than that of the planktonic forms of the open ocean, but their dense stands make them amenable to harvesting.

Seaweed has been gathered since prehistoric times for food, medicine, and fertilizer. Its use in the Orient has always been greater than in Europe or North America, although the value of Irish moss as a food and of kelps and rockwoods as fertilizer has long been known to the Western world. Agar, the first seaweed product to become an important item of commerce in the Western countries, was introduced from the Orient. It was first a novelty food, later it was adopted as a gelling agent for culture media in bacteriology, and finally it found a place in a variety of products and processes.

Three groups of marine plants (algae) are of commercial importance:[2]

1. *Chlorophyceae*, or green algae, are widely distributed in the oceans, with the greatest variety of species being found in tropical waters. Although they are of little economic value, some species are used as food in Hawaii, Japan, and the South Pacific.

2. *Phaeophyceae*, or brown algae, are characteristic of cold waters throughout the world and occur in tropical waters as well. To this group belong the giant kelps and intertidal rockweeds of our northern coastal waters. These are of considerable economic importance as a source of alginates.

3. *Rhodophyceae*, or red algae, occur in greatest variety in the tropics but are also abundant in cold waters. Certain genera of this group, from which agar and agaroids are obtained, are of economic value because of the presence in their cell walls of complex colloidal carbohydrates. These phycocolloids readily form a colloidal solution when heated and become a gel when cooled, for example, agar and carrageen or Irish moss gel.

The *Phaeophyceae* were at one time burnt and ashed as a source of soda for the soap and glass industries, and later were used as a source of potash and iodine,[3,4] but this kelp-burning industry collapsed near the turn of

[1] Johan T. Ruud, "International Regulation of Whaling: A Critical Survey," *Norwegian Whaling Gaz.*, no. 7, pp. 374–387, 1956.

[2] D. K. Tressler and J. McW. Lemon, *Marine Products of Commerce*, Reinhold Publishing Corporation, New York, 1951.

[3] *Ibid.*

[4] F. N. Woodward, "Creatable Resources: The Development of New Resources by Applied Technology," *Proc. United Nations Sci. Conf. on Conservation and Utilization of Resources*, vol. 1, pp. 131–134, 1951.

this century with the development of cheaper sources of these chemicals. At about the same time, E. C. C. Stanford, a Scotsman, discovered that kelp contains a colloidal substance, similar to cellulose, which he called algin or alginic acid. This material became the basis of an important industry in the United Kingdom, Japan, and the United States, because of its unique emulsifying, gel-producing, and other colloidal properties. These are of wide application in food and pharmaceutical products and in rubber and textile manufacturing.

The leading nation in seaweed harvesting, according to recent FAO tabulations,[1] is Japan, where some 300,000 tons a year is gathered, one-half being kelp. In the United States about 7500 tons of Irish moss, *Chondrus*,[2] is harvested annually from the waters of the North Atlantic. From it are extracted various materials used in the food, brewery, and pharmaceutical industries. The annual harvest of the giant kelp *Macrocystis* in California is about 150,000 tons per year. The crop is used for alginates and related products. Other countries listed by the FAO[3] as having significant seaweed production are Canada (13,000 tons), South Korea (23,000 tons), and Norway (17,000 tons). There is also a sizable seaweed industry in the United Kingdom.

According to Woodward,[4] a very great increase in the production of kelp is possible. He estimates that the standing crop of this plant is 45 million metric tons along the Pacific seaboard of North America and 17 million tons around the Falkland Islands. Comparable but unsurveyed beds exist off the Peruvian, Chilean, Argentine, Tasmanian, and New Zealand coasts. In addition to this resource of giant buoyant seaweed, Woodward points out the existence of unused quantities of nonbuoyant seaweed, such as *Laminaria*, in the sublittoral zone off the North American Atlantic, British, French, Norwegian, and Japanese coasts. He believes[5] that, from the Scottish coast alone, a million tons of brown algae could be harvested annually, yielding 70,000 to 110,000 tons of carbohydrate.

Petroleum and Natural Gas under the Continental Shelves. The continental shelves of the world, i.e., the land submerged in less than 600 ft of water, extend over about 11.8 million sq miles and include, according to Pratt,[6] an estimated 30 million cu miles of possible oil-bearing sediments. By comparison with the probable reserves of hydrocarbons per cubic mile of sediments in land areas where extensive exploration has been carried out, rough estimates can be made of the recoverable reserves

[1] Food and Agriculture Organization of the United Nations, *op. cit.*, Table C-12.

[2] Food and Agriculture Organization of the United Nations, *op. cit.*

[3] *Ibid.*

[4] Woodward, *loc. cit.*

[5] F. N. Woodward, "Seaweeds: A Source of Chemicals and Food," in *World Crops*, Leonard Hill, London, 1952, vol. 4, no. 12, pp. 403–407.

[6] W. F. Pratt, "Petroleum on Continental Shelves," *Bull. Am. Assoc. Petrol. Geologists*, vol. 31, no. 4, pp. 667–669, 1947.

of crude oil, liquid hydrocarbons, and natural gas under the continental shelves. The most recent estimates have been summarized by Weeks[1,2] and Hubbert.[3] According to the latter, the continental shelves of the United States could probably be made to yield, with present production practices, about 20 billion bbl of crude oil, divided as follows:

Shelf	Billion Barrels
Texas	9
Louisiana	4
California	4
Other states	3
Total	20

By using the commonly assumed ratios of crude oil to other hydrocarbons, it may be computed that the United States continental shelves contain a recoverable 3 billion bbl of the so-called natural-gas liquids and 150 trillion cu ft of natural gas. Both for natural gas and total liquid hydrocarbons (crude oil plus natural-gas liquids) the quantities under the continental shelves probably comprise about 20 per cent of the remaining reserves of the United States outside the oil shales. Their usable energy content is approximately 80 trillion kwhr of heat energy. If all remaining fossil-fuel reserves of the United States, including coal, lignite, and oil shales, are taken into account, however, the offshore reserves amount to slightly less than 1 per cent.

For the world as a whole, Weeks has estimated that there are 400 billion bbl of recoverable reserves of crude oil under the continental shelves. According to Hubbert's estimates, this is about one-third of the total remaining world reserves, excluding the oil shales and tar sands. The estimated recoverable hydrocarbons under the shelves would provide slightly more than 100 trillion kwhr of heat energy, forty-five times the annual world requirement in 1956 and 4.65 per cent of the total energy content of all the world's remaining supplies of fossil fuels.

Extensive geophysical and geological prospecting has been done in recent years in the Gulf of Mexico, off the coast of California, in the Persian Gulf, and elsewhere to discover these underwater petroleum deposits. Attempts to reduce the discoveries to recoverable resources have been successful in several localities. Figure 4.4 is a map showing the acres under lease and some of the fields already producing off the Texas

[1] L. G. Weeks, "Discussion: Estimates of Undiscovered Petroleum Resources, by A. I. Levorsen," *Proc. United Nations Sci. Conf. on Conservation and Utilization of Resources*, vol. 1, pp. 107–110, 1950.

[2] L. G. Weeks, "Concerning Estimates of Potential Oil Reserves," *Bull. Am. Assoc. Petrol. Geologists*, vol. 34, no. 2, p. 1947, 1950.

[3] M. K. Hubbert, "Nuclear Energy and the Fossil Fuels," *Drilling and Production, Practice*, American Petroleum Institute, pp. 7–25, 1956.

and Louisiana coasts. According to Parks,[1] the success of such operations depends on the solution of a broad complex of technical and economic problems, because the cost of operations to recover underwater deposits is initially very much greater than for comparable recovery on shore.

The chief physical problems, drilling, site preparation, and transportation, arise from wind, waves, and currents and become more difficult to solve as water depths and distances from shore and operating bases increase. So far, drilling operations have been confined to relatively shallow water at favorable locations, i.e., in depths less than 100 ft and less than 40 miles from shore. It may be expected, however, that present

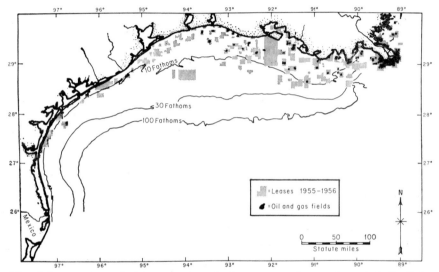

Fig. 4.4 Locations of oil leases and producing areas on the continental shelf off the Texas and Louisiana coasts.

rapid technical developments will make it possible to carry these operations into increasingly difficult conditions.

Minerals on the Sea Floor and in the Water. The floor of the deep sea is known to contain low-grade deposits of cobalt, nickel, and copper (0.1 to 0.7 per cent by weight of the metals) associated with deposits of iron and manganese. The problems of mining these materials, in the face of the great depth and pressure, have not been solved.

The sea water itself contains a large variety of minerals in the form of dissolved salts. The extraction of sea salt by evaporation is an ancient industry and is now highly developed, not only for the recovery of sodium chloride but also for the production of sodium sulfate, potassium chloride,

[1] M. H. Parks, "Petroleum Production from Continental Shelves," *Proc. United Nations Sci. Conf. on Conservation and Utilization of Resources,* vol. 3, *Food and Energy Resources,* pp. 21–23, 1951.

magnesium chloride, and magnesium oxychloride cements.[1] Bromine is also produced from the mother liquor, or bittern, of the saltworks.

The separation of elements directly from sea water, except as an adjunct to the production of salt, is an industry of recent origin, having started in 1924 when the Ethyl Corporation commenced commercial extraction of bromine from sea water for the manufacture of ethylene dibromide. This is the additive in "ethyl" gasoline. The production of magnesium metal from sea water was instituted by the Dow Chemical Company in 1941 at Freeport, Texas, employing a combination of chemical and electrolytic procedures.[2]

With sufficiently cheap power, and with the depletion of other sources, the production of these and other elements from sea water will doubtless become increasingly feasible economically. The total quantity of the minerals in the sea is tremendous, but most of them occur in very dilute solution. Thus, although this "mine" is essentially inexhaustible, it contains extremely low-grade ore.

Ocean Transportation and Defense.   Long-distance transportation of large cargoes by sea is the indispensable basis of international commerce. The economy of the United States is in large part related to the sea-borne commerce that flows through its seaports.

Many of the problems of ocean transportation, and opportunities for more efficient use of this resource, lie not at sea but at the boundary between the sea and the land. The transition from the land to the sea can be conducted economically only where the configuration of the boundary makes possible the close juxtaposition of the ship to the shore in a location sheltered from winds and waves. Such conditions obtain in the natural harbors, where nature has provided deep sheltered bays communicating with the open sea. In some locations, however, the natural harbors are not sufficiently deep or sufficiently protected; in these places dredging and building of jetties provide the required conditions for cargo transfer. Increased knowledge of the effects of waves, currents, and tides on dredged channels and structures can provide the basis of improved harbor design and development.

A further opportunity for more efficient and economic use of the sea as a transportation medium lies in the development of new methods of cargo handling. The shipping industry has come to realize that the characteristics and economics of bulk or container movements of cargoes on and off ships are not fully understood. Operations research has recently been initiated in an attempt to gain such understanding as a basis for improving the presently low efficiency of cargo transfers in American shipping.[3]

[1] Tressler and Lemon, *op. cit.*, chaps. 3 and 4.

[2] *Ibid.*, chap. 4.

[3] W. M. Roth, "The Problem of American Shipping: New Questions and Old Answers," *Operations Research*, vol. 5, no. 1, pp. 104–110, 1957.

Experience during World War II showed that it is possible to embark (and debark) cargoes off beaches and elsewhere outside conventional harbors. Whether techniques of beach loading and unloading without docking facilities can become commercially feasible in time of peace is doubtful, but they could become an urgent necessity in time of war. Since our sea-borne commerce funnels through a very few ports, the destruction or denial of use of these ports would be a primary objective of enemy action; means must be available for maintaining the flow of goods against such a contingency. From the point of view of national defense, it is thus of urgent importance to provide the necessary scientific and engineering knowledge to develop means of effective transfer of cargoes across the shores at locations other than developed harbors.

Waste Disposal.   Disposal of domestic sewage and industrial wastes is conveniently accomplished near coastal population centers by running them into the sea. The large volume and rapid mixing of the ocean waters dilute the wastes, and the microorganisms in the sea break down the organic constituents.

Haphazard dumping of wastes may, however, produce serious consequences. Where large volumes are run into the waters of nearly enclosed harbors, the rate of interchange with the open sea may be insufficient to provide rapid dilution, and high levels of the waste products, possibly including pathogenic bacteria, may be built up locally. An example is San Diego Bay, which has become dangerously polluted as a result of dumping about thirty-five million gallons per day of untreated sewage. Even on open coasts it is necessary to take careful account of local oceanic conditions, if large volumes of sewage and industrial wastes are to be disposed of without deleterious effects. In the cases studied to date, the residual waste concentrations in the immediate vicinity of the sewer outfalls have been high. Damage may have resulted to living resources in the vicinity, such as fish populations and kelp beds. Where the currents tend to transport the wastes along the beach rather than offshore, serious contamination of the beach and adjacent waters may result. Mixing is retarded if the waste liquids are not immediately diluted with a large volume of sea water during the process of discharge from the outfall. Because the density of the waste material is usually lower than that of the sea water, it tends to rise, without much further dilution, to the surface, where it can be rapidly transported inshore by the wind.

In any area where ocean disposal is contemplated, careful investigations should be made of tidal and wind currents as a function of time and depth, the density stratification of the water, the rates and volumes of mixing, the character of the bottom sediments, and the rate of disappearance of human bacteria in the mixture of sewage and sea water as a basis for choice of disposal sites and methods.

In the coming era of large nuclear-fission power plants, it may be necessary to dispose of very considerable quantities of radioactive wastes.[1] Careful consideration will have to be given to ocean disposal, particularly for countries with small, densely populated land areas and long sea coasts, such as England, Italy, and Japan. Some of the fission products, notably strontium 90, present a human health hazard even at very low concentrations. Others are concentrated from sea water, by factors of several hundred to more than ten thousand, in the bodies of marine organisms. The hazardous properties of these wastes disappear with time because of radioactive decay, but they cannot be reduced by any process of chemical or biological decomposition. They cannot be destroyed; they can only be isolated or dispersed.

Safe ocean disposal of radioactive wastes involves the use of sites where rapid and profound dilution will occur, or where sufficient decay can take place before the radioactive waters and their contained organisms come into contact with human beings. Low-level radioactive wastes are already being disposed of, apparently safely, in the shallow, rapidly mixing waters of the Irish Sea off the west coast of England. Small quantities are also being dumped off the east and west coasts of the United States. But it is certainly unsafe to dispose of large quantities of highly radioactive wastes in such coastal waters.

Deep ocean disposal may be possible, but we must learn a great deal more about the deep-ocean circulation, and the transfer of elements between the deep sea and the surface waters by physical and biological processes, before it can be stated with any certainty where and under what circumstances specified quantities of radioactive waste products can be safely disposed of at sea.

Recreation.   The recreational aspects of the sea and its contents are of great importance to coastal populations in the temperate and sub-tropical regions, not only in providing healthful sports and satisfaction of men's curiosity and their desire for beauty, but as the basis of large tourist and service industries.

The recreational uses of some of the living resources are a little more important commercially than their exploitation for food or industry. In California, for example, ocean sport-fishing enthusiasts during 1954 spent some $3\frac{3}{4}$ million man-days in angling, and their total expenditures through the service industries catering to them were correspondingly large. It has been estimated that, in the case of the striped bass, which is now reserved for sport fishing, California anglers spent $2.85 per pound of fish caught. This is a good deal more than these fish would be worth on the commercial market.

[1] Committee on Effects of Atomic Radiation on Oceanography and Fisheries, *Summary Report*, National Academy of Science—National Research Council Publication, pp. 73–83, 1956.

Water from the Sea.   It is frequently said that fresh water is becoming our most critical natural resource. During the last few years, serious attempts have been made to develop inexpensive methods for extracting fresh water from sea water. The basic principles involved are well known, and the theoretical amount of energy required is not large. Although 540 calories per g is taken up in evaporating sea water, almost all this heat is released on condensation. The energy required to separate the salt from the water is only a fraction of a calorie per gram. But even the most efficient of the existing and suggested methods for desalting water and pumping it to higher elevations are too expensive to provide water for irrigation (see Chapter 3).

The direct engineering attack may in the long run be less useful than an indirect one. Several alternative lines of investigation can be suggested: (1) Development of new and cheaper sources of power, for example, from nuclear reactors, would lower costs. (2) Development of methods of extracting useful trace substances from saline waste water might result in by-products that would, together with the fresh water, make the total operation economic. For example, the uranium in sea water has an energy equivalent, if all of it could be subjected to fission, of 50 calories per g, about 100 times the theoretical energy required to separate the salt from the water. (3) Agricultural crops might be developed by genetic experimentation that could use water of higher salt content.

The fact is that nature herself operates a most effective distillation system. Nearly one-third of all the energy of sunlight falling on the surface of the ocean is utilized in converting salt water into fresh water by evaporation. The quantity of solar power used in this way is nearly 10,000 times the power produced by our industrial society from fossil fuels and hydroelectric plants. The total quantity of water evaporated, if all of it fell on the surface of the land and was uniformly distributed, would result in an average rainfall of over 100 in. a year.

The trouble with the natural distillation process is not the quantity of fresh water produced, but rather that nature's pipelines are poorly distributed. Too much water comes to some areas and not enough to others; moreover, the valve systems seem to be capriciously managed. During some seasons the discharge is too great, bringing floods, while during others there is only a trickle and droughts occur.

Can anything be done about nature's pipeline system? The quantity of solar energy used in driving the engine of the sea and the atmosphere is so great, compared to any of the energy sources under man's control, that it would seem impossible to affect weather or climate materially by any human action. Yet a closer look shows there may be things we could do. Many of the processes in the atmosphere seem to be metastable: a slight action may initiate a very large-scale process. With sufficient knowledge of the mechanisms controlling weather and climate, we might be able to find "pressure points" in the atmosphere where actions within human capabilities could affect the running of the mighty heat engine of the sea and the air.

4.4 Some Problems in the Development of Marine Resources

Man is essentially a terrestrial animal. Only recently in our history have we ventured beyond the margin of the sea; it is an environment still largely mysterious, over which we have little mastery. This different environment brings economic and social problems in addition to technical ones. Our social customs, embodied in the statute and common law, have arisen in response to the necessities of living on the land and often apply imperfectly in the aquatic environment. The development of solutions to the new types of problems encountered in the sea is currently a source of much difficulty on the community, national, and international levels.

Increasing the Harvest of Marine Food Resources. Commercial fishermen will catch fish only if it pays them to do so, that is, if the cost of production is at least equal to the value of the product. Consequently, fish and marine invertebrate stocks will be unutilized or underutilized as long as the cost of catching the additional harvest cannot be met by the value of the additional catch. Increasing the harvest involves decreasing the cost of production, increasing the value of the product, or both. The problem is somewhat different for developed and underdeveloped countries and for different kinds of marine organisms.

Increase of Production and Decreased Cost. The potential of marine products for providing protein food and other organic materials has certainly not been realized, and the approach to full realization will be slow, because we simply do not know enough about the living resources to provide the basis for really new developments. Our knowledge of the extent and location of the latent resources is fragmentary. Even for those kinds of organisms which are now harvestable, we have inadequate knowledge of their biology and behavior and poor estimates of their potential yields.

Although modern fishing craft employ the most advanced aids to navigation, and some use has been made of underwater sound equipment and aircraft for locating fish schools, the various types of nets, lines, and trawls used for harvesting are basically the same as those employed for the past several hundred years. Consequently, the major fisheries are for the same kinds of organisms that have been exploited since man first went to sea, that is, those whose aggregation habits make them amenable to large-scale capture by the traditional kinds of gear.

According to Fleming and Laevastu,[1] commercial fishing with present

[1] Fleming and Laevastu, *loc. cit.*

methods is profitable only if the concentration of fish within a limited vertical range is more than 10 to 50 g per sq m, depending on the value of the product and the method of fishing. For comparison, the standing crop of salmon in the Bering Sea would be about 3 g per sq m if spread uniformly over their living area, while the concentration of pilchard in dense schools can be as high as 1 kg per sq m.[1] Except on the bottom in restricted shallow areas, the locations of concentrations of fish vary in both time and space, partly because of the diffuse and fluctuating character of the food supply and partly in response to such other factors as changing temperature and spawning behavior. Much of the fishermen's time and effort is spent in searching for fish. One of the most effective means of reducing present fishing costs would be the development of better methods for prediction of localities and times of concentrations. This must be based on a greater understanding of the changing oceanic environment and of the biology, not only of the commercially important animals, but of their food supply and predators.

In recent years previously unexploited stocks of commercially valuable marine animals have been located. Examples are the deep-bottom shrimp of the Gulf of Mexico, the king crab of the Bering Sea, and the large tuna living at depth in the equatorial regions of the central Pacific. Further exploration of this kind would inevitably lead to greater production at lower cost.

Other fish species, occurring in the sea more diffusely than those now commercially exploited, may well constitute a much larger biomass and be capable of yielding greater harvests. But these cannot be expected to support important fisheries with present fishing methods, because the costs of straining them out of the water with existing commercial gear are higher than the possible value of the catches. If man is to use these resources in the near future, it will be necessary to develop new means of capture, possibly, for example, the use of electromagnetic or acoustic fields to cause them to aggregate so that they can be netted. Unfortunately, the fundamental knowledge of the behavior and reactions to stimuli of these organisms, upon which such developments are predicated, is lacking.

Increase of Consumption in Developed Countries. In the United States and other developed countries, people are accustomed to eat only a limited quantity of fish, and then only a few varieties. The per capita consumption of marine food products in the United States is about 11 lb per year, and this, despite greatly improved refrigeration, transportation, and retail marketing facilities, is no higher than it was 20 years ago. There has been a rapid increase in the consumption of some products, such as frozen shrimp and canned tuna, but this has been mostly at the expense

[1] H. W. Harvey, "On the Production of Living Matter in the Sea off Plymouth," *J. Marine Biol. Assoc. United Kingdom*, vol. 29, pp. 97–137, 1950.

of competing sea foods. For a few species, the consumer demand outruns the supply—unfortunately, for at least some of these, the maximum sustainable harvest is already being attained. For most species, the fishermen know how to catch more than they can sell.

In such countries increasing the harvest of sea food is dependent, in large measure, on better processing, distribution, and marketing, and on creation of new products with greater consumer acceptance. Efforts should particularly be directed toward those species which can support larger harvests, where the fishermen already know how to increase the catch. The rapid development of the canned-tuna industry, which grew from nothing to a leading position in 40 years, illustrates what can be done along these lines.

The species now in great demand are not cheap, while others go begging on the market, even though they are capable of being captured and landed at lower cost. Tuna, for example, bring about 13 cents a pound to United States fishermen, and the canned product retails at about 75 cents a pound, not much less than beef. Salmon are even more costly. Pacific hake, a very abundant and easily obtainable species, are not now acceptable as human food fish (the small quantity marketed is mostly used for mink feed), and consequently they yield less than 2 cents a pound to the fisherman. A small increase in the value of the product through increased consumer demand would make economically harvestable this and other stocks that are now submarginal.

Improvements in Food Technology. One of the principal problems in increasing the use of marine protein food is the tendency for rapid spoilage of the flesh of marine animals. Even in highly developed countries, with all the resources of refrigeration and other preservative processes, fish can be kept fresh for only a short time.[1,2]

As the fish become stale, not only the flavor, color, and texture are affected, but also proteins and soluble nutrient substances are lost. With demersal fish, bacterial spoilage is most important; autolysis and oxidation of fats and oils play an important role in the deterioration of pelagic fish.

Deterioration begins with death, even in the death struggle during catching. In tuna, it has been found that the body temperature rises by almost 21°F (12°C) within 50 min after death. The rate of spoilage depends primarily on the temperature of the flesh, which determines the rate of growth, reproduction, and enzyme activity of the always present spoilage bacteria, as well as the rate of chemical changes leading to rancidity in the fatty fishes.

[1] F. Bramsnaes, "Handling and Chilling of Fresh Fish on Vessels at Sea," *FAO Fish. Bull.*, vol. 10, no. 1, pp. 25–41, 1957.

[2] E. Hess, "Current Technological Problems in Fish Canning," *FAO Fish. Bull.*, vol. 9, no. 4, pp. 161–180, 1956.

Recent research in several countries has shown that such preservatives as a weak nitrite solution can be used to delay spoilage. Certain antibiotics, especially aureomycin and terramycin, have proved even more effective. Dips, lasting $\frac{1}{2}$ to 2 min, in concentrations of 10 to 25 ppm of antibiotic in weak brine, doubled or trebled the keeping quality of the fish at ice temperatures. Traces of the antibiotics remaining before consumption are destroyed by the ordinary cooking processes. The use of antibiotics in most countries still awaits approval, however.

Intimately related to the problem of better preservation is that of assessing the quality of the raw material. Considerable effort is now being directed toward developing objective methods of grading fish products as they come into the market or enter processing plants.

Increase of Harvesting and Utilization in Underdeveloped Countries. Although the marine harvest plays only a secondary role in Europe and North America where there is an abundance of meat, the larger part of the world's human population suffers from a deficiency of animal protein, and it is here that the greatest need exists for development of the fisheries and a more widespread use of the catch. In densely populated countries, the raising of meat animals competes with more efficient use of the soil for the growing of human plant food. Moreover, in general, the cost of production of fish is far less per pound of protein obtained. Japan is an example of a nation with a heavily exploited land area in which the principal animal protein is derived from marine fish and other products of the sea, the average per capita consumption of fish being about 75 lb per year, seven times that of the United States.

In the countries of southeast Asia, with nearly half the world's population, few of the existing fisheries resources are even partially exploited. Coastal fishing is normally best developed. Deep-sea fishing in the Arabian Sea, the Indian Ocean, the Bay of Bengal, the Gulf of Thailand, the South China Sea, and the open Pacific Ocean is very limited. The solution, in general terms, requires exploration and surveying of the resources, improvements in fishing vessels, gear, and methods, better fish processing and preservation, a more efficient system of transportation and marketing, and stimulation of the demand for fish and other fisheries products.[1]

The hot climate of the region makes storing, preservation, and processing facilities of the utmost importance. Ice factories and refrigerating plants are a rarity, so that fish storage and preservation by the usual methods, if available at all, are very expensive. As a result, the fish catch can be used only immediately after collection and therefore very near the coast. New and cheaper techniques of preservation are needed. If these could be developed, they would provide the additional benefit of creating

[1] E. Szczepanik, "Problems of Fish Marketing in the Indo-Pacific Region," *FAO Fish. Bull.*, vol. 9, no. 2, pp. 85–92, 1956.

a number of subsidiary labor-absorbing industries. Transportation and marketing present other difficulties. Their solution involves a number of factors, such as the construction and improvement of roads and railways, the provision of insulated trucks and rail cars as well as sea and river vessels, the supply of suitable standardized containers, and improvements in wholesale and retail distribution systems.

In some parts of southeast Asia, fish is excluded from the diet on religious grounds. A typical case is the Indian state of Saurashtra where 92 per cent of the population believe in ahimsa (i.e., noncruelty to animals). Scaleless fish, sharks, skates, rays, and oysters are not eaten by the majority of Moslems. Elsewhere, the consumers do not like dried or cured fish. At the moment, however, probably the most important factor keeping the demand for fish at a low level is the unsatisfactory state of fish storing, preservation, and handling, which limits the availability of supplies. This is especially true of rural areas, where the purchasing power is often so low that the prices of fish are beyond the people's means.

Some countries are already trying to introduce specific measures to stimulate demand. In Pakistan, for instance, certain days have been declared as meatless in order to increase the consumption of sea foods.

Harvesting at Lower Levels in the Food Chain.   Despite the fact that the fishes are not yet being utilized to anywhere near the limit of their biological potential, many scientists have been fascinated by the possibility of gathering the organic material produced lower in the food pyramid, such as the zooplankton, and thereby obtaining a larger harvest. They have pointed out that other large animals, for example, the whalebone whales, make a prosperous living in this way. If an oversized mechanical whale, which might be a ship with an open bow leading to a water tunnel equipped with a filtration apparatus, were developed, the plankton could be harvested directly for man's benefit.

What is generally overlooked, however, is that, although the plankton production is large relative to that of the higher organisms, the standing crop represents a very small volume in a very large volume of water. Even in rich areas, the zooplankton constitute only a few parts per million parts of sea water. The problem of straining out a gallon of zooplankton from a million gallons of water at a profit, even if the plankton were worth as much per pound as the more costly kinds of fish, is formidable. Perhaps at some future time, when man's protein food needs are more pressing than now, and when new techniques have been developed, plankton harvesting may become commercially possible. In the immediate future, however, it can be expected that the food harvest will continue to depend mainly on the fishes and the bottom-living invertebrates.

Farming the Sea.   A similar long-range problem is that of farming the sea. At the present time, certain kinds of shellfish, oysters, and clams are cultivated in a manner analogous to agriculture, but except for these, man has been able to do nothing to improve on nature. The harvesting of fish resources is still essentially a "hunting" economy. In general, we do not yet know enough about the requirements for growth of marine plants and animals to be able to take measures to increase their productivity.

On land it is possible to increase the productivity of a given farming area by fertilizing it. At first sight, it would seem impossible to increase the fertility of the sea by any means available to human beings, because of its giant volume and the continual movement of its waters. It is possible, however, in semienclosed bodies of water and in oceanic regions where the water tends to remain for a considerable period because of eddying motions, that addition of a relatively small quantity of substances necessary for growth could greatly increase the yield of harvestable animals. This depends on the apparent fact that in many areas the substances that limit growth are present in extremely low concentration. The addition of a few hundred tons of these substances might increase the fertility of an area of many thousand square miles.

Conservation of the Living Resources of the Sea.   A self-renewing, living resource, such as a stock of fish, is maintained by reproduction and growth balancing losses due to deaths. Over a period of time, the losses from the population must be balanced by accessions to the population; otherwise it would become extinct. When the percentage rate of loss is increased, by whatever means, the percentage rate of accessions to the population changes also. If the changes are not too severe, the population again comes into balance, but usually at a different size. It is this resiliency of a population of organisms, its ability to compensate for increased mortality, that makes it possible for it to survive increase in its predators. The same phenomenon is the biological basis of fisheries since, from the standpoint of the fish, a fishery is simply an increase in the predation rate. A continuing fishery is possible only if the fish population reacts to the mortality produced by fishing by coming into a new balance under the environmental conditions that include predation by man. The size and composition of the balanced population can vary over a wide range, depending on fishing intensity and the size of the average annual harvests. Maximizing the sustainable harvest of the resource consists in choosing that level of fishing effort and corresponding mean population size for which the average catch over many years is a maximum. The problem has been formulated quantitatively[1,2] along the following lines:

[1] Schaefer, "Some Considerations of Population Dynamics and Economics in Relation to the Management of the Commercial Marine Fisheries," *op. cit.*

[2] Milner B. Schaefer, "The Scientific Basis for a Conservation Programme," papers presented at the International Technical Conference on the Conservation of the Living Resources of the Sea, United Nations, New York, 1956, pp. 14–55.

For each magnitude of population of commercial sizes of fish, there is a natural rate of increase. Under average environmental conditions, this is some single-valued function of population magnitude. That is,

$$\frac{1}{P}\frac{dP}{dt} = f(P) \tag{4.1}$$

where P is the magnitude of the population and $f(P)$ is a single-valued function of P which decreases with increasing population size to zero at the limiting size.

The catch C during a year is some function of the size of population and of the human and technical factors, which we collectively term *fishing intensity E*

$$C = \phi(P,E) \tag{4.2}$$

In the equilibrium state, the catch is equal to the rate of natural increase and may be termed the *equilibrium catch*. The average equilibrium catch is the long-term annual production of the fishery for a given level of fishing intensity and population.

From Equations (4.1) and (4.2) it immediately follows that, under equilibrium conditions, population size is some function of fishing intensity

$$P = \psi(E) \tag{4.3}$$

The natural first approximation to $f(P)$ is a linear relationship, and data from experimental populations and from some commercial fisheries indicate that this is adequate to describe them;[1,2] thus we have

$$\frac{dP}{dt} = K_1 P(L - P) \tag{4.4}$$

where K_1 and L are constants.

It also appears that, to a good degree of approximation for many fisheries, Equation (4.2) is represented by

$$C = K_2 EP \tag{4.5}$$

where K_2 is a constant.

Under equilibrium conditions, with $C = dP/dt$, we have

$$K_2 EP = K_1 P(L - P)$$

and, consequently,

$$P = L - \frac{K_2}{K_1} E \tag{4.6}$$

[1] Milner B. Schaefer, "Some Aspects of the Dynamics of Populations Important to the Management of the Commercial Marine Fisheries," *Inter-Amer. Trop. Tuna Comm. Bull.*, vol. 1, no. 2, pp. 25–56, 1954.

[2] Milner B. Schaefer, "A Study of the Dynamics of the Fishery for Yellowfin Tuna in the Eastern Tropical Pacific Ocean," *Inter-Amer. Trop. Tuna Comm. Bull.*, vol. 2, no. 6, 1957.

That is, for equilibrium conditions, average population size is a linear function of fishing intensity, and from Equations (4.5) and (4.6)

$$C = K_2 E \left(L - \frac{K_2}{K_1} E \right) \qquad (4.7)$$

for the relationship between fishing intensity and average equilibrium catch.

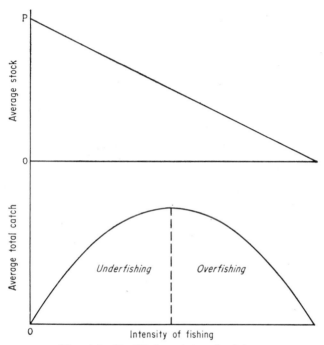

Fig. 4.5   Equilibrium states of a fishery.

The relationships (4.6) and (4.7) are shown graphically in Figure 4.5. It may be seen that as fishing effort increases the average population decreases, while the sustainable average catch at first increases, reaches a maximum at an intermediate value of fishing intensity, then falls off with increasing fishing effort. When the fishing intensity rises above the level corresponding to maximum average catch, the resource may be said to be overfished. Conversely, when the fishing intensity is less than this value, a greater average yield could be obtained, and the resource may be said to be "underfished."

The central problem of conservation is to determine these relationships for particular fish populations and so to provide the scientific basis for control of the amount of fishing in order to obtain the maximum continuing harvest. This is, however, by no means easy, because the renewal of the stock, in nature, depends not only on the magnitude of the unharvested population but also on variations in numerous environmental factors,[1] and these factors may vary in an unpredictable fashion. Indeed for some fisheries, such, for example, as that for the California sardine, the variability due to environmental factors has been so large that it has been quite impossible to arrive at a generally acceptable estimate of the effects of fishing on the stock and yield. For some fisheries, on the other hand, it is possible to arrive at useful estimates. For example, Figure 4.6 shows the values of fishing intensity, catch per unit of effort (as a measure of population size), and total catch experienced by the yellowfin tuna fishery of the eastern tropical Pacific over the years 1934 through 1955, taken from Schaefer.[2] On this figure is also shown as a broken line the estimated relationship between fishing effort and average population size, corresponding to Equation (4.6); from the intersection of this line with the equilateral hyperbola indicating total catch, one may read off the values of average catch corresponding to different values of fishing intensity [Equation (4.7)].

This simple theory is often adequate to describe fisheries that depend upon the entire reproductive stock. However, for some fisheries it is also possible to regulate the size and age at which fish are captured. In these cases a more complex mathematical model, involving the mortality, growth, and reproductive rates of different ages of fish, is required. Models such as these have been described in some detail by Beverton and Holt.[3]

In the foregoing it has been assumed that the objective of conservation is to maintain a fish resource in such a condition as to make possible the maximum sustainable harvest year after year. This objective has been generally accepted in the New World and has been written into several international treaties concerning specific fish resources, such as the Convention between the United States of America and the Dominion of Canada for the Preservation of the Halibut Fishery of the Northern Pacific Ocean and Bering Sea, and the Convention between the United States of America and the Republic of Costa Rica for the Establishment of an Inter-American Tropical Tuna Commission. The International Technical Conference on the Conservation of the Living Resources of the Sea, April 18 to May 10, 1955 (Rome), sponsored by the United Nations and attended by representatives of 45 nations, agreed that, "The princi-

---

[1] R. Revelle, "Fluctuating Fishery Stocks: What We Know about This World-wide Riddle," *Proc. Fisheries Products Conf. 47th Annual Convention Natl. Canners Assoc.,* Jan. 23–27, 1954.

[2] Schaefer, "A Study of the Dynamics of the Fishery for Yellowfin Tuna in the Eastern Tropical Pacific Ocean," *op. cit.*

[3] R. J. H. Beverton and S. J. Holt, "The Theory of Fishing," in *Sea Fisheries, Their Investigation in the United Kingdom,* Edward Arnold & Co., London, 1956, chap. 9, pp. 372–441.

pal objective of conservation of the living resources of the sea is to obtain the optimum sustainable yield so as to secure a maximum supply of food and other marine products."

On the other hand, Graham[1] has pointed out that such other considerations as the catch per unit effort, average size of fish, and monetary return

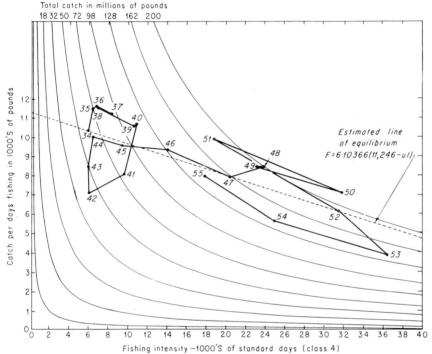

Fig. 4.6 Relationships among fishing intensity, abundance, and catch for the yellowfin tuna fishery of the Tropical Eastern Pacific Ocean. (*From Schaefer, "A Study of the Dynamics of the Fishery for Yellowfin Tuna in the Eastern Tropical Pacific Ocean," Inter-Amer. Trop. Tuna Comm. Bull., vol. 2, no. 6, 1957.*)

to the fishermen may be important. Several economists, for example, Gordon,[2] insist that a proper objective is the maximum net economic yield, that is, the maximum of the difference between the cost of making the harvest and its value. It may be shown, however,[3] that the maximum net economic yield must always occur at a lower level of total harvest

[1] M. Graham, "Concepts of Conservation," papers presented at the International Technical Conference on the Conservation of the Living Resources of the Sea, United Nations, New York, 1956, pp. 1–13.

[2] H. S. Gordon, "An Economic Approach to the Optimum Utilization of Fishery Resources," *J. Fish. Research Board Can.*, vol. 10, no. 7, pp. 442–457, 1953.

[3] Schaefer, "Some Considerations of Population Dynamics and Economics in Relation to the Management of the Commercial Marine Fisheries," *op. cit.*

(and lower fishing intensity) than the maximum total harvest, so that these two possible conservation objectives are, to a degree, inconsistent. Gordon[1,2] and Schaefer[3] have also shown that where the fish resource is common property, open to all comers on an equal basis, it is not possible to realize, in the long run, the maximum net economic yield, or indeed *any* net economic yield. The social question of just what *is* the human optimum, therefore, adds a further complication to the problem of the conservation of the living resources.

Legal and Economic Problems. In the preceding pages we have discussed some of the economic aspects of the development and conservation of marine resources, since all aspects of resource utilization are intimately and inevitably bound up with economic considerations. Certain additional problems of development of marine resources arise from the fact that legal and economic practices on the land apply imperfectly at sea.

The contents of the high seas have been, historically, regarded either as common property belonging to everyone (*res communes*) or as property belonging to no one (*res nullius*) until removed and reduced to possession. These concepts, which have served well enough for several centuries, are based on two assumptions: (1) the resources of the sea are practically unlimited and inexhaustible, so that one man's use of them cannot adversely affect another's, and (2) the contents of the sea are constantly shifting about so that private ownership of a part of a marine resource is not feasible. True, a certain narrow margin of the ocean, the "territorial sea," has been considered to be under the sovereignty of the adjacent coastal state, but even here the state has usually applied the concept of common property, belonging jointly to all citizens, to many of the resources of this zone.

The difficulty is that it has been discovered by experience that some of the resources of the sea which support extractive industries are *not* unlimited, so that it is necessary, for the common good, to control their use.

For such resources as oyster beds or oil deposits, which are attached to or imbedded in the sea floor, and are therefore fixed in location, the modern trend is to grant property rights to units of the resource, thus allowing their best use to be developed by the normal interplay of economic forces in the same manner as for resources on land. For the resources of the overlying waters, such a simple solution is much more difficult. A fish stock, for example, moves freely over a considerable area, and several

---

[1] Gordon, *loc. cit.*

[2] H. S. Gordon, "The Economic Theory of a Common Property Resource: The Fishery," *J. Political Economy*, vol. 62, no. 2, pp. 124–142, 1954.

[3] Schaefer, "Some Considerations of Population Dynamics and Economics in Relation to the Management of the Commercial Marine Fisheries," *op. cit.*

such resources often occur in the same area or in overlapping areas; consequently, it is not easy to define a property right by location. The elements of the resource cannot be marked or branded, like range cattle, to indicate ownership. Even where it might be possible to grant a property right to the harvesting of a particular resource, it would be necessary to have the right extend over the whole resource to enable the owner to control it effectively. Because these resources come in very large units, problems of monopoly occur in addition to the practical difficulty of revolutionizing long-established custom. The practice of treating these resources as common property available to all on an equal basis has therefore been generally continued, with the control required for conservation being exercised by government agencies. From the economic standpoint, however, this has the drawback that there can accrue no economic rent, or net economic yield, since under a system of common property with free access the net yield will at equilibrium be completely dissipated.[1,2] It has been suggested that such resources be managed as private property under government ownership or that a partial property right be established by limiting the number of persons permitted to engage in the industry.[3,4]

These problems are difficult enough where the citizens of only one nation are involved. Where people from several nations are simultaneously engaged in extractive industries based on the same resource, it is quite impossible to establish criteria for economically optimum utilization, because the economic factors vary widely from nation to nation. So far, the solution for the living resources of the high seas has been to give paramount importance to ensuring the maximum continuing harvest and to relegate economic considerations to secondary and subsidiary importance.[5] This also corresponds to practice in most nations with respect to the resources of the territorial sea.

Even where the maximum continuing harvest is chosen as the primary criterion of wise use, it may be possible to obtain at the same time some net economic yield by managing the harvesting so as to have a spread between the cost and the value of the products. This possibility has been seldom realized for resources of the sea, primarily because it requires modification of the simple common-property concept. There is a very great need for thorough studies, combining economics and the natural

[1] Schaefer, "Some Considerations of Population Dynamics and Economics in Relation to the Management of the Commercial Marine Fisheries," *op. cit.*

[2] Gordon, *loc. cit.*

[3] *Ibid.*

[4] Gordon, "The Economic Theory of a Common Property Resource: The Fishery," *op. cit.*

[5] "Report of the International Technical Conference on the Conservation of the Living Resources of the Sea, 18 April to 10 May, 1955," United Nations, N.Y., 1955.

sciences, of marine resources in order to develop a more rational basis for their exploitation.

International Problems.   International conflicts over the resources of the sea have been common in the past and can be expected to become more numerous in the future as the intensity and scope of exploitation of marine resources increase. The maritime history of the world is replete with disputes over rights of trade, navigation, and fishing. Recently, the matter of disposal of atomic wastes has brought up a new source of trouble.

Such conflicts arise from the natural desire of all peoples to secure for themselves as much of the sea's bounty as they can. There have been periods when powerful nations have attempted to exercise unilateral control over large areas of the sea, in some cases the whole of an ocean. None were long successful in such attempts. At present it is generally accepted that a nation has sovereign rights over only a relatively narrow belt of territorial sea. The large area of the high seas is considered to belong to all in common, although limited jurisdiction for defense and customs control has been exercised over a zone adjacent to the territorial sea up to some two hundred miles in width. Since a good many of the presently usable marine resources occur in waters at a distance from the coast, there is, in some quarters, a tendency to attempt to extend the breadth of jurisdiction of coastal states to ensure to their peoples special rights to the offshore resources.

International disputes over the resources of the sea have been of a number of kinds. Without attempting to list all of them in detail, we may mention some of the outstanding areas of disagreement.

Extent of the Territorial Sea.   There has never been common agreement on the extent of the territorial sea, although it is universally recognized that it extends seaward from the shore at least 3 miles. Until recent years, few claims have extended beyond 12 miles; there have, however, in the last decade, been some claims extending much farther. At the same time, there have been a number of disputes regarding the nature of the base lines from which the breadth of the territorial sea should be measured, and there have also been many disputes over the status of certain straits and bays.

Right of Innocent Passage.   The sovereignty over the territorial sea is not absolute, since it is generally agreed that vessels of all nations enjoy certain rights to pass through it in the course of commerce. Even here, however, there has been some disagreement as to the exact rights of the coastal state and the rights and duties of vessels passing through the territorial sea.

Contiguous Zone and Pursuit on the High Seas.   It has been common practice for nations to exercise in a zone outside the territorial sea controls necessary to prevent infringement of customs, fiscal, and sanitary regulations within the territorial sea and to apprehend and punish violators of such regulations. Under certain circumstances, a vessel believed to have committed offenses in the territorial sea may be pursued and apprehended on the high seas. The delimitation of the contiguous zone, the exact rights of nations therein, and the proper limits on the rights of "hot pursuit" have all been topics of serious disagreements.

Navigation on the High Seas. Although ships of all nations have the right of navigation on the high seas, this right is not completely unrestricted. As in all human affairs, it is necessary to establish some rules for the common good. These involve such matters as the nationality of ships, status of merchant vessels and government vessels, safety of navigation, slave trading, and piracy. There is a large measure of agreement on most of these matters, but there are some points of dispute on all of them.

Fishing Rights on the High Seas. While it is accepted that all nations have a right to fish on the high seas, there is a growing international consciousness of the need to establish principles and practices that will ensure the conservation of the living resources on which the fisheries depend. Such conservation has been attempted in respect to a few of the important fish species by means of bilateral or multilateral treaties. The recent United Nations Technical Conference on the Conservation of the Living Resources of the Sea, in 1955, showed that there is a large measure of agreement on the objectives of conservation and the scientific and technical principles involved, but the exact means of effecting it remain in dispute. This has given rise to continuing sharp conflicts over some of the major fisheries.

Exploitation of the Resources of the Continental Shelf. Recent technical developments making possible the exploitation of resources of the sea floor give rise to questions respecting the ownership of such resources. It appears to be generally agreed that these resources belong to the adjacent coastal state out to a depth of 200 m (the limit of the continental shelf as usually defined by geologists) or as much deeper as the resources can be exploited. There is, however, disagreement respecting the status of the waters over the shelf. Moreover, there is, as yet, no generally accepted criterion for designating what resources appertain to the sea bed and what appertain to the superjacent waters.

While the law of the sea has been a source of much international conflict, it is at the same time perhaps the area of human affairs that currently offers the highest possibility for peaceable international agreement. The International Law Commission, working under Committee Six of the United Nations, has been studying the international problems of marine resources for several years, and these problems have also been given much attention by the Organization of American States. The Law Commission has drawn up a set of draft articles on the Law of the Sea,[1] which offer a reasonable basis of handling most of the existing problems. An international conference was held in 1958 to consider the entire subject.

Domestic Conflicts over the Utilization of Resources.   Although the areas of conflict over the utilization of resources within the jurisdiction of a single state are rather less numerous than areas of international dispute, there are some sharp conflicts here also. These include disputes as to both different uses of the same resources and conflicting uses of different resources.

The most extensive, and historically the oldest, disputes involving the same resources are the conflicts over alternative uses of the living resources of the sea. Examples are (1) disputes between sports fishermen and commercial fishermen, (2) disputes among commercial fishermen using different types of fishing gear, (3) disputes among processors, or between processors and governmental agencies, as to the kinds of products to be manufactured from the raw material.

Some of these disputes involve social considerations about which there is no common agreement, for example, the question as to whether a fish stock that cannot support both extensive sport and commercial fishing should be reserved for recreation, or the question as to whether the use of fish for direct human consumption is somehow preferable to its use for other purposes, even if the latter are capable of yielding larger economic returns. In many cases, the cry of "conservation" is raised, although no real conservation issue is involved, as a means of enlisting popular support for some special interest. Many of the disputes between sports fishermen and commercial fishermen or between operators of different types of fishing gear fall in this category.

These disputes should be amenable to settlement on the basis of adequate fact-finding and public discussion. To provide a basis of facts, detailed study of the resources is needed, as well as a clear agreement on the proper objectives of conservation. But there should also be careful consideration of just what are the social objectives of the various uses of living marine resources and their relative merits.

Conflicts among the users of different resources in the same region are numerous and complex. The use of a part of the sea for waste disposal may interfere with its use for recreation or for commercial and sport fishing. The extraction of underwater petroleum may interfere with recreation and fishing in adjacent waters. There are conflicts of the harvesters of kelp with sports fishermen, who believe that kelp harvesting destroys

---

[1] "Report of the International Law Commission, Covering the Work of the 8th Session 23 April–4 July, 1956," United Nations, General Assembly, Official Records: Eleventh Session, Suppl. No. 9 (A/3159), New York, 1956.

the habitat of many game fish, and with users of beaches, who claim that the beaches are cluttered with cut kelp that escapes the harvester. Some of these conflicts would be resolved by more adequate scientific knowledge, which is often capable of indicating that supposed problems do not really exist and can frequently provide the basic technical improvements that can make the uses of different resources compatible. There will, however, always remain cases where incompatibility exists; in such cases hard decisions have to be made, but preferably on the basis of information rather than emotion.

5

The Atmosphere

MORRIS NEIBURGER

PROFESSOR OF METEOROLOGY
UNIVERSITY OF CALIFORNIA, LOS ANGELES

5.1 The Atmosphere As a Resource

No part of man's environment enters into his life more intimately than the atmosphere. Apart from the fact that it is "the air we breathe," it constitutes the milieu in which we walk, work, and build houses to seek shelter and on which we depend for the dispersal of many of the waste products of our activities. Too often imposed on or neglected, too seldom cared for or economically exploited, the atmosphere constitutes a natural resource the limitations of which are only now beginning to be appreciated and the possibilities of which have seldom received even slight attention.

That a well-cared-for atmosphere is essential to the health and well-being of the populace has been emphasized in recent years by a series of disasters, the greatest of which was the severe smog of 1952 in London, in which it was estimated that more than 4000 people died as a result of the pollution. In addition, people have become increasingly unwilling to put up with the discomfort of smoke, fumes, and dust in the air resulting from industrial operations and other human activities, and even aesthetic considerations have been considered adequate justification for requiring installation of equipment to reduce emissions of contaminants.

As the working substance in the solar engine which carries energy from equatorial regions, where it is received in excess from the sun, to polar regions, the atmosphere constitutes a source of energy which can under certain circumstances be tapped. The possibilities of exploiting power from the winds is discussed in Chapter 17. While the days of the sailing vessel as a major factor in marine transportation are over, the utilization of the winds to increase speed, extend range, and save fuel in air transport is far from negligible. By selecting the level and route of flight, commercial air lines are able to decrease fuel load and increase pay load. In particular,

110

use of the "jet stream" has enabled omission of refueling stops on trans-Pacific flights.

The possibilities of tapping other forms of energy from the atmosphere have received consideration. For instance, some experiments were conducted recently by the Geophysical Research Directorate of the Air Force Cambridge Research Center which suggest that it may become possible to tap the energy of dissociation of atomic oxygen in the E layer. It is conceivable that when intercontinental flight becomes possible at these high levels the sole fuel requirement will be for attaining the flight level, after which the solar energy stored by the dissociation or ionization of the environment will be adequate to provide the propulsive power.

The atmosphere plays the primary role in the hydrologic cycle. Both water supply and water power are subject to the vagaries as well as the regularities of the weather and climate. If and when it becomes possible to control the atmospheric circulation and in particular the evaporation and precipitation processes, an increase in usable water resources may be expected.

In addition to these actual and potential values of the atmosphere as a practical resource, the atmosphere has an aesthetic and emotional value beyond all measurement. Blue skies, golden sunsets, the myriad forms of clouds, and the varying degrees of haziness which contribute to the depth and variety of the landscape all appeal to the sense of visual beauty. Correspondingly, the balmy breezes of springtime, the bracing chill winds of the fall, the rhythmic successions of fair weather and rain, warmth and cold, and wind and calm appeal to the various other senses and sensibilities to enrich the process of living.

5.2 Composition of the Atmosphere

The atmosphere consists of a mixture of gases, most of which occur in relatively invariant proportions. Thus even oxygen, which participates in many reactions, both in connection with living processes and in inorganic processes such as the weathering of rocks, occurs in nearly constant proportion from pole to equator and from sea level up to at least 60 km. The major variable gaseous component is water vapor, which may vary from a few hundredths of a per cent to 2 or 3 per cent. Its variability is of course associated with the processes of evaporation and transpiration from land and water surfaces and of condensation to form clouds and precipitation. Carbon dioxide is another substance which is variable, because of its participation in photosynthesis, its formation by animal respiration and by industrial processes, and its interaction with the earth's surface and the ocean. In recent years, considerable attention has been given to the question of whether its average concentration has been increasing because of the increased consumption of fossil fuels, and whether this increase has been responsible at least in part for the general increase in temperature over the earth during the last half century.

In Table 5.1 are shown the concentrations of the various major components of the atmosphere. These are expressed as proportions of "dry air," that is, air from which the major variable constituent, water vapor, has been removed. It will be noted that the four gases nitrogen, oxygen, argon, and carbon dioxide together comprise more than 99.99 per cent of the dry air.

Table 5.1 Major Components of the Atmosphere, by Volume

Nitrogen (N_2)	78.08×10^{-2}
Oxygen (O_2)	20.95×10^{-2}
Argon (A)	0.93×10^{-2}
Carbon dioxide (CO_2)	3.3×10^{-4}
Neon (Ne)	1.8×10^{-5}
Helium (He)	5.2×10^{-6}
Methane (CH_4)	2.2×10^{-6}
Krypton (Kr)	1.1×10^{-6}
Hydrogen (H_2)	0.5×10^{-6}
Nitrous oxide (N_2O)	0.5×10^{-6}
Xenon (Xe)	0.1×10^{-6}

Table 5.2 Concentrations of Gaseous Pollutants in Los Angeles Air on Clear and Smoggy Days in 1950

Pollutant	Clear days	Intense smog
Carbon monoxide	2×10^{-6}*	40×10^{-6}
Hydrocarbons	....	2.0×10^{-6}
Oxidant (mostly ozone)	7×10^{-8}	6×10^{-7}
Oxides of nitrogen (NO and NO_2)	1×10^{-7}	3×10^{-7}
Organic acids	....	3×10^{-7}
Aldehydes	7×10^{-8}	2×10^{-7}
Sulfur dioxide	5×10^{-8}	2×10^{-7}

* 1×10^{-6} indicates one part by volume per million parts of air.

Aside from water vapor and carbon dioxide the variable gaseous constituents are mostly the consequence of the industrial activities of man. Table 5.2 gives as an example the concentrations of gaseous pollutants found in Los Angeles on clear days and on days of intense smog. Excepting for the high level of oxidant or ozone on smoggy days, these concentrations are representative of industrial communities everywhere. In coal-burning areas the concentrations of sulfur dioxide tend to be somewhat higher, with individual measurements as high as 3 ppm and average values greater than ½ ppm occurring in some places.

In addition to the gaseous constituents, there is always present in the lowest several kilometers of the atmosphere a considerable amount of suspended particulate matter. These particles range in size from a few thousandths of a micron to a few microns. The natural sources of this particulate matter include salt spray from the ocean, blown dust from the land, ash from volcanic eruptions, and meteoric dust from outer space. Human activities, including combustion, industrial processing, and mechanical erosion such as the wearing of automobile tires, all introduce particulate matter into the air as well. The concentration of particules in the air away from industrial areas and areas of high concentrations of domestic combustion sources is usually about 0.2 μg per cu m, except during dust storms and similar unusual situations. In heavily populated and industrial areas, the average values range from $\frac{1}{2}$ to 1 μg per cu m, and individual local values may range upward to several micrograms per cubic meter.

In the above discussion of particulate matter in the atmosphere, the most frequent and conspicuous occurrences of particles in the atmosphere were not referred to, namely, the products of condensation of water vapor, including fog, cloud, and precipitation. The amount of liquid (or solid) water in fog and cloud is usually of the order of 0.1 g per cu m, although in deep cumulus clouds it may reach several grams per cubic meter.

As was indicated earlier, the concentrations of the major constituents of the atmosphere do not vary materially through the lowest 60 km or more. However, starting at about 10 km the concentration of ozone increases from its normal level of a few hundredths of a part per million and reaches a maximum of 5 to 8 ppm at about 20 to 25 km. Above the level of the ozone maximum, the amount of atomic oxygen increases, although even at 100 km it is thought that only about 1 per cent of the oxygen is dissociated. Beginning some distance above 100 km, it is thought that most of the oxygen is atomic.

There are four main ionized layers, known as D, E, F_1, and F_2. The D layer occurs between 75 and 90 km, the E layer at about 110 km, and the F layers above 200 km. The last two are distinct only when the sun is at high elevations, and it has been suggested recently that the entire ionosphere forms a single continuous layer.

The dissociation of the oxygen and the formation of the ionosphere are due to the absorption of ultraviolet radiation by oxygen and nitrogen.

5.3 The Temperature Structure

The atmospheric temperature varies with latitude, time of day and year, location with respect to continents and oceans, and altitude. These variations are the result of the flux of short-wave radiation from the sun and long-wave radiation from the atmosphere and the earth's surface, together with the transport of heat by conduction from the earth's surface and motions of the air and with the release or absorption of latent heat by condensation and evaporation.

The variation of temperature with altitude is shown in Figure 5.1, which represents average conditions combined from observations by radiosonde balloon at levels up to about 30 km and rocket observations above that level. It will be seen that the temperature decreases rapidly to a height somewhat above 10 km, increases fairly rapidly above 20 km to a maximum at about 45 km, reaches a second minimum at about 80 km, and then

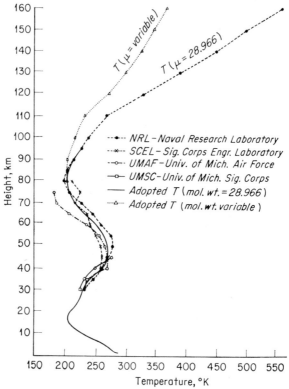

Fig. 5.1 The average variation of temperature with height. (*After The Rocket Panel*, *"Pressures, Densities and Temperatures in the Upper Atmosphere," Phys. Rev., vol.* 88, *p.* 1029, *December,* 1952.)

increases as high as data are available. The decrease near the ground and the approximate isothermalcy in the region from 12 to 18 km is associated with the absorption of solar radiation at the ground, the exchange of long-wave radiation between the ground and the carbon dioxide and water vapor in the air, and the convective activity in the lowest layers. The warm layer with maximum temperature at about 45 km is due to the absorption of ultraviolet radiation from the sun by ozone.

The variation of temperature with season and latitude in the lower 20 km of the atmosphere is shown in Figure 5.2. The dark lines in this figure, separating the regions in which the temperature decreases rapidly with height from those in which it is roughly constant or increases, show the position of the tropopause; the region of decreasing temperature below is the troposphere, while that of relatively constant or increasing temperature above is the stratosphere. The tropopause occurs at about 17 km at the equator and slopes downward with latitude to 8 or 9 km near the poles.

While through most of the troposphere the temperature decreases rapidly with height on the average, in winter in northern latitudes (and

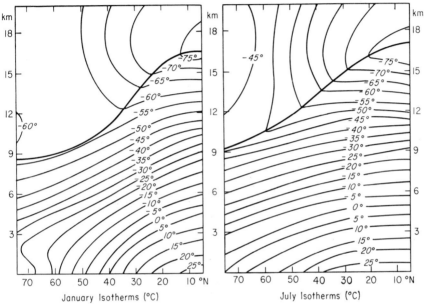

Fig. 5.2   Variation of temperature with season and latitude in the lowest 20 km. January and July vertical cross sections of the average temperature field, Northern Hemisphere (degree centigrade). (*After Wexler, "Annual and Diurnal Temperature Variations in the Upper Atmosphere," Tellus, vol. 2, p. 263, November, 1950.*)

over the antarctic continent in the Southern Hemisphere) there is a layer 1 to 2 km thick near the ground in which the temperature increases with height. A layer in which there is an increase of temperature with height instead of the normal decrease is called an *inversion*. While inversions occur in the average picture only over polar latitudes near the ground in winter, they occur occasionally at all latitudes, at any elevation in the troposphere, and during all seasons; and over land they are present on every clear night with light winds.

The significance of inversions lies in the fact that they are layers of extreme hydrostatic stability in which all convection and turbulent mixing is suppressed. Figure 5.3 illustrates the concept of hydrostatic stability in the atmosphere. When the air temperature decreases with

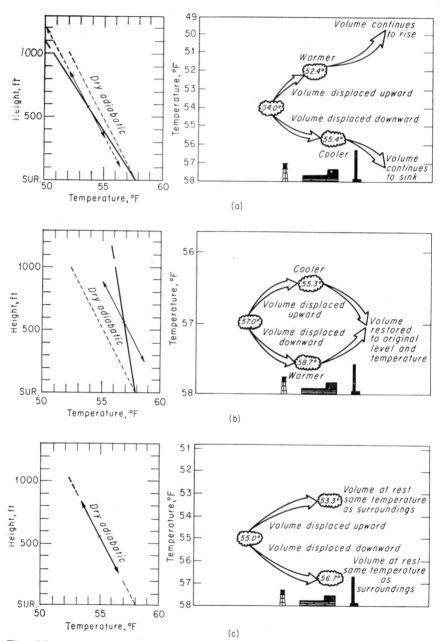

Fig. 5.3 The relationship between hydrostatic stability and vertical temperature variation. Effects of lapse rate on displaced air volumes. (*a*) Unstable lapse rate, (*b*) stable lapse rate, (*c*) neutral lapse rate. (*After U.S. Weather Bureau, "Meteorology and Atomic Energy," July, 1955.*)

height at the rate of 1°C per hundred meters or 5.4°F per thousand feet, as is illustrated in the bottom part of the diagram, a parcel of unsaturated air which is displaced upward or downward will undergo a change of temperature due to expansion or compression which is exactly the same as the change in its environment and, thus, will be subjected to no acceleration due to differences in density. The rate of temperature decrease with height in this case is known as the *dry adiabatic lapse rate*, or more properly, the unsaturated adiabatic lapse rate.

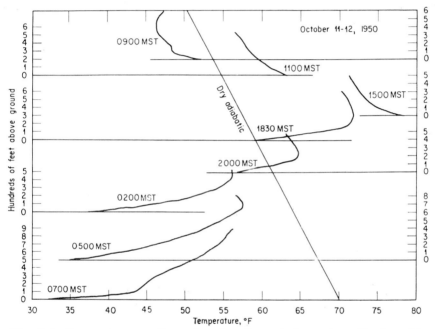

Fig. 5.4 Temperature soundings at various times during a day with clear skies and light winds. (*After U.S. Weather Bureau, "Meteorology and Atomic Energy," July, 1955.*)

If the rate of decrease of temperature with height is greater than the dry adiabatic rate, as is the case in the upper part of the figure, a displaced parcel will be accelerated in the direction of the displacement; the temperature variation with height in this case is called an *unstable lapse rate*. On the other hand, if the temperature decrease with height is less than the dry adiabatic rate, a parcel displaced upward will be cooler than the environment and thus be subjected to a downward acceleration, and a parcel displaced downward will be similarly subjected to a restoring force. In the case of an inversion, in which the temperature actually increases with height instead of decreasing, the restoring force will be very large and all tendencies for vertical displacements will be damped out. This damping action prevents the upward dispersal of contaminants injected into the atmosphere near the ground in a surface inversion, or confines it to the layer below the inversion if the inversion base is above the pollution source.

The development of a nocturnal inversion on a clear night with light winds is illustrated in Figure 5.4. In this figure the results of temperature soundings made at various times of the day are presented. In the sounding

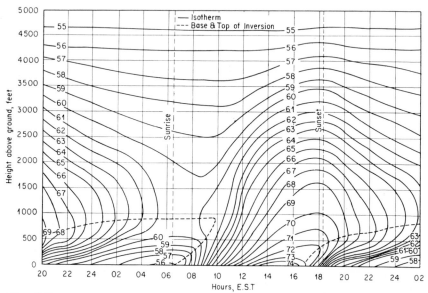

Fig. 5.5 Variation of average temperature at various times and heights at Oak Ridge, September–October, 1950. (*After U.S. Weather Bureau, "A Meteorological Survey of the Oak Ridge Area," Atomic Energy Commission, November, 1953.*)

taken shortly after sunset (1830) an inversion has begun to develop at the ground because of the loss of heat from the ground by radiation. Throughout the night the radiative cooling causes the inversion to become deeper and the air at all levels to become cooler, until at 0700 just before sunrise the inversion is at least 900 ft deep. With the heating of the ground after sunrise the elimination of the inversion begins, starting at the ground and working upward. In the morning (0900) the heating due to the absorption of solar radiation at the ground causes a superadiabatic lapse rate in the lowest layer, but the nocturnal inversion is still present above about 400 ft. By 1100 the nocturnal inversion has been eliminated and the lapse rate is superadiabatic throughout.

Figure 5.5, representing the average variation of temperature at Oak Ridge, Tennessee, as a function of height and time in the autumn of 1950, illustrates these effects in a single diagram. The top of the inversion layer, shown by a dashed line, progressively rises from about 500 ft in the evening to almost 1000 ft at sunrise. At that time the inversion base begins rising until about 2½ hr later, when the two are coincident and the inversion disappears. At about an hour before sunset the inversion forms at the ground again, and its depth increases rapidly at first and then more slowly.

Topography greatly affects the magnitude of ground inversions. If the ground is rolling or hilly, the cold air formed on the higher land surfaces tends to drain into the hollows, producing a larger and thicker inversion above low ground and little or none above the hills.

In middle and higher latitudes in winter, the solar radiation during the day is often insufficient to eliminate the inversion which has developed during the previous night, and ground inversions are augmented day after day during the periods of light winds. In these cases, fog which develops during the cooling may persist both day and night. The great valleys of California and the valleys of central Europe are characterized by persistent winter fogs of this type. If industrial plants emitting pollution are located in such valleys, severe smog may occur. In high latitudes an inversion of great magnitude, considerable thickness, and tremendous horizontal extent is present during much of the winter, particularly over the interior of high-latitude continental areas. Thus at Yakutsk, Siberia, an arctic inversion occurs in 98 per cent of the soundings during the winter, with an average thickness of 1720 m and an average magnitude of 18°C. The corresponding figures for Fairbanks, Alaska, are 91 per cent, 1355 m, and 14°C.

Other forms of inversion in middle and upper latitudes are turbulence inversions, frontal inversions, and subsidence inversions. Turbulence inversions develop when the wind blowing over rough ground stirs the air sufficiently to establish an adiabatic lapse rate in the lowest layer; the lower part of the unstirred layer above is warmer than the upper part of the stirred layer in this case. Frontal inversions occur when a cold mass of air and a warm mass of air are side by side in close juxtaposition. In this case the cold air mass extends like a wedge below the warm one, and the sloping boundary between the two air masses is called a *front*. Frequently the warm air moves upward over the cold air, producing clouds and precipitation. In this case the adiabatic cooling due to the upslope motion usually decreases the magnitude of the inversion or changes the frontal layer from a real inversion to a layer having smaller positive lapse rates than the air masses below and above.

Subsidence inversions are produced by the sinking and vertical shrinking of a layer of air. When a layer of air descends bodily, the increase in pressure compresses it so that the upper portion descends farther than the lower. The heat of compression will be greater for the upper part than the lower, and consequently the lapse rate of temperature will thus be reduced. If the air spreads out horizontally at the same time as it sinks, the upper portion will descend still more, and the compression may be sufficient to heat it to a higher temperature than the lower part, producing an inversion. In anticyclones the air near the ground tends to flow outward because of the influence of friction, and the air above must sink to take its place. In addition, because of the dynamics of atmospheric motion, the air moving around anticyclones and in equatorward currents must spread horizontally and shrink vertically. Subsidence thus occurs in anticyclones, especially in their eastern portions where the air flows equatorward.

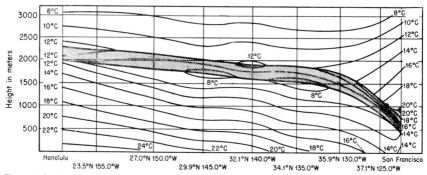

Fig. 5.6   Cross section showing average temperature at various heights, San Francisco–Honolulu. The inversion layer is shown by a shaded area. (*University of California, Los Angeles, Subtropical Pacific Project, supported by Office of Naval Research.*)

Anticyclones occur predominantly in the northern portions of continents in winter and over the subtropical oceans, particularly in the warm half of the year. The inversions associated with continental anticyclones are usually dome-shaped, with the inversion base at 3 to 5 km elevation to the east of the center of highest pressure and sloping downward in all directions to a level of about one kilometer. Where the subsidence inversion is low, it may merge with the ground inversion to produce an extremely large and thick inversion. Subsidence inversions in winter are frequently associated with persistent fog and stratus or stratocumulus clouds, with the valleys covered with cloud and the mountains which penetrate into the inversion enjoying clear mild weather.

Probably the most extensive and persistent inversions on earth are those associated with the anticyclones over the subtropical oceans. These inversions are present over the eastern portions of tropical and subtropical oceans. They follow the seasonal migration of the subtropical high-pressure belts and extend into middle latitudes in summer. They extend inland onto the west coasts of the continents and are largely responsible for the equitable climates characteristic of the west coasts, but they also lead to the unfavorable conditions with respect to dispersion of pollutants which are responsible for the smog found in large west-coast cities.

The characteristics of the inversion off the west coast of the United States in summer is shown in Figure 5.6. This figure represents a cross section of the atmosphere from San Francisco southwestward to Honolulu. The inversion base is on the average about 400 m above sea level at San Francisco. It slopes upward rapidly to the west at first, and then more slowly, extending somewhat above 2000 m at Honolulu. It is most intense just off the coast, with a temperature increase of about 12°C from base to top, and its intensity decreases as it gets higher. The layer below the inversion is characterized by high humidities, with stratus clouds in the region offshore where the inversion base is low, and stratocumulus and trade-wind cumulus clouds farther westward where there is room for convective activity to develop below the inversion.

5.4 The General Circulation of the Atmosphere

The view that the motions of the atmosphere consist of a dominant pattern called the *general circulation* on which lesser perturbations, the cyclones and anticyclones, are superposed is gradually giving way to the recognition that the "disturbances" in the flow, being as large or larger than the velocity one obtains by averaging them out, form as basic a part of the atmospheric circulation as the so-called fundamental flow pattern. In particular, when the winds are averaged completely around the earth by latitude belts, the north-south components practically cancel out so that the meridional circulation which is so frequently represented as the primary aspect of the general circulation involves net flow northward or southward at various heights and latitudes of the order of a few centimeters per second at most. On the other hand, the zonal component (west-east component) of the wind averaged around the earth by latitude belts gives a picture of the predominance of westerly flow (flow from west to east) in middle latitudes near the ground and at all but tropical latitudes aloft. Figure 5.7 shows the mean zonal winds from pole to pole and from sea level to about twenty kilometers in summer and in winter. In the figure, pressure in centibars is used as the vertical scale, and the approximate elevation corresponding to the pressure is given at the upper left. The speeds are given in meters per second, with westerly winds positive. The regions of easterly winds are shaded.

Over arctic regions the average wind is easterly at low levels, but westerly aloft. In middle latitudes the westerly winds increase with height, reaching maximum average speeds of about fifteen meters per second in summer and forty meters per second in winter at about ten kilometers elevation in the Northern Hemisphere. In the Southern Hemisphere the average westerly winds are estimated to be somewhat higher, but the data are not as reliable. The boundary between the middle-latitude westerlies and the tropical easterlies slopes equatorward with height from about thirty-five degrees latitude at the ground. The axis of maximum westerly winds likewise slopes equatorward with height. The easterly winds have maximum values near the ground in the trade-wind belts

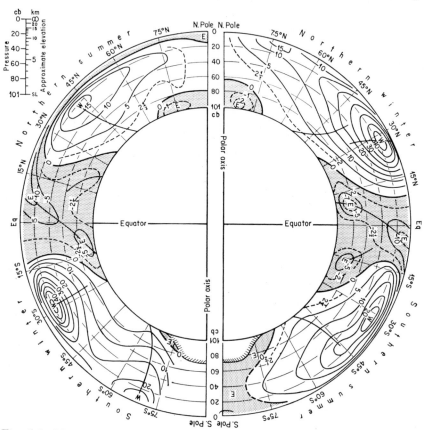

Fig. 5.7   Mean zonal (west-east component) wind averaged by latitudes, in summer and winter. Isotachs (lines of equal speed) are labeled in meters per second, with westerly winds positive. (*After Mintz, "The Observed Zonal Circulation of the Atmosphere," Bull. Am. Meteorol. Soc., vol. 35, p. 209, 1954.*)

about fifteen degrees north and south of the equator. In addition, a high-level easterly maximum occurs in the summer hemisphere in each season.

The distribution of pressure is closely related to the wind distribution, with the winds blowing approximately along isobaric contours in the free air in such a way that lower pressures are to the left in the Northern Hemisphere and to the right in the Southern Hemisphere. Near the ground the effect of friction is to deviate the wind slightly across the isobaric contours toward lower pressure. In addition to its direction, the speed of the wind is related to the pressure distribution, the rule being in general that the closer together the isobaric contours, the stronger the wind. Near the ground, the influence of friction is to reduce the speed by

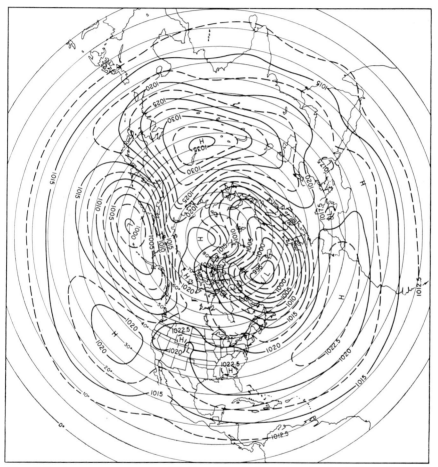

Fig. 5.8   Average pressure over Northern Hemisphere at sea level, millibars, January. (*Adapted from U.S. Weather Bur., Tech. Paper* 21, 1952.)

an amount which depends upon the character of the surface. Over the sea the factor is about two-thirds of the value corresponding to the isobaric gradient; over land it is one-third to one-half.

Figures 5.8 to 5.11 show the average pressure distribution in the Northern Hemisphere at sea level and at 500 mb (approximately 6 km) in January and July. The distribution at sea level is represented by isobars and that at 500 mb by the contours showing the height of the constant-pressure surface. Corresponding to the region of separation between the polar easterlies and the middle-latitude westerlies, there is a belt of predominantly low pressure at sea level, although in winter it is interrupted by high-pressure areas over the continents. The region of

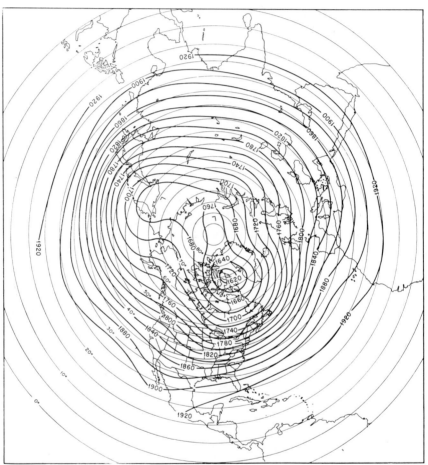

Fig. 5.9   Average height of 500-mb isobaric surface over Northern Hemisphere, tens of ft, January. (*Adapted from U.S. Weather Bur., Tech. Paper* 21, 1952.)

separation between the middle-latitude westerlies and the tropical easter-lies is a belt of high pressure which extends all the way around the earth at 500 mb, but it is interrupted by low-pressure areas over the continents in summer at sea level. Even on these normal maps, representing monthly averages taken over many years, the patterns are broken up into centers of high and low pressure at sea level and wave-shaped contours with troughs and wedges at 500 mb, with corresponding preferential areas of northward or southward major air currents. On weather maps for particular times the patterns are characterized by many more centers of high and low pressure, called anticyclones and cyclones, and upper-level waves. Figures 5.12 and 5.13 show the pressure pattern at sea level and 500 mb on a typical winter day, January 1, 1956.

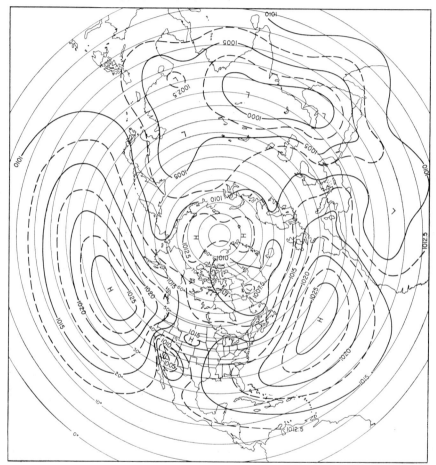

Fig. 5.10 Average pressure over Northern Hemisphere at sea level, millibars, July. (*Adapted from U.S. Weather Bur., Tech. Paper 21, 1952.*)

The broken-up pattern on these maps corresponds to much greater meridional exchange of air than suggested by the monthly normal maps. This meridional exchange results in transport of energy and westerly momentum, which is an essential part of the general circulation.

It will be noted that on the normal 500-mb chart for January there is a more or less continuous narrow belt along which the contours are close together all around the earth. On the 500-mb map for January 1, 1956, the closeness of the contours is more marked, particularly over the northern part of North America and the Atlantic Ocean. As has been stated above, the wind varies inversely as the distance between contours; so the wind in these regions is very strong. These narrow belts of strong winds

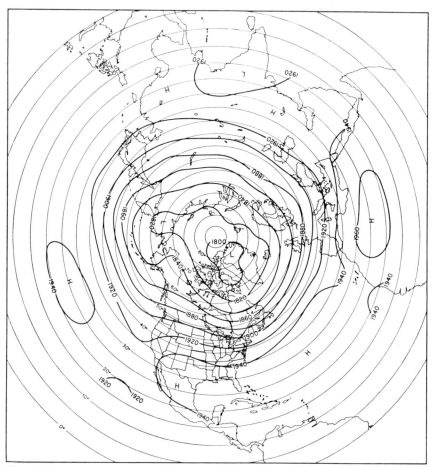

Fig. 5.11 Average height of 500-mb isobaric surface over Northern Hemisphere, tens of ft, July. (*Adapted from U.S. Weather Bur., Tech. Paper* 21, 1952.)

have been named the *jet stream*. The jet speeds usually increase with height to maximum speeds just below the tropopause. As shown on the map, the areas of closely packed contours do not form a single belt, but rather a series of meandering branches with interruptions at some longitudes. These branches and interruptions shift from day to day, as does the strength of the wind in the center of the jet, but through the winter months winds in excess of 100 knots are frequent, and values as high as 300 knots have been reported. The jet stream rarely forms a continuous belt around the earth, but it frequently covers large enough distances to enable great savings in fuel and time on transoceanic or transcontinental flights.

5.5 Medium-scale and Local Circulations

Associated with the differential heating of the continents and the oceans are wind circulations which are subcontinental in scale and seasonal in character. These are the well-known monsoon circulations. In winter, for instance, the Asiatic continent becomes much colder than the surrounding oceans, and the cold air flows generally outward from it, producing the northwest monsoon over China and the northeast monsoon over India. In summer, on the other hand, the heated interior of the continent becomes a low-pressure area toward which the wind blows from all directions, producing the southeast monsoon over China and the southwest monsoon over India, with accompanying heavy rains. North America has a less well-marked monsoon regime, although the continental-oceanic influence is adequate to modify the circulation considerably.

In North America and Europe the seasonal variations in wind are overshadowed by the fluctuations due to the passage of migrating cyclones and anticyclones, that is, areas of low and high pressure such as those shown in Figure 5.12. The low-pressure areas are characterized by winds blowing counterclockwise in the Northern Hemisphere and clockwise in the Southern Hemisphere around them, and vice versa for the high-pressure areas. The lows are generally stormy areas, with precipitation, and the highs are frequently areas of clear weather.

Cyclones frequently originate as waves on the boundaries between cold- and warm-air masses. The boundaries, when well marked, are called *fronts*. As these waves increase in amplitude, they become transformed into vortices of increasing intensity and affect the movement of the air at higher and higher levels. Alternatively, there are cyclones which originate at high levels and gradually work their way down to the ground.

These extratropical cyclones move in a generally easterly direction with speeds of about seven hundred miles per day in the winter and about five hundred miles per day or less in the summer. The more or less characteristic weather pattern associated with a cyclone formed by the deepening of a frontal wave is shown in Figure 5.14. As the warm front approaches there is increasing high cloudiness followed by middle and low clouds with continuous precipitation. In the warm sector generally fair weather is present, except for stratus clouds or fog in winter and local scattered heat thunderstorms in summer. With the approach and passage of the cold front there are usually showers and thunderstorms, with rapid clearing behind it. The cold front is frequently a line of severe thunder-storms with wind squalls. Occasionally a squall line develops in the warm sector ahead of the cold front, and along such a squall line or along the cold front itself tornadoes may occur. Most readers will be familiar with the characteristics of the tornado, the funnel-like cloud reaching downward

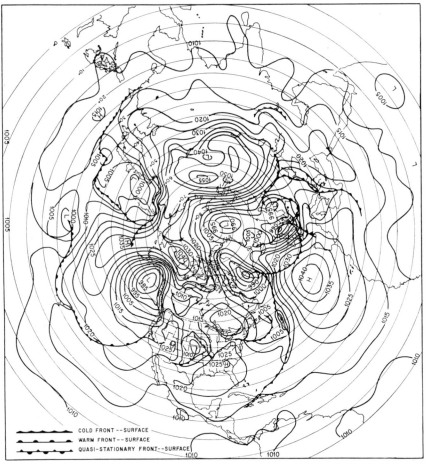

Fig. 5.12 Sea-level pressure over Northern Hemisphere, millibars, 1230 GMT, Jan. 1, 1956. (*Adapted from U.S. Weather Bureau, Daily Series, Synoptic Weather Maps, part 1, January, 1956.*)

to join the swirl of dust and debris carried upward from its path of devastation. Winds in tornadoes may reach 200 to 300 miles an hour or more, and the locally intense pressure gradients result in explosive destruction of structures in the path.

In equatorial and subtropical areas, changes are generally much more subtle. There are slight fluctuations from day to day, usually associated with perturbations moving westward in the easterly trade winds. The exception to the quiet conditions in the tropics is an extreme one, namely, the tropical cyclones which are known as hurricanes in the Western Hemisphere and typhoons in the Eastern Hemisphere. Hurricanes are

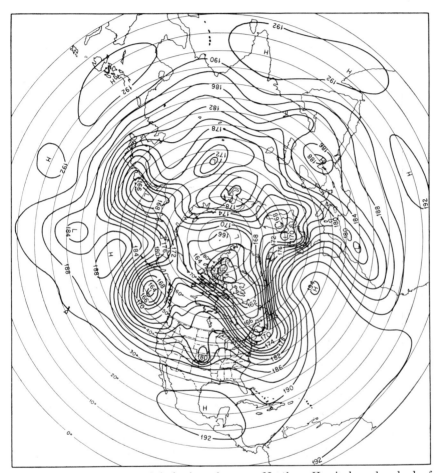

Fig. 5.13   Height of 500-mb isobaric surface over Northern Hemisphere, hundreds of ft, 1500 GMT, Jan. 1, 1956. (*Adapted from U.S. Weather Bureau, Daily Series, Synoptic Weather Maps, part 1, January, 1956.*)

formed characteristically between 5 and 15 deg of the equator and move slowly, first eastward, then curving poleward, and finally turning northeastward parallel to the coasts of North America or Asia or southeastward east of Australia or Madagascar. These tropical cyclones are much smaller in extent than the extratropical cyclones, but are frequently of greater intensity, with winds exceeding 100 miles an hour. They move with average speeds of about 200 miles a day while in tropical regions, in paths which are generally fairly regular but occasionally quite erratic.

In addition to the seasonal wind circulations on the continental scale and the migrant wind systems of the higher latitudes and the tropics, there are diurnal winds which are associated with local topographic features. These are the sea-land breezes and the valley-mountain winds. In both cases they are associated with the differential heating of topographic features. In low latitudes they are present almost every day, but

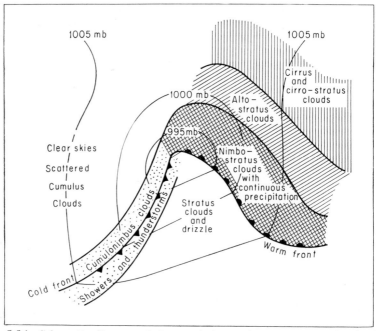

Fig. 5.14 Schematic diagram of characteristic weather pattern associated with a wave cyclone in winter.

in high latitudes they are usually dominated by the moving pressure systems and manifest themselves only in the absence of general pressure gradients, usually only in summer.

Sea breezes ordinarily start along the coasts at about 9 A.M. local time and increase in speed to reach maximum intensity at about 2 P.M. By 8 P.M. the wind ordinarily has died down, and shortly thereafter the breeze from the land begins. In the case of the valley-mountain winds, the situation is usually more complicated, with light winds normal to the slopes at the beginning of the flow periods, followed by larger-scale general flow up and down the main valley.

5.6 Conclusion

In the foregoing a brief presentation has been given of the main features of the atmospheric structure and circulation as a background for the consideration of the atmosphere as a natural resource. For details and additional information the reader is referred to the various standard texts on meteorology and the research papers on the various phases in which he may be interested.

As man gains additional means for its control, he may find it possible to modify the atmosphere by injecting energy in such a fashion that the circulation patterns are modified to give more favorable distribution of precipitation and remove the hazards of lightning, wind damage, and floods; or he may inject materials into the atmosphere which will affect the natural development or release of energy to produce these results. Before he achieves the knowledge and ability to produce these beneficial results of controlling the weather, he will have accidentally produced effects on the composition and circulation of the atmosphere. In addition to producing reduction in visibility, damage to vegetation, and irritation to humans, the pollution associated with industrial activity and transportation may have its impact on the occurrence of precipitation through the introduction of excessive nuclei of condensation. The production of carbon dioxide through the burning of fossil fuels may have its effect on the heat balance of the atmosphere. Certainly the conversion of large areas of vegetation to masses of rock and concrete has had its effect on the local climate of cities. And the introduction of radioactive debris into the atmosphere might, by changing the degree of ionization, the electric field, and the distribution of the particles in the atmosphere, result in changes in the weather as well as in the genetic constitution of life on the planet. A conscious appraisal of effects like these is essential to the exploitation of the atmosphere as a resource.

6

Air-pollution Control

ALBERT F. BUSH

ASSOCIATE PROFESSOR OF ENGINEERING
UNIVERSITY OF CALIFORNIA, LOS ANGELES

6.1 Management of the Air Resource

When the vital resources of the world are considered, it is appropriate to discuss the air about us. Though the estimated 11×10^{18} lb of air enveloping the earth (nine-tenths of which is within 11 miles of the surface) may be taken for granted, still it is necessary to concern ourselves with the general protection of its quality. In recent years, there have been areas where the production of pollutants has been so great and the natural ventilation so poor that the air resource was in short supply. In these areas the supply of pure air may be the one factor which will limit the size of cities, just as water resources have limited population growth in many areas of the world.

Protection of the air resource of a community to ensure a continuous supply of air of good quality may ultimately necessitate limiting population density and the extent of uninterrupted urban development. In principle, limitations of this sort have been used to prevent catastrophies such as communicable disease and fire, and in the long-range view these principles may be applied to the control of the air resource.

As plans are made for maximum beneficial use of the air resource in urban areas, qualitative and quantitative standards for appraising and protecting the resource should be established. It does not seem likely that the stipulation of the quality of discharges alone will be successful in providing all the information necessary for protecting the air we live in. Indeed, much information on the quality of natural, unpolluted air seems seriously lacking. Meanwhile, the community-wide concern over preservation of the air quality increases, thus making clear the importance of scientific engineering developments which may ultimately make it possible to manage the air resource for the benefit of mankind.

On a broad outdoor scale, man has not learned to influence or control the nature of his climate to any appreciable extent. Man has made progress, however, in the protection of cold-sensitive trees, and indoors he has brought about changes which make it possible for normal life to continue under adverse weather conditions.

There are appropriate comparisons which can be made between the development and management of water and food resources and the air resource. For instance, the distribution of water by nature has not been sufficient for sustaining large populations in certain areas. Man's ingenuity and engineering skill, however, brought water and improved its quality to a point where thousands of times as many people can survive in these regions. Similarly, the science of agriculture has brought forth food from the land in far greater abundance than that provided by nature under uncultivated conditions.

Large bodies of water influence local climate; natural currents of oceans and seas modify the air temperature and moisture content over the land along the coast. Air currents and area-wide ventilation have not been adequately evaluated as a possible preventative control of the irritating qualities of the air environment. As the potential pollutants contributed to the atmosphere by man-made sources at times alter the microclimate to an extent which can be felt and may be measured with sensitive instruments, selective control of emissions and encouragement of natural removal mechanisms may afford some measure of air management.

6.2 Air Needs of Man

In a quantitative sense human needs for air are small, but the quality is of concern. Man's average consumptive requirements for air, when breathing 16 to 18 times a minute a volume of 500 to 1000 cu cm, is about 0.3 to 0.6 cu ft of air per minute, or 30 to 60 lb per day. In the process of respiration, oxygen percentage is decreased from 21 per cent to about 17 per cent, amounting to a consumption of 1.5 to 3 lb of oxygen per day. Since the exhaled air contains about 4 per cent carbon dioxide, the total amount of carbon dioxide produced per person is 2 to 4.5 lb per day. The combustion process which goes on within the body liberates heat because of the oxidation of proteins, carbohydrates, and fats. For each pound of oxygen consumed, about 4500 Btu of heat is produced. The total heat production and the amount of oxygen consumed obviously vary with the degree of activity. Using a figure of 1.5 lb of oxygen per day, the heat production will be 280 Btu per hr; at 3 lb per day, the heat produced would be about 560 Btu per hr.

To support each individual's daily need for light, heat, transportation, food, refrigeration, and other services in modern living, it is estimated that nearly 1000 lb of air per person is required in combustion processes, while his consumptive needs are about 50 lb.

In considering the air needed for ventilation of buildings and homes and other closed spaces, a minimum rate of 15 cfm per person (or 1600 lb per day) is recommended, and in the future, heating and ventilation codes will probably be higher than this minimum value.

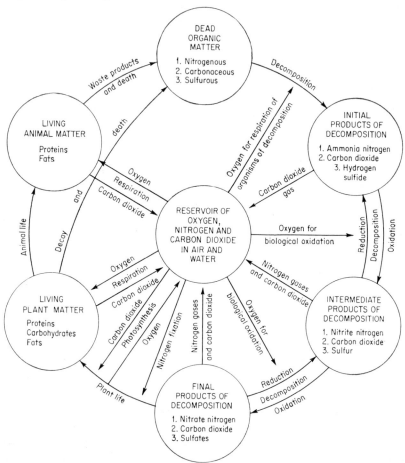

Fig. 6.1 Cycles of carbon, oxygen, and nitrogen. (*Reprinted with permission from Gordon Fair and John Geyer, Water Supply and Waste-water Disposal, John Wiley & Sons, Inc., 1954.*)

These demands are small indeed, however, in relation to the total air supply, and it is unlikely that consumptive demands will diminish the air resource in any quantitative way, particularly in view of the cyclic process in nature by which oxygen is continuously being given back to the atmosphere during the daylight growth of green plants and carbon dioxide is removed from the air by plants and the waters of the sea. The oxygen and carbon dioxide cycles are somewhat similar to the hydrologic cycle. Figure 6.1 illustrates the cycles of carbon, oxygen, and nitrogen going on in the air about us. The problem which must be faced is how to preserve the quality of the air for all its many uses.

6.3 Air-pollution Episodes

At least four different episodes in the history of air pollution indicate the severity with which polluted air can strike, and they clearly show the importance of protecting the air resource. Each is characterized by a prolonged period of air stagnation, or lack of ventilation, which confined the pollutants to the close proximity of inhabited areas. The build-up of foreign substances in the air first affects the elderly people, particularly those with bronchial, lung, or heart conditions. Acute illness in the major number of cases usually occurs within the first couple of days following the onset of severe air pollution, thus leaving little doubt regarding cause-and-effect relationship. The chronic manifestations are more insidious and will require further study to determine their true relationship to air quality.

The first major episode on record occurred in the heavy industrial area of the Meuse Valley near Liège, Belgium, in 1930 when 63 persons died from respiratory irritation during a 5-day smog attack; the second in Donora, Pennsylvania, where a severe smog, which hung over the Monongahela River for 5 days, beginning October 27, 1948, caused 20 persons to die and 5910 (43 per cent of the population) to become ill (a fatality-to-illness ratio of 1 to 300). The stagnation of the air was caused by a strong inversion and stable air mass which resulted in a valley fog. Little or no ventilation was provided. It seemed apparent that the accumulation of chimney emissions in the immediate vicinity was responsible for the illness and death in this instance.

Air polluted with hydrogen sulfide caused the death of 22 persons and the hospitalization of 320 others in Poza Rica, Mexico, on November 24, 1950. Poza Rica is located 130 miles northeast of Mexico City in the heart of Mexico's largest oil- and gas-producing area. The low-level temperature inversion and lack of wind confined the pollutants to the immediate area even though the terrain was nearly level. It was speculated that the fog and patchlike haze which drifted over the city were the result of the condensation of products of combustion from the wet-gas stack. The hydrogen sulfide escaped from the sulfur-recovery plant during a 20-min period between 4:50 and 5:10 A.M. The acute episode was over when the plant was shut down.

The fourth episode took place in London in December of 1952. More than 4000 persons died within a week because of the accumulation of smoke and sulfur dioxide in the air, while the air remained exceptionally stagnant and the absence of wind prevented ventilation of the 700-sq mile fog-bound area. Deaths followed 2 to 3 days after the onset of the attack.

Figure 6.2 shows smoke and sulfur dioxide observations from 10 sampling stations in Greater London, expressed in milligrams per cubic meter. The number of deaths per day is also shown. There certainly is no doubt about the cause of the high death rate.

The four episodes listed above involve fatalities and illness. Many other situations might be cited where damage to crops and property have occurred. Most notable perhaps is that of the Trail smelter in British Columbia on the international border between the United States and

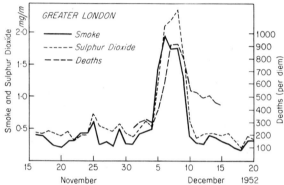

Fig. 6.2 Relation of deaths to smoke and sulfur dioxide concentrations. Greater London, November and December, 1952. (*The Times, London, April* 20, 1953.)

Canada. Devastation of vegetation has also been severe near Ducktown, Tennessee; Anaconda, Montana; and Redding, California.

6.4   Air Quality

The most common consideration of air-resource improvement is to control potential pollutants or contaminants at their source and thereby preserve the natural purity which the air is expected to possess. Pollutants and contaminants in the atmosphere of the earth are substances which alter the normal composition in such a way and to such an extent as to make the air irritating or produce undue damage to humans, animals, vegetation, or property.

While damage to humans, animals, crops, or other property is the most obvious manifestation of air pollution, in many instances nuisances or annoyances due to foreign material in the air may also be used as an indication of pollution. The criterion of visibility is often used to indicate pollutants where man-made operations are responsible for impairment of visibility. Seldom, however, are natural phenomena such as fogs, storms, or other acts of God considered as pollutants even though the visibility impairment and the damage to humans, animals, and vegetation may be much more acute.

Since man-made substances are considered pollutants, their source is the logical point to investigate and control when necessary. The complex problem of determining necessity and extent becomes the subject and objective of air-pollution control. Protection of health and welfare of man through control of environment is a governmental responsibility and quite properly a concern of political minds. Much has been written regarding the control of air pollution and the cleaning of the air.

Technology of treatment and complete understanding of the problem are not yet available. Before discussing means of control, however, it seems appropriate to indicate or classify the events in the air most frequently associated with pollution.

The nature of foreign material in air can be considered on the basis of its physical state and particle size. Attention must be given to solids and liquids occurring as particules and to foreign gaseous substances. The particules include dusts, fumes, smokes, fogs, and mists produced by physical and chemical means and pollens, bacteria, fungi, molds, viruses, etc., produced by biological processes. One distinguishing feature of particulate material in the air is its size. Figure 6.3 shows the usual sizes of particles in the air. The gaseous foreign substances in the air occur in the form of vapor or gas molecules which follow the gas laws.

The concentration of material in the atmosphere may be expressed on a weight basis as in Figure 6.4 which shows the range experienced under a variety of conditions. Gaseous substances may be expressed on the basis of volume of material per million volumes of air (ppm).

In most cases there is no acceptable standard concentration for pollution in the air. There are, however, threshold limits, useful for evaluating indoor working environment, such as those shown in Table 6.1. These values can serve as a guide to air-pollution control and may indicate the order of magnitude where difficulties might be encountered. Two cautions must be mentioned in the use of these values for outdoor environment. (1) They are originally conceived as the appropriate safe level for an 8-hr workday where the remaining 16 hr of each day would be free from the substance, thereby affording opportunity for recovery after short intervals of exposure. (2) The standards are based on average normal healthy adults. While in industry this is a fairly sound assumption, in a cross section of the entire population, including as it does children, retired elderly people, persons with allergies, and persons with predisposing diseases or states of physical stress, the indicated limits need revision downward.

From samplings of outside air in metropolitan areas (regions of high population density and much industrial activity), gaseous substances

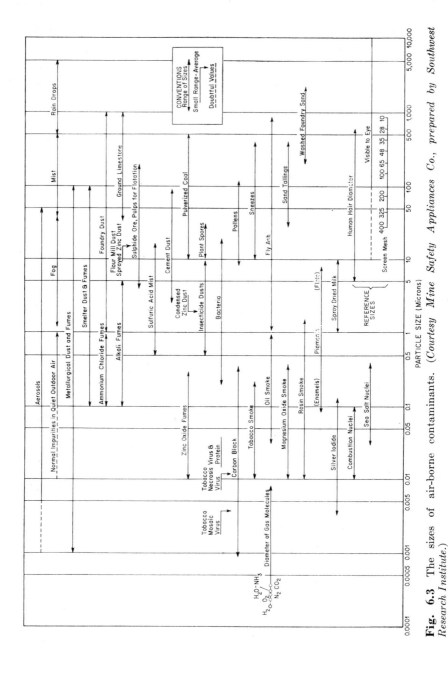

Fig. 6.3 The sizes of air-borne contaminants. *(Courtesy Mine Safety Appliances Co., prepared by Southwest Research Institute.)*

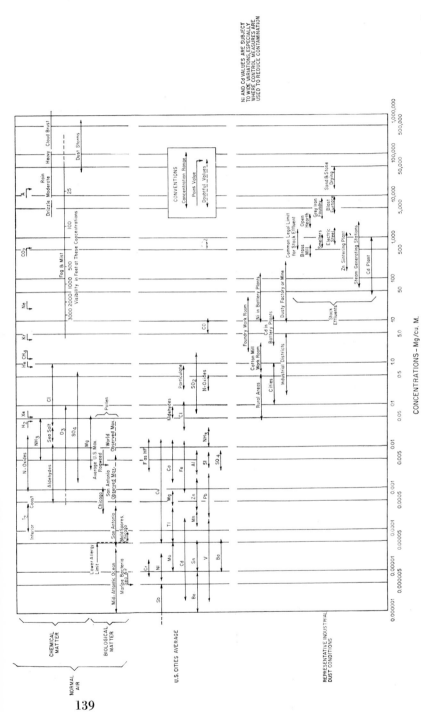

Fig. 6.4 The concentrations of materials in the air. (*Courtesy Mine Safety Appliances Co., prepared by Southwest Research Institute.*)

such as oxides of nitrogen, sulfur dioxide, carbon monoxide, ozone, and aldehydes and particulate material in the form of silica (which is not the kind of problem presented in dusty trades in industry except perhaps on a local basis) come closest to approaching the threshold. Dusts, mists, and fumes in the air may be of such chemical composition as to cause poisoning themselves, or they may carry bacteria, fungi, or viruses on their surfaces and convey them to people, thus causing diseases to spread. Another

Table 6.1   Sample of Threshold Limit Values for Aerosols

Gases and Vapors, Ppm of Air

Acetic acid	10	Hydrogen sulfide	20
Acetone	500	Iodine	1
Acrolein	0.5	Methanol	200
Ammonia	100	Methyl bromide	20
Aniline	5	Naphtha (coal tar)	200
Arsine	0.05	Naphtha (petroleum)	500
Bromine	1	Nickel carbonyl	1
Carbon dioxide	5000	Nitrobenzene	1
Carbon monoxide	100	Nitrogen oxides (other than N_2O)	25
Carbon tetrachloride	50	Nitrotoluene	5
Chlorine	1	Ozone	1
Chloroform	100	Phosgene	1
Cresol	5	Phosphine	0.05
Dimethylsulfate	1	Stibine	0.01
Ethyl alcohol	1000	Sulfur chloride	1
Formaldehyde	5	Sulfur dioxide	10
Gasoline	500	Toluene	200
Hydrogen cyanide	10	Trichloroethylene	100
Hydrogen fluoride	3	Turpentine	100
Hydrogen selenide	0.05	Xylene	200

Toxic Dust, Fumes, and Mists, Mg per Cu M of Air

Antimony	0.5	Mercury	0.1
Arsenic	0.5	Phosphorus (yellow)	0.1
Cadmium	0.1	Selenium, as Se	0.1
Cyanide as CN	5	Sulfuric acid	1.0
Fluoride	2.5	Tellurium	0.1
Iron oxide fume	15	Tetryl	1.5
Lead	0.15	Trinitrotoluene	1.5
Magnesium oxide fume	15	Zinc oxide fume	15
Manganese	6		

Mineral Dusts, Million Particles per Cu Ft of Air

Asbestos	5	Slate (below 5% free SiO_2)	50
Talc	20	Soapstone (below 5% free SiO_2)	20
Silica:		Total dust (below 5% free SiO_2)	50
High (above 50% free SiO_2)	5		
Med (5–50% free SiO_2)	20		
Low (below 5% free SiO_2)	50		

SOURCE: Taken from American Conference of Governmental Industrial Hygienists list prepared at meeting in Cincinnati, 1952.

possibility is that they may carry irritating or toxic chemicals upon their surfaces.

The type of air pollution known as smog is found in the Los Angeles area and elsewhere in the United States. Much research has been carried out to reach the present imperfect understanding of the smog problem. Frank M. Stead summarizes its nature as follows:

The following characteristics can be listed with reasonable assurance:

1. Smog results from reactions taking place in the atmosphere itself between raw materials or precursors (harmless in themselves at the concentrations found), catalysts, and atmospheric oxygen which form new compounds not originally present.

2. These reactions take place between gaseous compounds at extraordinarily low concentrations (less than one part of precursor or catalyst to one million parts of air).

3. Energy in the form of sunlight is necessary for these reactions to proceed and on removal of sunlight the reaction is partially reversible.

4. The precursors of these reactions are hydrocarbons; the principal catalyst is nitrogen dioxide (NO_2); and the reaction products are oxidized hydrocarbons and ozone (usually referred to as a group as oxidants).

5. The oxidants formed are capable, even at extremely low atmospheric concentrations, of causing irritation to the eyes and mucous membranes of humans and damaging or destroying certain types of growing plants. The aerosols (tiny particles of liquid or solid substance) associated with smog formation are capable of scattering light and destroying visibility.

The role of aerosols in the smog problem, aside from visibility interference, has not been clarified. There is reason to suspect, however, that aerosols may furnish the needed surfaces on which the atmospheric reactions take place and may also serve to absorb the irritating gaseous reaction products so as to intensify their effects on humans.

Efforts to maintain clean air in areas where pollution has become a problem have included measures to reduce visible emissions from industrial, municipal, and household burning operations and measures to reduce emissions of sulfur dioxide and hydrocarbon vapors from oil-refining processes.

In Los Angeles and other metropolitan areas the large amount of automotive exhaust now appears to have a major responsibility for air-quality impairment. Ways and means of reducing pollution of this type are being actively investigated.

6.5 Physiological Response of Human Beings to Contaminants in the Air

Irritation of the eyes, nose, and throat are probably the most frequent complaint of air pollution. Though it has been considered that the exact substances causing irritation are usually not known, substances such as aldehydes, sulfur dioxide, organic peroxides, organic acids, ozone, or ozonated hydrocarbons might be responsible in certain cases. On the other hand, the irritation from smog is believed to be due to short-lived intermediate reaction products which result from chemical reactions taking place in the air under the influence of ultraviolet solar radiation.

The type of health hazards or diseases involving pathological conditions in the lungs is not commonly associated with general air pollution. There have been many studies of the possibility that lung cancer could arise from breathing polluted air, but these conclude that many, many times the present concentrations of carcinogenic agent would have to be present in the air before it could be a true health hazard. There have been instances of beryllium poisoning several miles away from a plant where the material was being processed.

In episodes of extended air pollution, persons suffering from heart disorders and predisposed to lung disorders are the first to be affected. Noxious fumes, gases, and vapors may cause injury to health when present in sufficiently high concentrations and when the exposure time is sufficiently great. There are very few instances where the causative agent has been specifically identified. It seems fairly clear that the sulfur dioxide and smoke played an important role in London. At Poza Rica, hydrogen sulfide was the causative agent. The more insidious type of toxic agent such as lead, organic phosphates, halogenated hydrocarbons, and other organic solvents, which produce changes in the blood and cause damage to the liver, kidneys, and brain, are not well explored in relation to generalized air-pollution problems.

Smoke from chimneys is the first visible sign of emissions to the atmosphere, but even though it may cause decrease in visibility and dirt on laundry, the particles in themselves are seldom considered health hazards. The exact role of these particles in the physiological sense is not completely clear. However, the possibility that they are an important vehicle for transfer of contaminants still remains.

Metal fumes, insecticides, and solvent vapors occasionally contaminate the air in localized situations and may be causal agents of disease. Bacteria, fungi, and viruses also produce disease and are often carried on dust particles or in mist droplets, but since their origin is seldom man-made, or the result of man-made processes, they have not been considered in the usual classification of air contaminants. Future developments may bring biological agents into the classification of air pollutants. Insects and pollen might also be placed in this category. Man's cultivation of the soil often gives rise to the dust-storm phenomena, and wind-borne dusts may then be considered pollution. Coccidioidomycosis, or valley fever, a disease associated with the dust of the San Joaquin Valley in California, is an example.

Radioactive substances have recently become the subject of much discussion and under certain conditions can become the most far-reaching air-pollution problem known to man. It is fortunate, however, that potential health hazards from radiation are well recognized, and measuring-detecting monitoring equipment is well developed and sensitive to concentrations several degrees of magnitude lower than the dangerous level.

Though there are cases of health impairment and death due to air pollution, the most numerous complaints are the nuisances created by unusual amounts of dirt or odor or visible substances in the air. Irritation of nose, throat, and eyes and the confinement of vision to a small radius can at this time be classified as nuisances. There is also the possibility that attenuation of the ultraviolet portion of the solar spectrum by foreign substances in the air may have some effect on vitamin-D assimilation, and an indirect health effect may be experienced in regions where solar radiation is naturally low.

6.6 Psychological and Sociological Response to Air Pollution

Several studies have been made to measure the subjective reaction of human beings to atmospheric conditions and to evaluate the significant factors associated with a feeling of pleasantness or pleasurableness. Also, factors such as aesthetic enjoyment of natural scenery, visual beauty, and the "great-to-be-alive" feeling of invigoration associated with pleasant environment, though beyond measurement, are nonetheless real and important qualities which would be valuable to a community if preserved.

In a study by Winslow and Harrington, a group of 80 persons in Connecticut were questioned each day for more than a year about their feelings under various climatic conditions. It was found that there was a good correlation between the outdoor air pleasantness and sunshine and a good negative correlation with relative humidity as well as a fair negative correlation with total ion concentration in the air. The pleasurableness of outdoor air is highest when the sun shines and the air is dry and relatively free from ions. It is interesting to note that there was no correlation with temperature, wind, and other climatic variables. The ion count in the city is higher than in the adjacent countryside, and it rises in winter and falls in summer. It also rises with sea winds. Total ion counts are highest in cool, moist, relatively windy days. It was the authors' impression that the ion concentration resulted from combustion processes. The authors at that time did not call these ions pollutants, but their study does indicate that combustion processes were factors in reducing the pleasantness of the environment.

In another study of indoor environment, Yaglou, Riley, and Collings showed that there was an increase in body odors in closed spaces, and odor severity and carbon dioxide increase together. When the carbon dioxide reached 600 to 800 ppm, odors were definite, and they were strong at 2400 ppm. When ventilation rates were increased to 25 or 30 cu ft of air per person, the odors remained low.

Probably the most widely used study of psychological response to air is

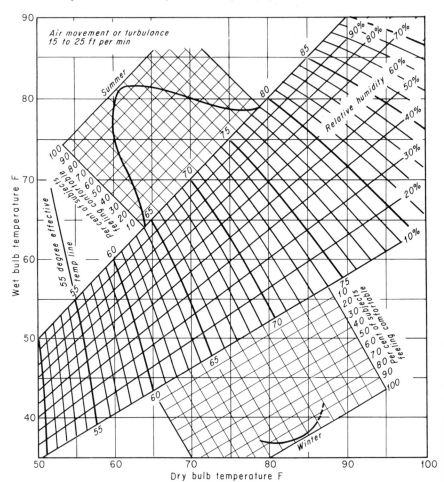

Fig. 6.5 Comfort chart. (*Copyright, American Society of Heating and Air Conditioning Engineers, Inc., reproduced by permission from Heating, Ventilating, Air Conditioning Guide, Chap. 6, 1956.*)

the comfort-zone chart, prepared by the American Society of Heating and Air Conditioning Engineers, Inc., in which the variables of temperature, humidity, and air motion are considered and a zone of condition for summer and winter comfort is defined. By measuring temperature and humidity under a large range of possible indoor climatic conditions, it was found that there are conditions under which almost everyone feels comfortable. (These areas are shown in Figure 6.5.) An interesting point to note is the effective temperature (ET) lines which connect points of equal warmth sensation. The chart does not, however, consider the quality of the air from a pollution standpoint. Perhaps future research will aid in evaluating quantitatively the comfort criteria for outdoor and indoor air. The chart does indicate how some of the subjective parameters of the air environment can be studied and quantified so that desirable, comfortable, pleasant surroundings may be produced.

One of the first and most obvious concerns of society relative to air is the presence of smoke, fumes, dust, dirt, etc., in the community air and the fact that it decreases visibility. This concern over confinement of vision to a small radius is not new; it happens in natural fogs and hazes as a normal part of climate; but man-made emissions which decrease visibility are always subject to public condemnation. There are a few facts regarding materials in the air which can be pointed out as an aid to evaluation of visibility problems. A study of the obscuring power of smokes and particles in the atmosphere has led to a measurement of total obscuring power (TOP) which is expressed in square feet per pound. Many different substances cause vision to be obscured, but the following are among the agents found most effective:

Substance	TOP, Sq Ft per Lb
Phosphorus	4600
Ammonia plus hydrochloric acid	2500
Navy smoke	1900
Tin chloride plus ammonia plus water	1590
Tin chloride plus ammonia	900
Sulfur dioxide plus ammonia	375

The concept of total obscuring power can be stated as follows: Consider a rectangular volume of air having a depth l and a cross-sectional area numerically equal to the total obscuring power of a particular material. If 1 lb of the material is introduced into the volume, with uniform density, visibility throughout the volume will be limited to a depth l. In other words, 1 lb of material will obscure visibility to a depth l throughout a volume of air V, where

$$V = |TOP|l$$

or   Volume of air = total obscuring power $\times$ visibility

The reaction of phosphorus in the air can be considered to be

$$4P + 5O_2 \rightarrow 2P_2O_5$$
$$2P_2O_5 + 6H_2O \rightarrow 4H_3PO_4$$

One pound of phosphorus, 1.3 lb of oxygen, and 0.9 lb of water yield 3.2 lb of H_3PO_4. One pound of phosphorus will obscure 4600 sq ft. If visibility is to be limited to 5000 ft by the reaction products of phosphorus, then the amount of phosphorus required in a basin of 25×10^{12} cu ft would be $25 \times 10^{12}/4600 \times 5000 = 1,080,000$ lb, or 540 tons. This sample basin is approximately the size of the Los Angeles basin when the base of the inversion is 1000 ft. If navy smoke were used, 1300 tons would be required. If visibility were confined to 5000 ft by fog, approximately 7500 tons of water would be required. It can be seen that the total amount of material to decrease visibility is in the order of a very few thousand tons for a large-area basin when the inversion base is low.

Particle size and concentration play an important role in the decrease in visibility, and therefore care should be taken in expressing pollution in tons of material. The amount and size distribution of particles in the atmosphere are important parts of any program of control. As the larger particles are removed, the remaining small ones become more and more difficult to remove. In the future we will have to look more carefully at the complete spectrum of particles in the air. In the meantime, study of their concentration may help to measure ventilation rates and patterns in local areas and aid in the prediction of the severity of air-pollution potential.

A problem which potentially endangers the lives and property of large numbers of people in civilized areas where population density is large is bound to concern society. It is encouraging to note that peoples all over the world are acting to prevent future air-pollution episodes and demanding study, understanding, and control measures: a healthy sign and a progressive attitude. In the future far-reaching measures may have to be taken to ensure adequate air supply to all people at all times. Regulation of population density and reserving areas of extended vegetation may be desirable. A fuller knowledge of the microclimate and warning signs of poor ventilation will no doubt be sought.

6.7   Extent of Air Resource and the Ventilation of Topographic Basins

A method of quantifying significance of air pollutants, in a local area, may be based on a mass balance on the air in a basin (i.e., the amount of pollution coming in minus what goes out should equal what is there). The extent of the air resource under critical conditions must be known and could be indicated by the volume of the receiving air and its dilution potential. The Los Angeles basin in California can be cited as an example since the data are readily available.

A prominent meteorological phenomenon known as *subsidence inversion*, discussed in the previous chapter, produces a strong discontinuity in the vertical profile of the lower air mass which prevents vertical mixing and for practical considerations acts like a lid on the basin. The height of this lid coincides with the base of the inversion, and from experience it has been learned that conditions may be critical when the base is below 2000 ft in elevation. Even though the subsidence inversion is mentioned here as an example, any inversion condition regardless of how it is produced would have the same effect; other types may not be as extensive.

Since the boundary of Los Angeles County, for which the full information is given, does not coincide with the boundary of the topographic basin, the mass balance is made on the Los Angeles County portion of the basin as shown in Figure 6.6. The map shows only the coast line, the 500-,

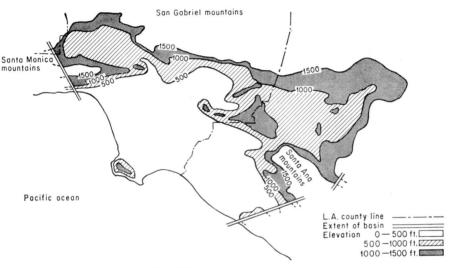

Fig. 6.6   Los Angeles basin.

1000-, and 1500-ft contours, and the Los Angeles County lines. If the total volume of the air in the basin below the base is considered, the volume of the basin air can be calculated with the results shown in Table 6.2.

Table 6.2

Interval, ft	Volume of Los Angeles basin		Volume of Los Angeles County	
	Cu ft	Cu miles	Cu ft	Cu miles
0–500	6.3×10^{12}	43	4.4×10^{12}	30
0–1000	24.8×10^{12}	169	15.8×10^{12}	108
0–1500	53.1×10^{12}	361	31.1×10^{12}	212

From the fuel data given in the 1954 Report of Stanford Research Institute, the calculations given in Table 6.3 may be made of the number of particles in the atmosphere, the carbon dioxide produced, the water vapor produced, and the heat released.

Table 6.3   Contribution of Combustion Processes to the Basin Atmosphere per Day

Combustion	Estimate fuel consumption in Los Angeles County (1953), tons per day	Total particulate material produced, particles per day	CO_2, tons per day	Water from combustion of hydrocarbons, tons per day	Heat, Btu per day
Fuel-gas.....	23,760	3.6×10^{20}	6.6×10^4	5.4×10^4	800×10^9
Fuel-oil......	8,830	1.5×10^{20}	2.6×10^4	1.6×10^4	350×10^9
Gasoline.....	14,380	5.8×10^{20}	4.2×10^4	2.6×10^4	350×10^9
Refuse (35% moisture)	7,560	1.0×10^{20}	0.6×10^4	0.5×10^4	70×10^9
Total......	54,530	11.9×10^{20}	14.0×10^4	10.1×10^4	1570×10^9

Total weight of air in basin $= 1.84 \times 10^{12}$ lb below 1000-ft inversion.

If it is assumed that the base of the inversion is uniform over the basin and at a fixed elevation (i.e., 500 or 1000 ft), then the volume of air shown in the table represents the volume available for diluting source emissions.

It can be seen that a relatively small shift in inversion height makes a substantial change in air volume. (A change from 500 to 1000 ft makes a fourfold increase in air volume, while a change from 500 to 1500 ft makes an increase of 8.4 times.) Basin topography, therefore, has an important influence on the volume of air below the inversion base.

The water produced from the combustion of hydrocarbons in the basin each day amounts to about 25 million gal, or 75 acre-ft. This amount of water would increase the relative humidity of the confined basin air by 2 per cent if the temperature were 70°F and the humidity about 35 per cent to begin with.

The total heat released from combustion processes is about 1.6×10^{12} Btu, or enough to raise the temperature of the 1.8×10^{12} lb of air 7°F, if there is no change in moisture content.

The total amount of carbon dioxide produced by combustion processes is 14×10^4 tons, or 28×10^7 lb. The human contribution of carbon dioxide to the air is about 7000 tons per day (enough carbon dioxide to raise the concentration by 150 ppm per day if none of it were removed by plant growth and large bodies of water). If it is assumed that all the 1600 sq miles of the basin floor is covered by plants, a carbon dioxide uptake during photosynthesis would be about 4 tons per sq mile, or 6400 tons per day in the basin. Since 147,000 tons is produced each day, it seems possible that fairly large concentrations of carbon dioxide may occur under conditions of low inversion height and poor basin ventilation.

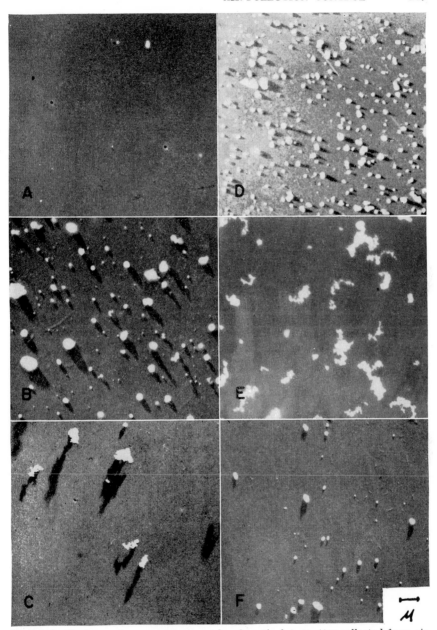

Fig. 6.7 Electron microscope photographs of particulate matter collected from air. A length of 1 micron (one thousandth of a millimeter) is shown to indicate particle size. (*A*) Air on clear day, University of California, Los Angeles. (*B*) Air on day of moderate to heavy smog, University of California, Los Angeles. (*C*) University of California, Los Angeles, boiler-plant output. (*D*) Industrial-incinerator output. (*E*) Household-incinerator output. (*F*) Automobile exhaust.

An interesting application of the particle-count data is the calculation of the time required for the concentration to increase from that observed on a clear day (0.06×10^9 particles per cubic foot) to the high level of 0.7×10^9 particles per cubic foot. It is calculated by using the following assumptions:

1. All particulate materials are confined to the air mass lying between the ground and the base of the atmospheric inversion layer.

2. All particulate materials are derived directly from combustion processes. It is possible that the size and number of particles in the atmosphere are increased by condensation processes and by chemical and photochemical reactions. These are not considered in the following calculation.

3. Particulate materials are uniformly distributed throughout the air mass.

4. The particles do not agglomerate, subdivide, or settle out.

5. The air mass remains static (i.e., no air flows into or out of the basin).

From the information in Tables 6.2 and 6.3, the "build-up time" (in days) has been calculated for two different inversion heights.

Inversion Elevation, Ft	Approximate Number of Days for Particle Concentration to Reach 0.70×10^9 Particles per Cubic Foot of Air
1000	10
1500	20

Particulate material in the air has been evaluated by using a thermal precipitator for collection and an electron microscope for analysis. Particle-count and size-distribution studies were made. Figures 6.7A to 6.7F show examples of the particles collected. Caution is required in casual interpretation of the results since all samples do not represent equal volumes of air sampled. A careful study will show that there are differences between the appearance of samples from different sources as well as variation in size.

Electron micrographs indicate the nature and magnitude of particle emissions from sources and will delineate the type of material which control devices will have to remove in order to reduce the particulate material which gets into the atmosphere from combustion processes. Even with particulate material completely removed, there may remain the problem of gaseous pollutants which will not likely respond to the type of controls used for particle removal, and these must be removed by other processes.

6.8   Effects of Air Pollution on Vegetation

In recent years the annual loss of crops due to air pollution has amounted to many millions of dollars in the Los Angeles area, and evidence of far-reaching influence of air pollution on crops in other areas of the world is gradually being accumulated. In studies by Middleton and others, the causative agents of crop damage by air pollution have been carefully studied, and the following materials are listed as those known to be injurious to crops in the concentrations which are frequently found in the atmosphere: ethylene, fluoride, herbicides, ozones, sulfur dioxide, and oxydized hydrocarbons in smog. Green leafy vegetables such as spinach, endive, lettuce, beans, and other green vegetables have been adversely affected, as have ornamental crops, by ethylene and other air pollutants.

Since plants are sensitive to air quality, they may be used as indicators to measure the degree of pollution in the air. Certain types of plants have been calibrated so that they may be used much like a sampling instrument. The pinto bean plant and several varieties of grass and weeds have been studied to determine their sensitivity to air quality and have been used in studies to evaluate air pollution. Vegetation has the characteristic of being able to integrate the influence of air pollution over a considerable period of time and therefore is far more effective than a single air-quality measurement. Although the differential diagnosis of crop damage due to air pollution and that due to other sources may, at times, be difficult, test plants under well-controlled conditions of nutrition and moisture may be excellent indicators of air quality.

When the broad problem of control of the atmosphere is considered, the influence that vegetation may have on the removal of contaminants from the air should not be overlooked. Although it is true that plants may be damaged when exposed to high concentrations of toxicants, it is also true that they remove many of the substances from the air, thus enabling the atmospheric composition to be kept in balance. An example is the amount of carbon dioxide removed from the atmosphere in the process of photosynthesis which helps to maintain the balance of oxygen and carbon dioxide. As more is learned about the importance of vegetation as a removal mechanism, it may be possible to set aside certain areas for vegetative culture to protect the air resource.

Continued study of air properties, its cyclic processes, and methods of air cleaning will certainly be vital to the expanding metropolitan areas. Practical, economical methods of control must be found if people, animals, and vegetation are to have air of the quality suitable for comfortable living.

7
Land as a Resource

ROBERT M. GLENDINNING

PROFESSOR OF GEOGRAPHY

UNIVERSITY OF CALIFORNIA, LOS ANGELES

and

RICHARD F. LOGAN

ASSOCIATE PROFESSOR OF GEOGRAPHY

UNIVERSITY OF CALIFORNIA, LOS ANGELES

USE OF THE LAND[1]

7.1 Introduction

Man's use of the land involves a host of factors. Some of the factors are cultural (human), the remainder are physical (natural). Salient among the cultural factors are the types of cultures (civilizations) and the stages of development within given cultures. The land use of a given area, of a particular type and at any one time, will vary in amount and kind and degree of success or failure, depending on the culture and the stage within that culture.

The physical factors are area (room), climate and weather, land forms, water, soil, native vegetation, wild animal life, and mineral resources. These, in combination, constitute the physical complex in which man lives and from which, in an economic sense, he makes a living.

The almost infinite combinations of the cultural and physical factors create, within area, the many detailed and general types of land use and patterns of land use over the face of the earth. In reference to these cultural and physical factors, we must remind ourselves that they do not exist, Shakespeare to the contrary, in the same relationship as a stage and actors on a stage. Rather, the relationship is essentially an ecological one. There

---

[1] This section was contributed by Professor Glendinning.

152

is mutual interaction as the land affects man and man affects the land, and the two are not logically subject to divorcement.

7.2 The Factor of "Room"

Although seldom emphasized, and often not even recognized per se, mere "room," or area, is a most valuable and basic natural resource. Fundamentally, man's use of the land at any time rests on how much land is available. It involves the matters of how much room to live in, how much room to grow in, and how much room to move about in.

The United States is fortunate in possessing comparatively large amounts of the vital room resource. Within it are some 3,000,000 sq miles, or about 3,600,000 sq miles if possessions and territories are included. Even if we confine ourselves to the United States proper, we find an area about twenty-five times the size of the British Isles, about twenty-two times the size of Germany (East plus West), about fourteen times the size of France, and even some two and one-half times the size of India. Only the Soviet Union, Canada, China, and Brazil are larger, and of these only the Soviet Union is appreciably larger.

Some aspects of room as mere area appear importantly in regions not now populated or only sparsely populated. Here there are scenic and recreational resources, as well as utility for transit and transportation and for military purposes. The military use of room, room not long ago regarded as nearly or completely useless, will continue to increase. Similar room, again not considered a resource or an important resource at the moment, may acquire appreciable status in land use as new types of plants and animals are developed or imported. Beyond this, it certainly is not full-blown fantasy to recognize the value of mere room in a future that portends widespread use of newly developed sources of power and the augmentation of our fresh-water resources.

Room per Capita.   The significance of room as mere area obviously is limited. Directly pertinent is the question of how much room per capita. In this aspect the United States again is in a favorable position, as shown by some comparisons (Table 7.1). In the United States there are approximately 54 persons per one square mile of room, as opposed to 447 per square mile in the British Isles, 510 in Germany, 202 in France, and 304 in India. On the other hand, and ignoring for the moment kind and quality of land, the population density of the Soviet Union is about 26 per square mile, that of Brazil about 18, and that of Canada about 5.

Kind of Room.   Much more significant than mere area or even area per capita is how much of what kind of room per capita. In other words, what is there in the way of type and quality of land available for each person? Here we are concerned primarily with arable land, pasture and woodland, forest land, and "other" land (including urban, waste, etc.).

In the United States (Table 7.1) about 23 per cent of the total area is classed as arable, 36 per cent as pasture and woodland, 23 per cent as forest land, and 18 per cent as other. The result is that there are some 2.7 acres of arable land, some 4.2 acres of pasture and woodland, some 2.7 acres of forest land, and some 2.1 acres of other land available per capita. Considering the extremely vital factor of arable land alone, it will be found that the per capita amount in the United States is over six times that of the British Isles, nearly six times that of Germany, over twice that of France, and slightly greater than that of the Soviet Union. Among the major nations, only Canada is in an appreciably stronger position. How-

Table 7.1   Some Comparisons

Country	Arable land*		Pasture and woodland†		Forest land		Other land‡	
	%	Acres per capita	%	Acres per capita	%	Acres per capita	%	Acres per capita
United States§..	23.0	2.68	36.0	4.22	23.0	2.68	18.0	2.11
British Isles....	29.2	0.42	47.8	0.69	4.6	0.07	18.4	0.26
France.........	38.0	1.20	22.5	0.71	20.0	0.63	19.5	0.61
Germany.......	38.5	0.48	20.0	0.25	28.0	0.35	13.5	0.17
Japan.........	16.0	0.17	2.5	0.02	66.5	0.69	15.0	0.16
China.........	9.5	0.50	20.0	1.05	8.5	0.45	62.0	3.27
India.........	38.5	0.82	0.0	0.00	12.5	0.27	49.0	1.07
Canada........	3.5	5.74	2.5	4.15	35.0	57.60	59.0	96.76
Soviet Union...	10.0	2.59	5.5	1.43	28.0	7.29	56.5	14.60

* Fit for tillage.
† Woodland usually grazed.
‡ Including urban, roads, railroads, waste, etc.
§ Figures for United States do not include Alaska.

ever, Canada's total area of arable land is far less than that of the United States. Other comparisons may be made including comparisons of pasture and woodland, forest land, etc.

7.3   The Physical Base of Land Use

Prior to any further mention of land-use categories, and before any examination of actual patterns of land use, it is important that we remind ourselves of the kind and distribution of the basic natural resources (additional to room) in the United States. It is the kind and arrangement of these resources which, under human utilization, result in the various land-use types, land-use regions, and land-use patterns.

The Land-form Base.   Land forms constitute, and very literally, a truly foundational resource. Here reference is made to major land-form expressions, such as plains, plateaus, hills, and mountains, and to minor land forms, such as river flood plains, deltas, alluvial fans, features of glacial erosion and deposition, and a legion of other forms. While these land forms are world-wide, the illustrations used are from the United States.

The general picture of what we have to work with in a land-form sense is perhaps best shown for the purposes here by two maps: a map of major land-form divisions of the United States, including some of the larger

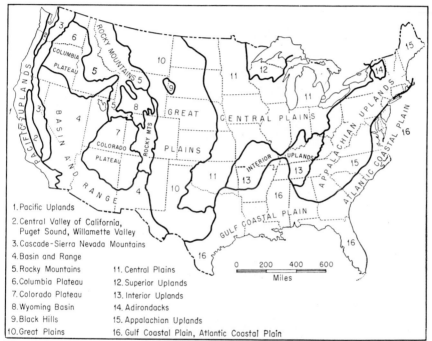

1. Pacific Uplands
2. Central Valley of California, Puget Sound, Willamette Valley
3. Cascade-Sierra Nevada Mountains
4. Basin and Range
5. Rocky Mountains
6. Columbia Plateau
7. Colorado Plateau
8. Wyoming Basin
9. Black Hills
10. Great Plains
11. Central Plains
12. Superior Uplands
13. Interior Uplands
14. Adirondacks
15. Appalachian Uplands
16. Gulf Coastal Plain, Atlantic Coastal Plain

Fig. 7.1   Major land surface divisions of the United States. (*After Kendall, Glendinning, and MacFadden, Introduction to Geography, Harcourt, Brace and Company, Inc., 1951.*)

subdivisions (Figure 7.1), and a physiographic map (Figure 7.2). Even brief glances at these maps quickly show the variety of land forms and the comparatively great extent of each land-form type, such as the range from the Atlantic Coastal Plain, the broad interior plains, the central plains plus the Great Plains, and the central valley of California, to the Appalachian Uplands, the Rockies, and the Colorado plateau. Most significant of all is the tremendous extent of plains lands. The interior plains alone represent an area roughly one-third as large as all Europe.

The Climatic Base.   Resting upon the land-form base is the quite different natural resource of climate, or climates. Again variety is the rule,

Fig. 7.2 Physiographic map of the United States. (Copyright, 1956, by Jeppesen & Co.)

as is the marked areal extent of most of the climatic types (Figure 7.3). It will be noted that climates range from subtropical to mid-latitude, from continental to marine, from humid to dry, and from lowland to alpine. Such spread and variety, considering climate alone, help engender a tremendous range in types of agricultural production and patterns of agricultural land use.

The Soil Base. Lying as a blanket over the land, albeit a blanket with some holes in it here and there, is the soil resource. As in land forms and climates, we find a resource varied as to kind and to a large extent in terms of individual kind. Reference to the soil map (Figure 8.8) shows a

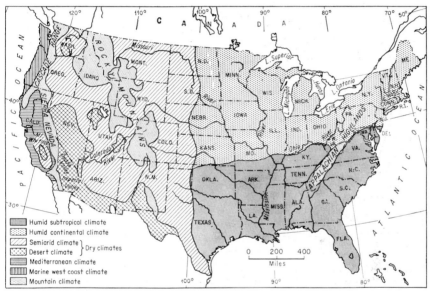

Fig. 7.3 Major climates of the United States. (*After Glendinning, Your Country and the World, Ginn & Company, 1954.*)

soil resource ranging from lateritics and podsolics to black prairie and chernozems. One is struck by the large square mileage of such extremely productive soils as the chernozem and black prairie, as well as the large extent of the brown forest soils.

The Natural-vegetation Base. Another vital resource, greatly modified by man's use and abuse, is that of natural vegetation. The original picture of this resource is shown generally by map (Figure 11.1). This picture is made up of different kinds of grasslands, forests, shrub lands, and intermediate types. The ax, plow, fire, and grazing animals have drastically modified the original conditions, but, even now, there is a variety and considerable spread of different kinds of forest, grassland,

and so on, whether these represent fragments of the original or culturally induced "reasonable facsimiles" of the original.

The Water Base.   By now, practically everyone is aware of another kind of basic resource. This we can call, simply, water. The amount, quality, and location of water are extremely significant factors in land use, whether in urban or rural areas, and whether in regions of dry or humid climates. The water resource is very much intermixed with other physical conditions. Part of the water resource is in the air, part is on the surface of the land, and part is within the soil and upper portion of the

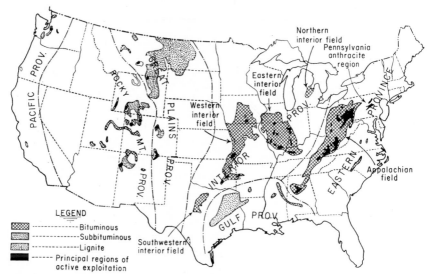

Fig. 7.4   Coal provinces and major coal-mining regions of the United States. (*After Bengtson and Van Royen, Fundamentals of Economic Geography, 4th ed., Prentice-Hall, Inc., 1956.*)

earth's crust. No single map, or other device, can portray even the general nature of our water resources. Especially pertinent are maps of precipitation, precipitation effectivity, water quality, water-power potential, and hydrologic provinces as given in Chapter 2.

The Mineral-resource Base.   Last, but not necessarily least, among our major natural resources are minerals. It is difficult to single out any particular mineral or group of minerals. As in other basic resources we are extremely fortunate, even if we are not self-sufficient in some minerals. Iron ore is vital as is coal, especially coal of coking quality. So are petroleum and natural gas. But, so also are such minerals as copper, lead, zinc, manganese, tungsten, aluminum, uranium, etc., let alone limestone, clays, glass sands, and salt. The United States is at least comparatively fortunate among the nations in the number, quality, quantity, and geographical location of many of the vital mineral resources, but it is not self-sufficient in some (such as aluminum and tungsten) and it lacks, for all practical purposes, a few (such as tin and manganese). It is not the purpose of this chapter to discuss and evaluate our mineral-resource position; that is covered in Chapter 14. The purpose here is merely to call attention to a kind of group resource that adds its bit to the variety of land-use types and patterns of land-use distribution. Accompanying maps (Figures 7.4

Fig. 7.5 Petroleum provinces of the United States. (*After Kendall, Glendinning, and MacFadden, Introduction to Geography, Harcourt, Brace and Company, Inc., 1951.*)

and 7.5) show part of the mineral-resource picture; other parts are shown or discussed in Chapter 14.

7.4   Selected Samples of Land Types and Associated Land Uses

As a result of the variety and extent of our physical-resource base, from land forms and climate to soils and water, we find a wide spread of land types, types of land use, and major and minor patterns of land use. Here the condition is so broad and, at the same time, so intricate in detail, that it cannot be properly covered in any short space. However, by means of a limited number of selected photographs, the point of variety in land types and land uses may be partially emphasized.

Figure 7.6 shows a portion of the Maine coast, characterized by rocky shore, thin soils, mixed forest, mid-latitude continental climate, and heavy recreational use during the summer period. Farther inland in upper

Fig. 7.6   Pemiquid Point, Maine. (*Photograph by Standard Oil Co., New Jersey.*)

Fig. 7.7   Farm land in New York State. (*U.S. Department of Agriculture photograph.*)

New York, a quite different setup is shown in Figure 7.7. It is marked by intensive and specialized agricultural use—an agricultural use that is mainly a summer one because of the severity of the winter season.

Jumping quite far to the west, Figures 7.8 and 7.9 portray land type and land use in parts of Wisconsin and Iowa. The first is a typical scene of hay and dairy belt economy in Wisconsin. The second is a view of the corn belt of Iowa; an area of hot, humid summers and cold, snowy winters, but

Fig. 7.8 Dairy pasture in Wisconsin. (*U.S. Department of Agriculture photograph.*)

Fig. 7.9 The corn belt in Iowa. (*U.S. Department of Agriculture photograph.*)

also an area of nearly level, easily cultivated black prairie soils. Another jump takes us into the Great Plains of Kansas (Figure 7.10), a region of semiarid climate, of blisteringly hot summers and blizzardy winters, and a sea of land that stretches monotonously to the horizon.

If we now go south, before going farther west, we find in Figures 7.11 and 7.12 additional variety in our land-use picture. The first is a view over part of the ridge and valley country of Tennessee, northeast of Knoxville.

Fig. 7.10   The Great Plains of Kansas. (*U.S. Department of Agriculture photograph.*)

Fig. 7.11   Ridge and valley country, Greene County, Tennessee. (*Photograph by Tennessee Valley Authority.*)

This is an area of subparallel ridges and valleys, a kind of corrugated iron-roof condition of land forms, often with ridges mainly in woods and pastured woodland, and valleys devoted to crops growing in the long summers of the humid subtropical type of climate. Figure 7.12 is illustrative of a quite different "south." It shows an area of swampy forested lowland in Arkansas.

Fig. 7.12   Cypress growing in grassy lake, Hempstead County, Arkansas. (*U.S. Forest Service photograph.*)

Fig. 7.13   Dream Lake in Rocky Mountain National Park. (*Photograph by Richard Kenyon.*)

Back west again, a contrasting variety to any of the previous scenes appears in the Colorado Rockies (Figure 7.13). Such rugged and scenic areas represent summer recreational use, but perhaps even more importantly, they are source areas for life-giving waters used in adjacent lowlands, especially the western margin of the Great Plains. Still other aspects of land type and land use farther west are shown in Figures 7.14 and 7.15.

Fig. 7.14 The eastern face of the Sierra Nevada range, Mono County, California. (*U.S. Department of Agriculture photograph.*)

Fig. 7.15 Citrus culture, with Sierra Nevada foothills in background, Tulare County, California. (*Photograph by Caterpillar Tractor Co.*)

7.5 The Land-use Picture of the United States

The over-all picture of land use in the United States is born from generalization of the numerous local uses; local uses as pictorially and partially depicted in Figures 7.6 to 7.15. The arrival at the over-all picture represents attempts to place major land uses on such a scale that "the forest is not lost because of the trees"—attempts to bring the "field" into the "office" in such fashion that the broad scheme of things may be analyzed and comprehended. The more important facets of the general land-use picture of the nation include major uses expressed percentage-wise and areawise and expressed cartographically in terms of major agricultural regions, manufacturing regions and districts, and major land-use regions.

Land Use in Areas and Percentages.   Figure 7.16 shows current land use in the United States in a simple and highly generalized manner. It indicates a total use of 1,904,000,000 acres. To this acreage, to obtain

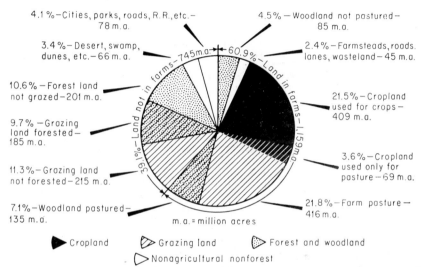

Fig. 7.16   Major uses of land, by acreages and percentages, 1950. Total U.S. acreage = 1904 million acres. (*U.S. Department of Agriculture, Neg.* 48391-X, *Bureau of Agricultural Economics.*)

completely total use, should be added some 14 million acres withdrawn from forest use for the purposes of parks and other special public uses. Close study of the chart provides considerable information. Full interpretation is not practical here, but items may be lifted out for purposes of emphasis. It will be noted that land in farms comprises about 61 per cent of the total, leaving 39 per cent not in farms. Most of the land in farms is used for crops and pasture, including cropland used only for pasture purposes; only small amounts of land in farms are used for farmsteads, roads, and lanes, or are wasteland. The total resource base of the nation, the large amount of land actually in crops (not including crops used only for pasture), some 409 million acres, is very significant; it is an acreage about three times the size of France. Beyond the large amount of land in crops are the tremendous acreages in farm pasture, of forest or forest-suited lands, etc. Conspicuous also, in an opposite sense, is the comparatively small amount of land in urban use or in waste (desert, swamp, dunes, etc.).

Another general method of portraying land use in the United States appears in Figure 7.17. Here is a rudimentary regional picture, still on a chart basis, but with a map background to provide the initial aspects of regional distribution of major uses. Perusal of this figure brings out a number of significant facts: the high percentage of cropland in the corn belt and the northern plains, in contrast to the lesser percentages of cropland in the Northeast, the South, and especially the mountain and Pacific regions; or the rather surprising percentage of forest land in the areas

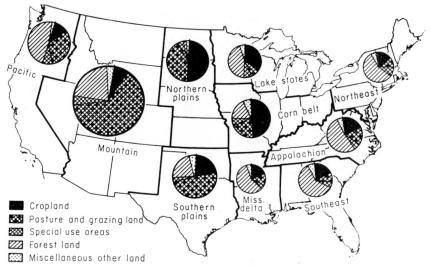

Fig. 7.17   Major land uses compared to total area, by sections, 1950. (*U.S. Department of Agriculture, Neg.* 48839-X, *Bureau of Agricultural Economics.*)

designated as the Lake states, Northeast, Appalachian, Southeast, and Mississippi Delta. Not surprising is the percentage of pasture and grazing land in the northern plains, southern plains, and mountain regions.

Land Use Shown by Maps per Se.   Perhaps more basically meaningful than any chart, or chart map, is the depiction of land use by true maps. These show not only major uses but also the more definite placement and distributional pattern of these uses. Figure 7.18 indicates the major agricultural regions. The names of the regions themselves (by their very number) emphasize the variety within our agricultural regional situation and also provide the keynote to the major character of each individual region. Witness the range from the subtropical-crops belt to the corn belt to the spring-wheat belt, and from the Atlantic truck-crop belt to the grazing lands and irrigated farming to the Pacific fruit- and vegetable-growing belt. Again it is not just variety, but also a real extent. As a case

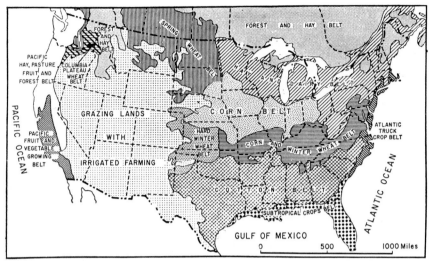

Fig. 7.18 Major agricultural regions of the United States and southern Canada. (*After Kendall, Glendinning, and MacFadden, Introduction to Geography, Harcourt, Brace and Company, Inc., 1951.*)

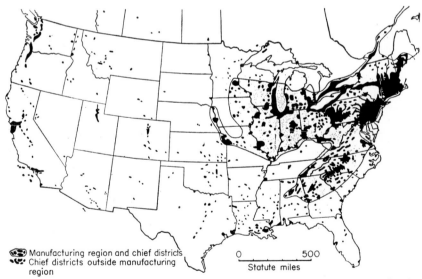

Fig. 7.19 The northeastern manufacturing region and the manufacturing districts of the United States. (*After Kendall, Glendinning, and MacFadden, Introduction to Geography, Harcourt, Brace and Company, Inc., 1951.*)

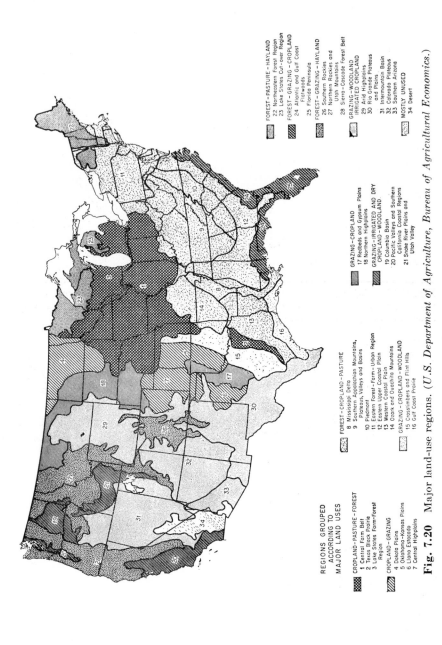

Fig. 7.20 Major land-use regions. *(U.S. Department of Agriculture, Bureau of Agricultural Economics.)*

REGIONS GROUPED
ACCORDING TO
MAJOR LAND USES

CROPLAND-PASTURE-FOREST
1 Central Farm Belt
2 Texas Black Prairie
3 Lake States Farm-Forest Region

CROPLAND-GRAZING
4 Dakota Plains
5 Oklahoma-Kansas Plains
6 Llano Estacado
7 Central Highplains

FOREST-CROPLAND-PASTURE
8 Mississippi Delta
9 Southern Appalachian Mountains, Plateaus, Valleys and Basins
10 Piedmont
11 Eastern Forest-Farm-Urban Region
12 Eastern Upper Coastal Plain
13 Western Coastal Plain
14 Ozark and Ouachita Mountains

GRAZING-CROPLAND-WOODLAND
15 Crosstimbers and Flint Hills
16 Gulf Coast Prairie

GRAZING-CROPLAND
17 Redbeds and Gypsum Plains
18 Northern Highplains

GRAZING-IRRIGATED AND DRY CROPLAND-WOODLAND
19 Columbia Basin
20 Pacific Valleys and Southern California Coastal Regions
21 Snake River Plains and Utah Valley

FOREST-PASTURE-HAYLAND
22 Northeastern Forest Region
23 Lake States Cut-over Region

FOREST-GRAZING-CROPLAND
24 Atlantic and Gulf Coast Flatwoods
25 Florida Peninsula

FOREST-GRAZING-HAYLAND
26 Southern Rockies
27 Northern Rockies and Utah Mountains
28 Sierra-Cascade Forest Belt

GRAZING-WOODLAND
IRRIGATED CROPLAND
29 Arid Highplains
30 Rio Grande Plateaus and Plains
31 Intermountain Basin
32 Colorado Plateaus
33 Southern Arizona

MOSTLY UNUSED
34 Desert

in point, the corn belt alone is over twice the size of the British Isles and a bit larger than France.

Figure 7.19 represents quite another type of land use and land-use distribution. Here is shown the major manufacturing region of the nation, including the major districts within it and also important districts which lie outside the major region. This map should be mentally superimposed on Figure 7.18. It is a reminder that for large portions of our land the

Suitable for Cultivation	*No Cultivation—Pasture, Hay, Woodland, and Wildlife*
I. Requires good soil-management practices only	V. No restrictions in use
II. Moderate conservation practices necessary	VI. Moderate restrictions in use
III. Intensive conservation practices necessary	VII. Severe restrictions in use
IV. Perennial vegetation, infrequent cultivation	VIII. Best suited for wildlife and recreation

Fig. 7.21   Land-capability classes. (*U.S. Department of Agriculture photograph.*)

basic agricultural and forestal areas and uses are complexly intermingled with perhaps equally important manufactural uses of the land.

Figure 7.20 presents a somewhat more detailed use and use-pattern picture than Figure 7.18. Again, mental superimposition of the manufacturing map is pertinent. On Figure 7.20, eleven major use regions are distinguished, but, in the explanatory legend, added detail is provided. For example, one finds the cotton belt broken down into several use categories and lesser land units, ranging from the eastern upper coastal plain and Mississippi Delta to the parts of the southern Appalachian and western coastal plain.

Some Details behind the General Patterns. Within the broad depiction of land use, as shown in Figures 7.16 and 7.20 particularly, lie the details that *in toto* make up the generalized picture. Even here the scale varies, depending on the objective. On the scale of "state units," patterns of land use emerge which are not discernible on the national scale. On the scale of strictly "local units," there is very little generalization—actual field reality as experienced by the observer "on the ground" is essentially attained. The great variations in land-use capability from an agricultural point of view are well illustrated in Figure 7.21.

7.6   Trends in Major Uses of the Land in the United States

Appreciable Changes in a "Half-century of American Land Use." From 1900 to 1950 the cropland acreage of the United States increased about 17.8 per cent, the pasture and range acreage decreased some 14 per cent, forest and woodland acreage increased about 7.8 per cent, and other acreage (urban, roads, railroads, etc.) increased about 4.4 per cent. During the 50-year period, land use pretty well "settled down" in terms of regional distribution of major uses and in terms of key products from such regions. This does not mean that changes are not still occurring, but they are mainly changes in degree rather than in kind.

Comparatively Little Change since 1930. While it is the common practice to deal with land use on the half-century basis represented by the 1900–1950 period, and to make generalizations and state conclusions for that period as a whole, the fact remains that most of the changes in major land uses took place between 1900 and 1930 (Table 7.2). This is borne out

Table 7.2   Trends in Major Uses of the Land
(United States, excluding Alaska)

Use	Per cent increase, or decrease, in acreage	
	1900–1950	1930–1950
Cropland..	+17.8	−0.96
Pasture and range (nonforested).................	−14.0	−1.1
Forest and woodland (grazed and ungrazed).......	+ 7.8	−0.16
Other (urban, roads, waste, etc.)...............	+ 4.4	+5.0

by the following: from 1930 to 1950 acreage in cropland changed very slightly (actually there was a 0.96 per cent decrease); pasture and range acreage continued to decrease, but only to a minor extent; forest and woodland acreage remained practically the same. Only in other use did the previous trend continue. The other use increase was associated primarily with the urban element (growth of towns and cities and increased amounts of land in railroads and highways). However, such increase, even though 5 per cent for the 1930–1950 period, represented only comparatively small land areas.

The changes that have occurred since 1930 have been mainly counterbalancing among different sections of the nation. For example, cropland increase west of the Mississippi was essentially balanced by cropland decrease east of the Mississippi; or, if we take an example entirely east of the Mississippi, cropland increase in the Lake states was offset by cropland decrease in the Northeastern states. In any event, such changes, counterbalancing as they may be, represent small changes percentagewise.

As of the moment, there is no sign of any imminent changes in major uses of the land or in the pattern of arrangement of these uses across the nation. Of course, the population continues to increase, but the needs of this population probably will be met within the present land uses and the present distributional pattern of these uses—met within the framework that seems to have practically "jelled" by about 1930. One cannot travel across the United States without feeling that the land we are now using can be made to produce far more than it does at present. Thinking of just the corn belt alone, it is apparent that we have not begun to use it to the point of full efficiency; and the same is true of most of our other areas. Looking to the future, it would appear that our present major land-use units possess the potential to support a still larger population—a potential based on scientific agriculture, scientific forestry, etc.

7.7   Competition for Use of the Land

Competition Is Mainly in Urban and "Rurban" Areas.   The many facets of competition for use of the land among the numerous and different land-use demands cannot be discussed at any length in this chapter—nor properly discussed in several chapters. It is a matter for volumes if it is done comprehensively. It includes competition among grazing and forestry, recreation and forestry and grazing, public use and private use, urban and rural use, etc. Despite this complex situation, certain general and dangerous, because of brevity and subject limitation, comments may be made.

The most pronounced and pressing competition for use of the land appears in connection with greatly increased urbanization, especially in the period since about 1930. Even though this competition actually affects only a small percentage of our total national area (land currently classified as urban, and including industrial land, amounts only to about 1.3 per cent of our total area), it is one that is exceedingly important and dynamic, and its effects are great in terms of numbers of persons affected in a nation that now is two-thirds urban in character. Within recent years cities and towns have almost literally exploded out of their former confines and have created marked conflicts among urban and rural land-use demands. Many rural sections adjacent to towns and cities first have become that mixture described as "rurban" and then have succumbed completely to urban functions and urban uses. In many instances this also has meant that areas still farther removed, and not previously used for commercial agriculture, have become important crop and animal districts. Often areas so utilized are physically better suited to other use; yet current economic demands dictate their utilization for agricultural purposes. To take one example, pronounced but certainly not unique, the growth of Los Angeles has swallowed up previously agricultural and suburban areas and has forced, or at least strongly encouraged, use of semiadjacent areas for crop and animal production, even areas in the Mojave and Colorado Deserts. The same growth and spread have tremendously increased the demand for recreational use of the land, particularly public recreational use, and have thus boomed the demand for recreational areas in local hill and mountain land, local shore lands, and even lands well out in the neighboring steppe and desert country. The same sort of thing, same in kind if not always in degree, has been happening in scores of areas across the nation as a whole. Yet, as noted before, all this actually affects only a small proportion of our territory and only minor segments of our now well-established major land uses and major land-use patterns. Because an extremely involved and extensive subject has of necessity been treated briefly, the reader is referred to the list of selected references at the end of this book.

UTILIZATION OF THE ARID LANDS OF THE WORLD[1]

7.8 The Nature of Deserts

As our world grows daily more densely populated, as the capacity of our arable lands to produce foods and raw materials is taxed more and more heavily, as our cities expand into what was formerly countryside, forcing their inhabitants to seek recreation in urban pleasures rather than in the open spaces, it becomes necessary for us to view every portion of the earth's surface, to determine its resources, and to evaluate its potentialities. And, after considering the humid areas of the earth, where wild vegetation grows lushly, where the agriculturist relies on the same precipitation to mature his crops, and where surface water is available to slack the thirst of city dwellers, it becomes necessary to look into the

---

[1] This section was contributed by Professor Logan.

assets and possibilities of the less-favored areas: the summerless poleward lands, the higher and more rugged mountains, and the lands of little rain. It is with these latter, the deserts of the world, that we are concerned here.

About deserts, the man in the street has a number of misconceptions. He thinks of a desert as a hot sandy waste and thereby may be wrong on

Fig. 7.22   A typical landscape in the warm-winter desert of southwestern Arizona. All the vegetation is either spiny or prickly. The large treelike saguaro cactus and the small cacti in the foreground are water-storing or succulent plants. The low shrubs and the paloverde trees have very extensive root systems. If water is available for irrigation, such an area can become very productive. (*U.S. Department of Agriculture photograph.*)

three counts. For some deserts are always cool, and very little of the typical desert is sandy. And the term *waste* implies an empty, useless void—an area that, now or in the past or future, must remain uninhabitable and can produce nothing of consequence. Yet out of the deserts of the Middle East have sprung the very essence of civilization: the

Mohammedan, Jewish, and Christian religions were conceived there, and the concept of monotheism itself was a natural result of the vastness of the desert landscape and the awe-inspiring magnitude of its perspectives, in contrast with the small horizons of the humid world.

If the man in the street is wrong about the hot sandy waste, what then are the characteristics of deserts? First of all, the notion of aridity has been omitted. For deserts are first and foremost arid lands, wherein moisture is lacking and things are adjusted to the dryness. Where precipitation exceeds evaporation, we consider the area humid. Where the reverse is true, with more potential evaporation from the surface than the rains can meet, we consider the climate semiarid. Truly arid lands are those in which the potential evaporation is at least double that of normal precipitation. Since evaporation is in part a function of the temperature, it is impossible to state a fixed number of inches of precipitation as the boundary of the arid or semiarid lands; rather, as the temperature increases, a given amount of precipitation has decreasing effectiveness.

To explain the presence of deserts, we must explain the absence of rainfall. On this basis it is convenient to divide the arid lands of the world into several types, as shown in Table 7.3. To these might well be added the polar lands, too, for they suffer from aridity of a sort. While they receive considerable precipitation, most of it is in a frozen form, and hence is

Table 7.3   The Causes and Characteristics of Deserts

Type of desert	Cause	Characteristics	Location	Examples
Low-latitude deserts....	Descent of hot, dry air from aloft in areas of subtropical high pressure	Hot summers, warm winters; dry at all times	15 to 30 deg latitude, both north and south	Sahara, northern Mexico, Kalahari Desert of South Africa, Australia
Mid-latitude deserts....	Precipitation of moisture on the windward sides of mountain ranges, creating moisture-deficit areas on the leeward sides	Hot summers, cold winters; dry at all times	Interiors of continents in the middle latitudes	Central Asia (Gobi Desert), western United States (Utah, Nevada, etc.)
Cool coastal deserts....	Air, chilled by passage across cold coastal current, is warmed on contact with hot land. Thus its moisture capacity is increased and it becomes a drying wind. It is unable to rise and produce rain	Mild to cool all year. Air moist at all times, with fog and dew, but no, or little, rain occurs	West coasts of continents between 15 and 30 deg, both north and south	West coast of Lower California, Mexico; coasts of Chile and Peru; Namib Desert of South-West Africa

unavailable to plants, creating what we term *edaphic drought*. Since an entirely different set of factors is involved here, any further discussion of this type of desert will be omitted.

The lack of plentiful precipitation naturally acts as a deterrent to the growth of vegetation. But it takes far more than this to exclude vegetation completely, for many organisms are able to adapt themselves to such disadvantageous conditions as the desert presents. Growing far apart, the perennial shrubs of the dry lands send their roots far out and far down into the soil in search of moisture, and their foliation and florescence coincide with seasons of higher humidity. Between them, the annuals, opportunists of the highest order, lie dormant awaiting the wetter and hence more propitious times. During the short period when water is available, the plants run through their foliating and flowering periods, producing seeds that may lie dormant for a decade, awaiting another favorable set of conditions.

Since the shrubs are always present (albeit dormant for long periods), there is always food of a sort for certain browsing herbivores, and diligent search in the lee of bushes will disclose accumulations of seeds where the wind has blown and cached them. This meager food supply supports a surprisingly large and varied population of insects, reptiles, birds, and rodents and, in turn, considerable numbers of carnivores dependent upon these. Some of the animals exhibit remarkable adaptations to the lack of water. The desert tortoise stores water for long periods in spare bladders, using it over and over again for his bodily processes. Rabbits seldom drink, getting their moisture requirements from the herbage they consume. Certain of the smaller rodents manufacture water metabolically, producing it within their bodies from even the most dehydrated materials by chemical rearrangement of the atoms to form water.

Primitive man probably did not select the desert as a most favorable home; rather, he was probably crowded into it by stronger and more warlike neighbors. But, nonetheless, he succeeded in making a living in areas that we consider today to be quite incapable of supporting man; he made use of every conceivable resource of animal and vegetable nature and of course had a living standard far below that considered to be minimal in the modern world. Remnants of this type of culture still exist in a few parts of the world, among the Australian aborigines, the Kalahari Bushmen, and the Papago tribes of Arizona, for example.

7.9 Present Uses of Desert Lands

Use in more modern times, or by more advanced societies, has virtually eliminated the primitive subsistent hunting and gathering existence and replaced it with other economies more in keeping with present cultures. This has had the effect of greatly reducing the population densities of desert areas, while raising the standards of the occupants. In some areas this replacement has been virtually complete, as in Australia and the western United States. In certain places, the primitive and the advanced still exist side by side, as in South-West Africa, where the grazier producing karakul for the luxury markets of the world or beef to feed newly industrialized South Africa may have some of his stock killed by the poisoned arrows of primitive Bushmen. In still other regions, subsistence, rather than commercial, grazing is carried on, based sometimes (as in the Sahara) on camels, sometimes (as in Persia) on sheep and goats, and even (as in Mexico) on cattle.

As far as meat production is concerned, the desert is usually insufficient in itself to produce the qualities of meat required for the modern market. As a result, the desert ranges become the youthful home of the animals, where they gain skeletal maturity; but the feed being insufficient to provide the right balance of fat and meat in their tissues, they are moved off to more favorable areas where feed is plentiful to complete their rounding out for market. The fattening areas are sometimes outside the desert, animals raised in Wyoming, for example, are shipped to the corn belt of the Middle West for fattening; but in other cases the irrigated oases are within the desert itself, where fattening on alfalfa and the culls and trimmings of vegetable crops is common.

Where situations are favorable, as on the peripheries of deserts, or where lofty mountains lift themselves out of the desert into the more humid environments of higher altitudes, transhumance is practiced. Flocks or herds graze in the desert areas during that season of the year when feed is plentiful there and move to the more humid environment during the ensuing dry season. In former times this was all done afoot (and it still is in many parts of the world), but in the United States today the animals are now largely transported by truck, it having been found that the loss of poundage of meat from the animals during such long drives afoot is a greater economic loss than the cost of transporting them by vehicle.

The absence of sufficient rainfall has always prevented agricultural development within desert areas. Development of dry-farming techinques has permitted the utilization of broad reaches of semiarid steppe lands, but it brings only soil erosion and economic disaster when practiced in truly arid zones.

Irrigation, on the other hand, has been most successful in desert lands. It has a long history, beginning with prehistoric agriculturists of Egypt, Mesopotamia, India, and Arizona, who planted their crops on inundated lands as the floods of their streams subsided. Eventually they learned the use of ditches to convey water to other lands and thus began the practice now so widespread in the arid lands of the world. Irrigated agriculture, it was soon found, has certain advantages over the ordinary humid-land farming: the hot sunny days are not interrupted by cloudy, cooler ones, hence growth goes on uninterruptedly; it is possible to regulate available water to the amount most beneficial to the particular crop, rather than depending on the unreliable supply provided by normal precipitation; and it is easy to control pests. On the other side of the ledger is the cost of procuring water and the damage done by permitting too great a soluble-mineral accumulation to develop in the soil.

In recent years, as a result of our rapid strides in technology, the irrigated acreage of the world has expanded rapidly. This has been especially true in desert areas settled by peoples of northwestern European extraction (in western United States and Australia particularly). For while irrigation was not part of their indigenous culture, these peoples have developed the technological skills and the capital necessary to carry out vast irrigation schemes. The North African and Middle Eastern world has not benefited to the same degree, owing largely to the lack of these two basic needs.

In another way, too, the two regions may be contrasted. The irrigated agriculture of the American and Australian deserts is principally commercial in nature, providing foodstuffs and industrial raw materials for other regions; the output of similar areas in North Africa and the Middle East is largely consumed locally. From the one there is a large economic return, from the other, virtually none.

Particularly in the United States, the irrigated parts of the warmer desert areas play a very important role in the food supply of the country. Because of their essentially frost-free winters, they are able to grow cold-sensitive plants which form an essential part of the winter diet of the colder areas. Similarly, a number of vegetables are planted so as to mature in midwinter, when the rest of the country is unable to produce them. Thus our deserts make a very important contribution to the variety and vitamin content of the winter meals of the nation.

Since in desert regions the bedrock is laid bare over large areas, mineral resources, if present, become more evident than in humid lands. As a result, mining has long been a major desert enterprise. Small mines are located in all sorts of situations, often operating at the cost of great hardship and deprivation. Where the product is of sufficient value and the management sufficiently enlightened, progressive communities with high living standards may be developed, usually at great expense and with the application of high-level technological skills. Such communities exist in all parts of the desert world—Chuquicamata, Chile (copper), Saudi Arabia (oil), Trona, California (chemicals), and Ajo, Arizona (copper), for example—developed by capital from Europe or humid America.

Within each desert, too, there are those who make their living because of the fact that the desert is a barrier between populous areas of greater economic importance and necessarily people have to cross the desert. In earlier times these were the drivers of caravans, of freight wagons, of pony express and stagecoach. Today, they are the men who maintain the railroad across Australia's Nullarbor Plain, who shovel sand from the rails in South-West Africa's Namib Desert, or who operate the Union Pacific and the Santa Fe railroads across California's Mojave. Similarly, they are the road-maintenance crews on desert highways, the pipeline patrolmen in Saudi Arabia, Jordan, and Arizona, the power-line and telephone patrols in the Mojave, and those who provide food and housing for travelers.

Thus, in the present time, we find the desert occupied by several groups: those who exploit it (the miners and oil men) supported largely from outside; others who use it productively (graziers and agriculturalists), sometimes on a subsistence basis, sometimes commercial; and those engaged in transportation and communications.

7.10   The Future of Desert Lands

To describe the existing is not necessarily to describe the optimum. Nor is it to portend the future. It is difficult, if not impossible, to augur the events of days to come. But something must be done along these lines, lest we drift on aimlessly, pursuing no set course and with no goal in view.

We must attempt, therefore, to find the optimum use for the arid lands and to try to direct their development in the way that will have most benefit to mankind.

Unquestionably, the world's greatest material need in the future will be the need for food, followed closely by industrial raw materials. Hence, the food and raw-material productivity of the arid lands should be given consideration and, where favorable, should be given high priority.

It has just been shown that crops can be raised in the arid zones only with the aid of irrigation. Hence, if the productivity of such areas is to be increased, it must be by means of an increase in the acreages under irrigation. This is obvious, and hence the solution to the problem should be obvious. But, on investigation we find that irrigation, using the technology available to us today, is beginning to approach its probable limits.

This comes about largely because of the lack of further water supply. We have already harnessed and diverted the major streams that are available as irrigation supplies. Most of these are exotic streams, which rise in areas of precipitation excess and flow across desert regions on their way to the sea. They include some of the most famous streams of the world—the Nile, supplying arid Egypt with water from the rainy equatorial highlands of Abyssinia and Uganda; the Tigris and Euphrates, watering Mesopotamia with water from the mountains of Armenia; the

Indus, supplying West Pakistan with the runoff of the western Himalayas; the Colorado and the Rio Grande, draining the Rockies across the deserts of southwestern United States; and the Murray and Darling, flowing westward from the Australian Alps. But most of the waters from these streams, and from thousands of lesser streams of the same nature, have already been allocated and are in use for existing irrigation projects.

Fig. 7.23   Where water is available in the warm-winter desert lands, frost-sensitive plants like these date palms yield bountifully. (*U.S. Department of Agriculture photograph.*)

Supplies in the future will have to come from extra-desert water-courses by large-scale diversions, many of them greater than any we have seen thus far. This will necessitate removing water in large quantities from humid-land streams and diverting it into arid regions. It will mean applying techniques already in use, albeit on a somewhat larger scale than at present. But it will be expensive, and it will raise important political issues.

In areas without surface water, explorations for underground supplies have often been successful. As a result, many basins in the western United States and in Australia are today utilizing water from deep wells. In some instances this water is being replenished as fast as it is being removed, for the aquifers surface in regions of heavy rainfall, or the basins receive much runoff from surrounding mountains. In other cases the withdrawal of subterranean water far exceeds the input, resulting in steadily lowering water levels. In some cases the water being removed is connate water, i.e., deposited with the original sediment from which it is now being pumped, and hence is totally irreplaceable.

The exploration for more underground water will go on and will no doubt be successful in many desert areas. In a large part of the arid world no attention has been paid to this source, the landowners and even the governments being economically unable to stand the cost of such work. But it is likely that areas such as Iran, Baluchistan, and Afghanistan will in the course of time develop irrigation based on deep wells. Such developments may in some instances be short-lived; in others, where replenishment is regular, they may be continued endlessly.

All in all, then, the case for continuing tremendous expansion of irrigation in the arid lands does not look too bright. However, new technological advances including the desalinization of sea water might alter the picture.

The climatic nature of desert areas makes it worth our while to consider the use of another form of power: solar energy, the subject of Chapter 17. The development of solar energy as a source of power would probably have much the same effect as hydroelectricity and coal. It *could* be developed anywhere, but the most logical place for its development would be those areas which have the greatest amount of sunshine, considered from both the astronomical and meteorological point of view. Astronomically, the equatorial regions receive the greatest amount of potential sunshine, but it is intercepted much of the time by a cloud cover. During its respective summer season, each pole receives continuous insolation, but the sun being relatively low in the sky, the input is weak (being filtered out, diffused, and reflected by the earth's atmosphere), and it is of course without any insolation for a 6-month period. The optimum is reached in the low-latitude deserts, which benefit from a day of moderate length, essentially equal throughout the year, from a high-angle position of the sun, and from very clear skies.

The utilization of solar energy might play an important role in attracting certain types of industry to desert areas.

In the minds of people from more humid areas who have had only passing experience with the desert, the question at once arises as to whether it would not be well-nigh impossible to convince people that they should live in desert areas, even if a good income is available there. To many, there is the idea of a desolate environment, cursed by heat and most unpleasant in all ways. Such was the case for the early pioneers, crossing the desert with heavy wagons, along the most primitive of trails, and fighting primitive man as well as nature. But such is hardly the case today. For with modern technology, desert living has come to be quite pleasant and by a large group of people much preferred to urban dwelling in many of our modern cities. With homes built along modern lines, designed to reduce glare and reflect rather than absorb heat, with air-cooling to overcome the worst of the heat, with swimming pools, lanais, and patios to utilize to the fullest the out of doors, with mechanical refrigeration, adequate water supply, and sewerage, and with telephone, radio, and the paved road to overcome isolation, the desert becomes an ideal place for living.

The interest in the desert as a home has not come about suddenly, or directly. It began a couple of decades ago with small-scale tourist enterprises at certain of the more attractive spots in the western United States and after World War II expanded rapidly into a tremendous recreational development.

The desert has become the center of interest of a great number of people, who are drawn to it because of its climate, its beauty, its solitudes. Even as people in other places are drawn to the seashore or the mountains, so here they are drawn to the desert.

Eventually the question arises in the mind of the city dweller spending a week end or vacation in the desert: "Why should I return to the urban area?" Most are forced to return of economic necessity; but a few, living on pensions or investments, or earning a living by some occupation that does not require their presence at an urban desk or machine, decide to remain in the desert permanently. Here the government has assisted by providing very cheap land for residential occupancy.

Because of the necessity for being accessible to utilities, most of these new desert dwellers come to live within the limits of the areas where water, electricity, etc., are provided, thereby creating open sprawling communities. Their presence creates a need for services, and towns develop to provide them. As a result, an urban aspect has developed over certain parts of the southwestern deserts of the United States.

At the present time, this development is entering upon a new phase. Real-estate promoters and businessmen, believing that the only sound economic basis for a community is industry (since it employs large numbers of people and creates, thereby, a broad income base), are forming chambers of commerce in many of these communities and endeavoring to attract industry there. It is most interesting to note the change in the nature of the advertising of desert communities over the past two decades. Cities like Phoenix which formerly stressed the climate, the beauty, the "out of doorness" of their areas as recreational assets are now citing the advantages of the city for industry. Thus, the base is being laid for a great industrial expansion in the desert areas, which may occur anyway, but which would certainly be greatly expanded were solar energy to come into use industrially.

The question at once arises as to whether this is the optimum use for desert areas. And this is a point which deserves very careful analysis. Until recently the deserts of America have been of relatively little value to the world at large. Consequently, they have been largely left alone, untrammeled and unspoiled. They have been too uncomfortable, too inaccessible, and too wild to be of interest to most of civilized society. But with technological developments over the past half century, the picture has changed. The automobile and the maintained roads have made these deserts accessible; pumps, refrigerators, thermos jugs, and canned foods have provided new comforts; and a new desire to see open spaces, to take Kodachromes with sweeping vistas, to sleep under the stars, and to get out of the bustling, crowded, smog-ridden city has brought a new race of recreation seekers into the desert.

To industrialize the desert is to destroy the very thing that these people are seeking. True, it will make it possible for them to live in the desert, but the things that set the desert apart from the rest of the world we know will be gone, the beauty, the space, the endless horizons. Already the open desert is being diminished, urbanization is encroaching from several directions, the highways that span the desert are lined with sign-boards, and the military have taken over large tracts for firing ranges, atom-bomb test areas, and the like.

It appears, then, that planning is necessary and that some thought should be given to the future. The professional planner will hasten to inform us that such has already been done, that there are just such plans already in existence. San Bernardino County, California, the largest county in the United States and one composed largely of desert, is already completely zoned. But a perusal of the zoning map will reveal that all the desert area is zoned for industry! The State Division of Parks and Beaches, endeavoring to set aside a large tract of economically worthless, but scenically valuable mountain land in the midst of this county, found itself not only unsupported by the county, but actually opposed by official elements therein.

What is needed then is a more comprehensive plan, not one geared solely to obtaining the highest possible dollar value from each piece of land. All elements of the population, all aspects of cultural development should be allowed their opportunity to develop. It is important that the desert be allowed to industrialize. Industrial occupance of presently worthless desert lands would free high-grade agricultural lands from the threat of industrial encroachment, as is happening throughout the country today. But, at the same time, recreational interests should be allowed an opportunity to develop, as well. The British have found it necessary to create a commission to preserve the open spaces in their crowded islands.

We who have so much open space fail to appreciate it and run the risk of obliterating it within a generation.

Such a plan should begin with the preservation of the fragile and irreplaceable items first. One of these is scenery. It is unlikely that a vista of desert mountains, appealing to the eye and stirring to the soul, will ever be lovely again once a cement factory has been erected on its slopes. Equally fragile, strange as it may seem at first glance, are rich agricultural lands. Once occupied as industrial or even residential sites, it is doubtful if they can ever be returned to anything approaching their former fertility.

Such a plan, then, would first seek out the scenic and potential recreation sites of the area and the present or potential high-grade agricultural lands and preserve them for all time, irrevocably, against invasion of any sort. The remaining areas could then be utilized for residential, commercial, and industrial occupancy.

At the present, the United States seems to be the only part of the world in which the desert areas are being extensively occupied, by industry or urbanization, or where they are being used for recreational purposes. However, trends begun in one area are likely to spread to others, particularly when they appear to have been successful in the first. Thus it is likely that the recreational aspects of deserts will in the course of time come to be appreciated in places as remote as the Sahara and Australia. If solar energy can be economically harnessed, industrial development may well follow into the low-latitude deserts, bringing with it many of the problems cited above. Hence, what appears at the moment to be purely an American problem of optimum land utilization may in the course of time become a world-wide one. Let us, then, strive to solve our problem in the best manner possible, that we may serve as a world model of effective utilization rather than an example of wasted resource management.

8

Soil as a Natural Resource

HANS JENNY

PROFESSOR OF SOIL CHEMISTRY AND MORPHOLOGY

UNIVERSITY OF CALIFORNIA, BERKELEY

8.1 The Question of Attitudes

If the early pioneers could have viewed from the skies what was to become the United States of America they would have seen a grandiose carpet of primeval vegetation, nearly two billion acres in extent. Half the vegetational colossus was dense forest, two-fifths was grassland, and the remainder was desert brush.

In an amazingly short period this immense Garden of Eden was eliminated with ax and plow, so completely that in the eastern half but few patches of original timber remain today. The prairies of the Middle West have been nearly extinct for decades.

The frantic slashing of the trees was not motivated by scarcity of lumber. The stimulus was a precious treasure hidden below the forest floor: rich virgin soil. In all parts of America nature had built up, in thousands of years, a fertile mantle of soil that was ready to release to man its pent-up fertility.

The settlers were forest men from Western Europe. They saw kinship in the new soils. They valued them. They knew by instinct how to treat them and how to keep them productive. In particular, the well-to-do religious sects furnished some of the finest farmers; witness the success of the Mennonites in early Pennsylvania.

But a psychologically interesting process soon set in. Surrounded by nature's riches and abundance, the exacting and land-loving European peasant underwent a curious transformation. He turned into an agricultural spendthrift who would acquire more land than he could handle, burn carelessly, exploit the soil, and let the soil wash away. If the land wore out, more and better land could be found out West.

A casual attitude toward soil developed that persists to this very day. It is unique among the progressive nations of the world. "Plenty of land" seems an unconscious American feeling. Not so much among the farmers,

184

but clearly among the urban dwellers. Today's steam-rolling expansion of homes, tracts, stores, factories, freeways, and turnpikes over productive fields and orchards constitutes a destruction of America's basic heritage that is alarming. It is not so much the total acreage that is at stake, but the extent of first-class land, for the urban dweller likes best the level, well-drained stretches. He devours the finest farms and the most fertile of soils (Figure 8.1). In parts of California, the fastest-growing state, covering of lands with concrete proceeds at a furious pace. The problem is becoming crucial, and attempts at zoning are being initiated.

Fig. 8.1 Housing development which has eliminated specialty-crop agriculture (artichokes) on fertile valley soil. The rolling uplands which are of low agricultural value offer beautiful views and attractive home sites at but slightly higher construction cost. Besides recreational parks, modern town planning might profitably include dairy and truck-crop areas.

Today, the fate of our national resource soil is first of all a psychological problem, a problem of attitudes. Soil technology is well advanced. The colleges of agriculture and the Soil Conservation Service know how to guard the land and make it yield, but such knowledge becomes academic unless the nation as a whole desires to save the good land for its children.

8.2 The Soil Profile

Anyone riding in the country or hiking over fields is aware that soils differ in color and in texture (sands, loams, clays). Yet, the surface of a soil is but a very poor indicator of the soil in its entirety. The most crucial soil properties are hidden below the surface.

Digging a trench into the soil will reveal its "profile," that is, the sequence of soil characteristics from surface to bottom. This sequence is not an accidental one. It is the product of soil genesis, and it reveals the soil's history. The soil profile is the fundamental criterion for describing, evaluating, and classifying soils, for either scientific or practical purposes.

Very few soils are uniform from top to bottom. Most soils exhibit a pattern of layers known as *soil horizons*. They are designated by capital letters and subscripts: A_0, A_1, A_2, B_1, B_2, C_1, C_2, etc. The A_2 layer, for instance, refers to a gray surface layer from which material has been removed. The B layers denote the accumulation horizons which, in extreme cases, may be a tight clay zone or lime-rich and iron-rich hardpan layers. The C layers pertain to the parent material. A sharply differentiated soil profile is shown in Figure 8.2. This podsol profile occurs in humid regions, in the Great Lakes area, in the New England states, and sporadically on the West Coast. It is also common in Europe. A less-differentiated but nevertheless well-developed grassland profile is illustrated in Figure 8.3. Organic matter is present in the surface and gradually fades out with increasing depth. This profile also has world-wide distribution.

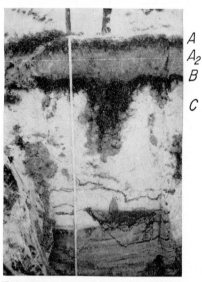

Fig. 8.2 A strongly differentiated soil profile (podsol). Depth about 3 ft. Dark-colored humic surface horizon (*A*) followed by a light-gray bleached zone (*A₂*) which rests on a brownish-black *B* horizon rich in iron and humus. Along a decayed root the *B* horizon intrudes tonguelike into the pale *C* horizon. (*Photograph by R. Bach.*)

Pedologists are stressing the unity of soil and environment. Soil and plant cover mutually affect one another. Each profile reflects a specific combination of the factors of soil formation, i.e., climate, biota, topography, parent rock, and age of soil. This holistic view supplants the old idea that soil is merely dirt, a mixture of organic and inorganic materials.

8.3   Processes of Soil Formation

Soils are dynamic. They are neither sterile nor inert. They team with life. Their properties change, from year to year, even from hour to hour (e.g., the numbers of bacteria).

It has been said that thousands of years are required to produce one inch of soil. This may well be true for hard rocks like granite or basalt. But soft rocks, such as shale, volcanic ash, sand dunes, fresh moraines, and river sediments, require little time, a few years or decades, to develop into soils that are able to support plants and acquire visible horizon differentiation. We shall examine a few soil processes that also have meaning for soil-management techniques.

Fig. 8.3   Virgin prairie soil in which organic matter gradually fades out with increasing depth. (*From H. Jenny, Factors of Soil Formation, McGraw-Hill Book Company, Inc., 1941.*)

Clay Formation in Soils.   Many rocks contain crystals which can be readily seen with the naked eye. Granite, for example, consists of quartz. feldspar, mica, etc.

Under the influence of temperature changes, hot days and cold nights, and the persistant action of water, the rocks and minerals break up into small atomic aggregates. These tiny clusters recombine to form colloidal clay particles which are so small that they cannot be seen with a lens or a microscope. X-ray studies reveal that the atoms in these tiny clay particles are arranged in orderly fashion as crystal lattices. Clay patterns are designated with special names, e.g., kaolinite clay, montmorillonite clay.

Montmorillonite clay (Figure 8.4) has the curious property of internal swelling. Water molecules enter the crystal between atomic planes and force them apart, thus increasing the volume of the crystal many times. Drying will shrink the crystal again. Soil rich in this kind of clay will exhibit large volume changes upon wetting and drying. Building foundations and highways may be seriously damaged by soil swelling and shrinking.

Fig. 8.4 Swelling and shrinking of montmorillonite clay. (*Left*) Dehydrated clay platelets in direct contact with each other. The thickness of an individual package of atoms is about 10 angstroms (about four-millionths of an inch). (*Right*) Hydrated clay with water layers (black) between platelets. The volume of the clay "accordion" is now doubled.

Under the influence of percolating rain water, clay particles migrate from the surface soil to the subsoil. The latter becomes dense. Eventually, in thousands of years, a clay-pan soil is formed having a very tight B horizon which restricts percolation of water and obstructs root penetration. The soil becomes of limited agricultural value. In moist seasons, soils with clayey B horizons stay excessively wet; on slopes they tend to slump and slide.

If only such soils that derive from similar rocks are compared, their quantities of clay display the impressive role of climate on soil formation. Since aridity retards weathering, desert soils of Nevada and Utah are low in clay. Across the Great Plains area soil clay increases, almost in direct proportion to the mean annual precipitation. Warm climate enhances weathering. In the eastern part of the United States, under a rainfall regime of 40 to 50 in., the content of clay in the soil is lowest in the north (less than 5 per cent) and highest in the south (over 50 per cent). Increasing temperatures from north to south are considered the cause of the sharp trend in clay formation.

Since 1850 it has been known that clay particles can be a store of plant food in the soil. On their surfaces they can hold (adsorb) large quantities of phosphorus, calcium, magnesium, potassium, and a good share of the microelements, especially manganese, zinc, and copper. The adsorption discovery was made by an English agricultural chemist who was so impressed by this device which effectively checks leaching of nutrients that he saw in it the wonderful hand of Providence. To complete the wonder, we now know that plant roots readily avail themselves of the nutrients adsorbed on clays.

The Build-up of Soil Nitrogen and Soil Organic Matter (Humus). The amounts of nitrogen and organic substance in a soil, exclusive of living roots, are often astonishingly high, as may be seen from Table 8.1.

Table 8.1 Total Amounts of Nitrogen and Organic Matter in Selected Soils

Type of soil	Depth of soil, in.	Total nitrogen, lb per acre	Organic matter, lb per acre
Grassland soils:			
Cultivated (Yolo soil, California)............	60	10,700	180,400
Pastured (Cayucos soil, California)...........	36	8,880	147,000
Forest soils (including litter layer):			
Under oak (Shaver Lake, California).........	50	5,650	104,000
Under pine (Shaver Lake, California)........	50	5,800	154,500
Tropical forest soils:			
Chinchina, Colombia, South America.........	50	31,400	404,000
Calima, Colombia, South America...........	30	22,400	328,000

Soil organic matter, of which humus is a part, has its source in vegetation. Dead roots decay and furnish humus to the lower horizons. Leaves and needles slowly rot on the ground. Small fragments are dragged into the mineral soil by insects and worms. The bulk is subjected to chemical decomposition by myriads of bacteria, actynomyces, and fungi. The processes are of highest complexity. Some of the products are the following: dark-colored organic molecules (humus), volatile carbon dioxide (CO_2), and mineral substances, such as the nitrates (NO_3), which are essential for plant growth.

It is now realized that in stabilized grassland and forest soils a sort of stationary condition exists between the annual production of organic substances by vegetation and their destruction by microbes, with the accompanying volatization and leaching of the decomposition products.

That is, the annual gains and losses of humus in the soil are nearly equal; the total amount of organic matter in the soil neither increases nor decreases. The soil has entered a biotic equilibrium with life.

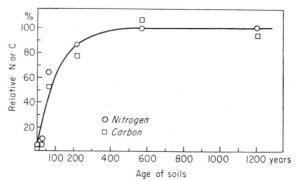

Fig. 8.5 Accumulation of nitrogen (N) and organic matter (C) in relation to time of soil formation, Mt. Shasta area, California. Note that a steady-state condition is reached after 500 years. (*After Dickson and Crocker, 1953.*)

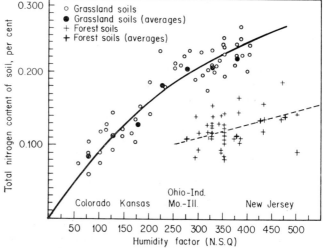

Fig. 8.6 Showing the increase of soil nitrogen with rising climatic moisture in regions having the same mean annual temperature. Samples taken from cultivated fields of former grasslands or forest lands. (*From H. Jenny, Factors of Soil Formation, McGraw-Hill Book Company, Inc., 1941.*)

The humus economy of the soil cannot be understood without considering the nitrogen problem. Fresh rock material will not support higher plants. It lacks the vital nutrient element nitrogen. Although air is rich in nitrogen gas, higher plants cannot utilize it. But certain bacteria and the blue-green algae can. Bacteria of the azotobacter group and the clostridium group as well as the rhizobia living in nodules attached to roots of legumes (clovers, lupines) fix nitrogen from the air and make it eventually available to plant roots. It is estimated that nodule bacteria in some tropical soils fix as much as 200 lb of nitrogen per acre per year.

Soil nitrogen and soil organic matter accumulate in the soil in a more or less parallel fashion. This is well illustrated in Figure 8.5, based on observations by Dickson and Crocker on virgin pine-forest soils of known age located on the slopes of Mt. Shasta, California. Nitrogen and organic carbon, to a depth of 36 in., accumulate at nearly the same rate. The 100 per cent mark signifies either 4148 lb of nitrogen per acre or 136,665 lb of humus per acre. It is significant to note that a steady state is reached in about 500 years (horizontal portion of the curve).

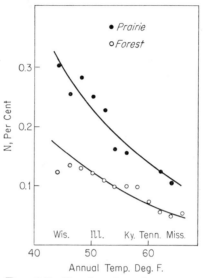

The nitrogen and organic matter content of the soil is sensitively geared to climatic patterns. Figure 8.6 shows how the nitrogen content of surface soils increases with mean annual rainfall at constant mean annual temperature. Figure 8.7 demonstrates how soil nitrogen decreases from north to south in the central part of the United States. The same shape of curves obtains in the tropics of South America, except that the tropical curves lie

Fig. 8.7 Showing that the average total nitrogen content of surface soils (loamy texture) decreases from north to south. Comparisons of cultivated soils whose original vegetation was prairie or forest. (*From H. Jenny, Factors of Soil Formation, McGraw-Hill Book Company, Inc., 1941.*)

far above the United States curves. These functions help to understand soil organic-matter problems on a continental scale.

8.4 Translocation of Mineral Substances in the Soil

As rock minerals break into smaller and smaller fragments, the resulting atomic clusters and ions become mobile and are displaced in the profile, or even removed, by percolating rain water.

In the *arid region*, where rainfall penetrates the soil but a few feet, translocation of lime ($CaCO_3$) from the surface soil to the subsoil is a most prominent feature. Lime horizons, seams and nests of lime concretions, are formed. They descend deeper in the profile as the annual rainfall increases. In general, soils of arid regions are not leached or are only slightly leached. Their soil reaction is neutral or slightly alkaline, which is often a desirable feature. Interestingly enough the limy nature of the arid and semiarid grasslands used to be viewed with suspicion by the West-European and eastern colonists who were used to leached and acid forest soils.

Below 20 in. of annual rainfall, alkali soils may develop in depression areas where water tables are near the surface. During the prolonged hot and dry season, ground water rises to the surface by capillary action, evaporates, and leaves its dissolved salts in the surface soil. Very harmful "black alkali" conditions are caused by sodium carbonate salt (Na_2CO_3), and less harmful "white alkali" is produced by sodium sulfate (Na_2SO_4). Alkali soils are widespread. Their chemistry is fairly well understood, but practical reclamation still poses a challenge to the worker in the field.

In *humid regions*, rainfall is sufficiently frequent and intense so that water will percolate through the entire profile and by seepage reach ground water, rivers, and oceans. Many of the soluble soil constituents, organic and mineral, are removed from the soil. Thus, in northern countries, e.g., Sweden, lakes and rivers often have a strong brownish tint, owing to dissolved humus.

As previously mentioned, clay particles are effectively translocated from A to B horizons. Lime horizons cannot form. The leaching of minerals over long periods of time is accompanied by development of soil acidity which may become so acute that plant growth is hampered. It creates special soil-management problems. It can be overcome by liming which, in effect, means imitating arid soils.

E. W. Hilgard (1833–1917), geologist in Mississippi and soil scientist in California, was the first to recognize and demonstrate the powerful impact of climate upon the mineral regime of soils. In doing so he changed the provincial outlook of the soil scientists in America and abroad to world-wide perspectives, both as to soil genesis and soil management.

8.5   Geologic Erosion of Soil

Long before man set foot upon this earth, mountains and hills were eroding and valleys were filling up.

Consider a virgin soil on a slope. Vegetation forms a cover that protects the soil, but not completely. Worms and rodents push and carry soil particles to the surface, where rain and wind will remove them, little by little, in a down-slope direction. At the same time, weathering and soil formation proceed at the base of the profile. The soil is really an open system; it gains material at the bottom and loses it at the top. Thus, there are annual rates of gain of soil material and annual rates of loss. They balance each other in mature soils. The soil appears stable although it descends vertically. Depending on the steepness of slope, hardness of rock, climate, and vegetative cover, the soil mantle will be either deep or shallow. At times singular events in environment, such as fires and cloud-bursts, may locally enhance the minute daily erosion by inducing mass flow, slips, and landslides. All this is called *geologic erosion*, in contrast to the disastrous widespread man-made erosion.

The sequence of soils along a slope is sometimes designated a *catena*, a chain, because soil depth, color, humus content, and reaction vary in regular fashion from crest to trough. This slope pattern of soils is especially striking when the lower end has a high water table which induces luxurious vegetation of swampiness or peat and muck conditions.

8.6   Soil Survey and Soil Classification

The United States possesses a system of soil mapping that is the envy of many a nation. The survey was inaugurated in 1899 as a Federal activity. It has since become a cooperative enterprise between the U.S. Department of Agriculture and the various state experiment stations. Parties of two or more surveyors map all the soils in a county, or other suitable area, describe their properties, and assess their agricultural value. The unit of mapping is the *soil type* and its phases which are segments of the landscape possessing recognizable individuality and agricultural significance. In the Merced district in California, for example, in an area of 1100 sq miles, 290 soil units have been recognized and mapped on a scale of 4 in. to the mile. In the United States as a whole, some 500 million acres have been mapped in detail, and over 14,000 soil types and nearly a hundred thousand phases have been described and recorded. In many instances the soil description includes detailed physical and chemical analyses and results of fertility tests.

Each soil type is named according to the locality where it was first found. To the locality name is added the texture designation of the surface, e.g., Hanford loam, Panoche clay, Marshall silt loam, etc.

The soil types are readily grouped into categories according to utilitarian purposes such as farm planning, land utilization, irrigability, potential productivity, reclamation, tax assessments, and many others.

The problem of arranging the multitude of soil types into a scientific system of soil classification that has world-wide significance has not yet been solved. New systems are being frequently proposed, but none has been generally accepted.

In the United States and elsewhere, soil types are often assembled into large classes, the *great soil groups*, such as podsols, yellow-red soils, lathosols, chernozems, desert soils, solonetz, etc., about twenty in all. Some of these selections and names are of Russian origin because Russian soil scientists, at the beginning of the century, were world leaders in scientific soil classification.

Figure 8.8 shows the distribution of the 12 great soil groups that make up the *zonal soils*. Their properties predominantly reflect the influence of climate and vegetation on soil genesis. This soil map was published by Marbut in 1935. In 1938 it was revised and reissued by Kellogg and associates. For the sake of clarity and simplicity, the 1935 version only is shown. An entirely new map is under preparation.

It is not to be construed that all soils in a given zonal area have identical profiles. The zonality pertains to mature soils only, soils believed to be in accord with the environment. Not shown are the thousands of soils incompletely developed, either because of youth, steep slope, poor drainage,

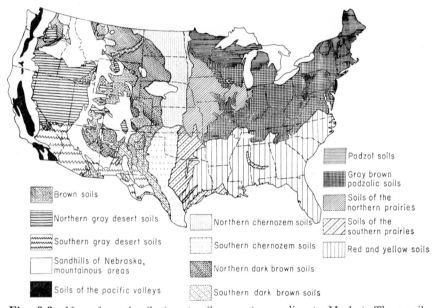

Fig. 8.8   Map of zonal soils (great soil groups) according to Marbut. These soils are closely related to climate and vegetation. (*After H. Jenny, Factors of Soil Formation, McGraw-Hill Book Company, Inc.,* 1941.)

or unusual rock material. Yet, in these immature bodies too, the soil processes operating are precisely those which produce the zonal features.

Note the heavy line running north to south, from the Dakota-Minnesota state line to near the tip of Texas on the Gulf. It is Marbut's major soil boundary or fringe. West of it, soils tend to accumulate lime; east of it they tend to lose it, acquire acidity, and develop grayish A_2 horizons (podsolization). One could say that the boundary roughly separates the arid from the humid region, as judged by soil behavior.

The podsol soils in the cool Northeastern states are low in clay and high in acid humus. For the red and yellow soils in the warm South the reverse holds true; clay content is high, organic matter low. The very productive gray-brown podsolic soils occupy an intermediate position.

Many soils have achieved prominence, even national fame. Some because of exceptionally high production and durability, others because of menacing threats (e.g., the Dust Bowl), still others because of the role they played in the history of the United States. A few brief illustrations may help to kindle interest in the unsung epic of soil and man.

At Plymouth, near the podsol belt, the Mayflower pilgrims soon found that they had fallen on comparatively sterile land (Gloucester and Merrimac soils). Had it not been for sea food and corn which was secured from the interior, they might have formed another lost colony. In 1635 Hooker led the main body of his church through wilderness into the Connecticut Valley and settled on the rich beaver meadows between Hartford and Springfield. These were young, fertile alluvial soils which became the lifeblood of each New England settlement. They were inordinately precious. When the towns were divided into lots, the utmost care was taken in the division of meadowlands; the surveys were carried out to inches and tenths with careful precision. New England became at once a land carefully marked out, and according to Hulbert, the moral tone of these exacting requirements wove itself into the people's lives, contributing to the Yankee's penuriousness, instinct for saving, cautiousness, canniness, and "nearness."

William Penn, whose forest empire was in the *gray-brown podsolic zone*, had received fair reports from the explorers: "a vast fat earth, like the best vales in England. . . . God, in his wisdom, having ordered it so, that the advantages of the country are divided; the backlands being generally three to one richer than those that lie by navigable rivers. . . ." In 1709 Pastor Hans Herr and Martin Kendig secured a warrant for 10,000 acres in the interior. They chose the land on the north side of Pequae Creek, in what is now Lancaster County. This splendid site had long been the home of the Conestoga Indians. The price paid, £500, was, however, about double the regular price Penn had set for other lands. Yet, it was the best land bargain ever made in colonial times (Hulbert). The soils are now known as Hagerstown soils, derived from nutrient-rich limestone rock. The immigrants' success was instant, and within less than a generation phenomenal prosperity was recorded. Soon Pennsylvania became the granary of the colonies and the agricultural keystone state.

The fertile limestone soils extended far south, along the Cumberland and Shenandoah Valleys. Many moved on, the Boones and the Lincolns and, crossing the Cumberland Gap, discovered the extension of these soils into Kentucky and Tennessee (1775). Soon thousands of families, on foot and in Conestoga wagons, traveled the wilderness road, eager to get a section of the famed bluegrass country. Today, the log cabins of the pioneers have been replaced by rich-men's horse farms. In beautiful design, they sprawl over Kentucky's Hagerstown and Maury soils which nature has so generously endowed with mellowness and with life-giving phosphorus.

But, good limestone rock is not enough to make a fertile soil, as many a Palatinate immigrant found out with sweat and with tears. As the settlers crossed the Mississippi River, they ascended the limestone area of the ancient Ozark Plateau. Here, in a zone of *yellow-red soils*, the land had been subjected to leaching for countless ages. The nutrients had mostly left the soil. In their place useless flint and chert had accumulated (Clarksville stony loam). After cutting the forest, fair crops could be secured as long as the meager supply of humus lasted; but sooner or later, the land gave out, and with it the efforts and dreams of the immigrants. All that is now left on these soils are a few orchard trees hidden in piny woods and forgotten cemeteries covered by brush.

The *gray-brown podsolic zone* contains another famous collection, the Miami soils, or Miami catenas, covering large areas of the Middle West. They are part of the undulating and rolling landscape that was carved by the huge retreating ice sheet of the last glaciation. The variegated relief consists of broad ridges, little valleys, dales, and depressions. In the native state the land sustained splendid beech and sugar-maple forests, interspersed with rich grasslands and wet meadows. To the colonist this was the Eldorado proper, for it possessed in abundance his three essential W's: wood, water, wild grass. The area was divided into small homesteads and was destined to become the heartland of American democracy.

Today the landscape is dotted with countless well-kept farms, barns, homes, and silos. It is the heaviest producer of the nation's corn and hogs. Together with the western extension into the superlatively fertile *prairie soils* of Iowa and the adjoining territory, the whole region is known the world over as the great American corn belt.

8.7 Management Aspects of the Soil Resource

To establish the American civilization, the native cover of a whole continent was removed. It was soon discovered that deforestation and plowing under sod cause soil instability.

The *natural nitrogen and organic-matter equilibrium is profoundly disturbed*. On the one hand, the return of plant debris is reduced to driblets; on the other, the rate of humus decay is enhanced by cultivation. A drastic reduction in soil nitrogen and soil organic matter takes place. This decline is depicted in Figure 8.9 for average farming practices on noneroding land in the central part of the United States. The nitrogen content of the virgin soil is arbitrarily set as 100 per cent. About one-third of the original reserve has disappeared in 60 years of farming.

Since the American agriculturist does not practice stable manuring, the humus reservoir is being progressively depleted. To counterbalance the resulting yield depressions, the farmer resorts to nitrogen fertilization with artificial products, manufactured by combining hydrogen gas and nitrogen gas from air at high temperatures and pressures. In 1954 over 2 million tons of nitrogen was applied to crop and pasture lands. It is less than 10 lb per acre, a small token compared to actual exhaustion.

The drain on soil nitrogen could be eased and production costs significantly reduced if an old dream of biologists could be made a reality: inducing nodule bacteria to live also on roots of nonleguminous plants, particularly grasses, small grains, corn, and cotton. Each plant would then run its own nitrogen factory.

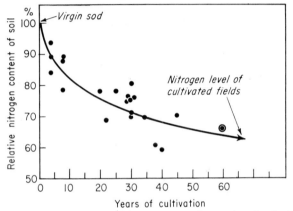

Fig. 8.9 Decline of soil nitrogen under average soil practices in the Middle West. (*From H. Jenny, Factors of Soil Formation, McGraw-Hill Book Company, Inc., 1941.*)

Although none of our major crops is native to the United States, they all grow splendidly, and their aggregate production is stupendous. Most of the food crops are consumed by urban populations, directly, or indirectly via milk, cheese, beef, and pork. The quantities of *soil minerals transferred in foods from farms to cities* have reached staggering amounts. Unfortunately the great bulk of these plant elements does not return to the land but is dissipated as sewage waste. Annually the soil resource experiences a sizable loss in nutrients. Mineral replenishment with artificial fertilizers is wholly inadequate, though, admittedly, fertilizer consumption in this country is sharply rising. According to the statistics of the Food and Agricultural Organization of the United Nations, the United States in 1952–1953 supplied on the average about 15 lb of total plant food to an acre of arable land, a trifle compared to Japan's 148 lb, Belgium's 220 lb, or the Netherlands' 340 lb per acre. In banker's language, we are still living on soil-resource capital rather than on interest.

The physical make-up of the soil, such as *texture*, which is the proportion of sand, silt, and clay, is a decisive factor in land use. Texture is the more crucial since man cannot change it to any significant extent. Loam soils, having favorable proportions of sand, silt, and clay, are considered best, but in certain localities sandy soils as well as clay soils have advantages for specialty crops (e.g., clays for rice culture). Marked texture variations within profiles may impede water and air circulation and limit root growth.

Texture very largely determines the amount of water a deep soil will hold and the quantity of water plant roots can extract. Soil physicists are intensely engaged in soil-moisture research, which is of vital concern to irrigation agriculture.

Deterioration of *soil structure* is now being aggressively combated. By soil structure is meant the "architectural" arrangement of soil particles, whether open-packed or close-packed.

Virgin soils largely have open structures. The clay particles are linked together as loose but water-stable aggregates, the links being organic molecules. Water and air circulate freely. The soil has good crumb structure, good tilth, and is friable. Exploitive cultivation burns out organic matter, the links disappear, the structure collapses, and the soil particles assume a close-packed arrangement. The soil becomes puddled and harsh. In humid regions water infiltration and water penetration may be reduced to such an extent that runoff and erosion become a menace. In arid regions, irrigation water may fail to wet the overcultivated soils to satisfactory depth.

In recent years, threadlike organic molecules have been manufactured which can act as artificial links between clay particles. They are fairly resistant to microbial attack. In many soils they create a favorable open-packed structure, simulating the behavior of stable manures and green manures. These so-called polyelectrolytes (e.g., krilium) hold much promise for the future, though they can hardly be expected to match the structure potential of a good grassland sod.

One of the great agricultural menaces is still *soil erosion*—accelerated erosion or man-made erosion—for it removes the soil mass irreplaceably. It fills up reservoirs, rivers, and harbors and silts the fertile lowlands. Gully erosion is especially dreaded as it interferes with the use of machinery in cultivation. Since these aspects are discussed in Chapter 9, suffice it to say that the Soil Conservation Service has done a splendid job in reducing erosion and in making a large segment of the public soil-conservation conscious. But, it is only a beginning.

8.8 Epilogue

It is estimated that by 1975 we will have 200 million mouths to feed in the United States alone. While we could not do it today, or tomorrow, we *might* do it by 1975, even without ersatz foods, such as algae proteins and sawdust cakes, provided we conserve the soil resource.

Proudly we hold the world's record in agricultural output per farmer. However, if we take as a yardstick the yield per acre, which is what counts in feeding people, we are behind East Asia, and far behind Western Europe. In fact, on prewar levels, little Europe (exclusive of the Soviet Union) produced many more millions of tons of caloric foods (grains, potatoes, sugar) than North and South America combined. There is no inherent reason why our agriculturists could not be equally productive and double and perhaps treble average yields in many areas. Some are doing it already. Besides, we still harbor sizable stretches of idle land: arid acres waiting for irrigation, alkali lands to be reclaimed, swamp lands to be drained. We can develop the skills to do all these things if the public recognizes its responsibility toward protecting the soil resource and if it will support agricultural research and finance the educational effort necessary to translate new knowledge into action on every farm.

9

The Physical Aspects of Soil Management

ARTHUR F. PILLSBURY
PROFESSOR OF IRRIGATION AND ENGINEERING
UNIVERSITY OF CALIFORNIA, LOS ANGELES

9.1 Introduction

The basic problem of soil management is to preserve, and even enhance, the utility of soil, at the same time that the soil is being used by man. Deterioration of a soil often results from management practices which adversely affect its physical or chemical properties or which affect its surface position. Important natural factors including the major factor of flood also change soils. Floods, through erosion and deposition, change both the nature and position of soils and are therefore discussed in their soil-management aspects.

9.2 The Soil Surface

The surface of soil is of particular importance in its management. It is the boundary between the soil and those forces which seek to change its nature. It is where water from precipitation, or other sources, enters and evaporates. It is where temperature changes and freezing and thawing are induced upon the soil. And it is where plant and animal life, macroscopic and microscopic, enters or emerges from the soil environment. Plant life often provides a canopy over the soil surface. The effects of utilization are usually surface or near-surface effects.

Soil is a complex system consisting of solid particles varying widely in size and arrangement, with air and water in the interstices. Above all, it is the home for a vast array of plant and animal life. Use of land to meet all man's varied demands can be expected to have important, and sometimes detrimental, effects upon the soil and upon the life it supports. Let us explore some of the principal factors affecting soil surface.

200

Compaction.   Traffic of any type on a soil may result in compaction of that soil. The effect of traffic in compacting soil was first investigated by engineers interested in utilizing soil as a foundation or building material. For instance, early engineers built earth-fill dams by placing the soil in thin layers and drove sheep back and forth to compact the soil to make

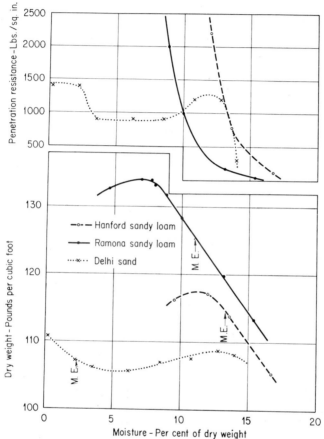

Fig. 9.1 Bulk density (dry weight per unit volume) and penetration resistance in comparison with the moisture content when the soil was compacted with the equivalent of the sheep's-foot roller. The Ramona sandy loam has the widest range of particle sizes, and the Delhi sand, the least. A lesser compactive force would have moved the peaks for bulk density down and to the right. (*From Huberty.*)

it denser and thus minimize seepage. It soon became evident that all soils did not react alike and that soils with a wide range of particle sizes were susceptible to the greatest compaction, while those with relatively uniformly sized particles would compact but little. Potential compaction increases with the moisture content of the soil until the soil reaches a certain dampness, then more water tends to hold the particles apart (Figure 9.1).

In agricultural terms, potential compaction peaks somewhat below the "field-moisture capacity" of the soil. By potential compaction is meant heavy compaction as exemplified by the sheep's-foot roller. With lesser compactive forces, maximum compaction occurs when the soil is wetter.

Compaction in agricultural soils is often excessive in a 6- to 12-in. layer immediately below that loosened by tillage implements. This is the well-known "plow pan" or "cultivation pan." There is usually a lack of roots in the compacted layer, and little if any water moves through the layer. In some soils, roots cannot grow when the bulk density exceeds 1.5g per cu cm, while for other soils the upper limit can be as high as 1.8.

Compaction, then, often adversely affects the soil as a medium for the growth of plant roots, both by excluding those roots and by diminishing their potential supply of air and moisture. It may make the soil more subject to erosion simply because surface runoff increases with decreased infiltration capacity. Compaction of a pathway, roadway, or any line along which some object has been dragged may create the beginnings of a channel, concentrating overland flow and accelerating erosion. As heavier and heavier equipment, and more equipment, is used in operations performed on the soil surface, compaction becomes more and more of a problem in agriculture. However, compaction may be desired for some structural uses of soil, and it has been employed in irrigated agriculture, to obtain longer furrow runs without excessive upstream infiltration and to reduce seepage in reservoirs and canals.

Tillage. Tillage affects the soil surface by causing compaction, as discussed above, and it has important effects upon the loosened mulch. Tillage may, if excessive, result in deterioration of soil structure, as frequently evidenced by reduced infiltration capacity and from the fact that tilled soil is more subject to erosion by both water and wind. Tillage also affects nutrient supply and organic-matter content, as described in the preceding chapter. Tillage is almost universally practiced in the production of food and fiber crops, particularly to control weeds and pests and to prepare a planting bed. It is used to break up and bury any natural cover, or other cover no longer required, to incorporate litter, crop residues, and other materials added to the soil, and possibly, to improve soil aeration. With surface irrigation, tillage is utilized to prepare the soil so as to direct the flow of water over the land.

Tillage of agricultural land should be such as to minimize structural deterioration of the surface and to minimize compaction below the loosened mulch. Hand tillage seldom deteriorates the soil. Soil compaction is, in the main, a relatively new problem created by heavy modern machinery. Improvement can come from (1) minimizing mechanical tillage and other traffic, (2) improving and extending chemical weed control, and (3) improving the design of tillage implements, tractors, and other vehicles (causing compaction) to reduce compactive forces by spreading the load and decreasing vibration.

Land Grading. It is often desirable to modify land surfaces in order to achieve efficient utilization. For structural purposes, the suitability of the soil as a medium for plant roots may not be important, but it is of prime importance in agriculture and wherever high crop production is desired. Where soils have a natural profile development, the practicality of grading may be limited. Minor smoothing of the surface is usually possible, but heavy grading adversely affects the nutritional and physical

Fig. 9.2 A carrier-type scraper used for land grading and pulled by a crawler tractor. It is typical of the heavy earth-moving equipment now widely used.

properties of the soil, thus inhibiting the growing of plants. The new surface usually has lower infiltration capacity and is more subject to erosion. For some time, at least, it may not provide a good environment for the growth of plants.

With deep soils lacking profile development, heavy land grading is often practiced. This is particularly true of irrigated lands, because uniform flat grades aid in distributing water evenly. Somewhat incidentally, water erosion is generally prevented by this grading operation because slopes are lessened. Sometimes the mixing that accompanies leveling of a stratified soil may improve the soil as an environment for roots.

Grading often results in compaction and adversely affects structure. Chiseling, ripping, or deep plowing may be resorted to after grading to help eliminate the compaction. Improvement of structure may come with cropping if the land is managed so as to eliminate excessive tillage.

Vegetative Cover.   Destruction of vegetation and its litter by fire, fumes, chemicals, or mechanical processes will affect the disposal of precipitation. This is particularly important on watersheds. Vegetation and its litter intercept some precipitation and break the impact of raindrops. Large raindrops striking a soil surface adversely affect surface structure and, hence, infiltration capacity. Being detached, the particles or aggregates are readily transported in any overland water flow.

Sometimes an important effect of vegetation is the accumulation of litter over the soil surface (Figure 9.3). Such accumulations may play a

Fig. 9.3 Litter underbrush. Such litter is of prime importance in minimizing flood peaks and erosion, but provides a huge fuel supply for wildfires to feed upon during dry weather. (*U.S. Forest Service.*)

greater role than living plants in protecting the soil surface. With some tilled soils, the presence of surface litter can result in significant improvement in soil structure. "Mulch tillage" is a cultural system used to retain litter on or near the soil surface.

Vegetation plays an important role in the management of untilled watersheds, particularly as regards floods, water yield, and soil erosion. Colman[1] has summarized information which indicates that burning of vegetation can reduce the infiltration capacity of untilled soils, while Burgy and Scott's[2] work shows that burning improved infiltration capacity on the soils studied. Runoff and erosion may well be increased by burning vegetation. The factors influencing this would seem to be rain-

[1] E. A. Colman, *Vegetation and Watershed Management*, The Ronald Press Company, New York, 1953.

[2] V. H. Scott, "Relative Infiltration Rates of Burned and Unburned Upland Soils," *Trans. Am. Geophys. Union*, vol. 37, pp. 67–69, 1956.

drop dispersion of the surface crust, temporary water-detention characteristics of litter, and differences in the hydraulic characteristics of overland
flow through litter as compared with flow over a bare surface. Kittredge[1]
reported that "field moisture capacity" in litter represents a rather minor
quantity of water, but such capacity is not an index of the far greater
amount temporarily detained under little or no suction force. Such
temporary detention serves to minimize the effective rate of precipitation
and to lessen the velocity of overland flow.

Fig. 9.4 Erosion in the Kennett area of California following denudation of watershed
by smelter fumes. Note large gullies down all the slopes. (*U.S. Forest Service.*)

Complete denudation of watersheds has occurred in the vicinity of smelt-
ers when the fumes therefrom have not been controlled. Such denudation
has been followed by an excessive increase in flood peaks and in erosion.
One smelter operating near Kennett, California, during the period 1905
to 1910, completely denuded about 8300 acres of brush and timberland
and left some 21,000 additional acres semibarren. Fumes were partially
controlled in 1910, operation was irregular thereafter, and the smelter
was abandoned in 1925. Nevertheless, there was little vegetation on the
worst affected areas in 1934, when a planting program was undertaken,
and cover is still obviously low.

Denudation without adequate measures to prevent excessive erosion
should be avoided. However, good management of watershed vegetation
may involve the substitution of one type of vegetation for another. Fire

[1] J. Kittredge, *Forest Influences*, McGraw-Hill Book Company, Inc., New York,
1948.

may be used as a tool in such conversion. Veihmeyer substituted grasses and forbs for brush, in connection with range-improvement studies, and found significant increases in grazing capacity and water yield, without adversely affecting erosion. Some grasses have shallow root systems, and the annual grasses grown had a life of only a few months. Therefore, there was carry-over of the moisture stored below the grass roots, and the moisture eventually reappeared as surface flow at lower elevations. Where precipitation is not sufficient to penetrate below the grass-root zone, or where the soil mantle is too shallow, little or no water can be conserved by vegetation management. When there is a wet series of years, sometimes considerable water can be saved, while during low-rainfall years, when water is most needed, little or none is saved.

Vegetation, then, plays an important role in the management of both tilled soils and watersheds in that it is an aid in the prevention of excessive erosion. Erosion per se, however, need not be considered a menace. Movement of soil downstream does not necessarily result in a net degradation of the resource. Upstream soils may be of low value because of position, profile, or climate. Moved downstream they may provide more of a soil resource for the valleys and deltas where unit values are often much greater.

9.3 Topographic Position of Soil

The position a soil occupies is of prime importance to its management. Location, with relation to climate, market, water supply, etc., will affect type and value of use. Of principal concern here, however, is the topographic position, which dictates the management practices which must be employed.

Soil is formed largely through the breakdown of rock materials by action of water, heat, and various forms of life. Its transport from the uplands toward the ocean is a natural phenomenon. We know that, prior to written history, marked climatic changes occurred on the earth, providing a dissimilar soil regime to that now known. Such cycles, if they are cycles, may repeat themselves, but in soil management we can look only into the immediate future.

Untilled Uplands.   Grazing, lumbering, mining, and recreation are important uses of untilled uplands. Often, however, an important or paramount use is as watershed, for the production and control of water. The uplands must also be considered a source of soil material, for all upland soil is eventually destined to be eroded and carried to the lowlands or to the sea. Damage to man's activities from downstream soil movement, an integral part of floods, may primarily be a result of the fact that a varying depth of soil material is deposited on the flood plain, where man often concentrates his activities.

In general, the value of untilled uplands per unit area is low. Water supplies may be of extreme importance. But the value is attained through extensiveness rather than intensity of use. It follows that relatively low-cost soil-management techniques are, or should be, employed. The most common technique, and the one given widespread publicity, is the maintenance of a vegetative cover on the land. This may be instigated by a desire to improve browsing potentialities of the area, improve lumbering, or decrease the erosion which accompanies water production.

Soil movement on watersheds is intimately related to overland flow of water. As velocities increase, soil-carrying power is increased exponentially. Finer material is carried in suspension, and coarser material is carried along the bottom as bed load. As volume and velocity increase, concentrations of soil in the water increase, until, in an extreme case, a mud flow exists. Mud flow becomes a significantly slower viscous flow wherein there is little or no size sorting of the material, as would be expected in suspensions. As the waters of overland flow concentrate, spots occur where the water tends to fall over the brink of an unstable bank. Velocities become supercritical, and the water hitting the bottom cuts downward and upstream, forming a gully head which advances upstream. While some soil is picked up in the initial overland flow, the greater source is from this gully action.

Another erosion factor results from ground water recharging into surface flow through stream banks. The adverse hydraulic pressure causes instability and bank sloughing. A similar phenomenon takes place when flood flows recede. Water moves into the banks during high flows and returns to the channel during recession.

During periods of long-sustained precipitation, the water content of subsoils can become quite high, approaching saturation. Under such conditions the soil load becomes great and the subsoil is lubricated by the water. Then, on steep slopes, landslides occur, providing sudden and appreciably large sources of soil debris. Landslides into a channel may temporarily dam water flow and wash out later in a surge heavy with soil material. Since the plane of slippage is generally in a soil horizon unfavorable to roots, or below rooting depth, the phenomenon appears partially independent of vegetal cover.

Not all soil material is moved from untilled uplands through the medium of water, although most of it is so moved. With sparse vegetation or following overgrazing or a fire, wind may move a little soil, but wind is generally unimportant in the absence of tillage. Not to be ignored, however, is the phenomenon of creep which occurs during dry periods on steep slopes covered with native canopy-type vegetation. Where there is an appreciable amount of surface litter, the surface soil may dry as loose crumbs. Possibly associated with wind action, and the traffic of animals, a marked downward drift of a mixture of soil and litter takes place. It can result in loose material being piled up in depressions and channels, ripe for erosion with subsequent precipitation.

Fire on a watershed can be a menace, destroying vegetation and structures of man. It can also be a tool in watershed management. Fire has been used for many centuries in parts of the world to clear areas of unwanted vegetation or to burn up stores of fuel that make wildfires uncontrollable. It was and is used by African natives to improve the grazing potentialities of the bush and was used by California Indians for a similar purpose—to increase the numbers of game animals upon which

Fig. 9.5 Landslides that occurred on steep slopes in southern California, March, 1938, after sustained precipitation. The debris first accumulated in the channels, and then was swept downstream.

they depended for much of their food and clothing. Use of fire in northern and southern California is increasing today as a means of minimizing unwanted brush and improving the browse for range animals.

Fire hazard increases not so much with the amount of vegetation as with the ever-increasing accumulations of dead vegetation and litter. Vegetation management may minimize this fuel accumulation by controlled burning. It sometimes involves only the burning of the forest floor. Other times, as with brush, it may be undertaken to modify the vegetation, i.e., increase the amount of grasses and forbs. If there is the probability of intense precipitation before new vegetation is established, there is increased danger of erosion during such period. The amount of soil lost from the watershed in such a case is not the important consideration. Rather, it is the effect of large amounts of soil debris being deposited on the lowlands or in reservoirs by floods.

The effectiveness of vegetation in minimizing erosion from slopes, and in the stabilization of channels, decreases as the intensity of floods increases. In other words, erosion control with vegetation tends to reach a saturation point and has relatively little effect during major floods, but great effect during lesser floods.

Other tools used in the management of vegetation on untilled uplands include replant programs on cutover forest land, grazing control, mechanical clearing, chemical spraying, seeding, fertilization, and irrigation. There is also evidence that the opening of small areas throughout a forest may delay snow melt and spread the production of water over a longer period of the year.

Erosion from mountain areas is increased by the gradual degradation of stream channels, with a consequent undermining and steepening of the side slopes. The stabilization of channels is, therefore, an effective erosion-control device. A series of temporary check dams can be effective during minor floods but can cause increased damage during major floods, except when located in the extreme headwaters of small channels. Small areas above channels have been paved, primarily as a means of increasing water supply. Paving also has the effect of preventing erosion. As cheaper methods are devised, paving can be expected to increase where water supplies are short and flood debris is a problem.

Tilled Uplands. Where climate, topography, soil characteristics, and economic considerations justify, uplands are tilled for the production of food and fiber crops. It is with the upland soils that soil-conservation practices are so essential to the continuous cropping of the land. Much has been written about these practices; so all that is needed here is a brief outline of the objectives of the common techniques employed:

1. Improve the structure of the soil to increase water-entry rates and thereby reduce runoff and erosion.

2. Roughen, alter, or otherwise modify the soil surface to the end that water is held on that surface for a period of time following precipitation. A danger in this practice should be recognized, as water thus concentrated may break down the slope suddenly, causing more erosion than if no conservation practices had been followed.

3. Reduce the grade over which water flows through the use of contour grade furrows and graded terraces. It is important that terraces and furrows be designed to prevent overtopping under any expected flood.

4. Provide a trashy surface, usually by tillage designed to leave the crop residue on the surface or to bury it only partially. This mechanically impedes erosion, and the organic matter improves soil structure. Difficulty may result where the decaying organic matter temporarily utilizes

nutrients, especially nitrogen, that would otherwise be available to the growing crops.

5. Provide contour strips of untilled vegetation (Figure 9.6).

6. Stop tillage and put land in pasture, tree lots, or a similar enterprise.

7. Utilize fertilization and irrigation to increase vegetation.

Any technique which concentrates surface-water flows must provide thoroughly stabilized wasteways. Design must be such that borders, terraces, etc., will not be overtopped.

Valleys. The term *valleys* as used here refers essentially to the upper flood plains. It is where the debris, eroded soil from the uplands, was

Fig. 9.6 Contour strip cropping to reduce soil erosion. (*U.S. Department of Agriculture photograph.*)

spread out by flood action and came to rest. It is above the basins where under natural conditions the gradient is very low and the water table is high. In general, the valleys constitute the area of greatest natural wealth, of ease of transport and communication, and of highest population density. Through good soil management, the productive capacity of the soil probably can be maintained for a long time. But, eventually, soils develop a profile which generally results in a degrading of their agricultural worth. The basic problem is the reconciliation of this natural soil aging and man's desire to preserve the surface as is. Further deposition may bury crops, may temporarily lessen fertility, and may create havoc in many ways with urban developments and communication facilities. Therefore, the general immediate objective is to regulate flow and prevent excessive soil deposition. This position cannot be maintained indefinitely, however, for aggradation must eventually come.

The old agricultural economy of Egypt was one of living with floods and their deposition. Flood waters would inundate the valley, leaving behind a deposit of new soil and soil moistened throughout the profile with water of low salt content. Crops were planted immediately and depended upon the stored moisture for their growth. In other words, these people adapted themselves to natural geologic processes.

Sicily provides another example of a permanent adaptation of the valleys to agriculture. There, alluvial fans and upper valleys are often divided by a rubble wall down the center, the wall being built up little by little. All stream flow is diverted to one side, where the stream meanders, and deposition of debris gradually raises the elevation. The other side is farmed. Then, after say 50 or 100 years, the process is reversed. The farmers live off to the side on terrace or upland soils. While only half the land is farmed at any one time, a truly permanent soil-management practice has been developed.

Basins.   Basins are lowlands with restricted drainage. The surface, in its natural state, may be periodically flooded or may be lake, swamp, bog, or even shallow sea. Particularly in arid and semiarid regions, the soils are usually saline or sodic. These lands require reclamation before they can be utilized for intensive agriculture. After complete reclamation the land may be highly productive, although the threat of flooding is always a hazard to be faced.

Examples of the reclamation of basin lands are found throughout the world. The Netherlands is a good example (Figure 9.7). This is a humid area, and once land is reclaimed from the sea and leached, salts do not constitute a major problem. The steps in reclamation which are usually taken are:

1. Encircling the area to be reclaimed by adequate levees.

2. Construction of a drainage system which will provide for the removal of excess surface and subsurface water. This might require pumping.

3. Removal of excess salines from the soil profile by leaching. This might include the addition of soil amendments such as gypsum.

With variations in techniques as necessitated by differences in climate and in the physical situation, much the same principles apply to basin reclamation throughout the world.

Basins often contain organic soils. These are formed from plants growing in shallow water or marshy areas. Lack of oxygen retards decomposition, and over the years organic material may accumulate to appreciable depth. When drained, organic soils are highly permeable and normally very productive. Both drainage and tillage, however, accentuate oxidation, with a consequent subsidence of the land and loss of soil. The tilled peat lands of the Sacramento–San Joaquin delta of California have been subsiding at a rate of about 0.3 ft per year for an extended period of time.

Burning of 3 to 5 in. of peat periodically on a few of the lands, wind erosion, oxidation, and compaction have contributed to this subsidence. In the Netherlands, the practice is to keep a high water table, eliminate tillage, and use the organic soils for pasture. This eliminates subsidence and preserves the resource. In some parts of the world, as in Ireland and in the Soviet Union, peat is used for fuel.

Fig. 9.7   Reclaimed lands in the Netherlands.

9.4   Precipitation Disposal and Soil Moisture

Precipitation falling toward a soil surface, or melting snow, is disposed of in several ways. Some is intercepted by vegetation. This is not all loss as it tends to reduce the transpiration or water loss through the plant. Water reaching the soil enters the soil up to the infiltration capacity rate of the soil at that particular time. This rate varies with different soils, and even with the same soil under various cultural practices. The water entering the soil goes first toward satisfying the soil-storage capacity, to the extent that water previously stored has been depleted by evaporation and plant transpiration. Water still percolating downward may next reach a stratum in the soil profile of lower permeability, may strike a bedrock of low permeability, or may reach a water table (sometimes a temporary perched water table created on top of a less permeable stratum by antecedent infiltration). Some fraction of the water may continue to flow downward, through the less permeable stratum, while other fractions move off laterally. These subsurface flows may reappear as delayed surface flows at lower elevations, tending to make streams perennial.

The infiltration capacity of a soil is a variable, dependent upon the basic nature of the soil, the effectiveness of any mulch of litter or other protectant on the soil surface, and the antecedent moisture conditions. A typical infiltration-capacity curve may take the form $I = Ct^n$, where I is the infiltration capacity rate in surface inches per hour, t is the time in minutes after wetting started, and C and n are constants. C varies inversely with initial wetness. A more complex curve can be expected with soils having a profile development, or where there is a shallow water table, or where the rate may become asymptotic with time. The amount of water entering the soil in a given time depends a great deal upon the prior treatment that soil has received. Undisturbed soils often permit a higher rate of water entry than those frequently tilled or of lowered organic-matter content. Maintenance of high infiltration capacity is important to soil management, as is the maintenance of good hydraulic conductivity through the profile.

Normal soils in which plants grow are said to be "unsaturated" because the pores between solid particles contain some air, in addition to the water which tends to adhere to the particles. Soil below a water table is said to be "saturated" because the water is under a positive pressure and pushes the air up and out, except for tiny bubbles of entrapped air. Because of the strong adhesive forces existing between water and the soil particles, water in unsaturated soil is under a capillary pressure (a negative pressure or suction). This suction or capillary pressure can be measured, and the amount of movement of water in soil, the storage of water in soil, and the availability to plant roots are all related to the suction values. Suction increases as moisture content decreases, and most movement takes place when the suction force is below 0.1 atm. ("Bars" is a presently proposed unit to express this suction and is approximately equivalent to one atmosphere.) Moisture movement diminishes greatly at a suction somewhere between 0.1 and 0.3 atm, but some movement, barely measurable, may continue up to suctions of 15 or 20 atm. When moisture movement becomes rather negligible, the soil is said to be at field capacity. This is not strictly a soil characteristic because the value will vary with the moisture content of the surrounding soil. It is a rough measure, however, of the moisture stored in a well-drained soil of reasonably uniform profile. Such moisture-storage capacities vary, in extreme range, from about 1.5 in. of water per foot depth of soil for sands to about 6 in. of water for clays.

Not all moisture stored in soil is readily available to plants. The permanent wilting percentage, representing a suction of about 15 atm, is in a range of rapidly lessening availability. Moisture remaining around and below this range is not available at sufficient rates to maintain turgor. Between field capacity and permanent wilting percentage, moisture is said to be readily available. In some instances plants grow about as well when the moisture is near the permanent wilting percentage as when near field capacity. Growth of other plants may be depressed when the moisture is under a suction of about one atmosphere or more, because of reduced rates at which moisture moves toward roots. One-half to two-thirds of the available moisture is by then used up. The storage capacity of soil for available moisture ranges from about 0.7 in. of water per foot of soil depth for sands to about 2.7 in. of water for clays. A basic requirement for intensive farming is to keep the soil moisture between field capacity and some lower limit, in the range from 1 to 15 atm suction.

Water required for the growth of various crops ranges from about 1 to 10 ft of depth per year, with the range usually between 2 and 4, depending upon climate. Perennial crops generally require the most water and annual crops the least, depending upon their growing season. Where irrigation is practiced, it should provide what precipitation does not. Not all precipitation or irrigation contributes to the evapo-transpiration requirement, or consumptive use of the crop. Some water may run off on the soil surface, while some may percolate deep below the root zone. In irrigation, if 60 to 80 per cent of the water applied goes to consumptive use (i.e., the efficiency is 60 to 80 per cent), the irrigation is considered highly efficient.

9.5 Drought

Under conditions of drought, management of soil for the conservation of water is of vital importance. This may take the form of eliminating weeds, which compete for the available moisture, of fallowing, or of irrigation. The main object of many tillage operations is to remove competing weed growth. Since the difficulties with surface structure of the soil and with compaction have become better recognized, and since the introduction of new herbicides, tillage has been lessened without commensurate loss of soil structure. Fallow practices provide a rest period between crops for a soil. They may also provide for some conservation of moisture.

Irrigation has been utilized since before recorded history as a means of augmenting precipitation for the production of plants. The techniques of irrigation vary, but all have a common objective: moistening the soil. Methods of irrigation can be classified as (1) subirrigation, (2) surface irrigation, and (3) sprinkler irrigation.

Subirrigation is the practice of moistening the soil through control of a water table. Moisture moves upward above a water table for an effective distance of about one foot in sands to over three feet in clays. The rate of movement, however, is much greater in the coarser, more permeable soils than in the tighter, fine-textured soils. In some cases of subirrigation the water table is held continuously at a desired distance below the surface to supply plant needs. In other instances, the water table is raised for a short period of time, and as soon as the soil is wet, the drainage facilities are opened, and the soil is permitted to drain. Subirrigation is restricted to open, permeable soils. The prime limitation on subirrigation is salt. When the precipitation is inadequate to keep salts leached away, subirrigation is not an effective irrigation method.

With surface irrigation, water is spread over the surface of the land through the use of furrows or by flooding methods.

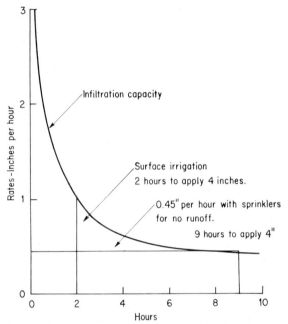

Fig. 9.8 Typical infiltration capacity rate for a soil, illustrating why considerably more time may be required to apply a given depth of water in sprinkler irrigation, avoiding runoff, than in surface irrigation.

Sprinkler irrigation utilizes water under pressure and distributes it through the air to the land surface. Sprinklers do not apply a uniform pattern of water distribution; a reasonable approximation of uniformity is attained by having overlap. Sprinkler irrigation is particularly advantageous with supplemental irrigation, is desirable where topography is such that surface methods are not efficient, and is well adapted to the irrigation of highly permeable soils or soils growing shallow-rooted crops requiring frequent irrigation. A disadvantage of sprinklers is that there is an additional cost resulting from the necessity for pumping to create pressure. Also, wind distorts patterns. The relationship between infiltration rates and time required to apply water by flooding and sprinkling is shown in Figure 9.8.

Salts are products of the decomposition of rock materials. Water, flowing through and over soil, picks up salts. In humid climates concentrations are normally extremely low because of dilution; in drier climates concentrations may become appreciable. As water progresses down a watercourse, concentrations increase. This is partly because the water passes through or over more and more soil, and partly because a part of the water is used in transport. Losses are through transpiration and evaporation, which processes take essentially pure water and leave the salt behind to concentrate in the remaining water.

Difficulty in agriculture from salts may arise because the irrigation water is saline or sodic. More often difficulties arise because of a high water table. Water moves upward through the capillary fringe above a water table to drier soil above. As this upward moving water is evaporated and transpired by plants, the salts remain and become concentrated. Also, in the process, the least-soluble salts—calcium carbonate, magnesium carbonate, and calcium sulfate, in that order—tend to precipitate. The resultant soil solution therefore becomes not only more saline but also more sodic. Remedy comes through judicious irrigation and adequate subsurface drainage.

Wind problems in soil management are primarily problems of drought, because it is a lack of moisture that makes soil subject to wind erosion. These problems are particularly important in the prairie region of the United States and in many of the arid and semiarid regions of the world. Besides constituting air pollution and visibility and deposition hazards, wind erosion removes fertile topsoil. Management practices to lessen wind damage may include vegetative or mechanical windbreaks or shelter belts. Where tillage must be employed, in utilizing land subject to wind erosion, it should leave a coarse rough surface (clods or furrows across the wind) or vegetative trash only partially buried. One of the most effective means of lessening wind erosion is to keep the land in a permanent vegetative cover, such as sod.

9.6 Flood

Flood is the great mover of soil. It erodes the uplands, deposits soil debris in the valleys, and builds deltas into the ocean. It is even a source of supply of sand for our beaches. Actually, man usually thinks of floods simply in terms of water, but without their load of soil debris they would be far simpler to regulate and would not constitute the problem they now do. Flood-regulation techniques are of three essential types: (1) storage, (2) disposal, and (3) zoning. All involve debris management to some extent.

Storage. Storage measures, largely upstream, provide for the decrease in peak flows through a lengthening of the period of flow. Some storage can be provided by improving the ability of the soil to absorb precipitation before runoff is initiated. The runoff of precipitation entering soil is significantly delayed or prevented. Therefore, management of watersheds so as to maintain high infiltration capacity is a part of flood regulation. The construction of reservoirs for detention storage or of multipurpose reservoirs with part of their capacity earmarked for flood detention may be highly important. Water in detention reservoirs is not stored, but is released, starting immediately, at such a rate as will ease the flood situation downstream and yet empty the reservoir fast enough so that storage will be available for the next possible flood. The effectiveness of detention storage decreases rapidly with increase in distance downstream. This is because watershed area increases rapidly, and there is thus only protection from a smaller and smaller percentage of the total area. This varies considerably, of course, with the shape of the watershed and with precipitation patterns.

Disposal.   Improving the disposal of flood water includes (1) confining waters flowing into a high-value area, such as a flood plain, in a relatively narrow channel and (2) removing inundating waters from an area as rapidly as possible. Methods used for both include levee construction to increase the size of the channel and prevent inundating the flood plain, channel straightening and improving, and construction of bypass channels. Flow in an improved channel is increased because of larger cross section, less friction loss, and steeper grade. Grade is increased because, as the channel is straightened, it is shortened. Increase in velocity, which accompanies channel confinement and channel smoothing, increases scour potential. Hence, channel improvement often requires paving or other type of stabilization as with jetties, fenced channel sides, etc.

The weakness of all disposal methods rests in the fact that soil movement is inherent in floods. What happens to soil brought down to the flood plain when deposition on that flood plain is denied? With improved channels and higher velocities, the debris is initially carried farther downstream. Then, either the channel will be lengthened by pushing out a delta, or the material will be deposited downstream. Either of these will lessen grade, lessen velocity, and push deposition upstream. Levees will have to be raised higher and higher above the flood plain. The stability of the system will thus deteriorate while costs accelerate. Bypass channels provide a means of improving disposal. These, opened only for large floods, can be tilled and successfully cropped most years. The area of a bypass should be of such capacity that the rate of debris deposit is not excessive.

Zoning.   Unfortunately, except to prevent encroachment on a normal stream channel, zoning is politically unpopular and rarely imposed. It should be employed to reserve parts of the flood plain for deposition.

Bypass channels are, in part, a zoning measure. Zoning is politically unpopular because it restricts use of land that is often most desirable for subdivision. To be possible at all, zoning must be initiated before serious encroachment takes place and must be rigidly and impartially enforced. Still, it is one of the best flood-regulation methods.

Debris Management.   As has been stated, debris management is an integral part of flood management, and both must be treated together. In areas of high debris load, however, some special treatments may be provided which either attempt to keep upland soil *in situ*, or to at least keep it above an intensely developed flood plain. Erosion-control techniques in the uplands are debris-management devices. Usually, the area on which such techniques can be practiced is so small relative to an entire watershed that such erosion control is largely ineffective in decreasing the flood magnitude or debris load of the whole.

Much of the debris produced on upland slopes moves intermittently to the downstream flood plain. There are usually flat upland areas, swales, canyons, valleys, where soil material may be deposited for a time, only to be scoured out in some later flood. Characteristically, canyon bottoms have an alluvial fill. This fill may be rather stable and support a large growth of phreatophytes, which give it further stability. When it is scoured out, the side slopes become undermined and unstable, so that erosion increases, filling the canyon bottom again even with moderate precipitation. At great cost, debris basins are sometimes utilized to remove soil materials from floods. The big expense comes in moving this material to where it can be permanently stored.

If the debris in upstream channels can be permanently stored, channel stabilization, with a series of really permanent dams, may have merit. Situations where the cost would not be prohibitive are extremely rare, and there would be continual need to increase such storage. Slope stabilization above the channels, through usual erosion-control devices and through paving, enhances the value of channel stabilization. Debris management may also become urgent in regard to the silting of reservoirs. The life of reservoirs, as gauged by a total loss of storage capacity, may be as little as 10 or 20 years. A life of 100 to 500 years may be more usual, however. The passing of silt-laden density currents through the reservoir, and out the discharge, is one possible way of alleviating this problem.

Quite the reverse of decreasing debris production is the practice, in some areas, of diverting streams to increase erosion. The reason, of course, is to increase the amount of good alluvial soil in the lowlands. Such soil building, over any appreciable area, would be quite slow and costly. It is indicative, however, of a significant change in thinking when a region becomes really short of good soil.

Generally speaking, all methods of debris management, except adapting lowlands to periodic flooding through zoning procedures, are expensive to begin with. In the future, there is the very real probability that costs will so accelerate as to become rather appalling.

9.7   Excess Subsurface Water

Subsurface waters are in excess when the water table is so high as to prevent the full utilization of the land for the purposes desired. In agriculture, most economic plants must have some aeration of the root zone, and the surface must be dry enough so that the soil will be suitable and have the necessary bearing power for essential tillage, planting, and harvest operations. In arid and semiarid climates, the water table must be deep enough so that salts can be kept conveniently at a reasonably low concentration and so that any salts which have accumulated in the past can be leached out. Proper bearing power for the foundations of structures likewise may require a lowering of the water table. In structural work, drainage may be simply a temporary procedure, such as unwatering a foundation site long enough to prepare a foundation. This may be done by pumping from a ring of well points driven or jetted into the soil.

The word *drainage* may refer to removal of excess downstream surface waters or to controlling the subsurface water table. It is used here to refer to the latter. The need for drainage is common, especially with basin and some valley lands, in many parts of the world. It is common with irrigated agriculture, especially where the water supply is from surface sources. Where ground water is utilized, either as part or as the whole supply, drainage problems do not often arise. Indeed, in areas such as the Salt River Valley of Arizona and in the Turloch-Modesto Districts of California, rather continuous pumping from wells was initiated as a drainage measure, but has been accelerated as the cheapest way to supplement the inadequate water supply. It is usually only under such circumstances that pump drainage is feasible. Otherwise, power and other pumping costs are too great. However, in ground-water areas where artesian conditions exist, it may be the only satisfactory method. The usual system of drainage is a gridiron or herringbone network of ditches or buried drain tile.

Land in arid and semiarid regions which has been drained is still usually adversely affected by saline or sodic condition. Although installation of a drainage system makes leaching possible, the soil must still be reclaimed. This is done by ponding water on the surface, often for a period of months. This water percolates downward, pushing the saline ground water down ahead of it.

9.8 Conclusions

Prime requirements in the physical management of soil are the maintenance of a soil surface favorable to the intended use and the proper management of water. Management of water includes artificial application when in deficiency and removal of excess. Management of water must also include recognition of, and some adaptation to, its transportation of soil from the uplands to the lowlands.

10

Photosynthesis

F. W. WENT

DIRECTOR, MISSOURI BOTANICAL GARDEN
ST. LOUIS, MISSOURI

10.1 Introduction

In magnitude, in its significance for the survival of life on earth, and in a biochemical sense, photosynthesis is a unique process. Each year approximately 10^{11} tons of carbon is fixed by plants using carbon dioxide from air or from sea water. This amount is approximately a thousand times more than the largest industrial production of a single substance, namely, steel. But, since in steel production we need coal, which was laid down in earlier geological periods as excess photosynthates, steel production also shows the importance of photosynthesis. Appreciable amounts of all photosynthesis, past and present, are being used in our industrial development.

At present there are only a few primary energy sources economically available to man. With the exception of nuclear energy, all energy has as its ultimate source the sun. Photosynthesis provides by far the greatest fraction of presently usable energy from the sun, the other major fractions being wind and water power.

Only a very small fraction of the wind power can be used as an energy source, and only a very small fraction of the sun's energy can be recaptured as water power. In addition, energy from both the latter sources can be stored to only a very limited degree, whereas the energy which results from photosynthesis can be stored over very long periods, as in fossil fuels. Photosynthesis is also remarkable in that it transforms light energy into chemical energy, which again among our natural resources is a unique achievement.

It is also interesting to point out that, whereas most biochemical processes occurring in nature have evolved in such a manner that a large number of analogous processes accomplish the same results, photosynthesis has not evolved any further in the course of organic evolution and is

221

almost exactly alike in all organisms. Chlorophyll is always present, and with only very slight modifications in different organisms. This contrasts strongly with processes such as respiration in which we know a number of fundamentally different pathways in which organic matter can be oxidized to release stored energy.

The over-all formula for photosynthesis is

$$6CO_2 + 6H_2O \rightarrow C_6H_{12}O_6 + 6O_2$$

DeSaussure in 1806 was the first to propose this formulation. He found that upon respiration of carbohydrates not only CO_2 was liberated, but that for each unit of CO_2 released there was an additional decrease in weight of the plant material, amounting to one unit of water. It was obvious that in photosynthesis one water molecule had to be incorporated for each CO_2 molecule.

Advances in chemistry or physics have almost immediately resulted in an increase in our knowledge concerning the processes going on in living organisms. It was only 5 years after the discovery of oxygen by Priestley, who also showed that plants were able to release oxygen, that Ingenhousz showed that the release of oxygen by plants occurred only in light and that heat energy was unable to produce photosynthesis.

The primary products of photosynthesis in plants are carbohydrates which are utilized by plants as energy sources for their own growth and development. Under a number of conditions, however, they will store these carbohydrates in the form of starch or sugar for future use. In this way more than half the photosynthates formed by the plant are available to them at a later date. In general, only a small fraction of such stored energy is collected for human use, and the greater portion of the photosynthates formed is eaten by animals or is metabolized by microorganisms. When an animal eats plants, only a small fraction, usually less than 10 per cent, of the energy present in the food is conserved in its own body, the rest disappearing through respiration or being used for growth and locomotion. Thus, not more than 10 per cent of the photosynthates formed in a pasture can be harvested as beef. In the ocean, this figure is very much lower, because of the large number of times that plankton pass through different organisms before we can collect any of the energy they capture in the form of fish. It has been calculated that at most one-thousandth of the energy captured by the plankton and laid down as photosynthates in their cells could possibly be obtained as human food in the form of fish.

Practically all the energy which goes into the production of leaves is also lost to human use when those leaves drop in autumn and are then decomposed by fungi and bacteria. It is obvious that, if necessary, a much larger percentage of the photosynthates now being produced by the wild vegetation can in the future be available for human needs if we increase the acreage under cultivation, because it is the cultivated plants which have efficient storage mechanisms of their photosynthates either in the form of seeds or of storage tissue.

Practically the only natural product in which the sun's energy is stored for considerable periods of time is wood, which as long as it is attached to a living tree is rather well protected against the attack of microorganisms and can be harvested as lumber or wood pulp.

10.2 Biochemistry of Photosynthesis

During the last half century a vast amount of study has been carried out on the process of photosynthesis from physiological, biochemical, and biophysical approaches, and although we are unable as yet to reproduce the process *in vitro*, the chemical and physical pathways of photosynthesis are now quite well understood. Originally it was supposed in the Baeyer hypothesis that CO_2 as such was reduced to formaldehyde (CH_2O) which was then polymerized to a carbohydrate. (The term *reduction* refers to the removal of oxygen. In a CH_2O molecule a carbon atom has one less oxygen atom associated with it than in CO_2.) In spite of a great deal of study, it has not been possible to substantiate the Baeyer hypothesis, and it is now quite clear that CO_2 is not reduced in such a simple step. Not only has it been impossible to show the presence of formaldehyde in photosynthesizing plants, but the photosynthesis of sulfur bacteria indicates a completely different pathway.

It has been shown that a number of photosynthetic organisms, particularly the green bacteria and the purple sulfur bacteria, reduce CO_2 only in light and in the presence of hydrogen sulfide. Since under these conditions sulfur is liberated, Van Niel suggested that the hydrogen from the hydrogen sulfide is used to reduce the CO_2. In this way, the photosynthesis of green bacteria falls in line with many other biochemical syntheses in living organisms which depend on hydrogen transfer, and the hydrogen sulfide acts in these green or purple bacteria as a hydrogen donor. Photosynthesis of higher plants can be considered analogous to photosynthesis of green bacteria if water is considered the hydrogen donor in the process of photosynthesis. This leads to the following equations:

$$CO_2 + 2H_2S \xrightarrow{\text{light}} (CH_2O) + H_2O + 2S \qquad (10.1)$$

$$CO_2 + 2H_2O \xrightarrow{\text{light}} (CH_2O) + H_2O + O_2 \qquad (10.2)$$

$$CO_2 + 2H_2A \xrightarrow{\text{light}} (CH_2O) + H_2O + 2A \qquad (10.3)$$

The parentheses in the equations indicate that a number of units of CH_2O comprise the final product, i.e., $(CH_2O)_6$ or $C_6H_{12}O_6$. Equation (10.1) stands for photosynthesis of green and purple sulfur bacteria.

Equation (10.2) represents photosynthesis of higher plants, and Equation (10.3) is generally applicable. The equations show that the equality of oxygen production with CO_2 utilization is not due to a liberation of oxygen from the CO_2, but that the oxygen liberated in photosynthesis is derived from the water. This has been actually proved by work in which the isotopic content of the oxygen in CO_2 and the oxygen in the water was different. The isotopic constitution of the released oxygen agreed with that of the water and not with that of the CO_2.

A second conclusion is that in photosynthesis it might be possible to substitute hydrogen itself for the hydrogen donors, and in green bacteria it is actually possible to obtain photosynthesis in the presence of hydrogen gas.

As a third consideration one could expect that a number of organic compounds could be used as hydrogen donors. Actually it was found that propionic and other acids can be decomposed in light by green bacteria. Simultaneously they take up CO_2 which becomes incorporated into the cell material, and thus we find photosynthesis in which CO_2 is reduced with the help of the hydrogen from, for example, propionic acid.

That we are actually dealing with oxygen liberation from water in the case of photosynthesis was also shown clearly by Hill, who in 1938 showed for the first time that preparations of isolated chloroplasts will liberate oxygen provided that a hydrogen acceptor (such as a ferri compound) is present. Subsequently, Warburg has shown that quinone can act in the same way. In the so-called Hill reaction, CO_2 does not necessarily have to accept the hydrogen liberated in photosynthesis, as several other hydrogen acceptors are effective. All available evidence at the moment points in the direction that the first step in photosynthesis is the transfer of hydrogen from water to a substrate which ultimately will be CO_2.

Willstatter, in his classic investigations on photosynthesis, had assumed that the CO_2 formed a compound with chlorophyll which then was reduced under the influence of the light absorbed by the chlorophyll. Recent work with carbon isotopes has shown that this picture is not correct.

The work of Calvin showed that CO_2, in which the carbon was labeled as C^{14}, was not found in any combination with chlorophyll. In darkness it formed labeled compounds in which the CO_2 was found as a carboxyl group in carboxylic acids. Within the first few seconds of illumination, this carbon became incorporated in phosphoglyceraldehyde, and within a few more seconds labeled sucrose was also present. This suggested that the CO_2 became originally incorporated in a C_3 carboxylic acid which was reduced with the hydrogen liberated from water. More recent work, however, has shown that this is not correct and that the CO_2 is first incorporated in ribulose diphosphate. In this way a transitory C_6 diphosphate is formed which then breaks down into two C_3 fragments which are further reduced to triose sugars. Further details about the biochemistry of CO_2 reduction by light can be found in the most recent papers of Calvin and collaborators.

10.3   Energy Relations

We now come to a consideration of the energy relations in photosynthesis. Near the end of the last century Engelmann proved that there was a quantitative relationship between the wavelengths which are absorbed by the leaf pigments and the effectiveness of the light rays to reduce CO_2. By a unique method, using bacteria which are mobile only in the presence of oxygen, he showed that only light which strikes the chloroplasts (green pigmented granules inside the cell) is able to liberate oxygen and that the absorption spectrum of the green cell is almost identical with the action spectrum of photosynthesis. In more recent work it was shown that over the whole spectral range in which chlorophyll absorbs light (except in the far red) the same amount of light energy is transformed into chemical energy, provided that the energy is expressed in quanta. Since Planck had shown that light energy comes in quanta, of which the energy is dependent upon the wavelength, it was recognized that photochemical reactions would require more energy in the blue than in the red part of the spectrum when this energy is expressed in calories. This was shown to be the case by Warburg in 1922 and was confirmed by Emerson and Lewis and many other investigators.

For the reduction of one molecule of CO_2, at least three times as much energy is required as is present in one quantum. In his famous paper in 1922, Warburg actually showed that under his special experimental conditions 3 to 4 light quanta were required for CO_2 reduction. This number has, during the last two decenniums, become the subject of a lively controversy, and the majority of investigators have found a minimal number of 7 to 10 quanta required for reduction of a molecule of CO_2. For theoretical reasons it is unlikely that these 7 to 10 quanta can all be present at the same time to reduce one CO_2 molecule. A simple experiment by R. Hill in England has shown how this can be explained. He carefully broke up leaf cells and by centrifuging separated the chloroplasts from the rest of the cell contents. When a suspension of these isolated chloroplasts was illuminated in the presence of ferric ions, oxygen was evolved by hydrolysis of water, the released H atoms being used to reduce the ferric ions. It was also found that only one quantum was needed for each H atom released. The oxygen released came from the water, as expected from Equation (10.2).

Therefore we now know that the light primarily reduces water and that the power thus released is available for CO_2 reduction, which consequently must go in a number of steps. To follow these steps, Calvin and coworkers perfected a method by which radioactive C^{14} in the form of C^*O_2 was fed to suspensions of algae for various durations, and then the cell products were analyzed by paper chromatography for radioactivity. Within a few seconds a measurable amount of radioactivity was found in several compounds in the cell, primarily in triosephosphates and secondarily in sucrose, a few dicarboxylic acids, and amino acids. The sucrose was clearly derived from triosephosphate, and the amino acids were formed by transanimation from organic acids. The original assumption that the triosephosphate was formed by addition of a CO_2 molecule to a 2-carbon compound was not verified, but a complex cycle in which the C^*O_2 was added to a 5-carbon sugar (ribulose diphosphate), including 4-, 5-, 6-, and 7-carbon phosphorylated sugars, was established. Details of this cycle are still being worked out and at present need not concern us. Suffice it to say that, through successive regeneration of ribulose diphosphate from fructose-6-phosphate by way of sedoheptulose phosphate, more of the CO_2 acceptor is being made, so that ultimately 12 molecules of CO_2 will appear in the form of a sucrose molecule, after having absorbed the energy present in 36 molecules of adenosine triphosphate and the reducing power of 24 molecules of reduced desoxyribose nucleotide. Both the reducing power and the high-energy phosphate are derived from the photolysis of water, as Arnon has recently demonstrated.

Thus a complicated but consistent picture emerges in which photosynthesis involves initially the light-driven decomposition of water and secondly the utilization of CO_2 molecules in the formation of sugar molecules.

10.4   Yield of Photosynthesis Process

We now should consider the physiological aspects of photosynthesis, that is, the conditions surrounding the photosynthetic CO_2 reduction. In a practical way we are interested in the over-all dry-matter production as indicated in the following:

Products: $CO_2 + H_2O \rightarrow$ carbohydrates $\rightarrow$ storage $\rightarrow$ plant-body products
                $+$ light

	A	B	C	D
Processes:	Photosynthesis	Translocation	Transformation	Respiration

The above diagram shows that photosynthesis consists of a succession of processes, first of which involves the photochemical reduction of CO_2. Once the carbohydrates are formed, they are moved out of the leaf cells toward the storage organs, or toward the places where new plant material is being produced, namely, the growing regions. This is where the sugars are transformed into cell-wall materials, proteins, and all other compounds making up the plant cell. Part of the photosynthates are used for respiration and go back to CO_2 and water. This, however, is usually only a small fraction of the total photosynthesis, being normally less than 20 per cent in young plants. Therefore, some 80 per cent of all photosynthates in young plants and in annuals can be harvested in the form of dry matter.

In most experimental work it has been found that by increasing the CO_2 concentration in the air above the normal amount (300 ppm) an increased rate of photosynthesis occurred. It is very likely that this was due to the particular experimental conditions, which decreased the rate of air flow past the photosynthesizing leaves. In general, plants had to be enclosed in tight containers or fully closed greenhouses to increase the CO_2 concentration of the air. Under such conditions there is not enough natural ventilation around the leaves to supply an adequate amount of CO_2 to them. In those experiments in which an extra air turbulence was created in the chambers in which the CO_2 concentration was increased, no indication of limitation of photosynthesis by the CO_2 concentration was observed.

The supply of CO_2 to the leaf cells is also dependent upon the diffusion resistance between air and leaf. This is determined by the degree of opening or closing of the stomata, which are tiny pores in the epidermis of the leaf, as shown in Figure 10.1. The opening width of these stomata can be controlled by the plant in response to light and moisture conditions. In strong light and with a favorable water balance in the leaf, they are open and allow a maximum rate of CO_2 exchange. But in darkness, or when the leaf is near wilting, the stomata are closed, reducing CO_2 intake and, consequently, photosynthesis.

The function of this closure of the stomata is probably not to restrict CO_2 intake, but to reduce water loss. For optimal photosynthesis, large amounts of light must be absorbed; so the leaf surface must be extensive. But a large leaf surface also produces large losses of water by evaporation. When a sufficient water supply is available, stomata can remain open and photosynthesis can proceed at a maximal rate. So, sufficient water, from rain or irrigation, is a prerequisite for maximal dry-matter production.

The close relationship which exists between water loss and dry-matter production is expressed by the term *efficiency of transpiration*, which means the number of grams of dry weight produced per kilogram of water transpired by a plant. For sorghum, a grain which does well in dry regions, this efficiency is 3 to 5, for corn it is 2 to 4, for tomatoes it is only 1.5. In general, crops of moist climates have a low efficiency of transpiration. But desert plants also have low efficiencies (0.5 to 1), which probably means that they cannot help but lose much water under the arid conditions in which they live.

In this connection the fundamental considerations of Blackman (1905) should be mentioned. He concluded that biological processes are chain

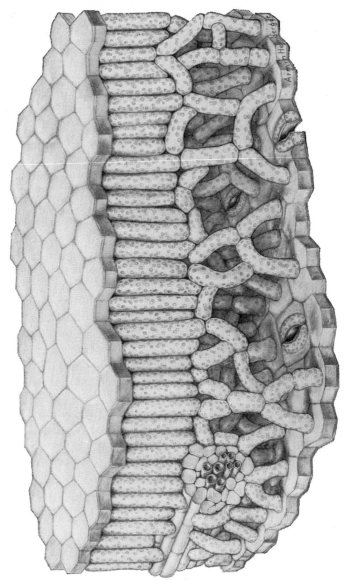

Fig. 10.1   Structure of leaf. (*Figure 6.4 from Sinnott and Wilson, Botany, McGraw-Hill Book Company, Inc.,* 1955).

reactions and that therefore the over-all rate was determined by the rate of the slowest process in the chain. He showed that at low CO_2 concentrations (below those present in the air) lack of CO_2 was limiting the rate of photosynthesis. At higher CO_2 concentrations, light was usually limiting, except at low temperatures. On this basis he concluded that, in photosynthesis after an initial photochemical process, a chemical process with a high-temperature coefficient followed. This accounts for the fact that at low-temperatures light intensity does not limit photosynthesis.

In most plants individual leaves are saturated at a light intensity of 1000 ft-c, which is approximately one-tenth of the maximal amount of light which reaches the surface of the earth at noon on a sunny day. This suggests that plants in general could be grown in partial shade since light above 1000 ft-c would not be usable. This, however, is not actually the situation. Except for shady plants, which usually form only one single layer of leaves, most plants have their leaves in tiers so that the higher leaves shade the lower. In this way we find that the average light intensity to which the leaves of a plant are subjected is usually 1000 ft-c or less. The plant is able to adjust the number of leaves it has to the average light intensity it receives, and thus a plant in full sun has a larger number of leaves than a plant in shade. Besides clouds often cut down the light intensity, and the 10,000-ft-c maximal intensity at noon lasts for only a few hours so that the early morning and late afternoon light is only a fraction of the maximum light intensity. Thus we can conclude that on the average the vegetation is adjusted to the average normal light intensity and that the amount of light reaching a piece of ground is normally the limiting factor in the amount of dry weight which is produced.

Work, particularly of van den Honert and of Emerson, has shown that there is a direct proportionality between the CO_2 concentration surrounding algal cells and the amount of photosynthesis which occurs. This proportionality holds up to a concentration of a few hundred parts per million of CO_2 in the air. Because of the direct proportionality, we can conclude that the CO_2 concentration at the chloroplast level during photosynthesis must be zero in these algae. We can assume also that this condition holds in the leaves of higher plants even though the experiments of Gabrielsen do not support this view.

Since the rate of CO_2 uptake during photosynthesis will be a function of the gradient which exists between leaf and surrounding air, and since we can also assume that the CO_2 concentration at the chloroplast level is zero, the CO_2 supply of the chloroplasts will be directly proportional to the CO_2 concentration in the air and the air-leaf gradient. This gradient can be changed by the rate of air movement past the leaves, and it has been found that in stagnant air of unventilated greenhouses this gradient becomes limiting. However, when a sufficient air circulation exists in the greenhouse, such as created by proper air conditioning, no further increase in photosynthesis is possible either by increased CO_2 concentration in the air or by increased air movement past the leaves. Apparently in nature there is usually a sufficient amount of air movement to give an optimal supply of CO_2 to the leaves.

The CO_2 supply in greenhouses is often severely restricted, especially during the winter when they are closed to prevent the loss of heat. Under those conditions there should be another supply of CO_2 in addition to the one from the air. This is usually provided in the form of organic materials which gradually decompose into water and CO_2. Useful for such purposes are organic manure, straw, or corn cobs, which are spread over the surface of the soil and which gradually decompose when kept moist. It can be calculated that the amounts of organic material added to the soil in the greenhouse can supply almost all the CO_2 which is required for the greenhouse crop so that only very little additional CO_2 has to enter with outside air.

Outside in the field there is practically an equilibrium in the amount of CO_2 which is absorbed by plants for photosynthesis and the amount of CO_2 which is liberated again from decomposing plant parts. In this respect the air and the carbonates present in the ocean act as a buffer for this CO_2 equilibrium. This means that, except for the effects of turbulence on the average most of the CO_2 in photosynthesis comes up from the soil. Therefore for enclosed vegetation we usually find a higher CO_2 content close to the soil than around the foliage.

With the use of fossil fuels, such as coal and oil, a vast amount of CO_2 is brought into the air from stored carbon. Calculations show that the CO_2 content of the air over the world has increased from about 290 to 330 ppm during the last hundred years. To what extent this process will continue is difficult to calculate because the buffering action of the oceans is not accurately known. The amount of CO_2 which is taken up by plants during the day is sufficient to cause a general decrease in CO_2 content of the air layer several hundred feet above the ground. During the night the CO_2 content increases again.

It can be shown that the amount of photosynthesis is influenced by the internal condition of the leaf, that is, by the amount of CO_2 acceptors. When plants have previously been kept for a few days in darkness, their subsequent photosynthesis is considerably reduced. However, it is possible to increase their light utilization by spraying them with sugar solution previous to light exposure. This shows that photosynthesis depends on the sugar content of the leaf, which presumably controls the amount of CO_2 acceptor.

Whenever an accumulation of photosynthates occurs in leaves, the rate of photosynthesis is reduced. This has recently been verified by determining the rate of photosynthesis of plants which had different levels of photosynthate accumulation. At very low levels, photosynthesis was reduced because of lack of a CO_2 acceptor, and at a high concentration of photosynthates, photosynthesis was also reduced because of inhibition of the photosynthetic reaction by high concentrations of photosynthetic products. Thus any treatment of the plant which will increase the concentration of photosynthates in the leaves will decrease their potential photosynthesis. These photosynthates can be removed from leaves in two ways: (1) by a translocation to storage organs and (2) by their transformation into other plant products such as cellulose, fats, proteins, etc. This latter transformation occurs during growth, and thus we find that the faster the growth of a plant, the higher its rate of photosynthesis. The reactions following photosynthesis have a strong effect on photosynthesis itself.

10.5 Conclusion

It has been found both in algae and in higher plants that, under optimal conditions and over short periods of time and at relatively low light intensities, up to 30 per cent of the light absorbed by algae can be transformed into the chemical energy of photosynthates. However, not more than 2 per cent of the light energy which falls on a field can be transformed into the chemical energy of the crop harvested from the field. This yield can be increased in the laboratory by growing the plants under optimal conditions so that the largest amount of photosynthates is being used in the production of new plant material. Thus we come to the conclusion that at present the world's total amount of dry-matter production through photosynthesis is still far short of the potential. Under efficient conditions we could expect that approximately 10 per cent of the light energy could be captured as chemical energy through the activities of plants. This presupposes ideal growing conditions, which at present do not exist but which might be created if the need for capturing the sun's energy becomes imperative.

In the case of algae, these ideal conditions have actually been obtained through the use of large plastic vessels in which the algal suspension is kept in contact with a 5 per cent mixture of CO_2 in air. Although a 10 per cent conversion of energy is potentially possible, it is not a practical way at present to capture the sun's energy. The 2 per cent efficiency of field crops like sugar beets and sugar cane is still far above the actual average light conversion for ordinary fields, where it is well below 1 per cent. By using our present agricultural know-how we can increase plant production several hundred per cent before the need for further fundamental improvements in the growing of crop plants becomes essential.

Much work has been done to determine how wild plants photosynthesize. Under conditions of water stress which are so common in arid regions, it was found that photosynthesis occurs largely in the early morning, whereas during the middle of the day there is practically a standstill in CO_2 reduction. The dry-matter production per acre under conditions of water stress is, therefore, severely reduced. It has also been recently found that, in areas with normally an adequate supply, periods of drought occur during which dry-matter production is restricted because of lack of water. So, practically anywhere in the world, irrigation at one time or another will increase photosynthesis.

Another generalization is that not only water but also lack of available nutrients in the soil restrict plant production. Under our present conditions it is very seldom that the photosynthetic process is restricting the utilization of the sun's energy. Rather, it is all the secondary processes which are required for optimal plant growth which prevent the full potential utilization of the sun's energy by plants.

11

Ecology, Wildlife, and Wilderness

WALTER P. TAYLOR

SENIOR BIOLOGIST
FISH AND WILDLIFE SERVICE
U.S. DEPARTMENT OF THE INTERIOR (RETIRED)
VISITING LECTURER, CLAREMONT GRADUATE SCHOOL

ECOLOGY

11.1 Introduction

The term *ecology*, introduced by Haeckel in 1869, was derived from the Greek words *oikos*, meaning home, and *logos*, meaning word or thought. From this beginning, ecology has come to mean the relation of living organisms to their environment. In 1935, we defined the term broadly as all the relations of all the organisms to all their environment. This is a bit comprehensive, but the definite idea is there—ecology is the science that gives attention to *environmental* relationships of plants and animals, including man. Therefore since natural resources (soil, water, atmosphere, plants, animals, minerals, etc.) are part of the environment, and since, in the business of living, man has to depend upon these natural resources, it is highly appropriate that in this volume attention should be given to ecology.

If one is trying to get the whole picture, the ecological approach is particularly appropriate. Ecology puts the emphasis on quality of relations discovered[1] rather than on quantity or even quality of specimens collected or on the mass of details compiled. Ecology warns the student that partial remedies or compartmentalized dealings with the environment may be wasteful and sometimes disastrous.

It is unfortunate that man has not fully employed the ecological approach in his dealings with nature. In fact, "civilized man has taken

[1] Charles C. Adams, *Guide to the Study of Animal Ecology*, The Macmillan Company, New York, 1913.

233

Nature on a number of sprees, and the poor lady is a bit bedraggled."[1] Notice the obvious soil exhaustion as a result of wasteful cropping processes (100 million acres of formerly good crop land now completely unproductive, another 100 million acres seriously damaged, and nearly all our farm land appreciably impaired[2]); decimation or even extermination of certain species of wildlife and of fishes; overgrazing, not only of the vast open ranges of the West but also of pasture lands in the East and South; wasteful logging of forests; destructive burning of brushland; plowing up of the native sod which should have been left exclusively for pasture; draining of marshlands for a prospective agriculture that might never be realized; reclamation of arid lands which often cannot pay the costs of development; and importation of pests through careless introduction of foreign plants or animals.

Yes, all these enterprises, entered into for the most part with the best of intentions, often have yielded poverty rather than prosperity, largely because, among other things, the ecological relations of the plants and animals and environments concerned were not understood or, if understood, were ignored.

Man has got himself in such a mental state that he sometimes thinks he is independent of nature. It is true that man can do many things, but he should not forget that in the prime essentials he is just as dependent on his environment as the humblest of his animal or plant associates. He must have food, water, air, and shelter as well as an appropriate range of other environmental conditions. A comparatively slight alteration of his environment could quickly disqualify him for living.

Everybody is acquainted with people who keep their religion in a watertight compartment, which they open on Sunday, but keep tightly closed the rest of the week. Unfortunately, all too often, scientists and engineers are like that, working blithely in their own little watertight compartments, not only on weekdays but on Sunday as well, oblivious of their fellows in their watertight compartments. And so, inevitably, serious conflicts develop. One group of engineers, for example, may be draining a marsh to increase the available farm land. At the same time, and not too far away, another group may be flooding a dry area to produce a more stable water supply or to encourage wildlife or fisheries. Both will be using stockholders' money, if employed by corporations, or taxpayers' coin, if they work for the government.

Ecology is the uncompromising enemy of the watertight compartment. Here is one discipline that stakes its life on the proposition that science is

[1] Walter P. Taylor, "What Is Ecology and What Good Is It?" *Ecology*, vol. 17, pp. 333–346, July, 1936.

[2] Ira N. Gabrielson, "Relation of Conservation to Engineering Projects," reprinted from *The Tech. Rev.*, vol. 50, no. 4, February, 1948.

a continuum. Ecology recognizes no hard and fast lines between the natural sciences, nor between the natural and social sciences.

11.2 Fields with Which Ecology Is Concerned

A better appreciation can be gained of the place and significance of ecology to human affairs if attention is given to some of the specialized fields in which it is important.

All who lived in the Dust Bowl during the 1930s will realize the importance of man's proper care of the soils, on which he must largely depend for his support. Land planning and land classification are among the most important of ecological enterprises.

In these days of industrial development, it is becoming more than ever apparent that not only water, but atmosphere as well, must be carefully protected from contamination and pollution. Investigations of these great resources are of the utmost ecological significance.

For a long time it has been recognized that forest and wildlife conservation, grassland management, biological control of insects and other actual or potential pests, fisheries and marine life, and the relation of environment to physical well-being are appropriate areas for ecological study. The pressure of growing population tends to accentuate these various interests.

Since life processes are in large part environmental, it is obvious that all biological sciences are in an important way ecological. Even industrial and engineering enterprises, so far as they deal with environment, are closely tied in with ecological inquiry. The Panama Canal could not be completed until the environment was altered to the extent necessary to permit engineers and workers to live and to get on with the job.

11.3 Some Useful Ecological Terms and Concepts

A further indication of the scope and meaning of the science may be gained by considering some ecological terms and concepts. Most of the sciences have developed a special language or vocabulary which, at its best, saves much breath in lengthy definition. Ecology is no exception. For additional details, reference should be made to Allee and others,[1] Clarke,[2] Odum,[3] and Woodbury.[4] Here we have sufficient space for but a brief reference to a few of the basic terms.

[1] W. C. Allee, Alfred E. Emerson, Orlando Park, Thomas Park, and Karl P. Schmidt, *Principles of Animal Ecology,* W. B. Saunders Company, Philadelphia, 1949.
[2] George L. Clarke, *Elements of Ecology,* John Wiley & Sons, Inc., New York, 1954.
[3] Eugene P. Odum, *Fundamentals of Ecology,* W. B. Saunders Company, Philadelphia, 1954 reprint.
[4] Angus M. Woodbury, *Principles of General Ecology,* McGraw-Hill Book Company, Inc., Blakiston Division, New York, 1954.

Autecology (from *auto* meaning self, same, or by or for oneself or the same individual), for example, refers to the relations to environment of an individual or of a single species. *Synecology* (from *syn* meaning with, along with, together) designates these relationships on the part of a group of species or a community as contrasted with an individual.

According to modern ecologists, the activities of living organisms, both plant and animal, are joined with the nonliving physical and chemical forces around them (soils, atmosphere, waters, etc.) in *ecosystems*. Thus plants, animals, and their habitat are considered as one interacting unit, "the materials and energies of one passing in and out of the others."[1]

It is obvious that, in every normal community of living organisms, plants and animals are as interdependent and inseparable as are flesh and blood in the human body. These interrelated plant-animal groups are known as *biotic communities*. The so-called plant community, without its animal life, is hardly a going concern. Neither is the animal community without the plants in which and on which its constituent animals live. But the biotic community, being composed of both plants and animals, is relatively complete and by some authors even has been regarded as a quasi organism. It will be noted that a biotic community is considered to be part of an ecosystem which includes the physical environment as well.

The world's major plant-animal or biotic communities possessing a characteristic structure and physiognomy (as tundra, forest, grassland, chaparral, desert, etc.) are known to the ecologist as *biomes*.

One of the most useful concepts in ecology is that of *ecological succession*, which refers to the orderly replacement as a result of *reactions* on environment of the biotic communities in a particular place. Let us take an example. Simple successions may start on areas of bare rock or in the waters of a pond or lake. As soil is naturally built up on the rock by the plants and animals concerned, and as the conditions of the substratum are altered to make possible other forms of plants and animals, the crustose lichens which form the original plant cover are replaced successively by foliose lichens, mosses, etc., these by herbs, these in turn by shrubs, and the shrubs at last by trees (if the succession is taking place in a potential forest area). Similarly in a water area, the simplest aquatic forms are replaced by more complicated organisms, then as the soil accumulates, by sedges and smartweeds, brush, and finally trees (again, if in a potential forest area). The ultimate successional stage is the climatic climax, a community of plants and animals which, theoretically at least, remains unchanged unless or until the climate itself changes.

Each species of plant and animal is an indicator of the conditions— climatic, soil, biotic, food, shelter, etc.—which it must have to live. Thus, if we know the limits of tolerance of a given animal or plant as we see it

[1] *Ibid.*

Fig. 11.1 Natural regions or biomes of North America. (*From A. W. Haupt, An
Introduction to Botany, McGraw-Hill Book Company, Inc., 1956.*)

Legend:

Tundra and snow fields

Northern evergreen forest

Eastern deciduous forest

Southeastern evergreen forest

Tropical evergreen forest

Prairie

Plains grassland

Western evergreen forest

Southwestern desert

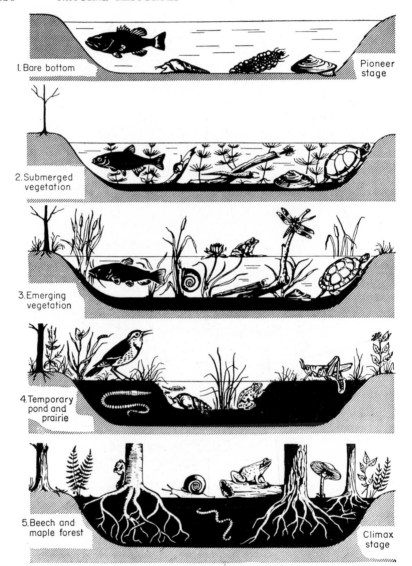

Fig. 11.2 Ecological succession resulting in a beech-maple forest. The stages shown here are based upon events which are thought to occur in the ponds at the south end of Lake Michigan. Other ponds in the Middle West will go through much the same succession. The succession in ponds with a very different climate will be different in detail; and, of course, the climax will be different. Humus laid down since the beginning is shown in solid black. (*From R. and M. Buchsbaum, Basic Ecology, by permission of the Boxwood Press.*)

in nature, we can tell a great deal about its environment without any further instrumental measurements. Each such species is an *ecological indicator*. The use of plant indicators has been found to be particularly useful in range management. A trained observer can assess the condition of a range by noting the occurrence or lack of occurrence of certain plant indicators.

Fig. 11.3 Aspen is replaced by conifers in a process of ecological succession. (*Photograph by Richard Kenyon.*)

In the same situation and without the use of plant indicators, an untrained observer might reach an erroneous opinion concerning the health of the range under study.

Each ecosystem is made up of numerous organisms and species and their physical environment. All animals, at one stage or another, are virtually *predators*, i.e., feeders on other animals or on plants. All in turn may at some time become predatees, i.e., be eaten by others. The interrelationships, of animals to animals, as well as of animals to plants, of plants to animals, and of plants to plants, are complicated and important. For on these interrelationships, and their proper functioning, depend the stabilization and survival of communities and of individual species.

Elton[1] uses the *pyramid of numbers* to illustrate some interesting aspects of community organization. Basic to the pyramid are some key species, such as the sardine off the California coast, which is eaten by some of the relatively small marine fishes, which in turn are consumed by larger fishes, which in their own turn are captured and utilized by man, who often stands at the summit of the pyramid.

Ecology is directly concerned with extreme or intermittent environmental conditions and with cycles of abundance in plants or animals, however caused. Indeed the study of animal and plant populations, including that of man, is one of the most significant in the field.

It should become increasingly clear that studies of these vital relations of organism and environment are among the most important in which man can engage.

11.4   The Engineer Ecologist

The supervising engineer of a drainage basin, forest operation, irrigation system, or indeed any similar enterprise involving the land and the water, the vegetation, and the animal life might well be something of an ecologist. Certainly in order to do a good job he must keep in mind the relation of the vegetation, whether grasses, herbs, brush, or trees, to the soil and the water; he must mind the effects of grazing, by domestic livestock, wild game, or rodents, on the vegetation and the soil; he must take into account the significance and effects of soil cultivation and cropping; and last but not least, he must not forget the relation of accelerated erosion on a watershed to the silting up of the lower portions of its streams and rivers and the possible impairment of the water-holding capacity of any downstream dam or catchment basin which may be in existence or be contemplated.

All these problems involve relations with many people. In reality, man deals here with human engineering outdoors. In a recent paper, Woodson[2] refers to the human factor in another connection. He writes: "Many human-engineering organizations currently are made up of phychologists, physiologists, anthropometrists, mathematicians, engineers, and physicists, who work together in the solution of man-machine design problems." Certainly in the great outdoors, teams of workers must increasingly pool their abilities in the solution of complicated problems. Seemingly, the science of ecology should be more and more employed by the engineer,

[1] Charles Elton, *Animal Ecology*, Sidgwick & Jackson, Ltd., London, 1935.

[2] Wesley E. Woodson, *Human Engineering Guide for Equipment Engineers*, University of California Press, Berkeley, Calif., 1954.

who, as Ralph Waldo Emerson might have put it, represents *man*, making useful to his kind the raw materials and the properties of matter and energy in the form of structures and machines.

11.5 Management of Natural Resources

In a very real sense the problems of management of natural resources are more urgent even than those associated with the atomic or hydrogen bombs. For mankind is pretty well alerted to the potential advantages and dangers from these. On the other hand, our manifold productive soils, forests, grasslands, mines, etc., are largely taken for granted. The wastage and continuing losses of these go largely unrecognized and unappreciated. But natural resources are in no way theoretical, academic, or imaginary. They are as close to us, as vital to our existence, as eating and breathing.

It is interesting to observe that a few chemists and engineers seemingly show little concern about the possible exhaustion of the fossil fuels (coal, petroleum, natural gas, oil shale) or of the soils, waters, or other resources mentioned. In this regard they resemble the general public which, while permitting a tremendous shortage of trained technical men to develop in the United States and appropriating relatively small sums of money for scientists' salaries and equipment, nevertheless possesses an almost pathetic confidence in the ability of the scientist to pull the rabbit out of the hat on demand. Thus, substitutes are promised for any of the essential natural resources which may run out and, when the substitutes themselves are used up, substitutes for the substitutes.

To a considerable degree the philosophy of this "enough and to spare" school operates as a "counterconservation" movement. Perhaps the statements of this group will have some value in compelling the conservationists to more rigorous scrutiny of their data. It would be regrettable, however, and might be exceedingly injurious, if they should succeed in impairing efforts to use the natural resources wisely and judiciously, especially the nonrenewable ones.

Seemingly some of those who show little concern over resources problems have overlooked one of the obvious facts of life, namely, the irresistible urge to multiplication. Illustrative of this, Woodbury[1] has written: "It is easy to show mathematically that if each of the young ones of any species which are started into life in each generation could grow, develop, and reproduce, a relatively small number of generations would produce standing room only for that species." The urge to reproduce is characteristic of every species of plant and animal, *including man*. It matters little how much he may have or produce in goods, materials, or energy, if his geometrically increasing numbers immediately expand to more than take up the slack.

[1] Woodbury, *op. cit.*

Sears[1] summed up the matter recently in the "form of an expression from mathematics expressing the ratio between resources and population as a function of culture." Sears' expression might be amended to read as follows:

$$\frac{\text{Resources} \times \text{culture}}{\text{Population}} = \text{standard of living}$$

Obviously, so long as the natural resources times man's cultural and technical treatment of them are maintained in generous proportions as related to population, man's standard of living can be kept up or even increased. But when the population figure of the denominator grows faster than the numerator, there will be a corresponding decline in the standard of living. All signs indicate that available supplies of food, energy, and other essentials may be augmented through technical ingenuity up to a certain point. But, if human population is permitted to follow Dr. Brown's description,[2] according to which "a substantial fraction of humanity . . . would not rest content until the earth is covered completely and to a considerable depth with a writhing mass of human beings," man's standard of living cannot help but be lowered. It might be remembered, too, that space itself, living room, is an important natural resource, and if human reproduction is unbridled, this too will eventually run out.

11.6 Cooperation and Competition

Since ecology stresses interrelationships, it is naturally concerned with competition and cooperation. As Allee and his associates[3] pointed out, the concept of competition has often been misapplied in recent years.

The importance of its implications and of its conscious misapplications in human affairs, both in economics and in interclass and international warfare, can hardly be overemphasized. . . . Fitness involves cooperation, and adaptations leading to coordination of parts of organisms and of individuals in populations are the result of evolution through natural selection. . . . The evolution of greater interdependence between organisms is correlated with progressive evolution.

Can one doubt that the application of ecological concepts to human affairs may exercise a refreshing and salutary influence on them? It may be hoped that such application may be of some slight help, at least, in correcting some of the perversions which apparently have come from the

[1] Paul B. Sears, "Biologists and Conservation of Natural Resources," reprinted from *Am. Inst. Biol. Sciences Bull.*, July, 1953.

[2] Harrison Brown, *The Challenge of Man's Future*, The Viking Press, Inc., New York, 1954.

[3] Allee et al., *op. cit.*

one-sided tooth-and-claw philosophy characteristic of some interpretations of organic evolution.

WILDLIFE

11.7 Scope and Magnitude of Wildlife Resources

As here used, wildlife includes the vertebrate wild animals, chiefly the fishes, birds, and mammals.[1] More accurately, the term should embrace every living organism, whether animal or plant, in a state of nature.

Fig. 11.4 The Canada goose is one of our finest waterfowl. (*Photograph by Rex Gary Schmidt, Fish and Wildlife Service.*)

Many persons are surprised to learn the magnitude of our fish and wildlife properties. According to Gordon,[2] "The . . . army of outdoor enthusiasts in the nation releases into the channels of commerce and trade over 4 billion dollars a year; supplying their needs has become one of the Nation's important industries."

In 1950, 1,500,000 fishermen and hunters bought licenses in California alone. Including sport fishing with the pursuit of game, it is currently estimated that California hunters and fishermen spend about 250 million dollars a year on their sport.

[1] Walter P. Taylor, "Land Wildlife Resources of the South," *Monograph* 4, Institute Research in Social Science, University of North Carolina, 1949.

[2] Seth Gordon, "California's Fish and Game Program," *Report to the Wildlife Conservation Board, State of California Senate*, 1950.

According to the annual report of the Director of the United States Fish and Wildlife Service for the fiscal year ended June 30, 1945,[1] the estimated capitalized value of wildlife to the United States is well in excess of 14 billion dollars, as follows:

	Wildlife	*Billion Dollars*
Waterfowl: ducks, geese, and swans		1.5
Fur animals		0.4
Big game		1.3
Commercial fisheries		5.8
Game fish		5.0
Total		$14.0

But these estimates do not even come close to telling the whole story. They do not, for example, include the wildlife not used for game or food, nor the benefits rendered the streams, fields, and forests by insect control through the agency of fishes, birds, mammals, and reptiles. It is pretty generally realized, and it should not be forgotten, that the plants and animals, all together, constitute nature's board of equalization, helping to keep things in balance so that the machinery will operate. Least of all do the above figures reflect the imponderable values of wildlife—beauty, recreational attractiveness, and spiritual inspiration. Taking these things into account, the Director of the Fish and Wildlife Service estimated that the grand total of the capitalized values of United States wildlife might conservatively be set at ten times the estimated 14 billion dollars.

Seemingly, it is a practical necessity to give attention to the dollars-and-cents side of the wildlife business. O. J. Murie,[2] the inspired leader of the Wilderness Society, refreshingly insists, however, that the real argument for conservation be advanced—not the commercial or economic argument alone. Man wants to perpetuate these wild creatures because he finds them interesting and attractive, he likes them, and he realizes that all mankind would be poorer and the world less interesting without them.

"How does one ever place in any formula such things as happiness, the good life, the elation that comes from being in high country in free, wild surroundings?" Or, Murie might have added, from a heart-warming association with birds, mammals, or other animals in their natural state?

11.8 For Some Species the Situation Is Critical

In many instances, valuable wildlife species simply cannot compete with man. The buffalo was harried from its ancestral range to make way

---

[1] Ira N. Gabrielson, "The Function of the Fish and Wildlife Service," in *Annual Report, Secretary of the Interior for the Fiscal Year Ended June 30, 1945*, U.S. Government Printing Office, Washington, D.C., 1946.

[2] Olaus J. Murie, "Wild Country as a National Asset," *The Living Wilderness*, no. 45, Summer, 1953.

for livestock, wheat, and dry-land agriculture. The passenger pigeon, a colonial nester, was exterminated for man's city markets. All remaining large and beautiful or unusual species have been and still are threatened by trigger-happy killers.

Fig. 11.5   The coyote, a predator, survives in spite of man. (*Photograph by E. P. Haddon, Fish and Wildlife Service.*)

Manipulation of habitat plays a big part in destruction or increase of various wildlife species. With human population increasing almost explosively, the future does not look promising for some of the native plants and animals.

Gone already are the great auk and Eskimo curlew.[1] The heath hen and most of the wolves and grizzly bears likewise are no more. Threatened with extinction are the tule elk of California, a number of the shore birds

[1] Ira N. Gabrielson, *Wildlife Conservation*, The Macmillan Company, New York, 1941.

including the upland plover, the Attwater prairie chicken, trumpeter swan, whooping crane, ivory-billed woodpecker, California condor, marten, fisher, wolverine, and many others.

In other parts of the world, likewise, a number of species of wildlife are threatened, among them the sea cow or manatee, various marsupials in Australia, New Zealand, and Tasmania, some of the African antelopes, and the white rhinoceros. For details on these and other threatened species, both in the Old World and the New, see Allen[1] and Harper.[2]

Fig. 11.6   Two mule deer bucks on the National Bison Range, Montana. (*Photograph by E. P. Haddon, Fish and Wildlife Service.*)

On the other side of the picture there are some notable examples of successful survival and adaptation to the new conditions on the part of the native species. Among plants these efficient types are usually known as weeds. Similarly the Norway rat, the house mouse, the European sparrow, and the starling widely are regarded as animal weeds. Even some of the more valuable native species, such as the North American deer, take astonishingly well to man's alterations in the environment. Indeed, the deer have become so seriously overabundant in parts of some 30 states of the United States as to be a real problem for the game administrators.

---

[1] Glover M. Allen, "Extinct and Vanishing Mammals of the Western Hemisphere with the Marine Species of All the Oceans," American Committee for International Wildlife Protection, Spec. Publ. No. 11, Cambridge, 1942.

[2] Francis Harper, "Extinct and Vanishing Mammals of the Old World," American Committee for International Wildlife Protection, Spec. Publ. No. 12, New York, 1945.

11.9 The Forgotten Millions

Universally characteristic of mankind is a taking for granted of present favorable conditions, social, political, economic, and natural, with very little thought indeed for the original bounties of nature, for which man was not responsible at all, or for the blood, sweat, and tears which have been invested in the welfare of the present generation by those who have gone before.

How infinitely less does man consider the thousands of individuals and species of wildlife, which, as a matter of fact, contribute to his welfare in countless subtle and unappreciated ways. It would be a good thing for man to think occasionally of the 240,000 described species of plants and the 823,000 kinds of animals[1] in the world. Every one of these is interesting, if man knew enough about them, and each is making its contribution to the exciting and sometimes baffling enterprise of living. Assuredly man's interest, concern, and care should be extended increasingly to the millions of nongame species, birds, mammals, reptiles, amphibians, fishes, etc., which help to keep the great world biotic community going.

Fortunately, most of the living forms continue to function regardless of man. But the game, which he harvests, and certain other forms require very special attention. What, then, are some of the ways and means whereby man tries to assure the maintenance of the valued game species?

11.10 Methods of Game Protection

Traditional methods of assuring a sustained yield of game are at least five in number: (1) protective laws, regulating the number and sex of individuals that may be taken and the period during which harvest is permitted; (2) control of the alleged enemies of game, usually including at least the four so-called principal predators, the wolf, mountain lion, coyote, and bobcat; (3) establishment of game preserves on which no hunting is permitted; (4) liberating birds or other game raised artificially on game farms; and (5) importing foreign game to supplement the local supply.

Each of these methods has been given a thorough testing, usually on a trial-and-error basis, seldom on a scientific foundation; but not one of them, nor, indeed, all of them put together, is sufficient to assure the desired result. Let us discuss each one of them briefly.

1. It is obvious that protective laws will accomplish little if there is a shortage of available food, cover, or water, for in such a case the game will decrease in spite of the most rigorous protection.

[1] E. L. Palmer, *Fieldbook of Natural History*, McGraw-Hill Book Company, Inc., New York, 1949.

2. The predators are seldom so numerous that they affect the numbers of game animals, unless something else, for example, an unfavorable alteration in the habitat by man, tips the scale in their direction. After all, what is a predator? Everything that eats animal or plant food may be regarded as a predator, and man, incidentally, is the bloodiest and most dangerous predator of all. Many persons feel that the four species just mentioned as predators are of interest in themselves and should not be exterminated.

Seemingly a revision is called for in man's "management" of predators. Public sentiment, in some instances, is definitely ahead of legislation. The wolf is extinct practically throughout the cattle country, where it used to cause havoc. The mountain lion does no appreciable damage to its principal prey, the deer, at least as a species, but rather tends to prevent the latter from becoming so numerous as to threaten its own food supply. Repeated painstaking studies have shown the food habits of the coyote and bobcat, except in the case of certain individuals in particular localities, to be beneficial to man. Should not man take a more realistic view of the problem and revise the rules in the light of the latest information?

3. Game preserves may or may not be beneficial to game numbers, depending on the available food and cover within them.

4. In most instances, liberation of game artificially raised in incubators and coops on game farms has not worked out satisfactorily. With a few exceptions, evidence is far from convincing that game-farm-produced birds have any appreciable beneficial effect on the numbers of birds taken by hunters. Furthermore, the distribution of game-farm birds lends itself with surprising ease to political manipulation and even, sometimes, to deterioration of native stocks.

5. The importation of foreign species is looked at askance by many game biologists, who point out that all too seldom is a careful ecological study made of the new environment prior to importation, so as to determine whether or not the new conditions are suitable. These specialists point out also that if the foreign species does not become established a considerable expenditure of public or private money is entailed with no corresponding benefit. If, on the other hand, the exotic becomes too well established (as has actually happened with the non game European sparrow, the starling, and the Norway rat, as well as with certain game species including the gray squirrel in England, the rabbit in Australia, the muskrat on the continent of Europe, and the elk in New Zealand), it may cause much trouble. One of the difficulties is that the natural enemies of the imported species are lacking in the new country and another is that foreign parasites and diseases may be imported with the game. Furthermore, if there is a native species of game on the ground already, the

foreigner may be found to be a competitor, and if the exotic chances to be stronger biologically, it may reduce both the distribution and numbers of the indigene.

11.11   The Habitat, Key to Wildlife

It has been found that, with a proper habitat (meaning, in the usual instance, an adequate forest, brushy, herbaceous, marshy, or grassy vegetation cover, with water and feed to go with it) ordinarily the wildlife, with reasonable management, may be relied on to do quite well. It may fairly be concluded, on the basis of rather overwhelming evidence, that the building and preservation of suitable habitat are more important in game conservation than any other single practice or, in fact, than all the rest of them put together.

Of course, if unharvested game becomes so abundant that it exceeds the carrying capacity of the habitat, there develops a poorly situated surplus, which immediately becomes vulnerable to starvation, winter cold, disease, parasites, and capture by enemies. As a rule, nature fills the habitat to capacity with game, always producing far more individuals than can possibly survive. This is the reason that artificial props, such as protection from predators, setting up of game preserves, game farms, and the introduction of exotics, are usually unnecessary and sometimes even detrimental.

Attention may now be called to one of the corollaries of the importance of the habitat. If the habitat is indeed as important as has been stated, then very often the farmer, the livestock ranchman, the forester, the range manager, and the engineer, indeed the land operator in general, are more important factors in what happens to the wildlife than the sportsman or the professional game manager.

11.12   Wildlife and the Engineer

Not the least of those just mentioned, the engineer, whenever he works with land or water, is sure to exercise a profound influence on the wildlife. An examination of some engineering works with the wildlife in mind may be profitable.

Installation of huge dams interferes in many ways with the original wildlife. The newly created artificial lake eliminates, at one fell swoop, not only all the farms, villages, cemeteries, parks, roads, railroads, and other cultural or natural phenomena below the new water line but also the wildlife.

Sufficiently far-reaching in its effect on wildlife to deserve special mention is the drainage of wet lands, usually in the supposed interest of agriculture. Let us consider a concrete instance of the wrong kind of

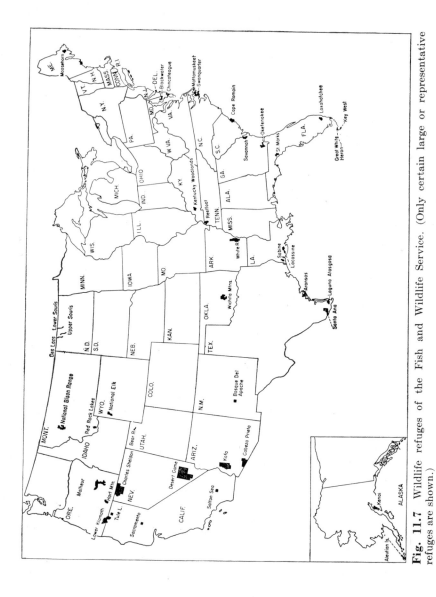

Fig. 11.7 Wildlife refuges of the Fish and Wildlife Service. (Only certain large or representative refuges are shown.)

250

drainage, which demonstrates the close connection between engineering and land and water management.

An enterprise in northern Minnesota was designed to provide 60,000 new acres of farm land.

A very extensive and expensive system of ditches through this marsh produced a total of 1200 acres that could be cultivated even during the driest years. The remainder of the land was totally unproductive. After more than 30 years, the Fish and Wildlife Service purchased and reflooded the land. It is now producing a fine waterfowl breeding and feeding ground and is of growing value in the production of muskrats and fish.[1]

The coastal marshlands possess special significance to Louisiana, Texas, and other Gulf states, as well as some of the South Atlantic states. Some years ago Stanley C. Arthur[2] pointed out the magnitude of the muskrat industry in Louisiana. As one editor put it, "Perhaps it is a mistake to agitate for the reclamation of the swampy belt fringing the Gulf, because it now yields great wealth at a minimum of expense and can be made to produce still more in skins. These, moreover, pay the State a severance tax on $5,000,000 of value." During the past several hunting seasons, wrote Arthur, Louisiana had produced more pelts of fur animals than had all the provinces and territories of the Dominion of Canada combined—with Alaska's catch thrown in for good measure.

Another item to be considered in connection with wet lands is the waterfowl (ducks, geese, and swans). The marshes of Texas, Louisiana, and the other Gulf coastal, South Atlantic, and Mexican states constitute an important part of the wintering grounds of these popular game birds, truly a continental resource which it will be remembered Dr. Gabrielson estimated to be worth 1.5 billion dollars. Thus these particular wet lands are a key to the waterfowl of the Western Hemisphere.

The many beneficial effects on the wildlife of certain engineering enterprises should not be overlooked. These include modern mechanical methods of soil working, fertilizer manufacture and application, irrigation, flooding and water control, pond and lake installation, forest planting, reseeding of grazing ranges, establishment of windbreaks and fence rows, game-food plantings, levees, fish ladders, etc.

To the writer, however, the combined total effect of all the beneficial factors may not compensate for the obvious impairment of wildlife habitat in the march of so-called civilization. Man's land and water management is paradoxical and even amusing if it were not so wasteful. Perhaps he can

[1] Gabrielson, "Relation of Conservation to Engineering Projects," *loc. cit.*
[2] Stanley C. Arthur, "The Fur Animals of Louisiana," *Louisiana Dept. Conserv. Bull.* 18, 1928.

learn from nature, if he is sufficiently open-minded, humble, and teachable.

Obviously, whatever happens to the habitat will affect the wildlife—and let it not be forgotten that the health or sickness of the habitat ultimately will be reflected in the status of man himself.

WILDERNESS

11.13 Wilderness More Valuable than Ever

Ecology and wildlife are intimately related to wilderness. Indeed, the alignment, in this discussion, of ecology, wildlife, and wilderness is a most happy one. What is this wilderness to which reference is made? According to Zahniser of the Wilderness Society,[1] the term applies to "areas retaining their primeval environment or influence, or to areas remaining free from routes which can be used for mechanical transportation." Some of the implications of this wilderness concept may profitably be considered.

The values which wilderness has to offer include scientific, educational, wildlife, recreational, and inspirational ones. The needs for these values become greater as the world becomes increasingly crowded and developed. The following editorial in *The Living Wilderness*[2] well expresses the situation:

Of course there is the practical need that resides in the fact that many people deeply want the wilderness, and there is a need for realizing our ideal of preserving for everyone the privilege of choosing to enjoy the wilderness if he or she wishes. We need also to preserve the wilderness because it is something superlative, and there are doubtless other ways in which we could define our various needs.

But deep down at the base of all our needs for wilderness is a profound, a fundamental need—a need that is not only recreational and spiritual but also educational and scientific, and withal essential to a true understanding of ourselves, our culture, our own natures, and our place in all nature.

This need is for areas of the earth within which we stand without our mechanisms that make us immediate masters over our environment—areas of wild nature in which we sense ourselves to be dependent members of an interdependent community of living creatures that together derive their existence from the sun.

Sufficient recreational and scenic areas of many types other than wilderness are also desirable and necessary, but the emphasis of this section is directed to wilderness because of its high quality and its unique and fragile nature. Wilderness and scenic areas are under continually increas-

[1] Howard Zahniser, "A Statement of Wilderness Preservation in Reply to a Questionnaire," Memorandum for the Legislative Reference Service, Library of Congress, Mar. 1, 1949.

[2] *The Living Wilderness*, Autumn, 1955.

ing pressures. Nevertheless it is encouraging to note that the forces working for wilderness preservation are also growing in strength. Two recent proposals are of tremendous importance to the preservation of our wilderness areas. They are the bills, first introduced in the Eighty-fourth

Fig. 11.8 The Teton Range rises abruptly above Jackson Hole in Grand Teton National Park. (*Photograph by Richard Kenyon.*)

Congress by bipartisan sponsors, for the establishment of a National Wilderness Preservation System[1,2] and the bills introduced in the Eighty-fifth Congress for a Scenic Resources Review. A proposal for a Scenic Resources Review was previously made by the Sierra Club Board of Directors in January, 1956.

[1] Hubert H. Humphrey, "Wilderness Preservation," Congressional Record, 84th Congress, 2d Session, June 7, 1956.
[2] John P. Saylor, "Saving America's Wilderness," Congressional Record, 84th Congress, 2d Session, July 12, 1956.

The originally proposed National Wilderness Preservation System would involve wilderness areas already in our national parks, national forests, wildlife refuges, and Indian lands. One of the motivations for the introduction of the bill "is the rapid growth of our population, and the resulting tremendous pressures for opening up these wilderness areas for commercial and economic purposes. If that trend continues, it will mean that our Nation, in the years to come, will be without our great system of national parks, recreational areas, wilderness areas, and forest preserves, which mean so much to the mental health, as well as to the physical health of our people."[1] No changes would be made in the administration of any area, except that the agency having jurisdiction at present would "have the sanction and encouragement of Congress and the legal responsibility for preserving the area's wilderness character."[2] The bills as originally proposed would include 163 areas and 55 million acres of wilderness land owned by the Federal government. An additional 3 million acres of wilderness is under state control.

These figures should be compared with the total area of the United States of $2\frac{1}{4}$ billion acres. The proposed wilderness-preservation program is based on the assumption that our land resources are sufficiently great "that we can have an adequate system of wilderness areas without sacrificing other advantages. . . . The needed sites for dams and reservoirs, the roads and landing fields for our mechanical travel in the great outdoors, places for recreation with the conveniences and facilities we so well contrive—all these can be located outside our wildernesses that we wish to preserve."[3]

The Scenic Resources Review was suggested to its backers by The Timber Resources Review, conducted by the United States Forest Service in cooperation with many agencies, itself a review which looks forward toward our optimum and maximum timber needs by the year 2000.

The Scenic Resources Review would need to concern itself with five basic questions:

1. *What are the needs* of this nation for scenic resources and their public use? . . .

2. *What optimum and maximum space* for scenic resources is likely to be required by the year 2000, considering probable trends in population growth, increase in leisure time, improvement in transportation, expansion of urbanization, and changing vacation habits? . . .

3. *What areas are suitable* for expansion of present scenic-resource reservation? . . .

[1] Humphrey, *op. cit.*
[2] Saylor, *op. cit.*
[3] *Ibid.*

4. *In areas where expanding use* of the scenic resources will conflict with expanding commodity utilization, for which use is a substitute more likely to be developed? . . .

5. *How may protection best be assured* for the resources for which there are no substitutes, that is, by what legislative or administrative authority, under what agency? . . .

We believe this review will put conflicting uses of land in fair perspective. . . .

The need for such a review is a very great need and very immediate. The native beauty of this land will not, by itself, survive the population and development pressure that is growing so rapidly. Our best talents, if used in time—and the time is now—can prevent irreparable and needless loss of the beauty of this country."[1]

A National Outdoor Recreation Resources Review Commission was established by the Eighty-fifth Congress[2], and it is strongly hoped that a wilderness-preservation system also becomes a reality. The supporters of wilderness-preservation legislation well appreciate the splendid contributions of the National Park Service and the Forest Service to wilderness preservation. They feel, however, that the legal basis for the fragile and unique resource of wilderness should be strengthened to face the increasing pressures of the times.

11.14   Norms Needed in the Management of Life and Land

Dr. Paul B. Sears[3] of Yale University has pointed out that

Just as the engineer in machine and industrial design must have at hand his theoretical apparatus of calculation, so the biologist and others who would design intelligent land use must have their norms or standards of measurement. And these norms, to a large degree, are to be found in the complex pattern of interrelationship represented by the undisturbed natural community. At present we have to rely largely on intuition—a wasteful and dangerous process, as is trial and error. It is a moral obligation to *know*, if we can.

R. D. Forbes,[4] a former Director of the Allegheny Forest Experiment Station, pointed out that 999 of every 1000 acres of forest land in the territory of the station had been lumbered off. The thousandth acre was in uncut virgin timber. "The thousandth acre," wrote Forbes, "will repay careful study." The wilderness is the thousandth acre for all the kinds and types of country around it.

[1] David R. Brower, *Sierra Club Bull.*, June and December, 1956.

[2] Kenneth B. Pomeroy, "The New National Outdoor Recreation Resources Review Commission," *American Forests*, vol. 64, no. 11, November, 1958.

[3] Paul B. Sears, "What Worth Wilderness?" *Bull. to the Schools of the University of the State of New York*, March, 1953, reprinted by the Nature Conservancy, Washington, D.C.

[4] Reginald D. Forbes, "The Thousandth Acre," *Am. Forests*, vol. 40, no. 2, pp. 51–54, February, 1934.

In much of our western and southwestern and plains country all the land has been settled on, grazed by livestock, drained, flooded, plowed, burned, irrigated, or otherwise modified by man or his domestic animals, and there just is no thousandth acre. Indeed, the extent to which man has taken over the land and altered it is almost beyond belief.[1]

Fig. 11.9   Azalea Lake in the Sierra Nevada near Donner Summit. (*Courtesy Sierra Club.*)

It is true that some of the ultra-arid country in the extremest portion of the desert area seemingly remains little altered; but the evidence of man's influence usually can be found without much difficulty on nearly every square foot, even of extreme desert territory. All this means that there is no longer any real norm with which to compare the soil, the vegetation, and the animal life.

[1] Walter P. Taylor, "The Need for Natural Areas," *Ecology*, vol. 15, no. 3, pp. 328–329, July, 1934.

One may interview old-timers and get from them valuable hints as to the early condition of the country—its soil, streams, grasses, brush, trees, and wild-life—but conclusive demonstration is lacking. The existing situation emphasizes in no uncertain terms the need for saving sample tracts in all important types under as nearly as possible original conditions to serve as a guide for present practice.[1]

Perhaps most needed just now are large areas of plains and prairie grassland. Obviously management of the 7 billion acres, more or less, of range land in the United States should be based on something more than old-timers' impressions. Adequate information is needed from studies of tracts of undisturbed grassland. Where are these to be found?

11.15   Recreation, a Vital Need

As everyone knows, world population, in the last 300 years, has risen five times over, from about half a billion persons to more than $2\frac{1}{2}$ billion. This surging increase is felt even in the United States, which, as compared with some other parts of the world, still is rather sparsely occupied.

The situation is unusually ominous, perhaps, in California, with a reported 1000 persons a day increase in population. Already Californians face almost insupportable pressures, such painful phenomena as congestion on the highways, insufficient parking places, disorganized municipal and interurban transportation, overburdened sewage systems, pitifully overcrowded schools, murkiness of the atmosphere, and eye-irritating smog.

In no field is the far-reaching baleful influence of overpopulation more obvious than in that of recreation. It is true that there seem to be plenty of taverns, night clubs, cocktail bars, and gaming places, but reference is not made to these, but rather to the opportunity for a certain amount of intimate and sympathetic contact with wild nature. Sometimes, man wants to be alone. Moreover he needs to be alone for the healing effect of nature on his spirit, all too often bruised and battered in the helter-skelter of man's increasingly crowded and plundered planet.

Murie[2] said, "a little lonesome space, where nature has her own way, where it is quiet enough at night to hear the patter of small paws on leaves and the murmuring of birds, can still be afforded. The gift of tranquillity, wherever found, is beyond price."

With pressure for recreation more intense than ever before in history, and continuing to build up as human population increases, those who love the outdoors encounter a frustration which bids fair to rob them of any possible pleasure in taking to the field. "Public camps during the summer, or on opening day for trout or deer, are a bewildering tangle of tent ropes,

[1] *Ibid.*
[2] Murie, *op. cit.*

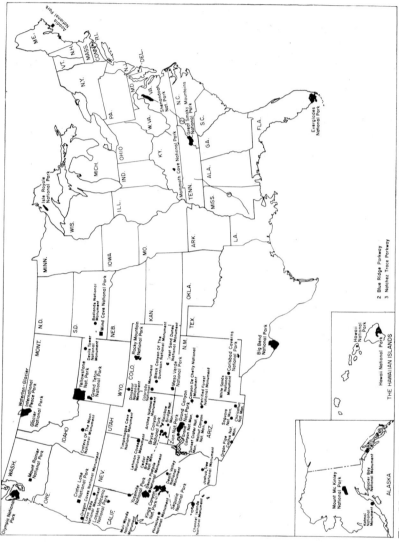

Fig. 11.10 National parks, national monuments, and parkways administered by the National Park Service of the Department of the Interior. The areas shown were selected because of special scenic, wilderness, or natural-history values. The National Park Service also administers other locations, including historic and battlefield sites, national memorials, and national recreational areas.

trailers, and tin cans."[1] Such conditions have been badly aggravated by insufficient appropriations for recreational purposes. "Operation Outdoors" of the Forest Service and "Mission 66" of the National Park Service are admirable recent programs which may be expected to provide some welcome relief.

As California sportsmen know, the pressure on possible hunting and fishing places in the state is growing with the population. One hundred thousand and more sportsmen in southern California alone, with no place to go! "No Shooting" and "No Trespassing" signs are everywhere. If open spaces are located, the hunters, in season, are crowded to the point where one must almost resort to a trench to save his life. Fishing is increasingly on a "put-and-take" basis, with the frustrated fisherman barely waiting for the state truck to depart before trying to beat his fellow anglers in pulling out the wretched fingerlings or their "catchable-size" successors.

Perhaps some readers have fished or picnicked at Crystal Lake, in the San Gabriel Mountains of southern California. From glamorous accounts the writer was prepared for a real gem. What an anticlimax!—a 3-acre mudhole, with scarcely room for the fishermen to stand around the shore on opening day in order to throw in their hooks, not to mention those in rowboats out in the middle of the puddle. Obviously, as the population pressure on recreational areas increases, the quality of recreation takes a nosedive.

11.16   The Mountains—Are They Being Worn Out?

And now for a moment let's turn to the mountains and discuss some of the threats and pressures with which Forest Service officials and others have to cope almost every day in the year.

1. The increasing pressures from thousands of picnickers and would-be campers, trying to get a breath of smog-free air and hankering for a few hours of rest and peace amid natural surroundings.

2. Increased pressure for home sites. There are thousands of cabins in the mountains already, potential fire hazards and threats to the all-important water-producing drainage areas.

3. The pressure for more "access" roads. Every new public road in the mountains, while promoting accessibility when a fire breaks out, tends to encourage accelerated erosion and to augment the danger of additional fires from careless tourists and campers.

4. The pressure for conference grounds, camps, summer retreats, etc., for various organizations. While highly commendable under other conditions, the mountains are becoming so crowded that this particular pressure is more and more difficult to deal with. People are discovering that the mountains are not the dreadful and dangerous places many have believed

[1] *Ibid.*

them to be, but rather, among other things, precious sanctuaries for the rehabilitation and sustenance of the human spirit. As a result, congestion in the hills becomes aggravated, the lonesome places lose their solitude, the recreational jewels take on a tarnish, and man's very love for the mountains results in their becoming less lovable.

5. Pressure from mining interests. These are among the most persistent of all the announced and involuntary exploiters of the general public's mountain properties. Some, unfortunately, are not above reproach. Claims are staked out with a view to possibilities in real estate, or timber, or summer home sites, or the location of motels or resorts. Legislation recently adopted by Congress, with the full cooperation of legitimate mining interests, will partially stop this type of malpractice, it is hoped. At times the pressure has been irresistible. Thus, Death Valley National Monument was forced open to mining, and vigorous efforts still were being made, at last accounts, to break down the Joshua Tree National Monument.

6. Pressures from commercial interests generally. Seemingly every patch of snow would have its competing ski lift and every available lot in the mountains its wayside shack for the sale of something or other to the traveling public were it not for the guardians of the larger interests of all the people in retaining at least something of the natural beauty of the scene.

7. Pressure from the alleged needs of national defense. Seemingly neither the high peaks of the mountains nor the wildest parts of the desert are immune from appropriation for one purpose or another by the Department of Defense. Not that anybody wants to interfere with any legitimate need for defense—but, already, thousands of acres of desert land have been closed to all public use because of the unexploded shells remaining from artillery practice. There is a growing apprehension lest the Department of Defense shall continue to take over acreages of wild lands out of all proportion to the need.

8. Pressure from grazing interests. Perhaps the most persistent and threatening examples of this in recent times were the D'Ewart Bill and the related Hope-Thye-Aiken Bill, introduced by a group of stockmen in the Eighty-third Congress. Had these measures been successful, priority of use of the national forests would have been assured to the grazing of domestic livestock—water production, timber, recreation, and wildlife would have been in second place.

So all these, and more, pressures are exerted on the precious and valuable mountain areas, the pressures increasing as population continues to grow. It is not too difficult to picture what would happen if a policy of *laissez faire* should suddenly be adopted and millions of people allowed to do what they would with the mountains. There is little doubt that the usefulness of these rugged areas to the settlements in the valleys would be reduced to the vanishing point and the communities themselves changed beyond recognition.

11.17 Conclusion

Too many of us, unfortunately, have mistaken the means, i.e., money and profits, for the ends, i.e., true happiness, healthful enjoyment, and spiritual inspiration. The means themselves have become the ends! Murie[1] says, "We are so eager to produce new wealth that we stumble in our haste, and the noise we make prevents us from hearing the quiet voice of history."

Must not man rely heavily on wilderness to assist him to rightful solutions of present-day problems? Here is nature, successfully accomplishing a tremendously complicated job, her checks and balances operating to bring about results outstanding in beauty and attractiveness. Perhaps in subjecting himself, at intervals, to wilderness influences lies man's best hope for ultimately balancing his own life equation and for building a civilization wherein a requisite equilibrium is attained between man and nature.

It is here suggested that the enjoyment of the harmony and beauty of wild nature, like music, art, religion, and the society and love of worthy men and women, is one of the true ends of existence.[2] Shall we permit its impairment or destruction by the shortsighted, or shall we guard this privilege well?

[1] *Ibid.*

[2] See also Julian Huxley, "Man's Challenge: The Use of the Earth," *Horizon,* vol. 1, pp. 48–55, September, 1958.

12

Forest Land and Forest Products

JOHN A. ZIVNUSKA

ASSOCIATE PROFESSOR OF FORESTRY
UNIVERSITY OF CALIFORNIA, BERKELEY

12.1 The Forest Resource

The first settlers on the eastern coast of North America landed on a forested continent. These great forests, with an extent and variety unknown to European eyes, exerted a high degree of control over the development of the early colonies. They provided a readily available material for the building of homes, an abundant fuel for the generation of heat and energy, and the primary elements of the early export trade which helped to pay for the badly needed imports from Europe. At the same time, the heavy stands of timber were a barrier to the extension of agriculture, requiring a Herculean effort in land clearing. In places they seemed more a menace than a blessing, serving as shelter for hostile Indians and wild animals. Heavy cutting and reduction of the forest resource were both the means and hallmark of progress.

This early tradition of abundant use of an abundant resource prevailed through the entire period of development of the United States. The great surge of population across the tall-grass and short-grass prairies was accompanied by the peak intensity of cutting in the pine forests of the Great Lakes region. Even the railroads' bands of steel which tied a sprawling nation into one unit rested on a forest of wooden crossties. Indeed, one of the major means by which the nation developed was through the cutting of a forest resource which was so great as to enable a nearly profligate use.

With the passing of the frontier, however, new attitudes toward the forests began to appear. It had become evident that forests were not limitless but instead were being rapidly reduced by heavy cutting and unchecked fires. With this realization, the cry of "timber famine" was raised and was heeded. New forces were set in action. In 1900 the now widely recognized concept of conservation of natural resources was gain-

262

ing its first foothold in the nation's forests. Today, more than half a century later, the forests remain a primary source of raw material for a greatly expanded economy, supplying nearly one-fifth of all physical-structure materials used in the nation. The forests are established as a major resource which can be used and renewed.

Throughout the world, forests constitute one of the most extensive forms of productive land use. The total forested area is some 9.5 billion acres, or nearly 30 per cent of the total land area. In contrast, agricultural land includes about 23 per cent of the total, with the balance being various forms of wild land, brush, or unproductive areas. More than half of this vast forest area is currently considered inaccessible, and less than one-third of the total area is currently in use.

The United States, with about 6½ per cent of the world's forest land, is the greatest producer and consumer of industrial wood. The nation produces about 31 per cent and consumes about 35 per cent of the world's total industrial wood, with the imports coming largely from Canada. Behind this heavy use lies a rich resource of highly productive temperate-zone forests. The nation's commercial forest land extends over 484 million acres, or 25 per cent of the total land area. An additional 163 million acres of alpine, swamp, or semidesert forests, woodland brush, and forests reserved for uses other than timber production is classified as noncommercial forest land. Thus the total forest area of the United States is 648 million acres, or 34 per cent of the total land area.

This forest area is widely distributed over the nation and includes a great range of forest types and conditions. The heavily populated and industrialized 21 Eastern states have 38 per cent of their land area in commercial forest land, with about 134 million acres of hardwood types and 35 million acres of softwood types. The 12 Southern states also have commercial forest land amounting to 38 per cent of their land area, including about 112 million acres of hardwood types and 82 million acres of softwoods. In these two regions are found the extensive oak-hickory type which includes nearly one-fourth of the nation's commercial forest land and the loblolly–shortleaf pine type which represents another one-eighth of the total. Here also are the common oak-gum-cypress and maple-beech-birch types, as well as the longleaf–slash pine, aspen-birch, oak-pine, spruce-fir, and other less extensive types.

Less than 13 per cent of the great area of plains and mountains in the 15 Western states is commercial forest land. These 121 million acres are largely softwood forests, with only limited areas of hardwoods. The widely distributed ponderosa-pine type and the highly productive Douglas-fir type are the most common forests, with lodgepole pine, fir-spruce, and a number of other types forming the balance. Here, too, is found most of the noncommercial forest land, with the plains and Rocky

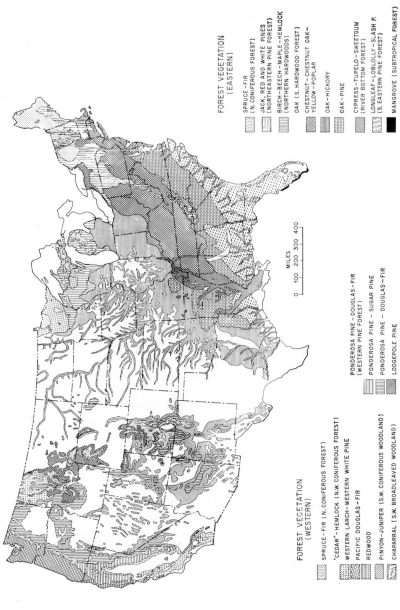

FOREST VEGETATION (WESTERN)

SPRUCE–FIR (N. CONIFEROUS FOREST)

"CEDAR"–HEMLOCK (N.W. CONIFEROUS FOREST)

WESTERN LARCH–WESTERN WHITE PINE

PACIFIC DOUGLAS–FIR

REDWOOD

PINYON–JUNIPER (S.W. CONIFEROUS WOODLAND)

CHAPARRAL (S.W. BROADLEAVED WOODLAND)

PONDEROSA PINE – DOUGLAS–FIR (WESTERN PINE FOREST)

PONDEROSA PINE – SUGAR PINE

PONDEROSA PINE – DOUGLAS–FIR

LODGEPOLE PINE

FOREST VEGETATION (EASTERN)

SPRUCE–FIR (N. CONIFEROUS FOREST)

JACK, RED AND WHITE PINES (NORTHEASTERN PINE FOREST)

BIRCH–BEECH–MAPLE–HEMLOCK (NORTHERN HARDWOODS)

OAK (S. HARDWOOD FOREST)

CHESTNUT–CHESTNUT OAK– YELLOW–POPLAR

OAK–HICKORY

OAK–PINE

CYPRESS–TUPELO–SWEETGUM (RIVER BOTTOM FOREST)

LONGLEAF–LOBLOLLY–SLASH P. (S. EASTERN PINE FOREST)

MANGROVE (SUBTROPICAL FOREST)

MILES
0 100 200 300 400

Fig. 12.1 The forest vegetation of the United States, adapted from Shantz and Zon's "Natural Vegetation" map of the United States in the *Atlas of American Agriculture*. (*U.S. Forest Service.*)

264

Mountain regions and California together having more than four-fifths of the national total.

Table 12.1 shows some important aspects of the geography of forestry in the United States. The West includes only one-fourth of the total area of commercial forest land, but it has practically all the remaining 46 million acres of old-growth timber. As the result of these heavy volumes per acre, the West has about two-thirds of the total board foot volume of saw timber and more than half of the cubic foot volume of forest-growing stock. Historically, the forest industries and especially the lumber industry have been migratory industries, shifting with the spread of population, changes in transportation, and the availability of forest resources. The characteristic importance of old-growth forests is reflected by the fact

Table 12.1 Highlights of Forest and Forest-products Geography in the United States

(Percentages of United States totals)

Region	Commercial forest area, 1953	Saw-timber volume, fbm, 1953	Growing stock, cu ft, 1953	Population, 1950	Lumber produced, 1950	Pulpwood consumed, 1952
East.......	36	14	22	58	13	33*
South......	40	18	23	26	38	50
West.......	24	68	55	16	49	17

* Approximately 29 per cent of the pulpwood consumed in the East was imported.
SOURCE: U.S. Forest Service and Bureau of the Census.

that the West produces about half of the nation's lumber supply from one-fourth of the nation's forest land.

However, the old-growth resources are being steadily reduced and the forest industries are settling down. As second-growth and third-growth "crop" timber is becoming the primary raw material, the importance of the various locational forces is shifting. In time, the ability to grow timber and the distance to the market will take control instead of the availability of existing forests. The East and the South, with three-fourths of the commercial forest land and more than four-fifths of the population, will probably increase their volume of forest-products output relative to the West in the future, even though some further increase in the absolute volume of output from the West can be expected. This shifting emphasis is already reflected to some degree by the location of the pulp and paper industry, although historical forces are still important in this. Thus, although the forest industries are settling down, further major shifts in the location of the forest industries must be expected in the coming decades.

12.2   The Uses of Forest Land

The extensive and variable forest-land resource has many different and important uses. Perhaps the most obvious use is in the production of a variety of familiar forest products—lumber, pulp and paper, plywood, veneer, shingles, cooperage, poles, piling, mine timbers, and many other lesser products. Another source of direct economic return is the forage and

Fig. 12.2   This fine stand of ponderosa pine in California is a part of the remaining 46 million acres of old-growth timber in the United States. (*Western Pine Association.*)

cover for domestic livestock and game animals which are produced by many forest types. A third and highly important group of uses lies in the influences of the forest cover on water runoff, snow melt, erosion, and wind. Finally, the importance of recreation and aesthetic values derived from the forests should be recognized.

Each of these forms of use is important in its own right. On any particular area, any one of these uses may be of dominant importance. Frequently more than one form of use can be obtained simultaneously from a forest area. Lands classified as noncommercial for timber production may sometimes have high value for certain of these other uses.

However, in this discussion, primary emphasis will be placed on forest products. The justification for this is evident throughout the economy. Probably more than 90 per cent of our single-family detached houses are of wood-frame construction, and wood is the most common exterior material. By 1955, the per capita consumption of pulp and paper had risen to more than 400 lb per year. In all, wood represents nearly one-fifth of the materials which furnish the physical structure of the things we make and use. It has been estimated that in 1952 timber-connected activity accounted for 6 per cent of the civilian labor force, 6 per cent of the compensation paid to all employees, and 5 per cent of the national income.

Although the primary use of forest land for purposes other than wood production will not be developed, the final part of this discussion will consider the compatibility of wood production with these other uses of our forests.

12.3   Forest Management and Wood Production

The forest tree is a living organism. After its establishment, there is ordinarily a period of rapid juvenile growth, the development of maturity, eventual decadence, and final death. Depending on species and circumstances, this normal life span may be less than that of man or it may extend over hundreds of years.

The forest tree is also a part of an ecological complex. It grows in a stand with other forest trees and with an understory of other woody and herbaceous vegetation. All these plant materials are rooted in soil with particular physical and chemical properties and with a very great variety of soil organisms. All develop under the influence of the climatic factors of the particular site. The tree cannot be considered in isolation from its surroundings.

It is with these living organisms and their total environment that the forester deals in managing a forest for wood production. His control on the forest must extend through all the stages of development.

The first stage is the establishment or regeneration of the forest trees. Commonly this is done by natural means, through the use of established seed-bearing trees. In some cases the artificial means of direct seeding or planting of nursery stock may be used. Stand establishment requires not only the source of seed or young stock but also the development of other needed conditions. For some species mineral soil should be exposed to direct sunlight, while other species may be favored by the maintenance of shade. Competition of other plants must be kept in check.

As the stand develops, a variety of intermediate cuttings can be carried out. By appropriate cleanings, thinnings, and release cuttings the forester can influence the species, sizes, and qualities of the trees on which the growth is laid down. With favorable markets he can recover considerable volumes of timber which would otherwise be lost to normal mortality in the development of the stand.

As the trees mature, harvest cuttings can be carried out, bringing in the main financial return to the operation and simultaneously providing for the regeneration of the stand. In some cases the trees for cutting may be selected on an individual basis, maintaining a cover of various ages of

Fig. 12.3   "Block cutting" in Douglas-fir in western Washington provides favorable conditions for the regeneration of this light-demanding species. (*U.S. Forest Service.*)

trees on the area. With such uneven-aged management, conditions favor the development of those species which are favored by shade. Many of the most valuable species, however, do not regenerate well under an established overstory. For these light-demanding species, some type of even-aged system of management must be used, with planned clear cuttings to ensure regeneration of the desired stands.

Through all these stages the forest must be protected from fire, insects, disease, and other injurious agents. General administration must be carried out, roads and other improvements must be developed and maintained, and the timing of operations must be carefully planned to give a balanced work load and desirable distribution of costs and returns.

Thus in its basic elements forest management for wood production consists of processes for deliberately controlling factors of the ecological complex represented by a forest in order to create certain desired conditions and results. The same philosophy and principles of management can be applied to the handling of any woody vegetation to produce the particular types of values desired from the area.

12.4   Wood and Its Uses

Wood as a Raw Material.   Wood is actually not a single raw material but, instead, is a group of closely related materials with variable properties and versatile uses. It is among the most widespread and familiar of all raw materials. Of particular importance in any consideration of natural resources is the fact that wood is renewable—that timber is a crop. Under good forestry practice the harvesting of mature trees for forest products is an essential stage of stand regeneration and optimum forest growth.

Both the physical nature and chemical composition of wood are fundamentally different from those of other common structural materials. Like all plant materials, wood has a cellular structure. However, there is considerable variation in this structure between different species and with different conditions of growth. This results in the wide variation in the properties of wood which is one of the bases of the versatility of wood as a raw material. Generally, wood is easily workable, strong for its weight, a good insulator, able to absorb shocks and vibrations, free from rust, easily fastened with nails or screws, and adaptable to a wide variety of uses. From their very familiarity, the qualities of wood are often underestimated. Because of the characteristic variability of wood, detailed studies of its physical properties and the establishment of clear specifications are essential for its most effective use.

Chemically, wood is composed primarily of carbon, hydrogen, and oxygen in definite proportions. No exact figures can be given on the composition of wood in terms of its different chemical constituents, since this varies widely among different types of wood. Its approximate composition, based on oven-dry weight, is as follows: cellulose, 40 to 55 per cent; lignin, 17 to 35 per cent; hemicelluloses, 15 to 30 per cent; water-soluble extractives, less than 1 to more than 10 per cent; and ash, about 1 per cent. Much of the chemical utilization of wood has centered around the delignification of wood, involving the separation of a fibrous pulp composed largely of cellulose from the lignin and other noncellulosic materials. The development of profitable chemical utilization of lignin is one of the great research challenges in wood chemistry.

The Use of Wood as a Fuel.   In a paradox typical of the qualities of wood, the ability of wood to support combustion, often considered a limiting factor of wood's usefulness, is actually the basis of its most common use. Throughout the forests of the world nearly half the volume of cuttings is for fuel wood, while large additional quantities of fuel are produced incidental to the industrial uses of wood. In the less-developed countries cuttings for fuel wood commonly wholly overshadow all other uses of wood, while even in Europe fuel-wood cuttings represent more than 40 per cent of the total volume of cuttings.

In an earlier stage in the development of the United States, fuel wood was also a major product of our forests. With increasing urbanization and the great changes in the availability of sources of heat and energy during the last 50 years, the total volume cut for fuel has declined rapidly. In 1952 less than 10 per cent of the cubic foot volume of cutting on the commercial forest lands was for fuel wood. This probably represented 20 to 25 per cent of the total volume of wood burned for fuel in the country, with the balance coming from manufacturing residues, dead trees, and other nonforest sources of wood.

As the direct result of this decline in fuel-wood cutting, the total volume of cut from the nation's forests has declined rapidly. The total cubic foot volume cut from the forests in 1955 was probably less than half that of 50 years earlier, even though the cut for the major forest industries has not shown any over-all decline.

The Lumber Industry. The lumber industry provides the main market for the trees grown in the forests of the United States. In 1952 about 70 per cent of the total cubic foot volume of industrial wood cut in the forests was for lumber mills, with 18 per cent for pulp, 5 per cent for veneer and plywood, and 7 per cent for other forest products.

Throughout the nineteenth century the production of lumber expanded at a rapid and sustained rate, reaching its peak in 1906 and 1907 at 46 billion fbm annually. Production then began to decline, rising to a secondary peak of 41 billion fbm in 1923 and again in 1925 during the building boom of that period. The industry was hit heavily by the depression, with production dropping to 13.5 billion fbm in 1932, after which it rose to around 35 billion fbm just prior to World War II. Since the war, production has been maintained at a fairly high level, averaging about 37 billion fbm for the period 1952 to 1954. Prior to World War II the United States was a net exporter of lumber, but since the war lumber imports have been substantially higher than exports. During 1952 to 1954 these net imports averaged just over 2 billion fbm annually, giving an apparent domestic consumption of 39 billion fbm.

The explanation of this production record involves both problems in demand and problems in supply. In general, it can be said that demand has not expanded rapidly enough to permit maintenance of the level of production in the face of increasing difficulties in supply. The major factors which have acted to limit the increase in demand include the ending of the period of territorial expansion in the nation, the increasing urbanization of the population, and the development of alternate materials. Many of the difficulties in supply have developed from the reduction of the forest resource by prolonged operation on a liquidation basis. This has involved increased logging costs due to operation in more difficult areas, increased logging and milling costs due to the handling of smaller and lower-quality logs, and increased transportation costs as production has shifted farther from the market centers. The industry has also been marked by rising labor costs as increases in wage rates have not been wholly offset by increases in productivity.

Although in the aggregate the lumber industry is one of the nation's major industries, it is characteristically an industry of small units. A bureau of census study in 1947 showed that the 50 largest companies in the industry provided only 18 per cent of the total value of shipments— the lowest concentration ratio of any of the 38 manufacturing industry groups covered by the study. And beneath these larger companies lie a multitude of small concerns, with more than 53,000 lumber mills having been reported in 1947.

Furthermore, the industry has been progressively breaking down into smaller units rather than aggregating into larger ones. For example, in 1929 the 120 mills producing more than 50 million fbm annually produced 26 per cent of the total output, while in 1947 the 43 mills reaching this size class produced 11 per cent of the total. The regional differences in mill capacity are also significant. In 1947, mills producing more than 10 million fbm annually accounted for 66 per cent of the production in the West, but for only 15 per cent in the South and 6 per cent in the East.

The explanation of this situation lies in the nature of lumber manufacture, the importance of transportation costs in the industry, and the changing nature of the forest resource. In the absence of diversified utilization, the direct economies of large-scale manufacture have been limited. The manufacture of lumber involves a very great reduction in the weight of the logs, with the dry lumber representing probably less than one-third of the green weight of the logs. As the size of the mill is increased, the average length of log haul increases. This increases total transportation costs from tree to consumer, and these higher costs soon offset the limited economies of scale. The result is a limitation on the maximum economic size of a sawmill under any given conditions.

As the possibilities of shifting to new areas of old-growth forests have been drawing to a close, the lumber industry has been faced with the problem of continuing operations in the same location. Since until recently lumber manufacture has been based on extractive techniques, this has involved increasing physical and economic difficulties. The shift to smaller timber, to stands of lower volumes per unit of area, and to scattered stands has been made in large degree by shifting to smaller units which can be brought close to the timber and which can be liquidated over a short period.

Although this type of adjustment to the changing forest resource has enabled the maintenance of production at a level higher than was once believed possible, it has also resulted in some major problems for the industry. Although there are exceptions, the small sawmill economy has been characterized by low wage rates, unstable employment, low and variable standards of manufacture, lack of programs of research and trade promotion, and little interest in long-term investment or planning.

Fig. 12.4 This portable sawmill cutting elm in Michigan is one of the thousands of small mills which are characteristic of the lumber industry, especially in the East and South. (*American Forest Products Industries.*)

This is not, of course, true of the entire lumber industry. Major differences exist among the various regions. As has been indicated earlier, the western lumber industry consists of larger units to an extent not found in the other regions. During recent years the average wage rate in western logging and lumber manufacture has been more than $2\frac{1}{2}$ times as high as that of the South and the East. In the same way, there are major differences among mills within each of the regions.

The Pulp and Paper Industry. The pulp and paper industry is the other major wood-based industry of the United States, ranking above the lumber industry in terms of total value added by manufacture and in terms of salaries and wages. However, in 1952 the cubic foot volume of cut in our domestic forests for pulp production was only 25 per cent of that for the lumber industry. This ratio is much higher now than in the past. For example, in the period 1925 to 1929 the pulpwood cut was 7½ per cent of the cut of logs for the lumber industry.

Throughout the history of the nation, the consumption of paper in the United States has expanded rapidly. The following spot data on the consumption of paper and paperboard will serve to indicate the trend: 1909,

Fig. 12.5 Pulpwood is the primary raw material for the rapidly expanding pulp and paper industry. (*American Forest Products Industries.*)

4.1 million tons; 1929, 13.4 million tons; 1941, 20.4 million tons; and 1954, 31.1 million tons.

Over the years the domestic pulp and paper industry has expanded with this rising consumption, but the United States remains a net importer of pulp and paper by a substantial margin. Eastern pulp mills import about one-fourth of their pulpwood from Canada. Paper mills in this region also import large amounts of pulp, primarily from Canada. The nation imports about 80 per cent of its newsprint paper, again largely from Canada.

Altogether, these various imports represented about 30 per cent of the wood equivalent of our 1952 consumption of paper and pulp products. Although this degree of import dependency may appear high, it actually represents a stage in a trend toward increasing self-sufficiency in pulp and paper. During the decade centered around 1930, it is estimated that the United States imported more than half of the wood equivalent of its paper and pulp requirements.

This trend toward increasing self-sufficiency is the result of technological changes in pulp manufacture which have enabled the industry to achieve a great expansion of its raw-material base within the existing forest resource. Under prevailing pulping processes, the wood-pulp industry was based largely on the spruce-fir forests of the northeast and Great Lakes region through the 1920s. Improvements of the sulfate process which enabled economical production of quality pulps from resinous woods such as the southern pines and Douglas-fir then led to revolutionary changes in the industry. For example, consumption of pulpwood in the South rose from 1.6 million cords in 1929 to 16.1 million cords in 1953, while total consumption of pulpwood in the nation rose from 7.6 million cords to 28.2 million cords in the same period. Technology had completely changed and greatly increased the pulpwood resources of the United States. Current developments in hardwood pulping suggest that a further expansion of the species base of the industry can be expected in the future.

Within the general manufacturing economy of the United States the degree of concentration within a limited number of large companies shown by the pulp and paper industry is fairly low. However, in comparison with the lumber industry, the pulp and paper industry consists of fairly large units. The major locational factors appear to be water supply, wood supply, power costs, and distance to markets, roughly in that order.

The industry has never been a migratory industry in the same sense as lumber manufacture. Although production has expanded into new areas in a search for cheap wood, the older producing regions have maintained and increased their operations. Because of high capital costs and the fixed and durable nature of the manufacturing plants, pulp and paper mills characteristically continue operations in the same location over long periods. This has had a great influence on the attitude of the industry toward the management of the forest resource.

Other Wood Industries.   Production of softwood plywood is one of the most rapidly expanding branches of the forest industries. Production has risen from 0.36 billion sq ft of three-ply equivalent in 1929 to 1.60 billion sq ft in 1941 and on up to 5.29 billion sq ft in 1955. This industry has been entirely a Pacific Coast industry, using primarily Douglas-fir. In its earlier years the industry was based largely on the purchase of logs in the open market, but with increasing recognition of the problem of log supplies, there has been a trend toward increased participation in forest-land ownership.

The softwood-plywood industry is of particular importance as a high-price market for the better-quality logs. In the past, plywood producers could use only top-quality material. However, through technological improvements and the widening of market uses of plywood, the grades suitable for the industry have been greatly extended in range. Although the industry remains a premium market for high-quality logs, technology here as in the pulp and paper industry has greatly expanded the resource base within the existing forests.

The hardwood-plywood and veneer industry located in the East and the South has also shown an upward trend in production, although the increase has not been so pronounced as in softwood plywood. During recent years this industry has faced heavy competition from low-cost imports of hardwood plywood.

In addition, there are a number of other minor forest-product industries. In the aggregate these industries represented 7 per cent of the total cubic foot volume of timber cut for the forest industries in 1952. These include such products as poles, piling, charcoal, hewn railroad ties, round mine timbers, and cooperage. Finally, there is the naval-stores industry of the South which is established on three different bases: on the tapping of living trees, on the distillation of stump wood, and as a by-product of the sulfate pulp process.

Future Wood Markets. In looking at natural resources, the past gives perspective, the present appears transient, and the future tends to become the frame of reference. In the forest-products industries, as in many parts of our economy in recent years, a number of studies of long-term prospects have been made. Independent studies covering all forest products were released by Stanford Research Institute in 1954 and by the U.S. Forest Service in 1955.

Both of these studies are based on the assumption of a continued rapid economic expansion. They anticipate an increase in population from about 164 million in 1954 to around 210 or 212 million by 1975. With such a population increase there is expected to be an increase in the gross national product by 1975 of around 75 per cent above the 1950–1954 average. Under such conditions there can be expected to develop a considerable increase in demand for forest products as for most other goods and services in the economy. However, the expansion of forest-products markets and production will be determined by problems of supply as well as by the level of demand.

In general, it is expected that increases in costs anticipated as involved in further expansion of lumber output would act to check any great expansion of lumber consumption. An increase in consumption of not more than 10 to 15 per cent is expected by 1975 under these conditions. These anticipated cost problems are based on the current availability of timber suitable for lumber production, since only limited increases in saw-log-size material could possibly be obtained over the next 20 years. In pulp and paper, however, consumption is expected to rise with very little check from rising costs, and an expansion of around 70 per cent in consumption expressed in pulpwood equivalent is shown for 1975. It is believed that this industry can solve the problem of rising wood costs by expanding its resource base through increased use of sawmill and logging residues, increased pulping of hardwoods, and the growth of material of pulpwood size in managed forests. A similarly rapid expansion in the consumption of plywood is anticipated, with the consumption of logs for plywood and veneer possibly doubling from 1952 to 1975. Here, too, technological developments are expected to widen the resource base through enabling the use of a wider range of species and log quality. Among the minor forest products it is expected that some lines will expand while others will contract, with little if any net change in the aggregate volume being anticipated.

Although there are considerable differences in detail in the two studies, the estimates of total consumption of industrial wood products in 1975 measured in cubic feet of round-wood volume and including the wood equivalent of net imports agree within 1.1 per cent. The indicated increase in such consumption from 1952 to 1975 is roughly 25 per cent.

On the other hand, the consumption of fuel wood is expected to continue its pronounced decline. This is not due to any problem of wood supply, but rather is because of the greater convenience and cleanliness of some other fuels and the high labor requirements involved in fuel-wood production.

However, in terms of the total timber cut, the significance of this anticipated fuel-wood decline is limited because of the relatively low level of fuel-wood cutting at present. Thus it is probable that the pronounced downward trend in total cut which has prevailed for the last 50 years because of declining fuel-wood use has come to an end. It can be expected that in the future the total cut will rise above the level of the early 1950s. Obviously an estimate of the amount of such increase involves many difficulties and uncertainties. The Forest Service study indicates an increase of at least 15 per cent in the total cut from our domestic forests from 1952 to 1975.

Trends in Wood Utilization.   A natural resource has meaning only in terms of the techniques which are available for its utilization. Improvements in utilization can be a major route to resource conservation.

In the forest industries there has been an accelerating trend toward

changes in techniques. New methods of logging and new types of equipment have changed inaccessible forests to accessible stands. Similar
changes have enabled the economical handling of materials of sizes and
qualities previously considered uneconomic and have made it possible
to salvage for economic use scattered dead trees and similar materials.
In lumber manufacture advances in metallurgy and improved saw design
have enabled increases in recovery in sawing, while improved drying
methods and yard-handling procedures have made it possible to reduce

Fig. 12.6 This operation of the Weyerhaeuser Timber Company at Springfield,
Oregon, includes a sawmill, plywood mill, ply-veneer plant, Presto-log plant, dry
kiln and planing mill, sulfate pulp mill, and container-board plant. Such integrated
and diversified utilization, by enabling full use of the materials cut from the forest,
provides a sound basis for good forest management. (*Western Ways, Inc.*)

degrade in seasoning. In both the pulp and paper industry and the plywood industry, technological advances have enabled a great expansion of
the potential resource base represented by existing forests. These and
many other developments in each of the forest-product industries considered separately have enabled the production of a greater quantity or
better quality of forest products from a given quantity of forest resource.
Further developments of these types are possible in the future.

Perhaps of even greater current importance, however, is the recent
trend toward the integration of several different product lines in the use
of the forest resource. In its most common form, integrated utilization
now implies the recovery of suitable residues from lumber manufacture
for use in pulp production. This has been made possible by the development of practical log-barking equipment for use at sawmills. The practice
developed first at the large mills in the Pacific Northwest but is now

spreading to smaller mills and promises to develop rapidly in the South. In 1952 about 6 per cent of the domestic pulpwood production came from this source without involving any additional cut in the forests. A large increase in this ratio is expected in the future.

Important though this is, however, it represents only a preliminary stage in the development of integrated utilization. The wood on any forest area represents a remarkable heterogeneity of sizes and qualities. Only widely diversified markets can enable a full return from such material. There is a need for plywood and veneer markets for the quality material, for lumber markets for the bulk of logs from the mature trees, for pulp-wood markets for the tops and early thinnings, and for pole and piling markets for the later thinnings. The returns from such diversified markets can make intensive forest management financially desirable and can greatly increase the volume and value of products obtained for the nation from a given volume of use of this resource.

Such integration of diversified product lines needs to be carried out at the mill level as well. The cores of logs cut for veneer and plywood can be used for the production of lumber or pulp. The residues from lumber manufacture can be processed for various wood specialties or can be chipped for use in pulp manufacture.

Thus full integrated utilization involves both the routing of each log and bolt cut in the forest to its most profitable use and the routing of the materials developed in processing each such log or bolt to their most profitable uses.

In moving toward such integration the development of new forest products can play an important role. The development of additional processes for manufacturing hardboard since World War II and the expansion of such production are examples of these possibilities, as is the even more recent development of particle-board production. Nonpulp fiber products are a little-developed field for using mill residues and perhaps also for the use of bark, which amounts to nearly 10 per cent of the volume of the wood. The waste liquors from pulping which now are a disposal problem are potentially a source of useful products.

There are now a number of examples of well-integrated forest-products operations and many more examples of preliminary moves in this direction. However, the trend toward such utilization is still in its early stages and has not yet become characteristic of forest industries generally. It is becoming evident that such utilization is introducing a major new aggregative force into the forest industries. It is possible that this may offset the historic forces which have led to a progressive disintegration in the lumber industry and to the short-term, low-capital, single-product concerns which have been prevalent in most of the forest industries up to now. It may well be that the advantages of integrated utilization will lead the forest industries into the development of larger, more diversified, better-balanced, and more permanent concerns in the coming years.

There are many difficulties to be overcome in the widespread development of such operations, and there is very little basis for estimating the rapidity with which such developments may occur. However, the trends in utilization are opening up a route by which the forest lands of the nation can serve as the resource base for a greatly expanded volume and value of forest products in the future.

12.5 The Ownership of Forest Land

The owner of land ordinarily makes the primary decisions controlling its management and use. Thus, in turning again to the management of

Table 12.2 The Ownership of Commercial Forest Land in the United States, 1953

(In millions of acres)

Class	East	South	West	Total United States
All ownerships...............	169	194	121	484
Total private................	137	177	44	358
Farm.....................	58	91	16	165
Forest industry...........	14	33	15	62
Other private.............	65	53	13	131
Total public................	32	17	77	126
Federal..................	13	14	72	99
State and local............	19	3	5	27

SOURCE: United States Forest Service.

the forest land which is the basic resource behind the forest industries, it is desirable to consider the current status of forest ownership.

The forests of the United States are primarily private property, with private owners holding three-fourths and public agencies one-fourth of the total commercial forest area. The public holdings are concentrated in the West, where they form about two-thirds of the forest area. These are largely Federal lands. State and local governmental agencies have only one-fifth of the public forests. Most of such land is in the East, with much of it having been obtained through the reversion of tax-delinquent areas.

The forest industries own a relatively limited area, amounting to about one-eighth of the total. About half of this industry land is in the South, with the balance split between East and West. The farm forests are the largest class of holdings, with one-third of the forest area. In the South, farmers hold nearly half of the forest land. The remaining one-fourth of the forest land is held by a wide variety of private owners, with much of this area being in small holdings.

It is estimated that private holdings of less than 100 acres total 25 per cent of the commercial forest area, or about the same as all public holdings. Another 20 per cent of the total is in private holdings of 100 to 500 acres, 9 per cent in holdings between 500 and 5000 acres, 7 per cent between 5000 and 50,000 acres, and 16 per cent in private holdings of more than 50,000 acres. Thus the control of the greater part of the commercial forest land in the United States is in the hands of a very large number of private owners of small forest properties.

Land Ownership and Forest Management.   The growing of forest trees probably involves the longest production period of any of the economic enterprises carried on within the United States. Under very favorable circumstances economic returns from early thinning cuts may be obtained within 15 years following the establishment of the forest stand. However, the main tree crop will rarely be obtained in less than 30 years, while periods of 50 to 100 years are far more representative. In some areas and for some products even longer growth periods are required.

The development of an established stand occurs through the growth of the trees which form the stand. Thus the trees which are to be the final product of this process are also a basic part of the means of production. To carry out effective forest management it is necessary to maintain and commonly to increase the capital investment in a growing stock of trees. In economic terms, forest management is a process of capital investment and capital accumulation based on the expectation of future earnings.

To carry out a productive enterprise of this sort the forest owner must have the necessary knowledge, motivation, and capital resources. Recognition of this is basic to an understanding of the current status and future possibilities of forest management in the United States.

During 1953 and 1954 the Forest Service carried out a carefully planned study of the condition of recently cutover lands. The public forests, the industry forests, and the large ownerships generally were found to have a high percentage of their recently cut lands in good condition for future forest production. In contrast, farm forests and small ownerships in general were found to have a relatively low percentage of their recent cutovers in such good condition. Small forest ownerships in the South, with more than one-fourth of the nation's commercial forest area, were held to be "the nub of the cutover land problem in the United States."

Such identification of " weak " areas is important in understanding the problem of improving the management of the forest-land resource. A lack of knowledge and an accompanying lack of motivation are undoubtedly of importance in explaining the attitude of many small holders to their forest lands. A lack of stability in ownership and the resulting lack of continuity in management interest are also surely of importance. However, it appears probable that in many instances a lack of capital resources and an income below that required for a desired living standard are basic to a lack of long-term forest management in many small properties. In short, many owners of small forest properties are not in a position to maintain or increase *any* long-term capital investments. The management of forest land cannot be considered in isolation from the economic and social needs and desires of the landowners.

Land Ownership and Wood Use. The industrial forest owners generally use directly the greater part of the products cut on their forest lands. The economic motivation of the operation commonly comes from the profit to be earned from the sale of wood products. It is looked upon as a manufacturing profit rather than a profit from wood growing. The impetus to forest management tends to come from a desire to ensure a wood supply needed to maintain a profitable wood-processing enterprise. In the past such owners have commonly tended to process their log supply in terms of their particular products rather than on the basis of obtaining the greatest value for the log. Increasingly, however, these industrial owners are recognizing that the variety of wood qualities involved in their cut can support a greater income if the product lines are diversified.

The other private forest owners are in quite a different position. They must rely on the sale of standing timber or of logs and bolts for the income from their forests. If there are a number of diversified forest industries actively buying wood in the area, the situation is favorable. Often, however, the nonindustrial owner finds only limited market outlets in his area. The market problems of the small holdings have often been particularly difficult. With a small volume and infrequent sales, the owner of such a tract is commonly poorly informed on market opportunities and timber values.

There is also an important converse relationship. The development of permanent diversified forest industries involves a large capital investment and requires a sure supply of timber in the future. The development of such ensured supplies of timber in an area dominated by small holdings managed on a short-term basis is very difficult. Such an ownership pattern favors small single-product mills established on a similarly short-term basis. The pulp and paper industry has for some years been carrying out a program designed to meet this problem, and recently a few lumber producers have also become active in such efforts. The ability to develop ensured timber supplies from these lands now in small holdings will have a great deal to do with the level and type of future forest-products output and with the management given the forest-land resource.

In the western United States this relationship takes on a special form because of the great importance of public ownership of the forests. The sale of public timber in small quantities and on a short-term basis tends to increase competitive bidding and to give the small operator a chance. On the other hand, the sale of large quantities with long-term contractual relationships can provide the resource base for heavy capital investment in diversified manufacturing facilities. Both objectives are important to the economy of the West, and the conflict between the two must be expected to be an increasing source of difficulty in public forest administration.

12.6 Public Influences on Forest-land Owners

Although the owner of forest land makes the primary decisions controlling its management and use, the people of the United States influence and limit these decisions in a wide variety of ways. All these ways might be grouped under a broad conception of public forest policy.

The development of improved management of the forest-land resource is a generally accepted objective of public policy in the United States. Probably the most widely known public action in "forest conservation" is the system of national forests and other public forests in which this objective is sought through direct ownership and control. However, the influences exerted on the remaining three-fourths of the commercial forest area which is in private ownership are also a very important part of public forest policy. Many programs have been developed to facilitate the management of these lands. Through state action supported in part by Federal grants an effective system of fire control has been established in most forest areas, and since 1947 there has been provision for state and Federal action in the control of forest insects and diseases. On the same basis a program of service forestry to provide owners of small forest properties with technical guidance has been developed, and a system of nurseries for the production of low-cost forest planting stock has been built up. The research branch of the U.S. Forest Service has made valuable contributions to the knowledge of forest-land management. At least 23 of the states have provided for the education of professional foresters through their state university systems.

In addition to these programs to facilitate good forest management, many of the states in which forests are important have enacted legislation which provides for the regulation of cutting practices and certain other management practices on private forest lands. This regulatory approach is basically a means of preventing forest devastation rather than a route to ensuring full forest production.

On the other hand, a number of our economic institutions have not been favorable to forestry. The general property tax has imposed a heavier burden on immature forests and forests held for deferred cutting than on most forms of business. Assessment of forest properties has often been erratic. Until 1953, regulations of the Federal Reserve System prevented member banks from recognizing standing timber as security for loans. Although there has been a recent increase in activity, up to 1955 neither forest insurance nor long-term credit facilities have generally been available to forestry operations.

It is through this entire setting of economic institutions and the general economic climate that the public has its influence on the forest resource. The rapid progress in forest management which has been made in recent years is the result of a total economic setting which on balance has been favorable to forestry rather than the result of any one program or policy.

12.7 Compatibility of Wood Production and Other Forest Uses

Wood Production and Water. Of the precipitation which falls on a forest area in the form of rain or snow, a part will be returned directly to the atmosphere by evaporation, a part will run off over the surface of the ground, and a part will be absorbed by the litter and soil. Of the water absorbed by the soil, a part is returned to the atmosphere by transpiration of the vegetative cover and a part by direct evaporation, while the balance is held as soil moisture or ground-water storage. The ground water in turn through percolation is a source of supply for springs, streams, and lakes.

By maintaining desirable soil conditions the forest cover favors ground-water storage by increasing absorption and reducing surface runoff. At the same time it increases evaporation as a result of interception and itself uses large quantities of the soil water in transpiration. With these various interrelationships it is difficult to determine with any precision the net effect on the yield of usable water of changes in the vegetative cover.

In the management of forests for wood production, it is the harvesting of the tree crops which involves the greatest direct impact on watershed conditions. The construction of roads and the skidding of the logs across the ground can involve major soil disturbances and upset the water regime of an area. However, such disturbances will also have a great impact on the possibilities of further wood production. A badly disturbed watershed with compacted soils or accelerated erosion is not a favorable site for establishing forest regeneration. If road development and logging operations are carried out with full provision for future wood crops, the disturbance to the watershed will usually be limited. A good productive forest is usually a good watershed.

It is probable that neither maximum wood production nor a maximum vegetative cover will ordinarily give the maximum yield of usable water. Further research can be expected to add to the knowledge of ways of safely manipulating the vegetation to increase water recovery. It is possible that such studies will show a need to modify methods of timber production to improve water yields in some areas. It is also probable that on certain highly critical watersheds not even limited disturbance of conditions should be permitted and wood production should be excluded along with other uses. However, in general, it appears the wood and water can be complementary products from most of our forest lands.

Fig. 12.7 In many regions of the United States the forest lands are the primary watersheds and important recreational areas. Good forest management can maintain and develop these values. (*U.S. Forest Service.*)

Wood Production and Forage.   The relationship between management of forest land for wood production and the use of the area for forage and cover for domestic livestock or game animals is extremely complex. The ecological relationships and effects vary with the species of animal, the size of the animal population, the type of forest, and the stage of development of the forest.

In most hardwood forest types and on farm wood lots generally, the use of the area by livestock is commonly in direct conflict with use for wood production. Frequently the result of such combined use is neither good forage nor good forest. Perhaps the primary grazing use of forest areas is developed on the intermingled openings which occur naturally in many forest types. Here the intermingling of the use pattern is a logical result of the intermingled vegetation types. The transition zone between primary use for forage and primary use for timber is a traditional and major tension zone in our land-use adjustments.

Fig. 12.8 These sheep grazing on a National Forest in Arizona represent the intermingling of uses which is a logical result of the intermingled vegetation types. (*U.S. Forest Service.*)

The extensive old-growth forests did not sustain a large population of the higher forms of animal life. In general the cutting operations, by breaking up the continuity of the forest cover, have resulted in increased feed and favorable cover conditions for game. Commonly the result has been an increase in wildlife populations, but often with a shift in the composition of the wildlife since any shift in vegetation may be favorable to one type of animal and unfavorable to another. The forest lands are a major source of game, and relatively minor modification of wood-production forestry can further increase the game-bearing capacity of these areas. However, under our existing institutions and customs, hunting is frequently a source of trouble to the owner and damage to the forest rather than a source of additional income. In addition, overpopulations of animals have developed in many areas, often with serious effects on the forests. Excessive numbers of deer, for example, often make forest regeneration extremely difficult or impossible. Effective game management under regulations sufficiently flexible to permit adjustment to local conditions of vegetation and animal populations is needed to reduce conflict and make game and wood complementary products of the forest land.

Wood Production and Forest Recreation. With increasing leisure time, improving transportation, and increasing urbanization of the population, there have developed rapidly increasing recreational uses of forest lands. These uses are extremely variable in their requirements and often conflict with each other. They range from the practically suburban developments of some commercial resort and cabin areas to the unmodified wilderness areas in which some difficulty of access is a prerequisite. The average skier desires mechanical developments and clear cuttings, while the park enthusiast may value each tree in its natural setting. Obviously the relationship of such uses to wood production depends on the particular circumstances of the individual case.

Generally, however, such recreational use of forest areas is a fringe use, concentrated along roadsides, lake shores, and spots of special beauty in the forests. The primary recreational role of most forest land is as an aesthetically desirable background and as a locale for hunting and fishing. The compatibility of this role with wood production has been demonstrated in many regions in which forest management is well established.

For intensively used camp and cabin areas, wood production must be accorded a secondary role, but the two uses often need not be mutually exclusive. However, for the special requirements of natural parks and wilderness areas, there must be acknowledged a conflict between forest management for wood production and recreational and aesthetic needs.

12.8 Forest Land and the Future

Wood as one of the nation's major renewable resources has value to our society primarily through use by forest industries which produce goods desired by consumers. If the forest industries develop the strength to expand their output along with the general expansion of our economy in the future, they can provide the economic base for the good management of all the forest land of the nation. Such good management for wood production can also give good watershed conditions, a desirable environment for recreational use, and substantial yields of forage and cover for animals.

The forest lands of the nation can sustain such an expansion of forest-products output. With the sharp decline in fuel-wood cutting and the lack of expansion of lumber production, the total cut from the forest lands has declined over the last 50 years. At the same time, increasingly effective protection of forest lands from fire and other destructive agencies and expanding forest management have had positive results. The growth of the forests has been expanding. Under these two types of forces, a stage of balance has now been reached. Estimates developed by the United

States Forest Service show the total growth of timber in the United States, measured in terms of cubic foot volume of growing stock, to have been more than 30 per cent higher than the total cut in 1952. In saw-log-size material, measured in the board foot volume of saw timber, the growth was nearly as high as the cut.

Within this general balance there are many problems of the distribution of the growth in terms of regions, species, sizes, and quality of wood. However, the most careful analyses which have been made indicate that

Fig. 12.9   The forests are a renewable resource. This fine stand of pine and hardwoods in Arkansas is skillfully managed with annual cutting of forest products. If such skillful management can be achieved generally, the forests of the United States can provide both increased forest products and other forest values in the future. (*U.S. Forest Service.*)

the stage has now been reached at which both the volume of cut and the volume of growth can move upward in the future. With a continuation and intensification of present trends in forestry, there can be a substantial increase in the volume of forest products available for consumption in the future, while at the same time the nation can achieve an increase in the volume of timber growth and timber inventory and a general improvement in the condition of the forest-land resource.

Timber is a crop. There is no longer any question of a "timber famine" in the nation. There remains the question of how fully the nation will use and benefit from the potential of its forest-land resource.

13

Food Consumption and Resources

MAYNARD A. JOSLYN and HAROLD S. OLCOTT

DEPARTMENT OF FOOD TECHNOLOGY

UNIVERSITY OF CALIFORNIA, BERKELEY

13.1 Introduction

The primal instinct of hunger, from the dawn of history, has given man a compelling interest in the problem of securing and maintaining his food supply. In the early food-gathering and hunting cultures, mankind passed periodically from food orgies into long periods of semistarvation. After transition to the food-production era, some eight thousand years ago, hunger and famine were still common, and even in recent times more people have died from famine than have been killed in war. While today frank starvation is periodic and limited largely to densely populated areas, suboptimal nutrition and malnutrition are widespread. Nevertheless, our knowledge of nutritional requirements for optimal health has been expanding, particularly in the last three decades, so that today we are close to defining the complete dietary constituents necessary for optimal physical and mental health. Unfortunately this knowledge has yet to be put into world-wide practice. It is estimated that about two-thirds of the population of the world is on a diet that is inadequate, i.e., on a diet supplying less than 2250 calories per capita per day, and some of the population is on a diet bordering starvation. Ignorance of the essential dietary requirements, poor dietary habits, and lack of ability to purchase or acquire the essential foods all contribute to this situation.

This situation and the explosive nature of the increase in world population during the last two decades have focused the attention of thoughtful scientists and laymen on the recurring question: Are our food resources adequate to meet the existing and foreseeable population requirements? This has been discussed in many recent articles and books by agricultural economists, nutritionists, and others. We here present our analysis of the situation on the basis of published statistical data and current investiga-

288

tions, with particular stress on present-day technological developments and from the point of view of food technologists.

At the present, as in the past, there is a wide disparity and contrast between the standards of living of populations in different parts of the world. Some twenty countries with a population of about 400 million, about one-sixth of the present world population, live in clean and comfortable surroundings, are relatively well clothed, sheltered, and fed. In sharp contrast, in the so-called underdeveloped countries, the great mass of people live in intolerably bad conditions and many suffer from disabling diseases and still more from malnutrition. Technically, there is no need for these contrasts to continue, for it is possible to abolish them by the sharing of skills and the development of resources. If the means were available for a more effective distribution of existing food supplies, some of the existing disparities in food consumption could be alleviated. Much more could be done by increasing the world's food supplies by methods already known, such as:

1. Reducing losses during production by plant pests and diseases
2. Reducing losses through infestation of stored products by insects, fungi, and rodents
3. Improving distribution and utilization by advances in food-preservation methods
4. Increasing the yield from areas already under cultivation
5. Developing new productive areas

The importance of action to increase the world's food supplies both to improve the diet of the existing population and to provide for the accelerating population increase is widely recognized. Although it is obvious that the earth cannot support an infinite population of anything, including men, the productive potential of the earth and the maximum population that the earth's resources can comfortably support are difficult to estimate. Technical advances in the production, processing, preservation, storage, and transportation and use of foods that have been made already markedly affect previous prognoses. It is possible that future developments in biological and physical sciences and their application to food production will result in unexpected new methods of increasing food supplies. Long-range predictions therefore can only suggest the upper limit to the population that the earth can support on the basis of our present knowledge of food production and food requirement.

While it is possible to arrive at a reasonable estimate of the population that could be supported by the existing land and sea resources under particular conditions of food consumption, it is difficult to foresee whether this could be achieved under the existing political and economic environment. Even more difficult is the determination of a fundamental relation, if such exists, between rate of increase in food production and population growth. There have been several attempts to formulate this relation on the basis of which the critical limit of population growth could be fixed. One of the most widely quoted of such estimates was that made by an English country clergyman, the Rev. Thomas Robert Malthus, about a hundred and sixty years ago (1798). Malthus observed, in his own village, that the limit to the increase in population was determined by the quantity of food available. On the basis of his belief that populations increase geometrically and food production arithmetically, he concluded that the human race would eventually run out of food. Famine, disease, and war would have to balance the discrepancy, unless man could adjust his rate of increase to the amount of food available by voluntary or imposed birth control.

The basic assumption that the population will inevitably increase faster than food production, however, cannot now be accepted. As Bennett[1] has pointed out in his analysis of the concepts of Malthus,

The power of population to increase is not necessarily exerted but lies within the control of mankind; and the power of food production or consumption level to increase has not necessarily a ceiling upon it and does not have to increase in arithmetic ratio only. Man is unlike animals and insects in that he produces food for himself by his own efforts and is not merely a gatherer of what nature has put before him.

Malthus could not foresee the effects of the Industrial Revolution, with concomitant improvements in agriculture and transport which made it so much easier to obtain food that during the next hundred years the population of Britain increased fourfold. Food supply during this period was not a limiting factor. The capacity to produce foods in various regions of the world has changed periodically, and even in the so-called underdeveloped countries of the world, food surpluses have accumulated in some districts while famine was rife in others. This regional overproduction created the anomalous condition which has been recognized for several decades. In 1935, Bruce in his famous speech at the League of Nations meeting directed attention to this situation: agriculture in the advanced countries was seriously depressed because farmers could not sell the food they were producing, and they were advised to produce less, while in less-advanced countries millions of people went hungry and suffered accordingly in health and efficiency. This situation still exists.

Recent analyses of our ability to meet the food requirements of a growing population have been of two types. On the one hand are those who have felt that we are close to the limit of the earth's resources. On the other hand, the more optimistic writers do not foresee a critical shortage

---

[1] M. K. Bennett, *The World's Food: A Study of the Interrelations of World Populations, National Diets and Food Potentials*, Harper & Brothers, New York, 1954.

of food in the near future. Lord Boyd-Orr[1] in discussing the agricultural potentialities of the world concludes

There seems no reason to doubt the estimate made by agricultural experts, that if modern improved methods were applied to all the land at present cultivated or grazed the world food supply would be doubled, and that if known measures were taken to increase the area of the earth under cultivation by irrigation, bush clearance, and other measures, the earth could support a population of 6000 million.

Killefer[2] too has no fear that the growth of population in the world will ever lead to famine because of the technological advances that have been made in improving the productivity of the soil, reducing losses, and synthesizing nutritional adjuncts. Brown[3] has estimated that it will be technologically possible to feed and clothe a world population of 7 billion but that the world will be a more desirable place to live in if voluntary control levels off population growth in the next century to less than the expected threefold rise. The quicker world birth rates drop, through the spread of birth control, the faster world living standards will rise, according to his analysis. Forbes and Brody stress the need to control population growth first. In their concept there is not, nor will there ever be, a "shortage of food" but, instead, an "excess of people."

De Castro[4] suggested that high fertility and birth rates are due in part to undernourishment and malnutrition and that improvement in nutrition would automatically reduce rates of population growth. Although this hypothesis is far from proved, Teitelbaum and Gantt[5] recently reported that starvation in dogs increased sperm count per cubic centimeter and per ejaculate and suggested that these findings have sociological implications. If these observations are reproducible, they will support the concept that improvement in nutritional status could be a factor in limiting birth rate.

The data on dietary requirements and food productivity, incomplete though they are, definitely support the conclusion that the world is not as yet close to the critical limit of food sufficiency for the existing and foreseeable population. Land, methods of cultivation, means of preservation and transportation are available to support the anticipated world

[1] L. Boyd-Orr, *Food and the Future*, George Allen & Unwin, Ltd., London, 1954.

[2] D. H. Killefer, *Two Ears of Corn, Two Blades of Grass*, D. Van Nostrand Company, Inc., Princeton, N.J., 1955.

[3] H. S. Brown, *The Challenge of Man's Future: An Inquiry concerning the Condition of Man during the Years That Lie Ahead*, The Viking Press, Inc., New York, 1954.

[4] Josué de Castro, *The Geography of Hunger*, Little, Brown & Company, Boston, 1952.

[5] H. A. Teitelbaum and W. H. Gantt, "Effect of Starvation on Sperm Count and Sexual Reflexes," *Science*, vol. 124, pp. 363–364, 1956.

population for at least one or two generations, provided that existing political, educational, economic, and other barriers are overcome. The latter are not within the scope of this survey of food resources. Freedom from want will be possible when governments, religious institutions, and other organizations will be able to collaborate freely and willingly in the solution of the existing problems.

13.2   Adequacy of Available Food Supplies for Existing Population

Several methods of estimating the adequacy of available food supplies have been used. These have included estimates of the quantity of food actually consumed on the bases of food balances, dietary surveys, nutritional surveys relative to dietary allowances recognized as necessary, and land-area requirements. The limitations of these measures have not always been realized by those who have used them in determining differences in the nutritional status of the population in various countries. Our knowledge of nutrition has advanced from the early emphasis on caloric requirements, to recognition of the qualitative factors inherent in the specification of a diet on an ingredient basis, and finally to the recognition of the important dynamic interrelationship between man, food, and environment. Lepkovsky[1] has called attention to the importance of nutritional stress factors and has developed recently a new concept of animal nutrition on the basis of factors influencing (1) transfer of nutrients from the environment to the gastrointestinal tract, (2) processing in the gastrointestinal tract, (3) transfer from the gastrointestinal tract to body cells, and (4) utilization by the cells. This concept was advanced also as the basis for sound information on nutrition by Gerard.[2] Our knowledge of several of these factors is still incomplete, and a better understanding of basic nutrition and possibilities and limitations of meeting this will not be available until the science of nutrition advances. In the meantime, hunger per se is differentiated loosely from "hidden hunger" due to inadequacies of the diet in less well understood but nonetheless appreciated factors.

Data on the quantity and types of foods actually consumed and their composition as prepared for consumption furnish one measure of food consumption and nutrition. It is customary to determine the total food produced in a region, correct this for food exported or imported, and then calculate average level of food consumed per unit of population. Such calculated average levels are rarely accurately known because of the difficulties involved in obtaining accurate data on consumption and popu-

---

[1] S. Lepkovsky, "Nutritional Stress Factors and Food Processing," in E. M. Mrak and G. Stewart (eds.), *Advances in Food Research*, vol. 4, pp. 105–132, Academic Press, Inc., New York, 1953.

[2] R. W. Gerard (ed.), *Food for Life*, University of Chicago Press, Chicago, 1952.

lation. The errors inherent in such estimates are largely unknown. The calculated average food consumption disregards such factors as age, ethnic origin, food prejudices, climate, and other stress factors determining both actual food intake and dietary requirements. They are useful, however, in comparing food consumption as it exists in various regions of the world with the average for the world as a whole and are important indices of existing and potential food consumption.

In addition to national food-balance data of this type, some information on food-consumption levels is also available from dietary surveys which indicate not only the average levels in a country as a whole but also their variation within different sections of the population. Such data, however, are limited to only a few countries which carry out comprehensive surveys of food consumption regularly on a national scale.

It is, therefore, difficult to estimate the actual food consumption and nutritional status of the world population. Nutritional surveys based on estimates of actual intake of nutrients are still limited, and too often regional surveys of this type are based only on average analyses of representative foods rather than on actual quantitative and qualitative analyses of nutrients present in the food as prepared and eaten. Physical evaluation of nutritional status for large sections of the population is limited or incomplete. While the necessity for a combination of the two approaches is recognized, this has not been widely used. More investigation of methodology and interpretation in this field is necessary.

It is now well established that inherent factors that determine body size and shape and physiological state (such as age, sex, physique, etc.) and environmental factors (such as climate, physical activity, etc.) determine both the basal metabolism and the requirements for growth and activity. The marked differences in the metabolic activity of one individual from another, however, have but recently been stressed and are still not widely recognized. In view of these factors, the average dietary requirements for a given population sample are not sufficient to define individual needs. Even when the difference in the dietary requirement of an individual from that of the "average" of a sample is disregarded, our knowledge of human nutrition is still too incomplete to specify the actual requirement of all factors.

Some of the essential nutrients required in small amounts (the micronutrients) are still unknown. The known requirement for many dietary factors is still based largely on small-animal feeding tests, or on very limited tests on humans, and is subject to correction.

Recommended Dietary Allowances.   On the basis of our present knowledge of nutrition, however, it is possible to specify partially the factors that must be present in a diet adequate to maintain good nutrition of healthy normal individuals subjected to ordinary environmental stresses. Such dietary allowances will be adequate only if the diet is composed of a variety of common foods which may provide less well-known nutrient requirements, and even this diet may supply the requirements for "adequate" and not for "optimal" nutrition. The recommended daily dietary allowances of the Food and Nutrition Board of the National Research Council of the United States, have been used as an index of the nutritional adequacy of various dietaries. These dietary allowances, however, apply to healthy persons, normally vigorous and living in temperate climates and consuming a variety of common foods. Even under these conditions marked variation is recognized in the dietary requirements of persons of different sex, age, weight and height, and physiological condition (e.g., pregnancy and lactation). It is recognized that the diet must supply:[1]

Energy required for basal metabolic rate and for normal growth and activity; this varies from 1200 to 2500 calories for infants and children and 1800 to 3300 for adults. The carbohydrate, fat, and protein constituents of a food supply this over-all energy requirement. No specific requirement for carbohydrates is recognized. Fats, however, are desirable in the diet because of the function they serve in absorption and utilization of fat-soluble vitamins, their high-satiety value, and their function as concentrated sources of energy; it is usually recommended that natural fats be included to the extent of 20 to 25 per cent of the total calories for moderately active persons and to 30 to 35 per cent of the total calories of children, adolescents, and very active adults. As a matter of precaution, it is recommended that the fat intake include "essential" unsaturated fatty acids to the extent of at least 1 per cent of the total calories.

Protein. Specific requirement for protein, both quantitatively and qualitatively, is recognized. Quantitatively this varies from 40 to 100 g per day, depending on personal and environmental factors. Qualitatively the protein intake must supply the essential amino acids, and these can best be obtained from the biologically complete animal proteins. The individual cereal and vegetable proteins are usually not biologically complete. It is difficult but not impossible to ingest a sufficient quantity of the variety of cereal and other plant proteins to meet the necessary requirement. The minimum proportion of animal protein in a mixed animal and plant-food diet cannot be specified.

Minerals. The essential need for inorganic constituents such as the cations (sodium, potassium, calcium, iron, copper, etc.) and the anions (chloride, phosphate, iodide, etc.) is recognized, but only calcium and iron are usually specified.

[1] U.S. National Research Council, Food and Nutrition Board, *Recommended Dietary Allowances*, revised, 1953.

Vitamins. Of the many vitamins now known, only two fat-soluble factors (vitamins A and D) and eight water-soluble factors (thiamine, riboflavin, niacin, ascorbic acid, vitamin B_6, biotin, pantothenic acid, and possibly folic acid) are considered to be essential for human nutrition. An adequate diet also must supply the crude-fiber constituents required for bulk for normal functioning of the digestive tract and the necessary requirement of water.

It is customary to use the caloric value of a diet as a measure of the quantity of food consumed, but the average minimum number of calories required daily for adequate nutrition cannot be given unequivocally. For an average family in the United States composed of two adults and two children under ten, it would be 2200 calories per person, and this is close to the value taken as border line by nutritionists of the Food and Agricultural Organization of the United Nations. There is no relatively simple unit for measurement of the quality of the diet, but the protein content is used as a yardstick on the assumption that foods rich in proteins are also comparatively good sources of other essential nutrients, especially vitamins and minerals. This is particularly true of foods of animal origin, and animal-protein intake is considered to be a better indicator of quality than the total protein intake.

Protein malnutrition is recognized to occur widely in underdeveloped countries such as Africa, Asia, and South America. Waterlow and Vergara,[1] for example, stress protein malnutrition in Brazil.

These and any other estimates of dietary sufficiency are not complete and must be used with caution as yardsticks of the adequacy of any diet. It is customary in evaluating and planning dietaries to classify foods into groups each of which has a characteristic function and which in combination provides the more important essential nutrients. In the FAO statistics and nutritional surveys, the following food groupings are used: cereals and flour, potatoes and other root crops, sugar, pulses and dry legumes, meat (including offal and poultry), milk and milk products, and fats and oils. The available data on food consumption in terms of these groups of foods and also in terms of total calories, total protein, per cent of total protein as animal protein, per cent of total calories from animal or cereal products indicate that a wide disparity in food supply and food consumption per person exists. This can be illustrated in various ways.

Table 13.1 shows the minimum and maximum values reported for different countries and regions. In Table 13.2, these extremes are shown for the United States in comparison with India; and in Table 13.3 are shown in more detail the world total and per capita production of milk.

[1] J. Waterlow and Vergara, "Protein Malnutrition in Brazil," FAO Nutritional Studies, No. 14, Rome, 1956.

Table 13.1 Existing Extremes in World Food Supply per Person per Year

	Maximum	Minimum
Cereals and flour in terms of flour and milled rice, lb per year..............	425 (Turkey)	165 (United States)
Potatoes and other root crops (including sweet potatoes and cassava flour), lb per year.........................	528 (Poland)	18 (India)
Sugar (as refined sugar but not including sirup and honey), lb per year........	128 (Australia)	2 (China)
Pulses and dry legumes, lb per year.....	48 (Brazil)	2 (Austria, China, and Denmark)
Meat (including poultry and offal), lb per year...............................	242 (New Zealand)	2 (India)
Milk (whole milk for consumption as such and as processed-milk products), lb per year...............................	858 (Iceland)	1 (China)
Fats and oils, lb per year..............	57 (Denmark)	2 (Japan)
Calories per day.....................	3380 (New Zealand)	1590 (India)
Per cent of calories derived from animal products.........................	49 (New Zealand)	4 (Japan)
Average total protein intake, g per day..	98 (Oceania)	50 (Far East)
Average animal protein intake, g per day.	67 (Oceania)	8 (Far East)
Per cent of total calories from cereals....	57 (Italy)	27 (Denmark)

SOURCE: Food and Agricultural Organization of the United Nations, *Yearbook of Food and Agricultural Statistics*, vol. 7, part 1, 1953; and The State of Food and Agriculture. Review of a Decade and Outlook, Rome, 1955.

Table 13.2 Comparison of the Yearly Average Food Consumption in the United States and India, 1949–1950

Food product	Consumption, lb	
	United States	India
Cereals and starchy roots............	279	277
Beans, peas, etc...................	15	44
Fruits and vegetables..............	447	90
Meat, eggs, fish, milk..............	856	110
Fats............................	42	7
Sugar...........................	103	29

SOURCE: Food and Agricultural Organization of the United Nations, "Second World Food Survey," 1952.

Table 13.3   Milk Production, Total and per Capita, 1953

Region	Total production, billion lb	Production, lb per capita
Oceania.....................................	24.1	1,788
Canada and the United States................	138.1	790
Western Europe.............................	202.5	662
Eastern Europe (excluding the Soviet Union)....	88.4	444
Soviet Union...............................	57.0	278
South America..............................	30.3	258
India......................................	42.4	115
Africa.....................................	23.6	112
Other Asia.................................	22.1	26
Total.................................	600.4	244

SOURCE: U.S. Department of Agriculture, Foreign Agricultural Service.

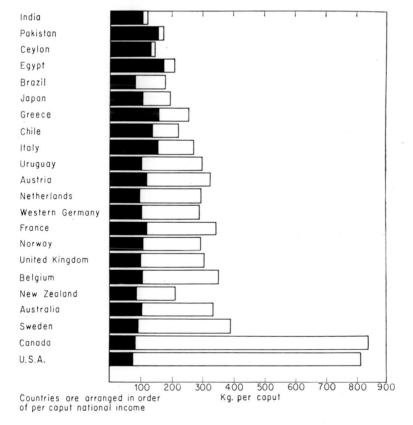

Countries are arranged in order
of per caput national income

Kg. per caput

Per caput consumption
for human food

Per caput consumption
for all purposes

Fig. 13.1   Per capita supply of cereals for all purposes (including livestock feeding) and for direct human consumption. (*FAO, Agriculture in the World Economy*, 1955.)

National income is one of the major factors contributing to variation in proportion of edible crops used directly for human food. This is shown graphically in Figures 13.1 and 13.2 for cereal foods and in Figure 13.3 for per capita supply of animal protein.

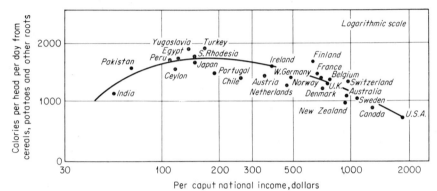

Fig. 13.2   Per capita consumption of cereals and foods in relation to per capita national income. (*FAO, The State of Food and Agriculture*, 1955.)

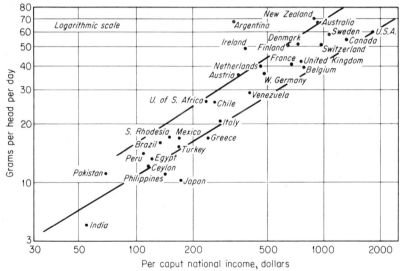

Fig. 13.3   Per capita supply of animal protein in relation to per capita national income. (*FAO, The State of Food and Agriculture*, 1955.)

Available Food Supplies.   Another way of estimating the present world situation would be to calculate the average available animal and plant crop produced per person. In 1952 the world (excluding the Soviet Union) produced an estimated 640 million metric tons of grain (largely wheat, rice, and maize), 37 million metric tons of sugar, 155 million metric tons of potatoes, 40 million metric tons of meat, 240 million metric tons of milk, 26 million metric tons of fish, 11.7 million tons of edible fats and oils, 45 million tons of fresh fruit (apples, pears, grapes, bananas, and citrus). Assuming that this production was available for equable distribution among the population of 2.2 billion persons, the available per capita supply of major food is shown in Table 13.4.

This estimate, though only approximate, indicates that at present distribution rather than production is the limiting factor in feeding the world population. Similar calculations of available food supply in terms of agricultural products have been made for particular countries and regions. A comparison of the pre-World War II situation for China with

Table 13.4 Available World per Capita Supply of Major Foods, 1952

Food product	Per capita supply	
	Pounds per year	Per cent of United States food supply
Cereals	640	256
Sugar...............	37	40
Potatoes.............	155	153
Meat................	40	24
Milk.....	240	43
Fish.................	26	237
Oils and fats..........	11.7	13
Fresh fruit...........	45	75

SOURCE: Food and Agricultural Organization of the United Nations, "Agriculture in the World Economy," 1955, and "Statistical Data."

other countries of the Pacific, made in 1945, is shown in Table 13.5. These data illustrate the possibilities of attaining sufficiency of food even under existing conditions in a densely populated underdeveloped country like China.

Land-area Requirements. Still another approach to the problem of estimating whether the present food production is adequate to feed the existing population is on the basis of land-area requirement. At present, of the total world's land resources (33.3 billion acres) only 10 per cent consists of cultivated land; 17 per cent is meadows and pastures, 29 per cent forests (see Figure 13.4). Almost half, 43.5 per cent, is land not used for production (e.g., built-on or waste land). Opinions differ as to whether or not the limits of cultivatable land have been reached; FAO experts believe that substantial expansion of crop area is possible. The actual percentage of land area that is arable varies from less than 5 per cent in the Near East and Oceania to 30 per cent in Europe. But unused tropical and arctic soils can be utilized; if 20 per cent of the unused tropical soils

Table 13.5   Available Food in China in Terms of Agricultural Products—with Comparisons for Various Countries—Prewar Average Annual per Capita, in Kilograms

Food product	China*	Japan†	Java‡	Philippines§
Cereals........................	223.0	208	159.0	130.9
Legumes.......................	32.2	17	10.6	
Root crops.....................	42.2	131	128.0	39.0
Other vegetables................	41.8	45	....	5.5
Fruit..........................	5.5	15		
Sugar.........................	1.4	12	7.0	9.4
Meat, fish, and eggs.............	9.4	52	4.4	106.9
Other.........................	8.3	...	....	45.0
Total......................	363.8	485	309.0	336.8
Unaccounted for.................	18.2	...	77.0	
Grand total................	382.0	...	386.0	

* Based on J. L. Buck, *Land Utilization in China*, Commercial Press, Ltd., Shanghai, China, 1933.
† Based on Ladejinsky's estimates, "Foreign Agriculture," U.S. Department of Agriculture, June, 1940.
‡ Annual Crop Reports 1933–1937 and Unreported Crops.
§ Amando M. Dalisay, Technical Adviser, Philippine Delegation, at United Nations Food Conference, May 18–June 3, 1945.
SOURCE: Owen Dawson, Agricultural Attaché, Embassy of the United States, China, 1945.

Table 13.6   Land Resources

Country	Acres per person	Per cent arable	Arable acres per person
Canada..................	247.0	3.9	9.6
Australia...............	247.0	2.3	5.7
United States...........	12.4	24.7	3.1
Ethiopia...............	17.5	10.4	1.8
Denmark...............	2.4	64.4	1.6
Mexico.................	17.6	7.6	1.3
Yugoslavia..............	3.8	30.3	1.1
Iraq....................	21.1	5.3	1.1
Brazil..................	41.2	2.2	0.93
Cuba...................	5.2	17.2	0.89
India...................	2.2	40.0	0.88
Italy...................	1.6	51.5	0.82
Thailand................	6.7	9.3	0.62
Ceylon.................	2.0	22.9	0.46
United Kingdom.........	1.2	30.0	0.36
Japan..................	1.1	13.8	0.15

SOURCE: *United Nations Demographic Yearbook*, 1953.

was cultivated, the present total arable area in the world would increase by 40 per cent. The present 33.3 billion acres of arable land and 7.7 billion acres of pasture on which graze approximately 2 billion head of livestock come close to producing the world's food requirement for the existing population as indicated above. The available land resources, however, vary markedly from country to country (Table 13.6).

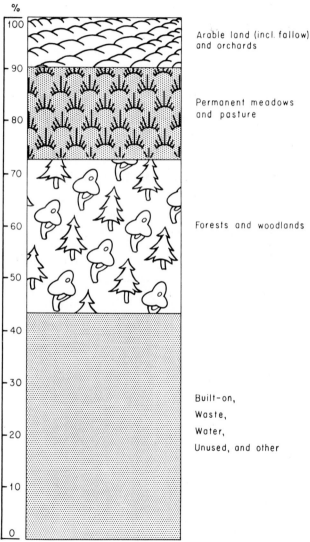

%

Arable land (incl. fallow) and orchards

Permanent meadows and pasture

Forests and woodlands

Built-on,

Waste,

Water,

Unused, and other

Fig. 13.4   Classification of the world's land resources. (*FAO, Agriculture in the World Economy*, 1955.)

It has been suggested that an area of 2.5 acres is required to produce an adequate diet for a single individual. On this basis, to feed the present 2.7 billion persons would require an arable area of 6.3 billion acres, almost twice that now available, not counting grazing lands. The existing dietary requirements, according to recent FAO statistics,[1] in the United States are produced on 2.67 acres,

. . . but of this 2.35 acres are required for the animal products in the American diet. In Denmark where diets are comparable with those in the United States, the area required per person is 1.1 acres. In Japan where agriculture is extremely intensive, the amount of land required for the prewar diet was 0.40 acre, a very low figure, but Japanese diets are supplemented to an appreciable extent by fish. In India where yields are low and the diets generally inadequate, the area per capita is estimated at 0.98 acre. The area needed in India to produce reasonably adequate diets, based on present low yields, is estimated at 1.56 acres per person.

If the productivity of the available arable land were raised to the Danish standard, the present population could be comfortably supported on the present available land area.

13.3 Possibilities of Improving the Diets of Existing Population

It is obvious that to improve the diet of existing populations it is necessary to increase the food availability, quantitatively and qualitatively. The chronic malnutrition which exists in the less-developed regions of the world requires special corrective diets higher in content of the more protective foods. To improve the situation, the FAO conference in 1951 recommended that all governments should aim at an increase in food

Table 13.7 Average Annual Increase in Total Agricultural Production Compared to Population from a Base, 1948–1951 to 1953

Region	Production per cent	Population per cent
Western Europe	4.1	0.8
North America	2.2	1.8
Latin America	1.8	2.4
Oceania	2.4	2.6
Far East (excluding China)	2.2	1.4
Near East	4.8	1.9
Africa	2.3	1.6
Average	2.8	1.5

SOURCE: Food and Agricultural Organization of the United Nations, The State of Food and Agriculture. Review of a Decade and Outlook, Rome, 1955.

[1] Food and Agricultural Organization of the United Nations, "The World Food Problem," 1954.

production of 1 to 2 per cent greater than the increase in population. By mid-1953 this was achieved, as the data in Table 13.7 indicate, but this was largely because of greater increases in the advanced and not in the underdeveloped countries. This relative growth of agriculture is shown also in Figures 13.5 to 13.7. The actual productivity of these countries is low by any of the standards that can be applied. Increased production in the economically advanced regions (Oceania, North America, and Western Europe) has increased agricultural surpluses and aggravated marketing problems. In the United States alone, the farm surplus for 1955 was

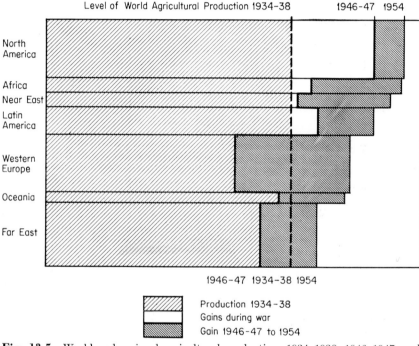

Fig. 13.5 World and regional agricultural production, 1934–1938, 1946–1947, and 1954. (*FAO, The State of Food and Agriculture*, 1955.)

estimated to be 4 per cent, and it has been predicted that farmers in the United States will produce 8.8 per cent more than the nation needs by 1965, in spite of the various controls now in effect. These surpluses are being produced on 350 million acres of harvested cropland. The total land area used for harvested crops in the United States has remained essentially constant since 1910, varying only from an average of 341 million acres in 1910–1919 to 350 million acres in 1953; the actual cropland used for food production, however, has increased from 215 million acres in 1910–1919 to about 300 in 1953, while the acreage used for feed production for horses and mules decreased from 89 million to 16 million. That used for

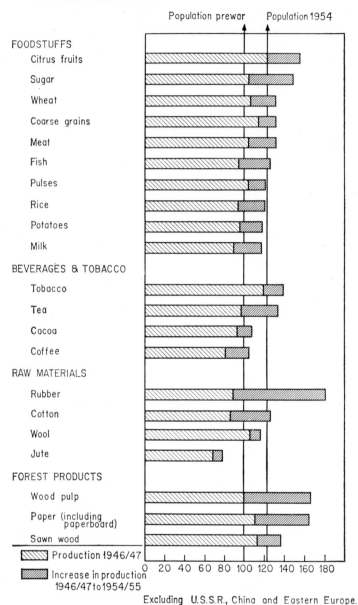

Fig. 13.6 Level of world production of certain commodities, 1946–1947, 1954–1955 (prewar average = 100). (*FAO, The State of Food and Agriculture*, 1955.)

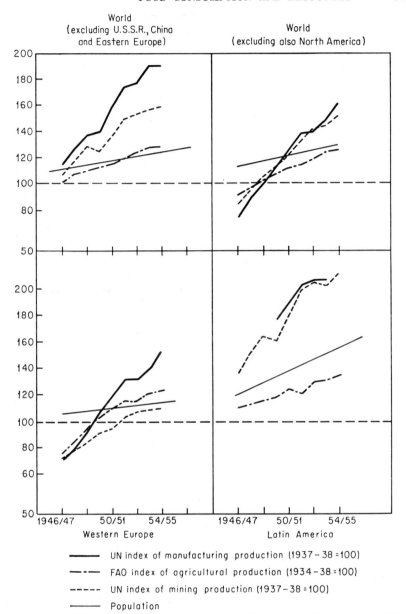

Fig. 13.7 Relative growth of agriculture, manufacture, mining, and population (prewar = 100). (*FAO, The State of Food and Agriculture*, 1955.)

cotton, flax, and tobacco has decreased from 37 million acres in 1910–1919 to 31 million acres in 1953. While the total area cultivated has remained essentially constant, the productivity of the land has steadily increased, in spite of artificial restrictions in the 1930s and post-World War II, in amounts more than sufficient to feed a growing population. This increase in productivity can be used as a goal for world-wide agricultural economy.

Reducing Losses. In meeting the short-time objective of adequately feeding the existing population, a first step is to prevent or reduce the losses in food supplies experienced at present. These are of several types: (1) losses in crops caused by plant diseases and pests (affecting field, forage, fruit, nut, vegetable crops, pastures, and ranges) as a result of use of infected seeds, by air-borne or insect-borne vectors of disease, and by damage to crops by insects and rodents during growth; (2) losses by diseases, internal parasites, and insects affecting livestock (meat and dairy cattle, hogs, goats, sheep, poultry, etc.); (3) mechanical deficiencies in harvesting field crops and rodent and insect damage during storage of crops or their products; (4) mechanical injuries, weeds, and hail damage to crops; (5) losses in marketing, processing, and distributing agricultural crops as a result of actual loss of food or decrease in food value (nutritive or acceptability). No over-all estimate of the extent to which such losses by these factors and by more difficult to control environmental factors (severe frosts, droughts, fire, predatory animals, etc.) affect total world production is available. Spectacular threats like locusts which can devastate the crops of the greater part of an entire area, foot-and-mouth disease, and rinderpest are now being controlled, and the spread of dangerous plant pests and diseases across national borders is being reduced. But the reduction or elimination of the more widespread and less spectacular plant pests and diseases is still limited.

Even in advanced countries like the United States, preventable losses in agricultural crops are large. Considerable crop acreage is still untreated with insecticides and fungicides. While the actual extent of such losses is not known, a preliminary appraisal of these losses was made recently by the Agricultural Research Service of the U.S. Department of Agriculture. In the comprehensive report issued in 1954, it was estimated that losses to crops (during production) due to insects and diseases, mechanical damage, hail, weeds, and inadequate harvesting amount to about 8.3 billion dollars annually in value of products lost. These losses constitute 20 per cent of the potential production of all farm and forest growth and are equivalent to the potential production from nearly 88 million acres (or about 25 per cent of the average harvested cropland). Plant diseases cause 7 per cent decrease in potential production; insects, 5 per cent; mechanical damage, hail, and weeds, 6 per cent; and losses and waste during harvesting, about 3 per cent. Losses from hazards to pasture and range lands (1 billion acres) amount to 17 per cent of the potential pasture and range production (equivalent to potential production of nearly 154 million acres), and livestock losses are equivalent to the potential production of 126 million acres additionally. Rodents destroy another 382 million dollars worth of stored crops (0.9 per cent) and insects reduce values by 217 million dollars (0.5 per cent). Marketing losses amount to 303 million dollars (0.7 per cent of potential) and processing losses to 271 million dollars (0.7 per cent of potential). Diseases, parasites, and insects cause a reduction of 2688 million dollars in the value of livestock and poultry and their products. This amounts to about 14 per cent of the total value of such products, and these postharvest losses are equivalent to the potential production on over 32 million acres. The total preharvest and postharvest losses on cropland are thus equivalent to the potential production on almost 120 million acres. Thus in the United States the over-all annual loss is estimated to be 33 per cent of the total production.

The FAO estimates that 10 per cent of the total world production is lost through infestation of stored products by insects, fungi, and rodents in comparison with the 6.6 per cent estimated for the United States. Losses during production must be at least as great in the world as in the United States, so that it is likely that existing losses amount to at least 33 per cent and possibly 50 per cent. Considerable reduction of such losses is technically possible, and appreciable reduction is economically achievable.

Increasing Productivity. Soil is the basic raw material in food production, and knowledge of the factors influencing soil formation and maintenance of desirable soil structure and fertility are basic to proper land utilization. Although much is known about soil formation and soil fertility, practical applications have in many cases outstripped fundamental studies in soil science. Thus although successful renovation of worn-out grasslands and rehabilitation of sea-flooded areas, for example, are based on well-established principles in soil chemistry and physics, the factors determining soil structure (upon which depend aeration, water absorption and movement, etc.) are still largely unknown. There are a large number of farmers who still follow outmoded practices, being reluctant to adopt modern aids to increase yields and improve quality of their product. With our knowledge in the field of soil science, it would be possible to increase productivity through adoption of good soil management practices, discussed in Chapters 8 and 9, including the improvement of soil structure and better control of weeds, through proper fertilization (including the use of legumes in crop rotation) to restore and maintain soil fertility, and by maintaining favorable soil moisture regimes by irrigation when precipitation is inadequate or poorly distributed. Thus in any given region of the world there are farmers who obtain higher yields than their neighbors because they apply better practices. It has been estimated that if the average level could be brought up to what is already obtained by the best 10 per cent of farms an increase of about 50 per cent could be expected.

With the exception of the tropical areas where the existing heavy rainfall introduces difficulties in maintaining soil fertility because of excessive leaching of water-soluble constituents, irrigation is often a limiting factor. Only a relatively small portion of the available arable land is irrigated although the high productivity of irrigated land is well recognized. It has been estimated that in the Middle East 1 dunam ($\frac{1}{4}$ acre) of irrigated land is equivalent in productivity to 4 to 6 dunam of land used for dry farming. In Europe the percentage of total arable land under irrigation varies from 0.1 per cent in France to 7.8 per cent in Greece; in North America it varies from 0.4 per cent in Jamaica to 20 per cent in the Dominican Republic (10 per cent for the United States); in South America, from 0.4 per cent in Ecuador to 45 per cent in British Guiana; in Asia, from 0.2 per cent in Burma to 75 per cent in Iraq; in Africa, from 2.5 per cent in Southern Rhodesia to 16 per cent in Somalia; in Oceania, from 0.6 per cent in Hawaii to 42 per cent in Australia.

The maintenance of soil fertility and the recovery of land areas that have been denuded of topsoil by erosion as a result of mismanagement depend on the return to the soil of the nitrogenous, phosphate, potash, lime, and other constituents depleted by crops that are harvested and the enrichment of soils deficient in these plant nutrients as well as in the micronutrients.

It is recognized that manure and urine (human as well as animal) markedly improve the fertility of grass and other lands, but proper grazing management, particularly avoidance of overgrazing, is necessary.

Cattle convert into food for man feeds, such as grasses, that humans cannot utilize directly. They return to the soil in manure and urine about four-fifths of the elements of fertility of the plants they consume. Pastures, provided that they are not overstocked, conserve soil better than most crops by retarding erosion and adding humus.

Agriculture is no longer as dependent on organic fertilizer as it was in the past. Synthetic nitrogenous fertilizers which, when first introduced, were not the equivalent of natural nitrate deposits can now be made so by the addition of the small quantities of essential trace metals present in the latter. Just as in the past mechanization contributed to improvement in soil management and reduction in cost and manpower requirement in agriculture, so now chemicalization is bringing advances in productivity and economy. Even with the knowledge available today, it is possible to improve soil fertility greatly by proper selection and application of chemical fertilizers alone or in combination with manures. Topical application of fertilizer close to growing roots or foliar application has resulted in considerable economy of fertilizer use. Better soil management and more effective use of fertilizers can result in increases of 25 to 50 per cent in crops and possibly even in much higher productivity.

In a recently published report on agriculture's capacity to produce,[1] it was concluded that in the United States it was possible to attain a total farm output 20 per cent greater than in 1951 within 4 to 5 years. With given land resources the effective limits on our present productive capacity are largely (1) lack of knowledge concerning effects and failure to apply the knowledge we have of improved production practices, (2) price and income incentives insufficient to encourage higher production, and (3) limited quantities of fertilizer, farm machinery, and other production goods at costs that would encourage their use as substitutes for land and labor. In the United States, for example, the percentage of crop acreage fertilized in 1950 was 3 per cent for sorghums, 25 per cent for hay and pasture, 29 per cent for wheat, 56 per cent for dry beans, 65 per cent for cotton, 98 per cent for potatoes, and 100 per cent for tobacco. The average percentage for 11 major crops and pasture land that was fertilized in 1950 was estimated to be 39.2 per cent, and the possible increased productivity of 20 per cent would require that 43.7 per cent of the total crop area would be fertilized. These figures, while approximate, indicate the possibilities of increased production by slight over-all increases in fertilizer application.

Many improved production practices require a higher degree of skill in management of farm operations than the usual or prevailing methods. Others, such as improved crop rotations, are not fully reflected in higher yields for several years. Considering only the known improvements which farmers could adopt and realize on, to some extent at least, in the relatively short period of 4 to 5 years, it was estimated that the yield per acre of major crops and pastures could be increased 114 to 197 per cent of that existing in 1950 in the United States. With sufficient incentive, even these yields can be surpassed and indicate what could be accomplished in the world as a whole if the existing limiting economic and technical factors could be overcome.

The use of clean and improved seeds in recent years has markedly increased productivity. Seeds selected for freedom from pests and diseases are available. In addition, by proper selection of varieties more resistant to existing plant pests and diseases, more suitable to particular soil and climatic conditions, and particularly by selection of hybrids, productivity can be greatly increased. Sound hybrid corn will produce a crop of about

[1] *U.S. Dept. Agr., Agr. Infor. Bull. No.* 88, June, 1952.

40 bu per acre compared with less than 20 obtained previously. The introduction of the high-yielding hybrid corn in Europe, where 6 per cent of the corn planted by 1954 was hybrid, resulted in an increase of 640,000 tons of grain. The yield of other grains increased in Europe by more than 5 per cent in 1948–1950 and in the United States by 26.5 per cent in 1946–1948. The yield of rice, the basic food of more than half the people of the world, could be greatly increased if Japonica varieties cultivated in Japan could be used instead of Indican varieties cultivated in the Asian tropics. Crossing of these varieties to establish hybrids which will combine the high response to fertilizers of the Japonica type with the climatic adaptation of the Indican is now being investigated.

MacGillivray[1] has stressed the importance of considering food production from the standpoint of yield of nutrients per acre instead of pounds of food per acre. On this basis a maximum food supply could be assured by (1) selecting organisms (plants or animals) that can produce the greatest amount of nutrients per acre, (2) selecting organisms that will mature in a shorter growing season, and (3) growing plants, where possible, for human consumption rather than for livestock feed. Such a program, however, would require changes in eating habits for greater efficiency in land use; human food preferences and cost would be limiting factors.

The efficiency of livestock production is much lower in underdeveloped countries than in Europe and the United States, where better breeding and better feeding have markedly increased growth rate and improved the efficiency of feed utilization. During the past 25 years dramatic changes have occurred in the principles and practices of farm-animal nutrition. Almquist[2] has described these as transition from ingredient-basis feeding to one of a nutrient basis, i.e., abandonment of empirical feed formulas in favor of the consideration of specific requirement of amino acids, vitamins, minerals, etc. The progress in nutrition accomplished by the new regime may be illustrated by the increase in weight attained by broiler chickens in 8 weeks of feeding on various commercial diets:

1930 diet	1.62 lb
1938 diet	1.89 lb
1946 diet	2.17 lb
1954 diet	2.81 lb

The time to raise a 3-lb broiler has been cut from 14 weeks to 9 weeks and the total feed used from 12 to 8 lb. Another illustration is the time required

[1] J. H. MacGillivray, "Factors Affecting the World's Food Supplies," *World Crops*, vol. 8, no. 8, pp. 303–305, 1956.

[2] H. H. Almquist, "Provision of Animal Nutrients," presented at the Meeting of the American Association for the Advancement of Science at Berkeley, Calif., December, 1954.

for 80-lb swine to reach 205 to 207 lb live weight. This was 148 days in 1910, 70 days in 1930, and 64 days in 1953.

Proper feeding, careful selection and breeding, and eradication of internal parasites and diseases have improved the egg-laying capacity of hens so that yields of over 300 eggs per year per hen are possible. The average yield of eggs per layer in the United States in 1953 was only 182; however, yields varying from 135 to 211 were recorded. Similar factors have increased the milk productivity of dairy cattle. Provision for obtaining adequate supplies of milk has always had high priority in any consideration of improving diet, not only because milk is the most nutritious food for growing children but also because it supplies animal protein in the greatest possible yield per unit of fodder expended. Dairy cows yield milk protein equivalent to 3.7 per cent of the energy value of the fodder which they consume. In comparison, fowls yield protein equivalent to 3.0 per cent of the energy value of their feed, pigs 1.8 per cent, beef cattle 1.6 per cent, and sheep 1.3 per cent.

Expressed in another way, 1 bu of corn consumed as whole corn meal provides 23 persons with food energy and protein sufficient to meet their daily requirement; converted into milk it contains the food energy equivalent to the daily requirements of 5 persons and the protein requirement of 12 persons; in the form of pork and lard it supplies the food energy for 7 persons and protein for 5 persons; in the form of eggs it supplies sufficient food energy for only 2 persons and protein required by 8 persons per day.

Important by-products of animal husbandry, wool and manure, and the ability of ruminants (cows, sheep) to subsist largely on grass which can be grown in yields higher in total energy value and with less labor than grain favor raising farm animals. In several of the advanced countries (e.g., the United States, New Zealand, England, etc.), the output of dairy products has steadily increased although dairy cattle numbers have fallen as a result of better feeding, better breeding, eradication of diseases, etc. The data for the United States, shown in Table 13.8 indicate that during the period of 1924 to 1953 the total milk production increased 4 per cent while the number of milk cows decreased 15 per cent. The milk flow per cow increased more than 24 per cent. The average annual yield of 5447 lb of milk per cow in 1953 is smaller than that obtained in other countries, particularly the Netherlands, as shown in Table 13.9, and is considerably below the yield of 22,000 lb of milk and 856 lb of fat obtained from test herds of Holsteins, and the 14,000 lb of milk and 812 lb of fat from test herds of Jerseys. This production can be achieved by proper selection, breeding, and management.

These improvements have not as yet been adapted to the underdeveloped countries, where the average efficiency of livestock used to provide draft power as well as milk and meat is very low. The yellow cattle of China, for example, yield only 300 lb of milk per year. Improvement in stock, control of diseases, and improvement in grazing management are needed. Overgrazing and consequent underproduction are too common in most of the world. Grazing management along with the conservation of

Table 13.8 Milk Production in the United States

Year	Milk production, total as fluid milk, billion lb	Milk cows, million head	Average annual yield, lb per cow
1924	115	26.25	4380
1939	109		
1940–1945	117.7		
1946–1950	117.0	22.75	5099
1951	115.3		
1952	115.6	21.62	5329
1953	121.5	22.25	5447

SOURCE: U.S. Department of Agriculture, "Agricultural Statistics," 1955.

Table 13.9 Milk Production per Cow, 1953

Country	Pounds of Milk per Cow
Netherlands	8576
Belgium	8160
Denmark	7993
Switzerland	6724
Sweden	6559
United Kingdom	6452
Germany, Western	6314
New Zealand	5985
Australia	5505
United States	5477
Norway	5023
Austria	4441
France	4334

SOURCE: U.S. Department of Agriculture, "Agricultural Statistics," 1955.

forage for periods when grazing is scanty could double or treble the carrying capacity. Improvement of grasslands by cultivation, fertilization, and reseeding could result in much greater yields.

The selection and breeding of livestock for particular regions and conditions are important. Ruminants like cows and sheep, able to digest the cellulose of herbage, are more economical to raise than nonruminants like poultry and pigs. Ruminants also can utilize nonprotein nitrogen. Beef cattle, for example, can efficiently utilize urea in amounts to supply up to 50 per cent of the total supplemental nitrogen in fattening rations and 25 per cent in wintering rations, according to Gallup.[1] Ammoniated molasses and ammoniated sugar-beet pulp have been introduced also as sources of enriched nitrogenous feed for ruminants. Poultry and pigs depend to a greater extent on cereal crops, which require more labor for their cultivation and could be used directly for human consumption. Even in poultry there are marked differences in feeding requirement. Geese, which can utilize a large proportion of grass in their feed, are more desirable for raising in densely populated areas where humans have to compete with animals for the products of the soil.

In animal husbandry, supplementation with synthetic methionine, and addition of antibiotics and other drugs have made important contributions not only in control of diseases but also in improving the efficiency of feed utilization and even in improving the storage life of carcass meat. The addition of crude antibiotics to feed has markedly increased the rate and efficiency of growth and has been found profitable under the economic conditions prevailing in the United States and elsewhere. It is possible that their use would be justifiable in many other areas of the world.

Wider Use of Sea Resources. Although land is the principal source of the world's food, the seas, the rivers, and the lakes contribute 30 million tons of high-quality food each year, but this may be only a fraction of the amount of food which could be obtained. Three-fourths of the world's fish catch before World War II was taken from the relatively shallow waters of the North Atlantic and the North Pacific. At present more than 90 per cent of the total sea-fisheries catch is obtained in the Northern Hemisphere. Fish and other sea food are used regularly in the diet of only a part of the world population. People living inland away from seas, rivers, and lakes rarely eat them. Previous difficulties in preserving and distributing the fish catch can now be largely overcome. Means are available for economic and efficient preservation of the food value of sea food. The food value of some of the presently caught fish is lost by diversion into industrial products (oils and fish meal), and more complete utilization of the fish caught would noticeably improve existing diets. Much could be done to popularize the less common species of fish as food; only a very few types of fish are today widely exploited by commercial fisheries. The total fish landings might be doubled without risk to the world fisheries resources. However, it is pertinent to stress the great lack of information concerning the amounts of total products in the ocean, how good they are for food, and how they can be tapped.

People who write on world food problems have often been impressed by the fact that the ocean represents a tremendous, fertile source of nutrients. Its surface is $2\frac{1}{2}$ times that of land area, it contains nutrient

[1] W. D. Gallup, "Review of Utilization of Non-protein Nitrogen in the Ruminant," *J. Agr. Food Chem.*, vol. 4, pp. 625–631, 1956.

salts in abundance, it is the home of thousands of species of flora and fauna, vast reaches are unexplored, etc. More reasoned analyses indicate however that these vast resources, if they exist, may not yield so readily to harvesting. In a recent careful survey of this problem, Walford and Wilbur[1] point out that to be profitable for fishermen a stock must be abundant, aggregated, regular in habits so that they can be found, accessible (that is, not too deep, or too far, or in inaccessible grounds), palatable and nutritious, firm-fleshed so that they can be transported, and amenable to some kind of preservation.

Most of the known edible fish live within a short distance from a coast line. This appears to reflect the requirement of their food, the minute plankton, for nitrogen and phosphate from the rivers. Hence these fish have been known and exploited as long as man has inhabited coastal areas. Walford and Wilbur suggest therefore that the yield of 27 million tons of marine products now consumed in the world cannot be reasonably expected to double unless strenuous and revolutionary efforts are made to change techniques and to expend more effort and energy toward this goal.

While the extent to which the oceans can contribute to man's food requirement is thus not unlimited, much progress can be made in improving fishing methods, in the farming of enclosed sea areas, and in the preservation and marketing of fish. Economic factors at present limit fishing mainly to continental shelves. In the deep oceans, nutrients are lost from the productive surface layers by the sinking of dead and decaying organisms to deeper layers, and it is only in certain areas where there is upwelling of deep waters that nutrients are returned to the surface. In tropical waters the very diversity of species, few occurring in the large shoals found in temperate regions, make productive fishing more difficult.

Fresh-water fish raised in fishponds contribute considerably to help the protein deficiency in many parts of the world. Carp has long been raised in China in ponds manured to increase productivity. Fertilization in fishponds with oilseed cakes is extensively used in Israel, in Louisiana, and elsewhere. While our knowledge of feeding requirements in such ponds is still limited, it is possible appreciably to increase animal protein supply by such means. Carp is more commonly raised in such ponds, but tench and pike can readily be grown also. The available information on fertilizer use in fishponds has been summarized recently.[2]

[1] L. A. Walford and C. G. Wilbur, "The Sea as a Potential Source of Protein Food," in *Advances in Protein Chemistry*, vol. 10, pp. 289–316, Academic Press, Inc., New York, 1955.

[2] C. H. Mortimer, "Fertilizers in Fishponds," British Colonial Office, Fisheries Publication No. 5, H. M. Stationery Office, London, 1954.

Supplementation. For optimum nutrition the daily diet must be adequate qualitatively and quantitatively and balanced with regard to nutritive constituents. Imbalance may be caused by feeding excessive amounts of carbohydrates in relation to protein, by alteration in balance of water-soluble and fat-soluble vitamins, by amino acid imbalance. Nevertheless, evaluation of nutritional deficiencies in individual foods and the fortification of particular foods with specific nutritive substances have been successful in eradication of several nutritional diseases and have improved the nutritive status of many persons in the United States and elsewhere. The fortification of evaporated and fluid milk with vitamin D (later also with vitamin A) has been largely responsible for the marked reduction in rickets in the United States; the addition of iodine to table salt has been an important prophylactic measure against goiter; the addition of thiamine, riboflavin, nicotinamide, and iron to flour partially to restore nutrients lost in milling has improved the nutritional status of many persons. Fruit products such as apple juice low in vitamin C are enriched by addition of ascorbic acid. This principle of fortification has now been extended to food proteins known to be deficient in essential amino acids. The fortification of gluten in milled wheat by the addition of lysine and addition of lysine to milk to improve the weight gain of infants with appetite problems have been proposed. However, although the fortification of animal feeds with methionine has been shown to be safe and desirable, fortification of human foods containing protein of poor biological value with synthetic amino acids such as lysine and methionine has not yet been proved to be without hazard. Amino acid imbalance has in some cases been demonstrated to cause decreased growth rates, excessive deposition of liver fat, and modification of vitamin requirements.[1] As our knowledge of the factors involved increases, however, it will be possible better to supplement protein deficiency by addition of synthetic amino acids to deficient diets. At present natural supplementation is preferred, i.e., addition of milk to cereals to supplement the known lysine deficiency of cereal grains, particularly dried and toasted breakfast foods. Killefer,[2] Williams,[3] Sure,[4] and others have stressed the possibilities of supplementing dietary deficiencies by addition of synthetic vitamins and amino acids. Williams has pointed out that, while the total cost of supplying the annual requirement for

[1] Anon., "Amino Acid Imbalance and Supplementation," *J. Am. Med. Assoc.*, vol. 161, no. 9, pp. 884–885, 1956.

[2] Killefer, *op. cit.*

[3] R. R. Williams, "Chemistry as a Supplement to Agriculture in Meeting the World Food Needs," *Am. Scientist*, vol. 44, no. 3, pp. 317–327, 1956.

[4] B. Sure, "The Critical World Food Situation, *Am. J. Clin. Nutrition*, vol. 4, pp. 211–223, 1956.

seven vitamins is \$1.14 per person (Table 13.10), all the major deficiency diseases of the world except kwashiorkor can be eradicated by the fortification of cereal and table fats with an outlay for vitamins of about 25 cents per person per year. This would be equivalent to an expenditure of about 700 million dollars for 2.7 billion people.

Kwashiorkor occurs in infants and children largely on a cereal diet deficient in lysine, tryptophane, and methionine. The cost of supplying these amino acids synthetically is considerably higher (\$44.35 per person per year) but would be decreased when the demand for large-scale production will have been established. Williams proposed that, when the

Table 13.10   Costs of Supplying the Annual per Capita Requirements of Essential Vitamins and Amino Acids, 1956*

	Cents per gram	Year's supply, g†	Cost per person per year, cents
Vitamins:			
Vitamin A................	7.25	0.62	4.5
Thiamine................	8.0	0.55	4.4
Riboflavin..............	8.0	0.55	4.4
Niacin..................	0.8	5.50	4.4
Vitamin C..............	1.6	25.6	41.0
Panthothenate...........	6.0	3.7	22.2
Pyridoxine..............	46.0	0.73	33.6
Amino acids:			
Lysine..................	2.7	292.0	\$ 7.88
Methionine..............	0.77	365.0	2.81
Tryptophane.............	33.0	102.0	33.66

* From R. R. Williams, "Chemistry as a Supplement to Agriculture in Meeting the World Food Needs," *Am. Scientist*, vol. 44, no. 3, pp. 317–327, 1956.

† Based on "Recommended Dietary Allowances of Food and Nutrition Board," National Research Council, Washington, except for amino acids.

child's yearly needs can be supplied for \$1 or less, an organization such as the United Nations International Children's Emergency Fund might be able to effect a substantial distribution to needy areas.

13.4   Possibilities of Meeting Requirements of Growing Population Demands

Population in recent years has increased strikingly in highly developed, economically advanced regions as well as in less-developed regions. In North America and Australasia, birth rates in 1950s are 30 to 40 per cent higher than in the 1930s. A recent FAO survey for those parts of the world for which statistics are available showed that the rate of annual increase in the period from 1948 to 1951 in the economically advanced regions varied from 0.7 per cent in Western Europe to 2.8 per cent in

Oceania; and in the less-developed regions, from 1.3 per cent for the Far East to 2.3 per cent for Latin America. While long-term trends of population are highly controversial and forecasts of world population 20 to 50 years hence are difficult to make, it is safe to assume that a 2 per cent annual increase will continue for some time. The present exceptionally high rate of increase in countries like the United States, Australia, New Zealand, and Argentina is particularly important because the people of these countries obtain about 40 per cent of their calories from animal products which are very expensive to produce in terms of agricultural resources.

To provide for this accelerating population increase and to improve the diets of the existing population, it may be necessary to cultivate new areas and exploit new sources of food in ways additional to those which have already been discussed. The rapid expansion of the world's cultivated acreage that occurred during the last century in the Americas, Australasia, and South Africa can never be repeated since those grasslands which could easily be cultivated are almost entirely developed and only small areas remain to be brought into this kind of use, chiefly in South America. Considerable areas of land, however, are available which are not under cultivation because of lack of water and fertilizer. Water supplies which are not fully developed for irrigation are available in many countries. Irrigation not only can increase yields but also can make areas available that would otherwise be useless. Considerable acreage of desert and semiarid land is available in the United States, Central America, Australia, Asia, the Middle East, etc.

Vast tropical rain-forest areas exist in Africa and South America, but these pose particular problems. In most such areas the soil fertility is low and nutrients are quickly leached from the soil by the heavy rainfall once the shelter of the forest has been removed. While the successful agricultural development of such areas is not possible on the basis of our present knowledge, it is likely that methods can be developed for the cultivation of such areas which do offer great possibilities for increased food production. One solution to the problem of excessive losses of plant nutrients from the soils of tropical rain areas is based on the concept that plant roots can obtain nutrients directly by ion exchange between soil colloids and root surfaces instead of by absorption from soil solution. When this principle is applied, it will be possible to supply the major nutrients and the trace minerals in an insoluble form. Land-conservation and land-utilization means for optimal use of temperate land areas have been developed as a result of centuries of patient applied research, and this is necessary also for tropical rain-forest areas. Even the failure of the groundnut (peanut) scheme in Tanganyika has contributed significantly to our knowledge of the factors involved. Much of the equatorial region can be developed, in spite of difficult living conditions, low natural fertility, and management problems. If only 20 per cent of the unused tropical soils was utilized for cultivation, the present total arable area in the world would increase by approximately 40 per cent. There are other potentially productive areas at present underdeveloped because of the prevalence of malaria, sleeping sickness, and other diseases. Here control of diseases and resettlement of land are possible by means already available.

It might be possible to increase the arable area further by making use of the potential land resources of the arctic and antarctic regions. Much has already been done to bring into production important areas of North America (the United States and Canada), the Scandinavian countries, Finland, and Siberia by development of cold-resistant short-season wheat crops, and much more is possible in this direction. Given the incentive it is possible by application of knowledge already available to double the area under cultivation in the foreseeable future, and it is not unlikely as research in improving productivity of land areas in nontemperate zones progresses that more can be done.

Hydroponics, plant culture without soil, has been used in wartime and emergency conditions, where water but not suitable soil is available; this use can be expanded if necessary. Marine and inland fisheries can be expanded. New sources of food supply, not only those which are currently being considered (direct use of plankton, algae, fungi, etc.) but some not now in sight, may be developed in the future. Thus it is technically possible to increase world food production to the extent necessary to provide adequate diets for the world's population even at the present rate of increase for an extended period. But social, economic, and administrative problems are formidable obstacles.

13.5   Factors Limiting Potential Food Production

The more important economic factors that limit increase in world food production are lack of incentives by world farmers to produce (unsatisfactory systems of land tenure, burdens of debt, inadequate credit, etc.) and the related lack of means of the population as a whole to purchase the products of the farmers' labors. Chronic poverty exists not only in the underdeveloped, less economically favored regions but also in economically more favorable countries. Even in the United States, in the period 1948 to 1954, while the number of families with high income increased greatly, the number of families with permanently inadequate economic resources (income of $2000 or less) showed little reduction. Nine per cent of the population of the cities and 27 per cent of the farm families had incomes of less than $2000. Families with incomes less than $1000 remained steady at 10 per cent.

Political factors as well as social factors are involved. Very few of the countries of the world are wholly self-subsistent even in food resources, and most countries depend on world trade to make up deficiencies of local and regional food supply. This trade at present is not free and is limited by political-social factors.

The socioeconomic factors governing the use of land for an agricultural crop are possibly best exemplified in the case of sugar. World production of sugar in the last few years has averaged about 13 million tons, roughly 10 lb per capita. Sugar can be grown both in tropical and in temperate zones, as cane or as beet. The cane can be produced more efficiently, but for many complicated reasons governments have often promoted home industry, and world marketing of sugar is now governed by an International Sugar Agreement.

Table 13.11 showing yields per acre of sugar is illustrative. It indicates that, if Peru were to be allowed additional sugar markets, for each

Table 13.11   Yield of Sugar per Acre, in Tons

Crop source	Country	1951	1952	1953
Cane..........	Hawaii	8.4	9.1	9.0
	Peru	5.9	6.6	6.9
	Cuba	2.1	2.0	2.0
	United States	1.3	1.7	1.7
Beet..........	Netherlands	2.1	2.7	2.6
	United States	2.0	2.0	2.2
	Sweden	2.2	1.8	2.7
	Italy	1.5	1.3	1.5

SOURCE: H. B. Hoss and O. H. Tamborn, "Economics of Sucrose," *Ind. Eng. Chem.*, vol. 47, pp. 1392–1396, 1955.

acre of cane planted, 4 acres could be released for other crops in the United States. The extremely high yields obtainable in Hawaii represent cutting every 2 years and are therefore not strictly comparable.

Farm Labor.   Approximately three-fifths of the world's population, or more than 1400 million people, live on farms and supply farm products for themselves and others. There are, however, wide discrepancies in the percentage of farm population between countries in the same region and also within countries. The active population engaged in agriculture varies from 5 per cent in the United Kingdom, and 10 per cent in the United States, to 85 per cent in Thailand, as shown in Figure 13.8. The percentage of farmers in most countries and in the world has steadily decreased in the past 150 years, while farm production, both total and per capita, has steadily risen. In rapidly industrializing countries, such as the United States, Canada, Sweden, Finland, and Japan, the proportion of workers in agriculture has declined over the last 80 years at the rate of

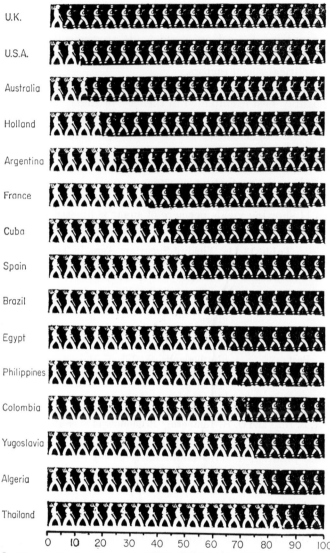

Fig. 13.8 Per cent of active population engaged in agriculture in 15 selected countries. (*FAO, Agriculture in the World Economy,* 1955.)

0.50 per cent annually. Industry did not only take people away from the land, it also expanded the demand for agricultural products and supplied improved tools, fertilizers, pesticides, etc., and thus encouraged and assisted agricultural development. The decrease in labor required for agricultural production is well illustrated in the following data on man-hours required to grow and harvest 100 bu of wheat in the United States:

Year	Man-hours
1800	370
1840	230
1880	150
1900	100
1940	43
1955	26

A similar startling statistic is revealed in a Senate report released in 1952. In 1941 the cotton crop required 203 man-hours of labor per bale. Only 10 years later, in 1951, the requirement had fallen to 130 man-hours. Machinery, fertilizers, and chemicals such as those used to control cotton pests and weeds accounted for the difference.

The processing of agricultural raw materials in industrialized countries is now generally carried out in towns, whereas it used to be done, and still is largely done in underdeveloped countries, on the farm. The same applies to marketing and distribution which has increasingly been taken over by specialist nonagricultural workers.

The actual minimum percentage of the total population that should or could be farm population will depend on the stage of development reached by the country and on natural resources, kind of farming, human skills, and political and social traditions. In view of the advances made in mechanization of farm output and in the use of chemicals for control of weeds, etc., it is not likely that shortage of farm labor will be a limiting factor in the foreseeable future.

Fertilizer Supply. The supply of three major fertilizing elements (nitrogen, phosphate, and potash) and of lime is not available in unlimited quantities. Before World War II, the world's farmers outside the Soviet Union consumed, on the average, about 8.1 million metric tons of commercial fertilizers per year (in terms of nitrogen, phosphate, and potash content). Now the rate of consumption is 13.5 million metric tons. The successful development of industrial processes for securing nitrogen from the atmosphere by fixation has relieved the world from dependence on organic supplies of nitrogenous fertilizers and natural deposits such as the Chilean nitrate deposits. The world fixed-nitrogen production capacity has increased from 8 million tons in 1954–1955 to over 10 million tons in 1957–1958, and the present rate of use of fertilizer nitrogen is about 4 million tons per year. The world potash resources as soluble potassium salts are large, over 37 billion metric tons, of which 65 per cent are in Germany and Russia, 23 per cent in Israel and Jordan, 6 per cent in France, and 1 per cent in the United States. The use of potash for fertilizer has increased markedly; in North America it increased from 400,000 tons in 1935 to 2.2 million tons in 1955, and the present annual world consumption is over 4 million tons. Even more marked increases in production and use of soil and fertilizer phosphate have occurred. In the United States phosphate consumption increased from 246,000 tons in 1900 to over 2,400,000 tons in 1950; and the world consumption increased from 3.5 million metric tons prewar to 5.6 million metric tons in 1951. The phosphate rock used in the manufacture of fertilizer is supplied from deposits in the United States, North Africa, Ocean Island and Nauru, and the Soviet Union. In 1951, the United States produced 10.7 million metric tons of phosphate rock, North Africa 7, Ocean Island and Nauru 1.2.

Improved methods of application of potash and phosphates have done much to conserve and extend existing supplies of these minerals. Nitrogen fixation by symbiotic microflora has always been an important factor in nitrogen enrichment of soil, but its application has been limited. The use of selected legumes as cover crop is still based largely on trial-and-error methods, and our knowledge of the nature of nitrogen fixation and nitrification is still limited. Kudzu grass, for example, has been imported to the United States as an important cover crop, but its use in its native habitat, Japan, and in China is limited. Even less is known about the nature of nitrogen fixation in the sea. The use of nitrogen-fixing photosynthetic microorganisms adapted to marine growth for improvement of the productivity of the seas and for use in fishponds is a possibility worthy of study.

It is possible to make improved use of animal manure and urine for fertilizer. At present, for example, cattle dung is used as an important domestic fuel in India instead of as soil fertilizer. Of the total available green dung (cow and buffalo), estimated as 900 million tons per year, 40 per cent is used as fuel, 40 per cent as manure, and the remainder is lost.[1] In China and Japan both animal and human manure are used as fertilizer, and special methods of preparing it for soil use by fermentation in pits have been developed. It is estimated that more than half the nitrogen content of such fertilizer is lost by seepage and dilution with rain water in such pits. In Europe animal and human manure are composted and returned to the soil. Our present methods of disposal of human wastes in the United States and elsewhere are wasteful of water (5 gal of water are required to remove 1 pt of waste) and fertilizer value. Only recently have attempts been made to utilize human waste and sewage better by converting it into innocuous high-protein feed and fertilizer by a combination algal-bacterial treatment. It is possible to increase fertilizer supplies by treatment of animal and human waste and improve their fertilizer value by supplementation with inorganic chemicals.[2]

[1] M. M. Saha, "Fuel in India," *Nature*, vol. 177, pp. 923–924, 1956.
[2] H. B. Gotaas, "Composting," *WHO Monograph Ser. No. 31*, 1956.

Food Acceptability.   Food habits and food prejudices have exerted a powerful influence on the acceptability of available foods. Dietary rules and regulations, religious and social, and other restrictions have been examined recently by Graubard,[1] Renner,[2] and Jensen.[3] These inherent food prejudices have influenced diets and necessitate production of particular types of foods for mankind of different nationality, culture, race, and climate. In China, rice is the staple food of the south and wheat of the north. In India, e.g., in recent years there has been an overproduction of wheat, unacceptable to many of the natives. There are wide differences in acceptability of particular foods, and these often result in rejection and waste. Lack of knowledge concerning the requirements of a good diet and poor dietary habits frequently lead to malnutrition even in the presence of plenty. Such factors can be overcome only by education over long periods of time. Differences in acceptability must be considered in planning an adequate diet even for maintenance levels.

Economic Considerations.   In the previous detailed analysis of food resources and possibilities, the technical aspects have been stressed to the exclusion of the economic aspects. Yet it is readily apparent that economic factors cannot be separated from technical factors in the solution of such problems as equidistribution of food crops, settling of new agricultural areas such as the tropics, and so forth. It is also readily apparent that other technological advances, not immediately related to food production, could play all-important roles in determining the economic feasibility of new advances in food production. Such would be, for example, the availability of very cheap energy, or a novel method of recovering fresh water from sea water, or revolutionary advances in soil chemistry and physics. These matters are discussed in part elsewhere in this volume.

13.6   Technology in Food Preservation and Distribution

Considerable advances have been made in extending the marketing season for farm-produced foods, in obtaining better products for consumption, in extending storage life, and in improving transportation. The commonly used methods of food preservation by drying, salting, smoking, pickling, and fermentation have been greatly improved in recent years so that products of better nutritive quality and higher acceptability are available. Newer methods of preservation such as radiation sterilization and the use of antibiotics are being developed. Marked advances also have been made in the development of improved packaging materials

[1] M. Graubard, "Food Habits of Primitive Man," *Sci. Monthly*, vol. LV, pp. 342–349, 453–460, 1943.

[2] H. D. Renner, *The Origin of Food Habits*, Faber & Faber, Ltd., London, 1944.

[3] L. B. Jensen, *Man's Food*, Garrard Press, Champaign, Ill., 1953.

and packaging methods for the better preservation of quality of both semiperishable and perishable foods during storage and distribution.

These technological developments have been made largely in the United States, and nowhere else is technology so far advanced in commercial processing, transportation, storage, and the use of farm-produced foods. This information, however, is being made available to other countries and already has led to marked improvements in conservation of desirable nutritive qualities of foods in many parts of the world. While all the methods and practices now established in the United States are not readily transferable as such to other countries, the principles developed are applicable and much of the technological know-how can be adapted.

In the United States, the increase in population, the continuing shift from farms to cities, and the growth in real income that has occurred in the past 20 years have resulted in a marked change in the pattern of living and particularly in food consumption. This has been facilitated and encouraged by technological progress in food preparation and marketing.

A recent survey of food consumption in the United States[1] during the period from 1909 to 1948 has indicated that the per capita consumption of meat has not changed appreciably in this period, the decreased consumption of beef being balanced by increased consumption of veal. The total per capita consumption of fish did not increase, but the proportion of fresh and frozen fish consumed increased markedly, that of canned fish increased appreciably, while the consumption of cured fish dropped from 3.9 lb (35 per cent of total fish) in 1909 to 0.8 lb (7 per cent of total) in 1948. The consumption of poultry and eggs increased appreciably.

The per capita consumption of milk and milk products remained essentially constant, but the proportion of fluid milk, cream, cheese, evaporated milk, and ice cream increased. The total oil and fat consumption did not increase appreciably, but the consumption of fresh fruit increased largely as a result of marked increase in consumption of citrus fruit even though the consumption of apples decreased by over half. Citrus fruit today are as important in our diet as apples were in 1908. During this period, the consumption of canned fruits increased by more than fourfold and the consumption of canned fruit juices by over thirty-six-fold. The consumption of dried fruits was practically unchanged, but the consumption of frozen fruits increased about a hundredfold. The total per capita fresh vegetable consumption increased by about 30 per cent, largely because of an increase in consumption of leafy, green, and yellow vegetables and tomatoes. Marked increases also occurred in canned and frozen vegetable consumption. The per capita consumption of

[1] *U.S. Dept. Agr., Misc. Publ. No. 691.*

potatoes decreased by about 50 per cent, that of sweet potatoes by about 30 per cent, while the consumption of dry edible beans increased. The consumption of wheat, rye, and rice decreased as did that of corn, oats, and barley. This decrease was marked in cereal flour (about 35 per cent), while the per capita consumption of prepared cereals increased slightly. The consumption of cane and beet sugar increased from 73.1 lb per capita in 1909 to 95.9 in 1949, that of coffee doubled, while tea consumption decreased about half.

At present a considerable proportion of the total farm crop is prepared for distribution and use by various methods ranging from those in which the inedible portions are removed by cleaning and separation operations; to refining such as milling of cereal grains into flour, recovery and refining of sugars, starches, oils, and fats; to preparation and preservation of foods to retain as much as possible of their desirable qualities, flavor, color, nutritive value, etc.; to the preparation and preservation of derived food products, juices, preserves, candied and glacéed products, fermented or pickled products, etc.; and finally to precooked foods prepared for consumption with minimum preparation for table service. The proportion of the crop processed for food use varies with the type of crop and end use. Thus cereal crops (wheat, corn, rice, etc.) are subjected to varying degrees of processing and refining. About 89 per cent of the total rice crop harvested, 59 per cent of the total wheat crop, 7 per cent of the total corn crop, and 3 per cent of the total oat crop are processed in the United States. All the sugar cane and beet crop, all the nut crop, and all the spice and condiments are processed. Of the oilseeds, 97 per cent of the flaxseed, 89 per cent of the cottonseed, 84 per cent of the soybean, and 10.5 per cent of the peanut crop are cleaned, crushed, and converted into crude oil or fat and subsequently refined.

13.7   Fiber Resources

The major natural fibers, cotton and wool, deserve brief mention inasmuch as their by-products furnish important foodstuffs. Thus cottonseed oil is the world's fourth most important oil crop, following coconut, peanut, and soybean oils. Also arable and forage acreage devoted to fiber production is potentially available primarily for food crops. As an illustration of this it is interesting to note that cotton is fourth in acreage among the crops of India and Pakistan. During the period from 1900 to World War II, this acreage amounted to 80 per cent of that used for cotton in the United States, but production was only one-third that of the United States. If the Indian yield per acre had been as high as that in the United States, an additional 11 million acres would have been available for food crops. Meanwhile in the United States during the 20-year period from 1925–1932 to 1944–1949, production techniques had improved so much that the total acreage devoted to cotton had dropped by half without a decrease in total yield. This trend is continuing.

As this is written, cotton is still in such surplus that additional restrictions in acreage are in force. It is an interesting example of the complex interrelationships in world trade that the existence of a ceiling price for United States cotton has served to bolster the world price structure. With this incentive, several smaller nations have increased their cotton production and are enabled to sell it on the world market just under the United States price.

Table 13.12 gives data on the per capita consumption of textile fibers in several countries. A comparison of the rates of use in the "have" with the "have-not" countries suggests that, if and when a rising standard of living is achieved, there may be a potentially tremendous increase in fiber use. In this as with all other material possessions *except food*, man's potential ability to possess and consume seems to have no limit.

Table 13.12   Amounts of Certain Textiles Used in Different Countries, 1952

Country	Pounds per Person
United States	37.2
Australia	27.9
Canada	25.1
United Kingdom	21.6
Denmark	17.2
Japan	12.3
Cuba	10.6
Brazil	8.1
Egypt	7.9
Yugoslavia	5.5
India	4.4
Indonesia	2.4

SOURCE: Food and Agricultural Organization of the United Nations, The State of Food and Agriculture. Review of a Decade and Outlook, Rome, 1955.

In our discussion of food availability, it was mentioned that supplementation of natural foods with synthetic vitamins and amino acids would be a possibly effective way to improve inadequate diets. It did not seem likely, however, that synthetic food substances would displace the great bulk of carbohydrates, fats, and proteins obtained from agricultural sources. The same situation does not necessarily hold for fibers. In the past few decades, organic chemists have developed fiber-forming polymers which have already made inroads on the markets for natural fibers. As an example, in 1939 cotton furnished 80 per cent and wool 9 per cent of the per capita fiber utilization in the United States. By 1955, these percentages were down to 66 per cent and 6 per cent, respectively. The synthetics accounted for 28 per cent of the total of 36.6 lb.

Rayon and nylon are the best known of these, but at least seven others have properties which appear to be of sufficient value to make them industrially successful. While a growing world population and rising standards of living would appear to ensure a market for the natural fibers for an indefinitely long time, nevertheless the synthetic fibers, which can be made to order with tensile strength, flexibility, drape, etc., "built in" and of constant properties must eventually prove more satisfactory.

14

Nonfuel Mineral Resources

DONALD CARLISLE

ASSOCIATE PROFESSOR OF GEOLOGY
UNIVERSITY OF CALIFORNIA, LOS ANGELES

14.1 Introduction

A mine is a classic example of a fund of wealth. It is wealth because the minerals it yields are both useful and scarce. It is a fund because those minerals can be taken from it only once and once taken cannot be renewed. But it has become a mine only because its operators, presumably in search of a profit, are able and willing to extract those minerals from it. One of the objectives of this chapter is to direct more attention to this last consideration.

Along with energy, minerals have become associated with industrial might and with prosperity more closely than any other natural resource. The known economic reserves of most minerals, however, are strikingly limited in relation to projected needs and are most unevenly distributed among nations. Mineral consumption is growing more rapidly than population itself. It is not surprising then that minerals should be singled out in discussions of natural resources for special and urgent concern. These are the "stock" resources, exhaustible, nonrenewable, and depleting at what seem to be extravagant rates. Yet there is reason to believe that much of the concern for minerals may be misdirected. Many of the references to minerals and plans for their conservation suggest that too much emphasis may have been given to the apparently fixed and limited supply of minerals and not enough to other important characteristics of the mining industry. There appears to be considerable misunderstanding of how an ore reserve is created in the economic as well as the geological sense. The classical concepts of a mine as a fund of wealth and of minerals as a stock resource require some reexamination.

Not all the known mineral deposits are worked as mines today, nor are all parts of the few workable deposits included in the commercial ore reserves. In general, only the richest and the best-situated deposits are worked. Of these few, the only parts that are included in ore reserves are those for which the amounts and grades are reasonably well determined by surface exposures, by mine openings, or by drill holes, and for which there is thought to be a profitable margin between the cost of recovering the mineral product and the price to be received. Other deposits or parts of deposits as yet unknown in grade and tonnage or economically marginal or submarginal are potential ores. Many of the potential ores will be explored more thoroughly in years to come, and many of them will be placed in production if suitable conditions are met. The conditions could be the establishment of a large enough tonnage of a satisfactory grade, a rise in the price of the mineral product, a decline in costs with the appearance of some new technology or facility, or management by operators that are more competent, aggressive, or optimistic, or perhaps only more willing to accept a cost-price differential that others would not.

In addition to the commercial and known potential resources there are the hidden resources, deposits which present techniques and incentives for exploration have not yet discovered but which must surely occur beneath the blankets of barren rock or water that cover the greater part of the earth's surface. Without much doubt the number of undiscovered workable deposits that lie beneath thin coverings of soil or barren rock greatly exceed the number of known deposits. Many deposits without outcrop or visible evidence at the surface have already been found, and more will be discovered as the demand grows and as the opportunities for additional surface discoveries decline.

One should not generalize too readily about materials that are produced in such a variety of ways, from so many different kinds of deposits, and for so many uses as minerals. Some, such as the ores of iron, copper, lithium, or sulfur, for example, are produced for the elements they contain whereas others, such as clay, coal, or corundum, are consumed in their natural forms as minerals or rocks. For some, such as sand, gravel, clay, or limestone, the costs of the refinery plant and of refining, transportation, or marketing may be the major costs, but for scarce metals or precious gems these costs may be unimportant relative to the value of the raw ore itself. Some minerals are predominantly by-products or coproducts from the recovery of some other mineral, and their output, therefore, is tied closely to the output of the principal mineral. Over 90 per cent of the silver produced in the United States, for example, comes from copper, lead-zinc, and gold ores; the bulk of the world's cobalt, platinum, and platinum-group metals are by-products of copper-nickel recovery; cadmium, bismuth, indium, and thalium come almost entirely from zinc, copper, or lead refining.

For the most part minerals are durable producer goods used for manufacturing and for heavy industry, but a few such as building stone, coal, oil in some degree, and gem stones appear directly as consumer goods. Minerals consumed as fuel, paint, or ceramics cannot be used again, but minerals applied in some kinds of construction or manufacture may be reclaimable as scrap and used indefinitely. In the United States, excluding production from foreign ores, scrap is a major component in domestic output of iron (about 50 per cent), lead (about 60 per cent), copper (about 30 per cent), and zinc (about 12 per cent). A few minerals enjoy a virtual monopoly in the market, and many minerals have a monopoly in a few applications or a partial monopoly in several. For example, there are no economic substitutes for sheet mica in some electronic uses, for diamond as an abrasive, or for mercury in some pharmaceuticals. On the other hand, depending largely upon their relative prices, aluminum and copper substitute for each other readily as electrical conductors. It is no paradox to find a large copper company installing aluminum transmission lines for their operations in South America, while the power to aluminum refineries travels over copper cables.

The variety of tenure of mineral deposits also imposes some limitations upon the generalizations one can safely make about the economics of mineral resources. Many deposits are owned and operated by a single company concerned only with working the one deposit or perhaps with recovering a single kind of mineral. Others are leased by their owner. Still other deposits are owned by an enterprise that consumes all or a large part of the mineral produced. Many coal, aluminum, and copper mines are in this category. Finally, there are innumerable deposits, each with a more or less unique geological environment and unique problems of uncertainty and of cost.

14.2   Mineral Uses in the Industrialized World

Metallic and Nonmetallic Minerals.   One has only to look about in any but the most remote parts of the country to realize how important minerals have become in our society. In the building in which the reader is sitting, there are probably a dozen readily identifiable metals serving in more than a hundred functions. In addition there would be several alloying elements in steels or other materials that would not be recognized. Nonmetallic mineral products are even more prevalent. They are so commonplace, in fact, that one may tend to forget that they are mineral materials at all. Actually nonmetallic minerals may have entered into the composition or the manufacture of nearly every article in the building. The brick, cement, and plaster, the glass, and the paint are made largely or entirely of them. The roof may be in part rock granules and the floor covered with tile or linoleum containing a large proportion of mineral filler. The shapes and surfaces of wood and metal articles were probably obtained with the help of mineral sands and abrasives. The land outside has probably been fertilized, the food and water we consume may have been treated, and the air we breathe may be polluted with the help of nonmetallic minerals.

The distinction between the so-called metallic and nonmetallic minerals is not always clear. Iron oxide, for example, can serve either as an ore of iron or as a component of certain cements and pigments in which it is added directly to the mix. The most logical distinction is between (1) minerals that are mined with the purpose of extracting one or more of the elements they contain and (2) minerals and rocks that are mined for use without separation of the elements. The former are sources of the elements, mainly metals, but include a few nonmetals such as sulfur, selenium, or fluorine; the latter are perhaps better termed industrial minerals and rocks. Many of the former group are metallic in appearance and yield metals, whereas most of the industrial minerals and rocks are nonmetallic in appearance.

Metals and Their Uses. Before the industrial era, it was customary to think of the metals as belonging to two major groups: (1) the *noble metals*, gold, silver, and platinum, highly valued for their rarity and for their resistance to oxidation and for their permanence in air; and (2) the *base metals*, including iron, lead, zinc, and all others inferior in value to gold, silver, and platinum. Today, base metals dominate the scene although the value per unit of weight for the most essential of them remains much less than that for the noble metals. Cheapness, in fact, is their virtue. In their applications the base metals tend to fall into groups, partly according to their relationship to steel. The whole picture is about as shown in Table 14.1, though in recent years it has become common to refer only to the major nonferrous metals as base metals.

The Varied Uses of Nonmetallic Minerals. The nonmetallic minerals and rocks are much more difficult to classify than the metals. Unlike the metallic minerals, most of them are consumed in their natural mineral form. Commonly the only treatment given is some cleaning or physical beneficiation, grinding or screening to desirable particle size, or mixing with other materials. A few require some preliminary chemical treatment such as a mild acid leach, but the object is generally not to extract a contained element for use. Their value depends very much upon the particular use to which they are put. Specifications for purity, grain size, and other properties vary with the particular use and, unlike the metals, range widely from one use to another. A large proportion of the nonmetallics are valued for their physical characteristics. A good example is asbestos, a rather sparsely occurring silicate mineral with a most unusual ability to split into silklike fibers. Because of this and its infusibility, it can be spun into yarn and woven into a completely non-inflammable cloth. It is excellent for brake linings. It also serves as a

Table 14.1   Common Metals and Their Uses

Metal	Use, 1953*	United States consumption, 1953
Noble metals		
Silver..............	Money, jewelry and arts, silverware, chemicals, etc.	106,000,000 oz
Gold................	Jewelry, electroplating, filling, leaf, dentistry, instruments, and laboratory ware. (United States monetary reserves have changed only slightly in more than 10 years.)	$75,000,000
Platinum and platinum group (palladium, iridium, osminium, rhodium, ruthenium)	Catalysts, electrodes, laboratory ware, alloys, electronics, dental and medical, jewelry and arts	533,298 oz
Base metals		
Ferrous		
Iron..............	The raw material of steel	74,708,000 tons† (pig iron)
Ferroalloy metals....	Used to make steel and steel alloys but having other uses as well	
Manganese........	Essential to steel production. Ferroalloys 97%; dry cells 2%; chemicals 1%	2,196,000 tons (ore, 35% or more Mn)
Chromium........	Ferroalloys 56%; refractory brick cement, etc., 33%, chemicals 11%	1,336,000 tons (ore, avg. 42.7% Cr_2O_3)
Nickel............	Ferroalloys 43%; nonferrous alloys 37%; electroplating 13%; catalysts, ceramics, magnets, etc., 7%	105,681 tons
Molybdenum......	Ferroalloys 90%; nonferrous alloys, chemicals, etc., 10%	14,800 tons
Cobalt...........	Nonferrous alloys 60%; ferroalloys 26%; enamels, pigments, chemicals, etc., 14%	5400 tons
Tungsten.........	Ferrotungsten and steel; tungsten carbide wire filaments, chemicals, etc.	3900 tons
Vanadium........	Special steels 90%; other alloys, catalysts, chemicals, etc.	(1600 tons, 1947)
Silicon...........	Iron and steel alloys 87%; nonferrous alloys	260,000 tons (approx Si content)
Boron, columbium, phosphorus, titanium, and rare earths are also used in ferroalloys		
Nonferrous		
Major nonferrous metals		
Copper...........	Wire 50%; brass 46%; chemicals, paints, etc., 4%	1,494,000 tons

Table 14.1 Common Metals and Their Uses (*Continued*)

Metal	Use, 1953*	United States consumption, 1953
Lead..............	Storage batteries 30%; tetraethyl lead 13½%; cable covering 12%; pigments 11%; many other	1,202,000 tons
Zinc..............	Galvanizing 41%; zinc-base alloy 31%; brass 18%; metal; chemicals	986,000 tons (slab)
Tin..............	Tinplate 37%; solder 24%; bronze and brass 23%; babbit 5½%; chemicals, foil, etc.	96,000 tons
Light metals		
Aluminum.........	Wrought aluminum 74%; cast 21%; paints, etc.	1,542,000 tons
Magnesium........	Castings 35%; wrought 27%; aluminum alloys 20%; powder, chemicals, etc.	50,000 tons
Titanium.........	Pigments 95%; welding rod coatings 2½%; alloys, ceramics, etc.	430,000 tons (TiO_2 equiv)
Radioactive metals		
Uranium..........	Energy production, chemicals, ceramic, electrical	1¼ tons (U_3O_8 nonenergy)
Thorium..........	Gas mantles, chemicals, magnesium alloys, filaments, abrasive and refractory	9.5 tons (ThO_2)
Radium...........		
Minor nonferrous metals		
Mercury..........	Electrical apparatus 18%; instruments 10%; insecticides, etc., 13%; pharmaceuticals 3½%; many others	52,000 flasks (76 lb)
Antimony.........	Battery metal 21%; antimonial lead 16%; bearings 7%; ceramics 7%; other metallic and nonmetallic uses	14,000 tons
Cadmium.........	Electroplating 71%; bearings 11%; pigments 7%; pharmaceuticals 27%	4800 tons
Bismuth..........	Fusible and other alloys 51%; solder 19%; pharmaceuticals 27%	780 tons
Beryllium.........	Beryllium-copper alloys 83%; metal 9%; ceramics 5%; other alloys, etc.; neutron moderator	2661 tons
Zirconium........	Refractories 28%; foundries 27%; ceramics 20%; metal and alloy 12%; nuclear applications; chemicals	45,000 tons

Table 14.1 Common Metals and Their Uses (*Continued*)

Metal	Use, 1953*	United States consumption, 1953
Lithium............	Grease, ceramics, brazing, batteries, metallurgy, and many others	1700 tons (domestic ore only, Li$_2$O equiv)
Boron.............	Ceramics and glass 50%; agriculture, cleansing compounds, pharmaceuticals, chemicals, fuels, steel alloys, and many others	576,000 tons
Niobium (columbium), tantalum	Special steels, nonferrous alloys, many others	450 tons
Selenium, germanium......	Electronics	560 tons

* Some nonmetallic uses are included.
† Tons refer to the short ton, 2000 lb.

binder in various composition products, hard rubber, plastics and porcelains, roofing paper, millboard, floor tile, and heat-resistant tables. Because it is acid resistant and a good electrical insulator as well, it is also useful in chemical and electrical equipment. Diatomite, a porous earthy material composed of the silica remains of a tiny marine plant, is another example of a rock with many different uses that are applied in the manufacture of several hundred articles. It is widely used as a filtering agent for sugars, beverages, water, pharmaceuticals, oils, or other liquids, but another major use is as an absorbent or filler in rubber, paper, asphalt products, plastics, explosives, insecticides, and paints. It is also a good insulator for heat and sound and appears, therefore, in construction materials. It is a mild abrasive, a catalyst carrier, a raw material for ultramarine pigment and silicate glass and has many other minor applications. As other examples of the varied uses of the nonmetals, abrasives such as diamond, garnet, or corundum are valued for their hardness and toughness, but some varieties because of their unique appearance as well, and perhaps their rarity, are used as gem stones.

Another large proportion of the nonmetallics is valued for chemical properties even though the chemical components are not separated prior to use. Examples are the fertilizer minerals, the raw materials of cement including limestone and clay, and metallurgical fluxes such as fluorite, limestone, or silica. One of the most important nonmetallic mineral groups, the clay family, has a multitude of uses, many of which are derived from physical-chemical properties that are not fully understood. Finally, according to current usage and perhaps not altogether logically, the nonmetallics include a group of minerals and rocks from which industrial chemicals or compounds and some nonmetallic elements are extracted. The brines, borates, and natural sodium carbonates and sulfates are examples.

The list of nonmetallic minerals and their uses in Table 14.2 is not complete although it includes all the principal minerals. It is presented mainly to emphasize the great number of minerals in use and the variety of applications.

Table 14.2   Some Uses of the Nonmetallic Minerals and Rocks

Fuels.....................	Coal, petroleum and gas, asphalt, oil shale, and oil sand
Abrasives.................	Diamonds, corundum, emery, garnet, zircon, natural silica, pumice, diatomite, talc, several rocks
Ceramic minerals...........	Clay, feldspar, talc, pyrophylite, quartz, fluorspar, diatomite, bauxite, sillimanite minerals, borax, magnesite, lithium minerals, barite, and others in minor uses
Chemical minerals..........	Salt and brines, borax and borates, sodium carbonate and sulfate, calcium and magnesium chloride, bromine and iodine, potash, sulfur and pyrites, nitrates and nitrogen, strontium
Dispersing materials (minerals that swell and disperse in fluids)	Bentonite, montmorillonite
Fertilizer minerals..........	Potash, nitrates, phosphates, limestone, sulfur, gypsum, borax, magnesium carbonate, oxide, and sulfate, manganese, zinc, and copper
Fillers (inert cheap powders used in paper, paint, insecticides, fertilizers, rubber, composition products, plastics, textiles, etc.)	Clays, limestone, quartz, feldspar, diatomite, pumice, shale, slate, serpentine, soapstone, talc, pyrophylite, asbestos, mica, vermiculite, gypsum, anhydrite, magnesite, graphite, iron oxides, etc.
Filter minerals (to remove colors, odors, sulfur, or solids from foods, beverages, oil, water, chemicals)	Diatomite, fullers earth, bentonite, sand, bauxite, alunite
Gem stones.................	Diamond, ruby and sapphire, emerald and beryl, opal, jade, quartz, tourmaline, topaz, zircon, spinel, spodumene, peridot, garnet, lapis lazuli, feldspar
Glass minerals..............	Quartz, feldspar, fluorspar, limestone, other minor components
Heavy minerals (for oil-well muds, heavy media, etc.)	Barite, celestite, galena, iron minerals
Insulators:	
Electrical................	Mica, sillimanite group, ceramics
Heat and sound..........	Vermiculite, asbestos, mineral wool silicates, diatomite, gypsum, magnesite, pumice, perlite
Lubricants.................	Graphite, talc, pyrophylite, soapstone, mica, petroleum

Table 14.2 Some Uses of the Nonmetallic Minerals and Rocks (*Continued*)

Metallurgical minerals:

Fluxes..................	Fluorite, cryolite, limestone, silica, iron oxide
Foundary sands..........	Common sand, quartz, zircon
Optical and electronic minerals	Quartz, calcite, fluorite, tourmaline, mica, selenite
Pigment minerals..........	Limonite, hematite, manganese oxides, chlorite, gypsum, barite (titanium, zinc, lead, chromium, cadmium, cobalt, mercury minerals are also sources)
Refractories...............	Chromite, magnesite, dolomite, bauxite, silica, sillimanite group minerals, graphite, clays, diatomite, zircon
Structural materials.........	Gypsum, magnesite, asphalt
Cement materials........	Limestone, clay, quartz, iron oxide, fluorite
Aggregate...............	Sand and gravel, crushed rock, pumice and volcanic cinders
Building stone............	Sandstone, granite, limestone, marble, slate, etc.
Roofing granules.........	Opaque, weather-resistant rock

The total consumption of nonmetallic minerals excluding fuels in the United States is only slightly less in dollar value than the consumption of metals. Only about one-tenth of the nonmetallic minerals consumed, in dollar value, is imported, whereas almost 40 per cent of the metal value consumed is imported metal.

The Aggregate Demand for Minerals.   Because minerals are predominantly producer goods, used by industry, rather than direct consumer goods, the demand for them is more sensitive to industrial activity than to price. If business is good, minerals are consumed in great volume. Moreover, in most articles requiring minerals for their manufacture, the cost of the raw mineral material is not a very large proportion of total cost, and if business is good, a moderate change in the price of minerals does not greatly change the amounts consumed. Nor does a decrease in the price of minerals generally add much to the amounts consumed during a depression. Aggregate demand for minerals, then, tends to be price inelastic, and aggregate consumption of minerals, unlike the consumption of agricultural products, follows the business cycle (Figure 14.1).

An amazing growth in the use of minerals has taken place in the industrialized world during the past 50 years, outstripping the growth of population and the use of all other natural materials. Between 1900 and 1950 the population of the United States doubled; gross national output increased fivefold; and per capita income in constant dollars increased a little over $2\frac{1}{2}$ times. Consumption of all raw materials increased about $2\frac{1}{2}$ times in amount over the same period; agricultural products increased $2\frac{1}{4}$ times; fishery and wildlife products a little more than this; and forest products declined 1 per cent.[1] But the amount of minerals

[1] Paley Report, vol. 1, p. 4, 1952.

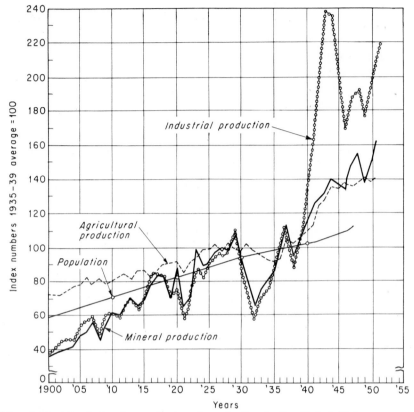

Fig. 14.1   Physical volume of mineral production in the United States compared with agricultural and industrial production and population. (*Minerals Yearbook*, 1951.)

consumed, including fuels and excluding gold, increased sixfold. Approximate multiplications in use for typical minerals are:

Iron ore	4	Chromium	40
Lead	4½	Aluminum	300
Manganese	5	Crude oil	35
Copper	7	Natural gas	47
Zinc	10	Coal	2

In 1950 the apparent consumption of minerals in the United States was $12,678,000,000 consisting of:

$2,204,000,000 . . . . For crude metallic minerals and unwrought metals excluding silver and gold

1,951,000,000 . . . . For crude nonmetallic minerals excluding fuels

8,523,000,000 . . . . For fuels

This is about five times the value of forestry products and almost half the value of agricultural, fish, and wildlife products. The volume of minerals used by the United States alone since 1900 undoubtedly exceeds that of the entire world prior to then.

War forces a huge demand upon mineral resources. The United States consumption of relatively minor metals such as antimony, tungsten, and mercury having critical applications in munitions or weapons increased two to more than three times between 1939 and 1941. It has continued to grow but not nearly at that rate since the war. Copper and iron-ore consumption almost doubled between 1939 and 1941, and since the war copper consumption has declined slightly and iron ore has continued to grow. So much of the material permanently lost during wars will be replaced only with much greater effort from higher-cost deposits.

Energy, Steel, and Mineral Consumption. Up to the present it has been those countries with the best-developed energy resources and the best-developed steel industry that have acquired the world's minerals. The United States, for example, with approximately 6 per cent of the world's population and about 8 per cent of the land area consumes about one-half of the world's yearly production of antimony, asbestos, molybdenum, and nickel; a slightly lower proportion of the bauxite (aluminum ore), copper, iron, fluorspar, and phosphate rock; about one-third of the chromite, lead, mercury, tin, gypsum, agricultural nitrogen, and salt; and disproportionate amounts of most of the other minerals (Table 14.3). The great mineral consumers, however, are not necessarily the most richly endowed with mineral deposits. All of them are grossly deficient in some minerals and partly dependent upon other nations for several more. But they are, in general, nations with large deposits or with access to deposits of iron ore, coking coal, limestone, and manganese, the requisites for steel, and they are nations that have been successful in other respects in the competition for resources and material wealth. They constitute what C. K. Leith has called the "power belt," a string of nations around the Northern Hemisphere with better-developed energy resources than the rest of the world and with a steel industry, the capital, and the technology to find and to develop new resources. The ferroalloy metals, the nonferrous base metals, petroleum, and even iron ore have poured into this power belt.

Will this grossly uneven consumption of minerals continue? With the ever-rising price of labor concomitant with rising standards of living and with continued mechanization and automation, there seems every reason to believe that low-cost power will continue to attract industry and continue therefore to govern the use of minerals. A pointed example is the transportation of bauxite ore from South America, through the Panama Canal, to northern Canada for extraction of the aluminum with low-cost hydroelectric power. The industrial nations are still well ahead in the development of low-cost power, but their advantage will not last

Table 14.3 Production and Consumption of Some Principal Minerals and Metals, 1953

	World mine production	United States production, per cent*	United States consumption, per cent†
Metals			
Antimony....................	29,000 m‡	12.7	50
Bauxite......................	14,000,000 m	11.5	41
Chromite....................	3,900,000 m	.....	31
Copper.......................	2,750,000 m	30.5	44
Gold.........................	33,500,000 oz	5.9	6.4§
Iron ore.....................	331,000,000 m	36	37.6
Lead........................	1,810,000 m	16.3	36
Manganese...................	9,300,000 m	....	23.6
Mercury.....................	161,000 f	8.9	32.5
Molybdenum.................	28,200 m	92.7	50.3
Nickel.......................	203,000 m	....	47
Platinum group...............	750,000 oz	3.5	62.5
Tin.........................	179,000 t	....	30
Tungsten (60% WO₃).........	73,000 m	12	10
Nonmetallic minerals			
Asbestos....................	1,375,000 m	3.6	49
Cement......................	178,000,000 m	25.6	25
Diamond (industrial)..........	16,400,000 k	....	77.8
Fluorspar and cryolite.........	1,310,000 m	22	40.7
Graphite.....................	180,000 m‡	....	17.6
Gypsum.....................	24,500,000 m‡	30.7	37
Nitrogen (agricultural)........	5,012,539 m‡	28	32
Phosphate rock...............	25,500,000 m	48	42
Potash (K₂O, equiv)..........	6,700,000 m	26	24.6
Salt........................	56,000,000 m	33.7	33.6

k = carat.
t = long tons.
m = metric tons.
f = flasks of 76 lb.
* Of mined metal or ore.
† Of primary or new metal or ore.
‡ Excluding the Soviet Union.
§ United States monetary gold reserves increased <10 per cent between 1940 to 1956.
SOURCE: U.S. Bureau of Mines, *Minerals Yearbook.*

indefinitely. Great Britain among other industrial nations can obtain coal only at increasingly great cost. Discovery of new petroleum resources in the United States has fallen off in the face of rising demands, and the enormous supplies in the Middle East upon which Europe depends have been threatened. The more easily developed hydroelectric resources in the older industrial countries are harnessed, and new sites will be more costly to prepare. Against this are the imminent possibilities of nuclear- and perhaps solar-energy supplies which may not have the same geographic restrictions and advantages that coal and hydroelectric supplies have imposed. On this basis alone one might predict a wider diffusion of industry and of mineral demand among the nations in the not-too-distant

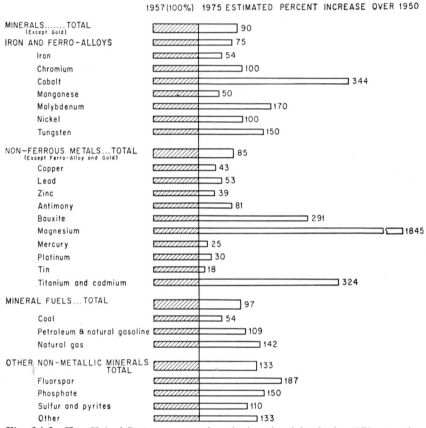

Fig. 14.2 How United States consumption of minerals might rise by 1975, assuming no relative change in prices. (*Paley Report, vol. 1.*)

future. There will be a trend as well for industry to develop in areas where labor is still relatively cheap, and added to this will be the efforts of hitherto undeveloped nations to evolve industries of their own. All this points to more and more nations with larger and larger populations competing for raw materials. How will the world's mineral reserves stand up under this strain?

14.3 The Occurrence and the Supply of Minerals

Known Economic Reserves of Most Minerals Could Be Consumed in One Lifetime. The perennial problem of mineral resources

is their presumably limited and short supply. If the whole world were
consuming minerals at the rate at which the United States is using them,
the known economic reserves of all, except coal, would be depleted within
a lifetime (Table 14.4). Even though the rest of the world is not industrialized to the same extent as the United States, projection of

Table 14.4   World Reserves of Some Minerals, in Years Supply

Mineral	At current world rate of consumption	Assuming world at current United States per capita consumption
Iron ore, iron content:		
Actual reserves..............................	200	25
Potential reserves...........................	625	74
Manganese ore, 50 per cent Mn ore equivalent.....	250	50
Chromite, metallurgical, chemical, refractory......	47	8
Tungsten, 60 per cent WO_3.....................	125	34
Copper, recoverable content.....................	45	5
Lead, gross content............................	33	4
Zinc, gross content............................	39	6
Tin, recoverable content........................	38	6
Bauxite, crude ore............................	200	31
Petroleum, recoverable:		
Proved and indicated......................	22	2.5
Ultimate.................................	160	18
Coal, all types................................	2200	340

SOURCE: E. W. Pehrson, "Estimates of Selected World Mineral Supplies by Cost
Range," *Proc. United Nations Sci. Conf. the Conservation and Utilization of Resources,*
vol. 2, *Mineral Resources,* 1951, pp. 2–4. The data are for 1947–1948 and are not strictly
comparable among minerals owing to varying sources and bases for estimating reserves
and consumption.

current trends suggests that a world rate of consumption may be reached
by 1975 that will accomplish the same thing.[1] In view of this critical
supply of several minerals, serious doubt has been expressed whether
the world standard of living ever could be raised to that of the United
States. The rate of discovery of new mineral districts in the great consumer nations has not kept pace with the rising demand. Increasingly
these nations have turned to imports for minerals they need and for
minerals which they once exported. In the United States, copper, lead,
zinc, and petroleum are examples. Because of these developments the
United States along with other industrial nations is said by some to have
become a "have-not" nation.

[1] Paley Report, vol. 2, 1952.

For several reasons the impressions given by such projections and comparisons may be grossly misleading. They give only a partial picture, and they fail to include some highly significant geological considerations and economic incentives.

The Supply of Minerals in Common Rocks.   If the earth's crust were homogeneous or if the useful minerals were more or less uniformly

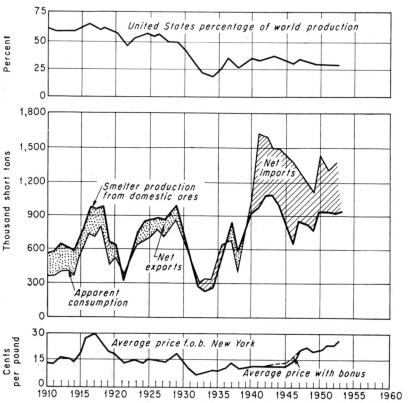

Fig. 14.3   Production, consumption, and price of copper in the United States, 1910–1953. (*Minerals Yearbook*, 1953.)

distributed through it, the problems of mineral discovery, exhaustion, and conservation as we know them would not arise. With one exception the economic criteria would be much the same as for the extraction of magnesium from sea water or nitrogen from the air. As long as the costs of extracting a mineral from average rock with existing technologies and organization were less than the price consumers would pay, the mineral could be produced. One piece of land would be as good for its production as any other, although unlike the removal of magnesium from sea water or nitrogen from the air, mining would have to be carried to new areas or to deeper rocks as extraction proceeded.

The composition of the earth's crust is generally taken by geochemists as the average composition of the igneous rocks which predominate in its make-up. This average (Table 14.5) shows some interesting and sur-

Table 14.5 Tons of the Elements Contained in 1 Million Tons of Average Crustal Rock

(One million tons would have a volume of about 100 by 100 by 1300 ft)

Oxygen	466,000	Cerium	46.1	Bromine	1.6
Silicon*	277,200	Tin*	40	Thallium	1.3
Aluminum*	81,300	Yttrium	28.1	Holmium	1.2
Iron*	50,000	Niobium*	24	Europium	1.1
Calcium	36,300	Neodymium	23.9	Antimony*	1(?)
Sodium	28,300	Cobalt*	23	Terbium	0.9
Potassium	25,900	Lithium*	22	Lutetium	0.8
Magnesium*	20,900	Scandium	20	Mercury*	0.5–0.08
Titanium*	4,400	Lanthanum	18.3	Iodine	0.3
Hydrogen	Present	Gallium	16	Bismuth*	0.2
Phosphorus	1,180	Lead*	15	Thulium	0.2
Manganese*	1,000	Molybdenum*	15–2.5	Cadmium*	0.15
Barium	1,250	Thorium*	11.5	Silver*	0.1
Fluorine	700	Germanium*	7	Indium	0.1
Sulfur	520	Cesium	6	Selenium*	0.09
Rubidium	350	Samarium	6.5	Rhenium	0.05
Carbon	320	Gadolinium	6.4	Argon	0.04
Chlorine	314	Praseodymium	5.5	Palladium*	0.01
Strontium	320	Arsenic	5	Platinum*	0.005
Chromium*	200	Hafnium	4.5	Gold*	0.005
Zirconium*	185	Dysprosium	4.5	Helium	0.003
Vanadium*	150	Uranium*	4	Tellurium	0.002(?)
Zinc*	111	Boron*	3	Rhodium*	0.001
Nickel*	80	Ytterbium	2.7	Iridium*	0.001
Copper*	55	Erbium	2.5	Osmium*	Present
Tungsten*	69–1.5	Tantalum*	2.1	Ruthenium*	Present
Nitrogen	46.3	Beryllium*	2	Radium*	0.000001

After K. Rankama, *Isotope Geology*, Pergamon Press, London, 1954.

* Listed in Table 14.1.

prising relationships. The range in abundance among elements is enormous. And, except for iron, aluminum, and magnesium, the relative abundance of an element in the crust as a whole bears little or no relationship to its availability and its economic importance to man. Such familiar elements as antimony, mercury, bismuth, cadmium, and the noble metals are much less abundant than the rare earths cerium, yttrium, or neodymium. Lead is about as abundant as gallium and along with nickel, copper, tungsten, and tin is much less abundant than rubidium. The reasons for these apparent inconsistencies lie mainly with the chemical characteristics of the elements. Some of the unfamiliar elements, such as rubidium and gallium, though relatively abundant, are dispersed throughout the crust as trace amounts in rock-forming minerals. They are difficult to detect and expensive to extract. Others, such as zirconium and cerium, appear as major components of readily identified minerals, but the minerals themselves are for the most part widely dispersed as minor accessories in common rocks or else can be made to yield the element only at too great a cost.

The elements that are most familiar and most important in commerce are those which tend to be concentrated by geological processes into large rich deposits where they occur as major components of specific minerals which are easily recognized and from which the element can be extracted at a reasonable cost. Gold and silver, for example, though exceedingly rare in the crust as a whole, are among the oldest and best known to man because they occur as visible particles in rich deposits from which they are easily extracted. Similarly, mercury is recovered easily from its bright red sulfide cinnabar, antimony from stibnite (Sb_2S_3), lead from galena (PbS), tin from cassiterite (SnO_2), and so on. Practically all the prospecting in the world so far has been directed toward elements that are concentrated in this way. It is interesting to compare the concentrations of various elements in the earth's crust and in typical ore deposits. The ratios of concentration in ore bodies to that in the earth's crust for some major metals are given in Table 14.6.

Table 14.6

Metal	Typical concentrations in ore bodies, %	Ratio
Aluminum	30–60	4–8
Iron	30–50	6–10
Manganese	20–40	200–400
Uranium	0.05–0.5	125–1,250
Copper	1.0–4.0	200–800
Zinc	2–8	200–800
Chromium	20–60	1,000–3,000
Lead	2–8	1,300–5,300
Mercury	0.2–1.0	4,000–20,000

Next in commercial importance to the metals which occur as major components in ore-forming minerals are the by-product metals which tend to concentrate either with or within minerals containing the principal metals. Bismuth, cadmium, germanium, indium, and the platinum-group metals are examples. These metals merely contaminate the ores of zinc, lead, nickel, and copper, but as demand and technology have developed it has become profitable to recover them as by-products. More recently, technologies of extraction and use have encouraged the production of "new" metals from minerals that are exceedingly rare or from minerals that heretofore have been too costly to treat. Beryllium is an example of the former and titanium of the latter.

Some of these new and less-available metals actually have more useful properties for man than many of the familiar available metals.

The amounts of all elements in the dispersed state vastly exceed the amounts estimated to occur in economic or near-economic concentrations. For this reason no appreciable error has been introduced in the abundance data for the crust as a whole in Table 14.5 through omitting the known ore deposits. These data, however, are not in themselves a guide to the amounts of metals that might be available in presently submarginal deposits or in some very abundant common rocks. Most ore deposits occur in metamorphic rocks or in the relatively thin accumulations of sedimentary rocks not well represented in Table 14.5. Very little is known about the amounts of metal in very low-grade deposits, but considerable information is now available for economic concentrations on the one hand and trace concentrations on the other. Data from minable deposits suggest that, in general, fairly regular grade-tonnage curves can be drawn between the aggregate amounts of metal in economic deposits and the amounts in marginal concentrations. For some metals the aggregate known abundance increases logarithmically with declining grade. Lasky has shown this to be the case for individual porphyry copper deposits and for particular deposits of nickel, manganese, and vanadium and phosphate.[1] A similar relationship appears to hold for trace amounts. The abundance of many trace elements in specific igneous rocks increases inversely as concentration and in much more than linear proportions down to an average concentration.[2] Although each element has a unique distribution in the crust, it is reasonable to expect that a similar relationship will apply, at least crudely, for intermediate concentrations. General observation also supports the conclusion that lean deposits are enormously more abundant than economic ones. Without doubt, the supply of the major industrial metals in deposits at minable depths but at concentrations down to one-tenth of those now mined is, for all practical purposes, inexhaustible.

Obviously with such low-grade ore as common rock and with today's technology the costs of recovery would be extremely high. For most metals they would be prohibitive in relation to the costs and usefulness of alternative materials. For a few metals though, the concentrations even

[1] S. G. Lasky, "Mineral-resource Appraisal by U.S. Geological Survey," *Quart. Colo. School Mines*, vol. 45, p. 24, January, 1950.

[2] L. H. Ahrens, "Lognormal-type Distributions—III," *Geochim. Cosmochim. Acta*, vol. 11, pp. 205–212, 1957.

in some common rocks are sufficient and the uses of the metal are so unique and so difficult to replace with less expensive substitutes that the metals might be worth extracting anyway if there were no other source. As a matter of fact there is a very real possibility that within a century aluminum will be extracted from rather abundant high-alumina clays and later, perhaps, from certain igneous rocks (anorthosite) and that uranium will be extracted from some granitic rocks. Is it unreasonable to expect that other "dispersed" elements will eventually be extracted from common rocks?

Many of the nonmetallic minerals would not be available at all, however, from a homogeneous crust or from common rocks. Minerals like asbestos, diamond, and talc require unique or at least unusual geological circumstances for their growth, and not merely the presence of their constituent elements. The common rock-forming minerals, quartz, feldspar, and olivine, would be abundant enough though not in the crystal size or concentration that we find in certain deposits today.

One wonders what might have happened had none of the rich concentrations of metals that we mine today ever existed. Would technology and needs ever have developed to the stage where we would extract metals from common rocks or from sea water; or, indeed, would man ever have advanced beyond the Stone Age if he had never found unusually rich concentrations of copper and tin close to the surface.

The Genesis of Mineral Deposits.   Fortunately the earth's crust is highly differentiated. A myriad of geological processes, some acting at the surface of the earth, some within it, continuously change the assemblages and concentrations of minerals. The waves, the wind, and the flowing streams each sort mineral fragments according to the relative ease with which they are carried along. Minerals of higher-than-average specific gravity, such as gold, magnetite, or diamond, tend to accumulate locally and to enrich the sands and gravels sufficiently to form workable placer deposits. Meteoric water charged with oxygen and carbon dioxide helps to decompose surficial rocks and, along with organisms and other agencies of weathering, produces soils which are either enriched or depleted in various elements. Under the extreme weathering conditions of the tropics, all the more soluble minerals may be leached from a soil and only oxides of iron (iron laterite) or aluminum (bauxite) or perhaps silicate of nickel (nickel laterite) may remain. All our present-day aluminum ore and much of our nickel ore were formed in this way. In other areas the meteoric water may seep downward through soil and fractured rock and, dissolving copper from scattered grains of copper sulfide, carry it in solution to depths where it is again precipitated. In this way huge and enormously profitable blanketlike deposits of secondarily enriched copper have accumulated. Ground water and streams carry most of the salts dissolved during weathering to lakes or to the ocean where they accumulate over the centuries. Here, through evaporation or through chemical reactions with each other or with organisms, they may again precipitate in some partly enclosed bay or shelflike area. If they are then left in a place where man can find them and if the deposit is large enough and rich enough in some desirable salt, they constitute a workable mineral resource. These are the evaporites.

Still other processes, many of them complex and not well understood, have concentrated minerals of many kinds within the earth's crust, along fractures, faults, and folds, within certain beds of sedimentary rocks, or within igneous and metamorphic rocks. One of the most common agents of transportation for a great variety of processes of this sort appears to have been hot water or water vapor in which the elements have been dissolved. The precise source and nature of these "hydrothermal" solutions is uncertain, but they appear to have come from considerable depth and to be related to the intrusion of great bodies of granite, gabbro, or other igneous rocks. In many cases the solutions have made their way to the surface, mingled with meteoric water, and dispersed their load through hot springs and similar phenomena. In other cases the dissolved materials have been precipitated as the solutions moved along in various channelways, and mineral deposits of many different sizes, shapes, and grades have formed. Practically all the vein deposits and most of the large irregular "replacement" deposits of precious and base metals are of this origin. Usually more than one kind of mineral occupies a single deposit. Common constituents are metallic sulfides of copper, lead, zinc, mercury, or other metal; native gold; and such common nonmetallic minerals as quartz, calcite, fluorspar, and barite. Still other important metallic and some nonmetallic deposits are formed at the contact of invading igneous rocks and the invaded host rock. These are the so-called contact metamorphic deposits. Usually, they are extremely irregular in form and grade. And finally there are the concentrations of minerals formed within igneous rocks at the time they were emplaced. Diamond deposits are of this sort and so are the only occurrences of sheet mica.

Each concentration of minerals is unique in size and shape, and each extends for varying depths beneath the surface of the ground. There are all gradations from country rock only slightly enriched to almost pure deposits of the source materials. Some are fairly uniform. Others range continuously or erratically from thick rich zones of concentration to irregular, barely traceable stringers of mineralization. Some have sharp boundaries against barren rock; others grade almost imperceptibly from minable to unacceptable concentrations.

While most deposits tend to fall into some sort of a family group with several features in common, the detailed mineralogy and structure and

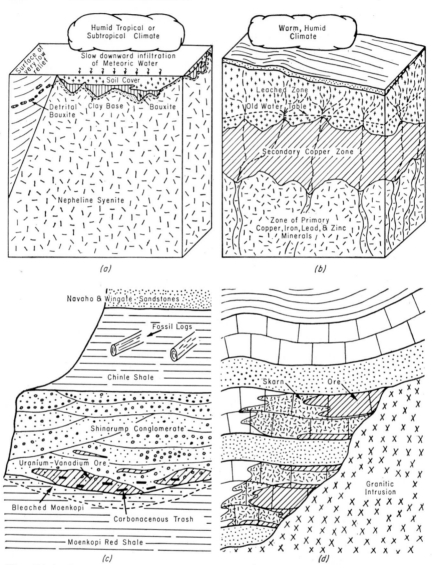

Fig. 14.4 Geological processes yielding ore deposits: (a) residual concentration, block diagram of a bauxite deposit; (b) secondary enrichment, of a low-grade copper deposit; (c) concentration by circulating waters, cross section of a Colorado plateau uranium deposit; (d) introduction during contact metamorphism, cross section of a tungsten deposit.

Table 14.7   Geological Processes That May Yield Ore Deposits

Process	Some minerals or metals concentrated
I. Mechanical concentration	
Rock fragments and mineral grains separated by weathering are transported differentially by streams, winds, waves (mechanical sediments)	Placer gold, platinum, precious stones, quartz sand, gravel
II. Chemical concentration	
A. In bodies of surface waters (chemical sediments)	
1. By interaction of solutions or by organisms	Limestone, chalk, dolomite, magnesite, diatomite, sedimentary iron and manganese ores, phosphate rock
2. By evaporation of solvents (evaporites)	Gypsum, anhydrite, borates, sodium and potassium salts, nitrates
B. In bodies of rocks	
1. By concentrations of substances contained in the rock itself	
a. By weathering and by meteoric ground water (residual and secondary deposits)	Clays, bauxite, lateritic iron, nickel, manganese, copper, lead, silver
b. By ground water of deeper circulation and by metamorphism	Sulfur, magnesite, talc, asbestos, graphite, garnet, sillimanite group minerals
2. By introduction of new substances into the rock	
a. By hot ascending waters possibly or definitely related to igneous activity. (Hydrothermal replacements and open space fillings. Includes nearly all vein deposits.)	Copper, lead, zinc, silver, gold, tin, mercury, nickel, antimony, molybdenum, uranium, vanadium, fluorspar, barite, quartz, calcite, and many others
b. By direct igneous emanations (contact metamorphic deposits and sublimates)	Iron, copper, tungsten, lead, zinc, tin, molybdenum, asbestos, sulfur
C. In magmas	
1. Magmatic segregations	Diamond, chromite, iron
2. Pegmatites	Mica, feldspar, quartz, beryllium, rare earths

the detailed problems of exploration and extraction, therefore, tend to be peculiar to each. Table 14.7, showing geological processes and some metals and minerals that may be concentrated to ore grade thereby, is taken from a famous classification of mineral deposits devised by Waldemar Lindgren.[1] It is presented here to give the reader some feeling for the

[1] W. Lindgren, *Mineral Deposits*, 4th ed., McGraw-Hill Book Company, Inc., New York, 1933.

prodigious variety of processes by which minerals are concentrated. It must be pointed out in all fairness that geologists are by no means agreed on the details or on the relative importance of many of the processes. Working out the genesis of a deposit, moreover, does not necessarily ensure that predictions of grades and amounts of mineralization in unexplored areas will be much more reliable.

The Uneven Distribution of Economic Deposits. Most of the minerals listed in Table 14.7 can be concentrated in several different ways, and as a result they become associated with many kinds of rocks. Uranium is a good example. The largest known economic deposits are in conglomerates (consolidated gravels) that were enriched in uranium either by placer concentration at the time the conglomerate was deposited or by hydrothermal solutions much later. Other large deposits are in veins, in beds of sandstone and limestone, in pegmatites, in layers of lignite, in fossil logs, and in phosphate rocks.

Several minerals, though, have a tendency to concentrate in one or a few kinds of rocks. Hardrock deposits of diamond, chromite, chrysotile, asbestos, nickel, and platinum metals are found only or predominantly in certain coarse-grained dark-colored igneous (basic and ultrabasic) rocks. Tin, tungsten, and uranium tend to concentrate in or near the light-colored quartz-rich granitic rocks. Sheet mica is found only in granite pegmatites. Many copper deposits are near bodies of igneous rock of intermediate composition, and so on.

For much the same reason many minerals, particularly the metallic minerals, have tended to concentrate in a few parts of the earth's crust. The world's deposits of tin, for example, are in and near the Malay Peninsula, in Bolivia, and in Cornwall (now exhausted). North America has no workable tin deposits. Diamonds have concentrated in South Africa and in Brazil. Russia and India have more high-grade manganese ore than all the rest of the world. Great copper-rich provinces are found in western and northeastern North America, in the Andes, in central Africa, and lesser ones elsewhere. Over 60 per cent of the world's nickel now comes from the Sudbury district of Ontario, Canada, which is only 40 miles long and 20 miles wide. Three more huge nickel deposits have recently been found a few hundred miles to the north and northwest. About half the world's molybdenum comes from a single deposit in Colorado, and another four-tenths from molybdenum and copper deposits in other western states.

The uneven distribution of economic deposits among nations is further illustrated in Figure 14.5. The figure gives an example of estimates made by the U.S. Bureau of Mines and Geological Survey,[1] the first organiza-

[1] U.S. Bureau of Mines and Geological Survey, *Mineral Resources of the United States*, Public Affairs Press, Washington, D.C., 1948.

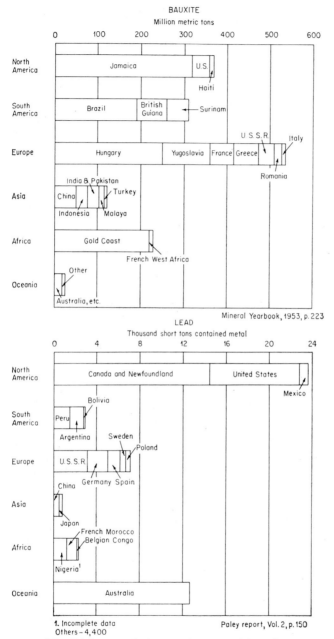

Fig. 14.5 World reserves of commercial grade.

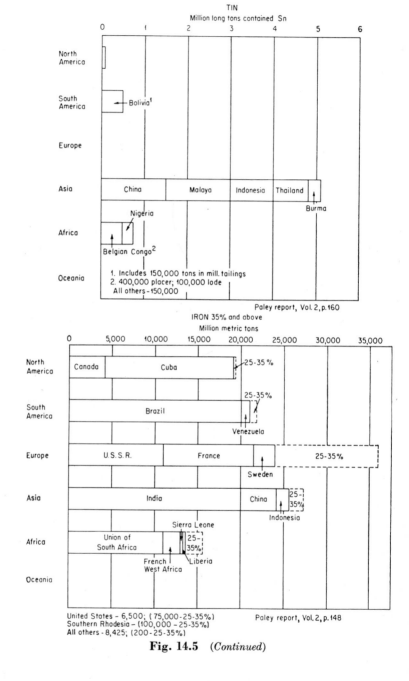

Fig. 14.5   (*Continued*)

tions known to have attempted detailed estimates of this sort. The following definitions adopted by these organizations for the purpose may be of interest to the reader because they illustrate the kind of information upon which estimates of mineral reserves are based.

Measured reserves are those for which tonnage is computed from dimensions revealed in outcrops, trenches, workings, and drill holes and for which the grade is computed from the results of detailed sampling. The sites for inspection, sampling, and measurement are spaced so closely and the geologic character is so well defined that size, shape, and mineral content are well established. The computed tonnage and grade are judged to be accurate within limits which are stated, and no such limit is judged to be different from the computed tonnage or grade by more than 20 per cent.

Indicated reserves are those for which tonnage and grade are computed partly from specific measurements, samples, or production data and partly from projection for a reasonable distance on geologic evidence. The sites available for inspection, measurement, and sampling are too widely or otherwise inappropriately spaced to permit the mineral bodies to be outlined completely or the grade established throughout.

Inferred reserves are those for which quantitative estimates are based largely on broad knowledge of the geologic character of the deposit and for which there are few, if any, samples or measurements. The estimates are based on an assumed continuity or repetition, for which there is geologic evidence; this evidence may include comparison with deposits of similar type. Bodies that are completely concealed may be included if there is specific geologic evidence of their presence. Estimates of inferred reserves should include a statement of the special limits within which the inferred material may lie.

The starting points for the estimates are the known deposits of presently economic or near-economic grade. Concealed deposits other than extensions of known deposits or for which there is no specific geological evidence are not included. Thus, if an estimate of this sort had been made for Canada in 1935, probably not more than one-third of about thirty major mineral discoveries made there during the last 20 years would have been included. At least half of those included would have been "inferred reserves" of relatively small size. The estimates for deposits well below commercial grade are even less complete because, for the most part, such deposits attract little attention and they do not warrant much exploration. For some minerals, the known very low-grade deposits are of a different genesis and in quite different rocks from the principal deposits of commercial grade. In other words, the tonnages suggested for deposits at the low-grade end of the curves are undoubtedly very conservative.

Discovery, Technology, and Mineral Reserves. The discussion so far has emphasized two qualifications of the term *stock resource*. On the one hand is the likelihood of new discovery. On the other hand is the

Table 14.8   Trend of United States Copper-reserve Estimates

Year	Recoverable copper,* tons	Price, cents	"Life," years	Annual rate of production used to estimate "life"	Reference
1931	At least 18,500,000	9	31	600,000†	Barbour, Percy, "World Copper-ore Reserves," *Eng. Mining J.*, vol. 131, p. 178.
1931	18,800,000	9	31	600,000†	Rawles, W. P., "The Nationality of Commercial Control of World Minerals," *Am. Inst. Min. Met. Eng., Contr.* 41, 1933.
1934	18,900,000	10	32	600,000†	Barbour, Percy, "World Copper-ore Reserves," *Eng. Mining J.*, vol. 135, pp. 448–449.
1935	16,000,000 23,500,000	10 12	22 32	750,000‡	Leith, K., and D. M. Liddell, "The Mineral Reserves of the United States and Its Capacity for Production," Natural Resources Commission, p. 55, Washington, 1936.
1936	23,700,000	12½	33	725,000	Leith, K., and D. M. Liddell, "The Mineral Reserves of the United States and Its Capacity for Production," Natural Resources Commission, p. 55, Washington, 1936.
1944	20,000,000 30,000,000	13§ ¶	25 38	800,000	Cannon, R. J., M. Mosier, and Helena Meyer, "Mineral Position of the U.S.," pp. 240–241, U.S. Department of the Interior, 1947.
1945	29,200,000	13§	36	800,000	Federal Trade Commission, *Report on the Copper Industry*, p. 4, 1947.

* Recovery factor, 90 per cent.
† 1925–1935 average.
‡ Predicted by the estimators from trend. Actual production in 1935 was about 400,000 tons.
§ Premium price plan.
¶ More favorable than 1944.
SOURCE: S. G. Lasky, "Mineral-resources Appraisal by U.S. Geological Survey," *Quart. Colo. School Mines*, vol. 45, p. 22, January, 1950.

possibility of tapping ever larger reserves of metal as new technology and increased demand lower the acceptable grade. Even in the United States with its monstrous rate of consumption, these two factors have offset depletion for a few minerals. Copper is a good example (Table 14.8), and iron will be an even better one as the taconites, very low-grade iron deposits, are made economic through new technology.

The critical question for mankind, then, is not merely "How will the world's mineral reserves stand up under the strain of accelerating consumption?" but "How likely and under what conditions can discovery and new technology continue to unlock supplies of minerals?" The answer in our economy depends very largely upon individuals and upon economic motivations and conditions.

14.4 Uncertainty and Risk in Mining

Geological Risks Are Unique. While a mineral deposit is a nonrenewable fund of wealth, it is not a stock of known and absolute amount, as some appear to believe. For one thing, the operator is uncertain about the amounts and the kinds of mineralization beyond exposed faces of the ore, and he is uncertain about future costs and prices.

Mining differs from most but not all other industries in that unusually large, and frequently the largest, uncertainties are associated with the supply of the raw material. This is not quite so true for the low-priced nonmetallic minerals, since with them the ability to gain and hold a market may be critical; but it is especially true for most of the higher-priced minerals. The great uncertainties of discovery and of estimating the quality and extent of the unseen resource are unique to mining, and the physical risks of production can be very large. Moreover, the investment in mine plant is usually large, fixed, and often in a remote area, so that it commonly has no alternative use or salvage value.

The risks of mining are:

Geological risks, involving the quantity, grade, and mineralogy of the ore both within measured blocks and in extensions beyond exposed faces.

Technological risks, including the physical risks of mining and excessive inflow of water and the uncertainties of recovery in mining and in processing. The risks of managerial efficiency might also be included here.

Economic risks, especially those of market or product price arising mainly from the uncertainties of demand and from the possibility of serious competition from newly discovered ore bodies or techniques in the hands of competitors. Also in this category are the risks of factor supply, particularly of the supply of labor.

Sociopolitical risks, which include those of excessive or discriminatory taxation, of nationalization, expropriation, or revolution.

In North America, the uncertainties of ore supply and of market usually exceed the other risks, and of these two, in metal mining at least, the geological risks are commonly the larger. Ordinarily, the geological risk in a new mine is reduced by a step-by-step procedure; first a preliminary examination, followed, if warranted, by a more thorough investigation, usually with an option to continue, and then a series of piecemeal additions to the investment as the results warrant. The risks involved in sampling are purely technical, even the probability of error being calculable in some deposits.

All the estimated ore in the mine is finally classified into three groups, usually labeled positive, probable, and possible ore. Only positive and probable ore are included in the ore reserves, for with these two classes the risk is either negligible or not too large. Possible ore, sometimes called "geological ore," is purely speculative. Most or nearly all properties offered for sale, however, and all prospects owe their chief attraction to this possible ore; positive and probable ore reserves are small, and available information is meager. The uncertainty of estimating ore in the early stages of a mine can be reduced, of course, by more intense mine exploration and sampling, but this reduction is offset by the increase in the amount of capital risked in the process. In spite of the best technical facilities, the estimates of possible ore are highly subjective. Some well-organized, competent mining firms have been rather unsuccessful in their prospecting programs, while good mines have been found by sheer luck, or at least by people without training. It would appear that somewhat less than 1 per cent of metal prospects that are judged promising enough to receive serious exploration become successful mines.[1]

In a few mines the amounts and the grades of ore are known only as they are encountered from day to day. This is the state of affairs in some very high-grade and erratic silver deposits. In others, enough exploration is done to maintain ore reserves at a level where they will last a few months or a few years at the current rate of mining. In these situations, although the total amount of recoverable mineral in the deposit is a fund, the size of that fund may not be known until the deposit is exhausted. The distribution of ore bodies within a district may be similarly difficult to foresee. In several of our oldest and geologically well-known metal mining districts, the details that have controlled the location of ore bodies are not well enough understood to guarantee that ore does or does not occur in some unexplored sections. New mineral districts are even less predictable. Indeed if it were not so, mineral exploration would not be so expensive. Frequently the costs of mine exploration, the potential market, and the requirements for amortizing the mine plant do not justify blocking out reserves to last much more than about ten years. However, for

[1] D. Carlisle, "Maximum Recovery through Mining High-grade and Low-grade Ore Together Is Economically Sound," *Can. Min. Met. Bull.*, pp. 21–27, January, 1953.

several metallic deposits and for many deposits of the lower-priced non-metallic minerals, such as coal, limestone, or phosphate rock, the reserves of ore, even without a great amount of exploration, are much more than this. These factors need to be considered in evaluating estimates of future mineral supplies.

The geological risk of ore supply is peculiar in another way. Most risks of an enterprise accumulate over time. That is to say, the longer a person remains in a risk-taking situation, the more likely he is to suffer from some untoward event. The risks of fire, labor unrest, destructive competition, and most other economic, technological, and sociopolitical risks are of this sort. But geological risks are not. Whether one looks for the expected ore today or a year from now, or whether the exploration is spread over a month or 10 years, the odds that the ore will be found, assuming no change in the data available, are the same. So there is no reduction of geological risk by mining or exploring more rapidly. Mining slowly, and thoroughly in fact, may increase the chances of enlarging the ore reserve because of the added time available for exploration.

On the other hand, the risks of market do accumulate over time and do justify rapid mining. When mineral prices are unstable, miners are encouraged to "gut" their ore bodies, that is, to mine out the more profitable ore as rapidly as possible at the cost of losing less profitable ore.

The Risk of Price Is Large for Many Minerals.   Unfortunately the risk of market for many minerals is unduly and perhaps unnecessarily high. In the first place, production and sale of many of the metals are highly competitive. Copper, lead, zinc, and mercury, for example, have many producers, an open market, and a nondifferentiated product. In the second place most minerals are producer goods with a relatively inelastic demand. Each fluctuation in industrial activity, therefore, is reflected by a similar fluctuation in demand for those minerals accentuated perhaps by the stock piling activities of the industrial consumers. A very large change in price is induced by sellers in an attempt to increase sales if the demand is low or by buyers bidding for the mineral if the demand is high. The result is the sort of price record shown in Figure 14.6.

Price instability discourages long-range planning and the recovery of low-profit ore along with the high-grade ore, and though some mineral may be recovered from marginal mines while prices are high, much mineral may be lost through the flooding and collapse of those marginal mines when prices again fall. Price instability has a serious effect as well upon the people who work mines for a living.

Many attempts have been made to stabilize mineral prices through subsidies, premium price plans and stock pile quotas, tariffs, enforced price ceilings and floors, production control and cartels both private and governmental, and buffer stock piles of various kinds. Most of the

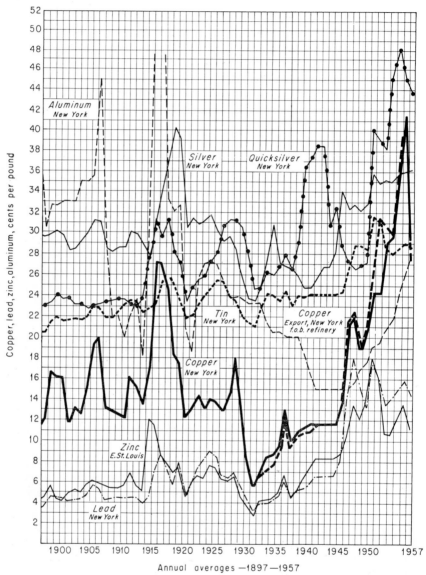

Fig. 14.6 Metal prices, 1897–1956. (*Engineering & Mining Journal*, February, 1957.)

attempts have failed or have been declared unnecessary or illegal after a few years. Monopolistic combinations or cartels in aluminum, nickel, tin, mercury, and diamonds have had varying periods of success. Since 1956 the International Tin Council has done rather well with a buffer stockpile plan, although in 1958 it was forced to set up export quotas to offset the sale of tin by the Soviet Union at discount prices. Most private plans have been designed for the benefit of producers, of course. Publicly operated buffer stockpiles appear to offer considerable hope for both producers and consumers of minerals.

14.5 Determinants of Mineral Output

Profit, Cost, and Price. Of the innumerable mineral deposits, it is economic to mine only the few deposits or parts of deposits so concentrated, so shaped, and so situated that they can be expected to yield their mineral at a profitable cost. Expectations, however, are subjective; each entrepreneur makes his own estimates of risks and expectable profits and invests in that enterprise which for him seems wisest. To be more exact then, and neglecting other "noneconomic" incentives, a deposit or part of a deposit will be operated as a mine only if, when compared with all the alternative opportunities for investment, it appears, in the minds of the individuals concerned, to offer the best opportunity for profit. The size of the "stock" of ore in a mine, therefore, is in large part discretionary; it depends upon expected costs and prices and also upon what the operator is able and willing to mine.

Costs are determined by:

1. *The nature and location of the deposit.* The shape, structure, and geological setting of the ore bodies affect the costs and the uncertainties of mining and the amount of waste rock that must be taken with the ore. The size of the deposit determines the size of the plant that can be amortized and the economies of scale. The grade, mineralogy, and texture of the ore determine the costs of milling and extraction of the mineral.

2. *Technology and economic conditions.* These include the methods and the means for mining and extraction, prices of labor, materials, and capital, costs of transportation, rentals, royalties, and taxes.

3. *Decisions made by management.* The major considerations here are the rate and the level of recovery. Some aspects of these decisions are discussed below.

Price, on the other hand, is determined for most minerals by the demand of the market and the rate at which mineral suppliers satisfy that demand. Markets range from highly monopolistic (gem diamonds) to highly competitive (lead and zinc). The rate of output from a mine supplying only a small fraction of the market has relatively little effect on price. A major nickel, aluminum, or iron producer or the only sand and gravel plant in a community, however, can affect the mineral price profoundly by its own supply and must take this fact into account.

The Rate and the Level of Recovery. The operator of a farm or factory or any renewable resource must decide on a most satisfactory scale of production, or quantity of output per time period which is the same thing. But the miner, who is continuously using up his source of supply, must decide not only how fast he is to exhaust the deposit but also how much he is to take out of it. He must choose between alternative rates of recovery, the amounts of mineral product per time period; he also must choose between alternative levels of recovery, alternative fractions of the absolute total assumed to be present in the ground. This latter choice includes such variables as the grade of ore to be mined, the completeness of removal of ore from the mine, and the per cent extraction of valuable product from the mined ore. It is extremely important, for it frequently happens that low-grade or high-cost ore can be mined at a profit only if it is removed and treated along with the neighboring high-grade ore. The two parameters, rate of recovery and level of recovery, may influence each other, but there is no inherent relationship between them.

Consider, for example, a mineral deposit of irregular shape, of varying thickness, grade, and mineralogy and extending through an appreciable vertical range, but sufficiently uniform nevertheless that any or all of it might be blended into an acceptable (from a technical viewpoint) mill feed. How much of it is ore? The alternative levels of recovery are shown on the abscissa of Figure 14.7, and the alternative costs for each level and the price and profit are shown by the curves. In practice, of course, the data are never so regular and continuous or so well known as this, but the purpose of the example is to illustrate the relationships and the importance of the decisions in mines beyond the prospect stage.

Mining lower-grade and less-accessible ore and extracting larger percentages of the mineral content have both advantages and disadvantages, and in accordance with the economic law of nonproportional returns the tendency for costs per ton to decrease with fuller recovery, that is, the economies, will ordinarily outweigh diseconomies up to a point of diminishing returns. Many of the economies arise from the fact that some costs, such as the costs of acquiring the right to mine, of exploration, and of much of the primary development and essential equipment, are more or less fixed as a total for the whole supply of ore regardless of the level of recovery, at least within wide ranges. These "fixed costs" are spread as larger and larger alternative tonnages are considered. Other costs, which can be called "variable costs," may at first decrease as a total for the whole supply of ore and then increase as the higher alternative levels of recovery are considered. Among these, for example, are most direct labor and material costs, ordinary depreciation on plant and equipment, and royalties on the gross product. Included also are several costs, such as interest on borrowed capital and costs of pumping, obsolescence, and the minimum amount of management, that remain at a more or less fixed rate per day if the mine is to produce at all and, therefore, vary directly as a total with the time required to exhaust the ore body. The further one pushes the level of recovery to lower grades, less accessible ore, and fuller extraction, the more markedly do variable costs rise with each higher alternative level. The point is illustrated by the effect of mining widths on costs. Wider stopes may yield lower costs per ton both because of the spread of more or less fixed preparatory costs and because of more

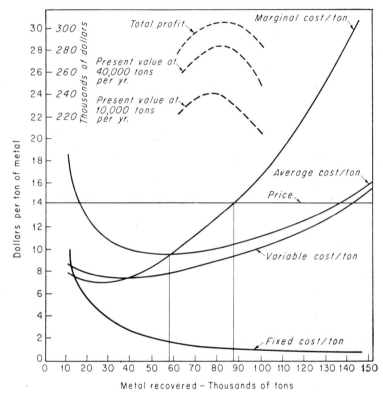

Fig. 14.7   Alternative levels of recovery. Price is assumed to remain constant regardless of the level chosen. Smooth curves have been drawn between alternative costs.

favorable mining conditions in the wide stopes. In almost every case the decrease in cost per foot of added width becomes less at very large widths, however, and it may be reversed.

   Average cost per ton is the sum of fixed plus variable cost per ton. Now if the mineral product sells for $14 per ton, how much of the deposit is ore? Apparently 130,000 tons can be recovered "at a profit." Obviously, the total profit is meager at this level of recovery, and it is more profitable to mine a somewhat smaller amount of richer or lower-cost "ore." Costs per ton are at a minimum between 50,000 and 60,000 tons, and some might seize upon this level as the optimum, saying that the operator should make as much profit as possible. The criterion of maximum profit may be acceptable, but the least-cost level is actually not the maximum-profit level. Instead, as various methods of calculation will show, total profit on the whole deposit (neglecting the distribution of this profit in time) is maximized at about 87,000 tons.[1] To mine more than this would be an error for it would reduce total profit, even though much more low-grade material could be mined "at a profit" if it were blended with richer ore into a uniform mill feed. Conversely, much of the "ore" included within the 87,000-ton cutoff could not be mined at a profit if it had to stand upon its own merits. It is "ore" only by virtue of its association with richer material. Yet neglecting it would reduce the total profit from the whole ore body.

It is not correct, however, to neglect the distribution of profits in time. Profits in the future are worth less than profits today and need to be discounted at some rate of interest. The rate to be used is a matter for the recipient to decide, but it should reflect, in general, the risk that the profits may not be realized at all. High risks justify a high rate of discount, and this in turn justifies a more selective form of mining. The higher the risks, the more rational does it become to "gut" the ore body, that is, to leave otherwise minable rock in the ground. Geological risks however, as we saw above, are not compounded with time, and they do not justify a high discount rate and overly selective mining.

Price Instability and Overly Selective Mining.   But large market risks do justify a high discount rate. These are more or less dependent on time and are reduced, therefore, by rapid mining of the best ore first. For some kinds of mining, notably for small-scale coal production and for many nonmetallic enterprises, the risks of market may far exceed those of ore supply, and this can also be true, as price history shows, for producers of mercury, tungsten, chromium, and other metallic minerals. The greater the likelihood that the market will not last, as with war markets, with cutthroat competition, or with limited-term contracts, the more advantageous does rapid-selective mining become.

A similar analysis can be made for the rate of recovery. Also the effects of rate and level on price can be taken into account. In each case, the theoretical optimum rate and level of recovery are those which yield maximum present value.

Apparently in many average-sized mines the uncertainties of market and of future costs and the demands of shareholders encourage a level of recovery closer to that yielding a maximum yearly rate of profit or per-

---

[1] "Marginal cost" is the net increment in total cost incurred by adding one more unit, the "marginal" unit, to total output. Total profit is greatest where marginal cost equals marginal revenue or price in this case.

haps a predetermined rate of profit objective than to a maximum present value optimum. Management and the technical staff, on the other hand, usually favor a long-life stable operation, and the trend in larger mining companies at least is strongly in this latter direction.

14.6 Future Mineral Supplies

One purpose of the above discussion has been to emphasize that, while a mine is a fund of wealth, the size of that fund may be highly uncertain, that it varies with current technological and economic conditions, and that it depends in large part upon the will and the abilities of its operators. Another purpose has been to call attention to the enormous increase in workable mineral resources occasioned by a decline in acceptable grade. The world's supplies of most of the important metals at concentrations one-quarter to one-tenth of present cutoff grades are not "stocks" in any practical sense for living man. So many pessimistic predictions are made for mineral resources, so commonly are they cited in resource discussions without reference to these fairly obvious relations that it has become difficult for many of us plagued much more with marginal deposits than with clamorous demand not to lean over backward in compensation. If the term *stock resource* is not misunderstood by some who so commonly use it, it must surely be misconstrued by many readers. The Paley Report, quoted several times here for its sober findings, labels a graph showing a threefold decline in the average grade of copper ore "forced to low-grade, high cost copper ore."[1] It might equally well have been labeled "New technology creates today's ore from yesterday's waste." The text implies that rising price encourages new technology, recovery from lower grades of rock, and substitution by other materials (aluminum and plastics), suggesting that the poor correlation between price and grade actually shown by the graphs results from rigidities of production and uncertainty. It can be argued equally well that new technology and larger markets reduced the cost of production and of marketing and made the recovery from low-grade ores profitable. Substitution of aluminum and of plastics for copper is not necessarily dependent upon a rise in the price of copper but reflects the new profitability of producing these materials through new technology. The effect of the eye-catching summaries in Volume I of the Paley Report upon many readers can be illustrated by the following comments from a draft report in *British Political and Economic Planning*, January, 1955, quoted by Ordway:[2]

[1] Paley Report, vol. 1, p. 18, 1952. A typographic error shows the grades 10 times too high.

[2] S. H. Ordway, Jr., "Possible Limits of Raw Material Consumption," in W. L. Thomas, *Man's Role in Changing the Face of the Earth*, University of Chicago Press, Chicago, 1956, p. 993.

On the other hand, copper will be exhausted in about 50 years; lead, zinc and tin before 1980. And the supply of other important minerals is likely to be exhausted before the year 2000.

The Paley report estimates that if the rest of the noncommunist world achieved the present American materials standard, the world consumption of minerals would be multiplied by six. It is quite obvious that to supply such standards would mean an impossible demand on the world's mineral resources.

The quotation then goes on to say that technology cannot necessarily be counted upon to provide alternatives or substitutes before existing supplies are exhausted or become excessively expensive, perhaps by about 1980 for lead, zinc, and tin.

The concept of mineral resources as a chest of wealth lying in the ground, inherently valuable but limited in size, exhaustible and non-renewable has lead to a widely held conclusion that we should become more restrictive in the use of these precious stocks, that we should find some equitable way of rationing them or at least of apportioning what little remains between present and future generations. For nearly all the mineral elements and for most of the nonmetals, the concept is fallacious. Man's needs and ingenuity created the chest. They control its size. If man is clever enough, and if he does not first run out of sheer space and energy, the chest for most minerals can be inexhaustible.

The critical issue for most mineral resources, then, is not how shall we preserve those we are now mining, but by what route and in which vehicle shall we travel from the bonanzas of yesterday to the low-grade refractory ores of tomorrow. We do not deny that the journey may be perilous and that many individuals may be hurt along the way. But slowing down will never get us there, and the bonanzas are already passing out of view. Assuming that the vehicle will continue to be private enterprise, what are the prospects for the trip?

Underlying much of the above discussion has been the assertion that in a private enterprise economy mines are worked to make a profit. This is not to deny that there may be other incentives as well, personal or group, rational or irrational, but the overruling criterion for operation is that the mine be profitable or give promise of making a profit. In a very real sense minerals are the mere by-product of that profit. In developing mines, as in developing any new business, entrepreneurs turn to the best opportunity available to them. Should the best opportunities appear to be in foreign lands, they will turn there. This does not mean that domestic deposits are exhausted or that no more will be found. Rather it means that in the eyes of those entrepreneurs the opportunities to make a profit, taking into account social, political, economic, and geological conditions, are more favorable abroad than at home. Similar reasoning applies to foreign purchases of minerals. It is the best deposits that are scarce and limited and exhaustible. They are also more unevenly distributed than the poor deposits. As long as the world is partly unexplored and as long as international trade is possible, rich deposits abroad will outbid lean deposits at home, and there will be less incentive to develop new technologies for lean ores than if those alternative opportunities did not exist.

But as the low-cost deposits are depleted, will miners then turn to higher-and-higher-cost deposits and will they provide the minerals in ever-greater amounts and at comparable costs? The record so far is very encouraging. The world average grade of ore for nearly every metal mined (excluding gold) is lower today than it was 50 years ago and in some cases several times lower. Yet the price that consumers have had to pay for the metals, measured in constant dollars, has held steady or has declined. Productivity, the output of metal per man day, has risen steadily in every case where data are available. In every case where the demand has been expressed, mankind has a larger annual supply of metals, spends less direct labor to obtain them, and so far as can be told, has larger known world economic reserves than 50 years ago. To be sure, cases can be cited where the economic ore grade has risen, as for example when the discovery of new high-grade boron deposits made the older low-grade ores no longer competitive. Cases can be cited, too, the rare earths for example, where ore reserves are so large relative to demand that there is no incentive to develop new reserves.

It is an error to claim that consumption is constantly pressing supply. In some degree, suppliers create their own demand. The producers of molybdenum and of nickel have spent large sums on research to create new markets for their huge supply, just as the owners of a single large rare-earth deposit are doing today.

Men are as intrigued as ever with the prospects of converting waste rock into profitable ore. Recent developments in cheap metallurgical leaching and other extractive processes are evidence. Every mining engineer and metallurgist in the industry knows that if he can cut costs of mining or recovery by 50 cents per ton he can create millions of tons of ore. Mining-equipment manufacturers know this too, and know that they can share in the profits. Large mining companies have found that the big low-grade long-life deposit makes a very desirable operation. But, as yet, there are still rich deposits to be discovered in less-explored countries. It is still advantageous to look for mines in Africa and in northern Canada, and there are still great hopes for geological and geophysical methods of discovery even in countries like the United States that have been thoroughly explored by surface prospectors. For most metals, therefore, full pressure has not yet been placed on technology and invention. When it has, as for the taconite iron ores, the results have been highly satisfactory. Whether they will continue to be satisfactory with extremely low-grade deposits and with metals that are dispersed or tightly locked in common rocks is impossible to know. Increasingly greater amounts of energy almost certainly will be required.

Should discovery and invention and new supplies of cheap energy fail to hold costs in the face of declining grades, the price of metal need rise by only a small proportion to convert a much larger proportion of the known deposits into ore and to encourage enormously the search for new deposits and new methods. A substantial permanent rise in the real (constant dollar) price of a metal would indicate, of course, that a larger proportion of man's effort was needed for its production. This would suggest, in turn, that man's standard of living was being impaired in some degree by the metal shortage.

The future is not quite so promising for some of the rarer nonmetallic minerals which are required in their unique mineral form. The world reserves of sheet mica, radio-grade quartz, and cryolite are already heavily depleted. Attempts to substitute or synthesize the mineral have been successful for the latter two and are promising for mica. This will be the pattern for many others. Except for petroleum the situation will not be particularly critical for the world as a whole for a very long time.

The adjustment to very low-grade deposits will not be simple. Many writers doubt that the profit mechanism alone will be sufficient. Very little is known about the submarginal deposits of some important metals. For a few the difference in grade between current ore and the kinds of deposits that will be needed to supply the market is very great. For some there is as yet no obvious technique by which costs of extraction can be drastically reduced, and the prospects of discovery do not look very good. It is interesting, however, that each of these things could have been said of uranium prior to 1943, and today the economic and potential reserves in North America alone are fantastic. The cutoff grade in the Algoma District, the largest known commercial deposit, is only five to ten times the grade of several extremely large masses of common rock.

More interesting is the economic climate that was created for the uranium rush. A stable effective price more than four times the 1943 price was guaranteed until 1963. Extremely efficient new prospecting instruments, the Geiger and scintillation counters, were placed in the hands of thousands of persons in search of a fortune. Public agencies made as much technical help, information, and encouragement available to all as they felt they could and undertook much of the riskiest exploration. Nothing was done to dampen the boom thus created. In the United States, mills and ore-buying stations were built by the Atomic Energy Commission, and government capital was loaned for some of the exploration and development. The United States price schedule provided a bonus for selective mining in the belief that the mills could not produce uranium economically from low-grade ores alone. In Canada, individual contracts were negotiated with the U.S. Atomic Energy Commission through a crown corporation for production from major deposits. These required that private operators erect the mills and provided a price estimated to yield a profit on all costs, including amortization within the guaranteed price period. Contract prices were confidential but close to the price in the United States for similarly low-grade ores. These contracts made possible debt financing from large capital sources at a scale heretofore extremely rare in mining. In addition, new uranium discoveries in Canada benefited, along with other kinds of mining, from mineral land laws that give reasonable access and security and from financial regulations that encourage the expenditure of risk capital in the ground and rapid release of the property if exploration fails. New mines in Canada are also exempted from dominion taxation for 3 years after the start of economic operation.

The price for uranium to producers in the United States was later extended for another 5 years with approximately one-third reduction, but this extension was drastically curtailed in November, 1958, because of the abundance of known uranium ore reserves. Larger operators outside the United States with their plants amortized and with large proved reserves should be able to produce at a much lower price after 1963.

The uranium rush has emphasized once again the uneven distribution of the richer mineral deposits among nations. This maldistribution has been a source of international friction many times in the past, and it can be again. Although future mineral supplies for the world as a whole appear reasonably promising, they are not promising for a nation deprived of access or the means for international trade. Moreover, access to foreign supplies does not replace the loss of a wealth-producing home industry. It behooves each nation, therefore, to adopt mineral land laws and economic and tax policies which tend to reduce the risks of exploration, operation, and particularly of price, but which encourage high levels of recovery from the deposits now in operation and which ensure that mineral technology will continue to advance and not fall behind as it can so easily when alternative kinds of investment become more attractive than mining. And, although it is not within the scope of this chapter, more thought should be given to incentives that will encourage the most efficient and appropriate use of minerals.

These and not merely the preservation of known reserves are the things that need attention in the mineral industries.

15

Some Aspects, Mainly Geophysical, of Mineral Exploration

LOUIS B. SLICHTER

DIRECTOR, INSTITUTE OF GEOPHYSICS
UNIVERSITY OF CALIFORNIA, LOS ANGELES

BACKGROUND

"The point to remember is that the reserves are being used up at an unbelievable rate."—Julius A. Krug, Secretary of the Interior, 1949. "Secretary Krug might have added that the *acceleration* in the rate is even more unbelievable."—Palmer Putnam.[1]

15.1 Introduction

The American economy is distinguished by its high per capita consumption both of power and of metals. In our factories, the average worker consumes an amount of power equal to the energy output of about 250 men. When one uses a gasoline engine, each gallon of gasoline burned provides the mechanical energy of a gang of 25 laborers working throughout an 8-hr day. Thus at 25 cents a gallon, the fuel costs correspond to hiring labor at 1 cent per 8-hr day. These comparisons between the trivial energy output of an unaided worker, and the enormous increases obtained by the use of controlled power, do not, of course, tell the whole story. No mention has been made of the large outlays of capital per worker needed to supply his power, tools, and facilities for work. But the factor of over a thousand between the cost of human labor and the cost of its equivalent in electrical or mechanical energy is the reason for the enormously increasing use of power in our factories and homes. Energy at present prices is the great bargain of all ages. That is why the world is using record amounts today, and will constantly achieve new records in the future. In

---

[1] Palmer Putnam, *Energy in the Future*, D. Van Nostrand Company, Inc., Princeton, N.J., 1953, p. 71.

368

this country, almost everyone is personally conscious of the rapidly increasing use of power, and of metals, stimulated by bargain prices. Despite familiarity, however, the true figures remain almost unbelievable. The report of the Advisory Committee on Minerals Research to the National Science Foundation[1] begins its second paragraph with the remark, "In the prosperous twenties C. K. Leith called attention to the fact that mineral production since 1900 had exceeded the entire mineral output from the dawn of history to the end of the 19th century. In 1955 we can again claim that within the past quarter century more minerals have been extracted from the earth than in all preceding history." The prodigious consumption of the world's nonrenewable mineral wealth has aroused increasing recognition of the importance of mineral-resources problems. "This mounting strain upon resources that cannot be replaced has become the most challenging aspect of our present economy."[2]

Among the challenging aspects of mineral-resources problems are many which belong purely in the province of science and technology—problems of developing better methods for finding hidden mineral deposits, of developing substitute materials for metals in short supply, of working lower-grade ores, and most important of all, the development of new sources of low-cost power. Fortunately, the explosive increase in the use of nonrenewable mineral resources has been accompanied by a remarkable growth in technological research. Thus we are witnessing a continuing race between the depletion of our richest mineral reserves and the growing power of science to mitigate the effects of depletion. We shall be especially interested here in a narrow aspect of this contest, namely, the recent efforts to develop new methods for discovering concealed minerals. But before proceeding to these details, it seems well to review some of the broad features of the mineral-resources situation.

15.2   Relation between World Consumption of Fuels and of Metals

The annual consumption of mineral fuels and of the eight most important metals of industry, iron, copper, aluminum, lead, zinc, nickel, silver, and tin, is shown in Figure 15.1 for the 60-year period 1880 to 1940.[3] The vertical scale is in dollars of constant value (1939 dollars). In this 60-year interval, the annual world output of both fuels and metals increased nearly tenfold. This increase is the more significant because it was so largely accounted for by so small a part of the population. Two-

---

[1] Report of the Advisory Committee on Minerals Research to the National Science Foundation, 1956, p. 1.

[2] Report of the President's Materials Policy Commission, *Resources for Freedom*, vol. I, p. 5, 1952. (Referred to in Chapter 14 as the Paley Report.)

[3] C. K. Leith, J. R. Furness, and C. Wilson, *World Minerals and World Peace*, Brookings Institution, Washington, D.C., 1943, pp. 211–213.

thirds of the world's peoples make almost no use of the industrial minerals, whereas the United States, with 6.2 per cent of the world population, uses nearly half of the world output of metals and fossil fuels.

A notable feature of the chart is the parallelism between the output of fuels and of metals. Except for brief intervals during World War I and the depression of 1931, their relative output remained nearly constant, at 35 cents worth of the eight chief metals to each dollar's worth of mineral

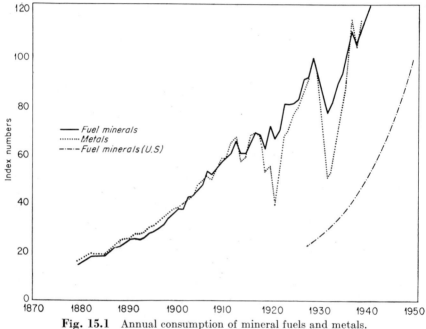

Fig. 15.1   Annual consumption of mineral fuels and metals.

fuel. The graph in Figure 15.2 shows by years the ratio of the value of the annual world production of metals to the corresponding value for fuels and brings out the essential constancy of this ratio throughout these years. It is evident that the world requires energy and metals in nearly constant ratio. The mineral-resources problem is a problem of the supply both of metals and of fuels.

Energy and Metals for the Future.   Energy resources have recently been reviewed in impressive treatises by Putnam,[1] Ayres and Scarlott,[2] Hubbert,[3] and others. An important trend is the increasing use

[1] Putnam, *op. cit.*

[2] E. Ayres and C. A. Scarlott, *Energy Sources—The Wealth of the World,* McGraw-Hill Book Company, Inc., New York, 1952.

[3] M. K. Hubbert, "Nuclear Energy and the Fossil Fuels," Drilling and Production Practice, American Petroleum Institute, 1956.

of fluid fuels. In the United States, in 1953, fluid fuels were carrying nearly 57 per cent of the total. "By 1970, the proportion may reach 70 per cent."[1] Before 1970, the production of petroleum in the United States is expected to attain its maximum, and to decline. The large potential production in Canada will be dependent on the United States market, via pipelines.

As domestic oil production falls behind demands, the energy deficits are expected to be made good in three major ways: (1) by importation of oil, purchased under the handicap of increasing competition from other oil-deficient countries, (2) by large increases in domestic production of coal,

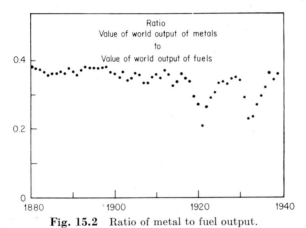

Fig. 15.2   Ratio of metal to fuel output.

and (3) by the introduction of new sources of low-cost energy. Of the fossil fuels—coal, petroleum, natural gas, oil shales, and tar sands—coal is easily in largest world supply, representing about 70 per cent of the total energy budget. The energy reserves theoretically represented by uranium deposits are enormous. Known deposits of uranium in the United States have an energy content "probably several hundred times greater than that of all the fossil fuels combined."[2] To what extent, how soon, and at what cost uranium or other new sources of power can come to the rescue is still a guess, but "by the time nuclear energy is abundant, we shall be thankful for it."[3] Despite technological advances, energy, like money and gold, will continue to be in short supply. Its price will tend to be upheld and stabilized by the myriads of new competing uses which are encouraged as new sources become available.

In comparison with reserves of many of the essential metals, energy resources are large indeed. Thus an important feature of the rising con-

[1] Putnam, *op. cit.*

[2] Hubbert, *op. cit.*

[3] E. Ayres, *Mines Mag.*, vol. 14, p. 42, July, 1955.

sumption of energy seems to be the correlated acceleration in the consumption of metals. With the notable exception of iron and aluminum, many metals are in short future supply, under present economics, and at prices approaching present low costs.

15.3 Factors in the Growth of Mineral Consumption

The increase in world use of minerals is a growth compounded of three major factors, (1) the increasing use per capita in industrialized nations, (2) the spread of industrialization to nonindustrialized countries, and (3) the increase in world population itself.

1. Up to now, the increase in the world consumption of minerals has been chiefly accounted for by the heavily industrialized areas, North America, Western Europe, Japan. Thus the graphs in Figure 15.1, with minor corrections due to the increase in the populations of these countries, are primarily indicative of the rapidly increasing per capita demand in industrialized nations.

2. If all the world's peoples were to achieve the per capita use rate now existing in the United States, world mineral production would have to be increased sevenfold. In addition, large quantities of metals would be required to provide the capital facilities—buildings, bridges, machinery— needed to establish an industrial society. In the United States, the per capita amounts of steel, copper, lead, zinc, and tin already being used in various forms represent about ten to twenty times our present annual per capita consumption of these metals.[1] Thus to create in the nonindustrialized two-thirds of the world an industrial plant like that in the United States would absorb the entire present world production of the chief metals for about 75 years. This is in addition to the mentioned sevenfold increase needed to feed such an industrial plant. Reserves of copper, lead, zinc, nickel, silver, or tin of traditional type, sufficient to create and to support such an expansion, are certainly not known today, nor does there appear to be any possibility of finding them.

3. The rapidity of the increase in world population in modern times may be visualized by reference to the graph in Figure 15.3, which shows the trend in world population since the time of Christ. "It required over 1600 years, or 85 per cent of the Christian era, for the population to double. The next time, it required 200 years (1650 to 1850) to double the population, and the third time, only a hundred years, or 5 per cent of the Christian era."[2] More recently, we find in the United Nations 1956 Demographic Year Book the information that the current rate of increase of world population is 1.6 per cent per year, which means a doubling in only 44 years. According to 1957 U.S. Census Bureau figures, the 1956–

[1] H. Brown, J. Bonner, and J. Weir, *The Next Hundred Years,* The Viking Press, Inc., New York, 1957, pp. 20, 157.

[2] W. Weaver, "People, Energy, and Food," *Sci. Monthly,* vol. 77, no. 6, p. 359, 1954.

1957 rate of growth in the United States represents a doubling of its population in 40 years. The dotted line in Figure 15.3 shows a projection, for 25 years into the future, of the world population at its present frightening rate of growth. It is obvious that a continuation of the indicated projection soon becomes absurd; for within a short period, as nations measure history, the ensuing population would quite literally be crowded into the sea.

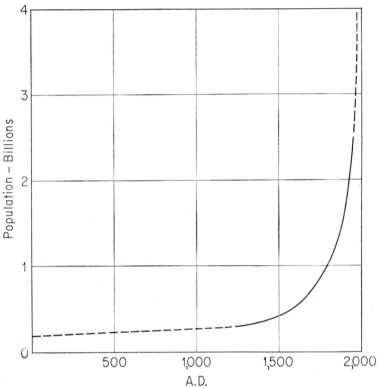

Fig. 15.3   Trend in world population.

More than half the present world population lives in a dangerous state of hunger. "Even if the population of the world should increase no further, an increase of total caloric production of about 35 per cent would be required to bring the world average up to the Western average."[1] It has been estimated[2] that a total population of 7 to 8 billion could theoretically be supported at a reasonable standard of living, if (1) present agricultural acreage were increased by 40 per cent, through subjugation of the warm and cold wet regions of the earth, and (2) Japan's intensive agricultural

[1] H. Brown, *The Challenge of Man's Future*, The Viking Press, Inc., New York, 1954, p. 113.

[2] Brown et al., *op. cit.*, p. 68.

yields were achieved on one-third of the earth's agricultural acres and that of Western Europe on the other two-thirds. (Japan's agricultural production per acre is threefold that in the United States, Western Europe's one-and-two-thirds-fold.[1]) If the present growth rate of 1.6 per cent per year continues, this critical population level of 8 billion will be attained in 69 years—within the lifetime of many persons now living. This certainly leaves little time for the enormous task of educating the masses in the use of the postulated intensive agricultural techniques and for financing such a huge expansion. Although the increasing population entails increasing demands upon nonrenewable mineral resources, there are more fundamental aspects of the population problem which are more deeply disturbing. At last the world seems to be approaching its saturation level, where the attainment of human aspirations requires limitation of population by means more humane than starvation.

15.4   Extending the World's Metal Resources

The problem of supplying the world's essential metals will apparently have to be solved by a combination of many means: by more efficient exploration techniques for discovering hidden deposits; by improved technology in the mining and recovery of metals; by higher metal prices, reduction of waste, substitutions of other materials, more complete recovery of scrap metal; and perhaps by reducing trade barriers in the interest of establishing a more efficient economy in the world as a whole. In the past, improved technology has often succeeded in more than compensating for the depletion of higher-grade ores. For example, the average grade of copper worked in the United States decreased during the first half of the century from 3 per cent to 1 per cent; yet the real price of copper in dollars of constant purchasing power dropped by a half during this interval.[2]

The advantages of cheap, abundant sources of minerals, and of other raw materials, to the economy of an area, whether it be as small as a mining community or as large as a nation or continent, clearly are great. These advantages are, of course, relative and involve the element of competition. The richness of the "have" areas, and of rich mining districts being developed, is enhanced by contrast to the "have-not" areas, or of mineral areas on the way to depletion. The differences in costs of mining obviously are especially large during the era of exploitation of large frontier areas, when the rich finds of a new continent come into competition with the leaner, partially worked-out ores of older lands. However, the era of bonanza strikes in frontier areas is gradually coming

---

[1] *Ibid.*, p. 57.

[2] Report of the President's Materials Policy Commission, *op. cit.*, vol. I, pp. 18, 19, Figs. 1 and 6.

to a close. There is relatively little new land to be explored for easy finds at the surface. In the long term, there will be smaller differentials in mining costs as all areas become older mining districts, whose richest ores have been partially depleted. Depletion of the richer ores will lead to higher metal prices. How much more can we afford to pay for essential metals?

As Evan Just has recently emphasized,[1] the price we could easily afford to pay for the scarcer metals is manifold higher than their present low prices. To illustrate: cotton, which is harvested annually, costs about $0.33 a pound, and about 27 lb per capita per year is now consumed in this country, namely $9 worth per capita. Zinc, which is mined once, has recently been selling at $0.10 per pound. Our per capita consumption in 1954 was 16 lb, or only $1.60 worth per capita at recent prices. There seems to be little doubt that society could pay ten times, or more, the current prices for its essential needs of such metals as copper, lead, and zinc. In the United States today, the average per capita annual income from all sources is about $2000. In 1954, the per capita consumption of the plentiful metals, steel and aluminum, was $50, whereas a total of $13 worth of the seven less plentiful metals, copper, lead, zinc, manganese, tin, nickel, and antimony, was consumed per person. In comparison with this figure of $13, we are paying farm subsidies of $30 per capita for food which we do not need and cannot use. If, by virtue of shortage, the world price of these seven metals were increased *tenfold*, our indicated increased per capita cost would be 6.5 per cent of the average per capita income. Because of savings from use of substitute materials, by curtailment of waste, by increased recovery of scrap, etc., the actual per capita cost would certainly be far less than this indicated figure. The present low prices of the major metals and their consequent lavish use provide an important cushion against hardships resulting from tighter supplies and higher prices.

It is generally agreed that the effect of large price increases in developing additional reserves of metals would be enormous. Within limits, the cost of producing metals seems to be approximately inversely proportional to the grade (see page 407 and Table 15.2). Estimates of the amounts of world reserves of ores as a function of grade still involve large elements of human judgment and uncertainty. The indications are that copper reserves would be doubled by reducing the cutoff grade from 1 per cent to $\frac{1}{4}$ per cent.[2] In the case of zinc and lead, a factor of 2 to 4 may result in reducing the cutoff from 4 per cent to 2 per cent.[3] Certainly large price increases, which could easily be afforded, could greatly multiply the effective lifetime of the reserves of the scarcer metals.

[1] Evan Just, *Science*, ser. 2, vol. 122, pp. 317–318, 1955.
[2] Report of the President's Materials Policy Commission, *op. cit.*, vol. II, p. 144.
[3] *Ibid.*, pp. 149–150.

15.5   Need for New Tools for Prospecting

"Practically, the prospector has worked himself out of a job in the metallic field because he has discovered virtually every worthwhile deposit that can be found by visual and simple instrumental means within the confines of the United States."[1] This statement is rapidly becoming applicable to the surface of the earth in general. The old-time prospectors succeeded in discovering almost all the visible ore showings in our Western states in a little more than a generation. The rise and fall of their fortunes

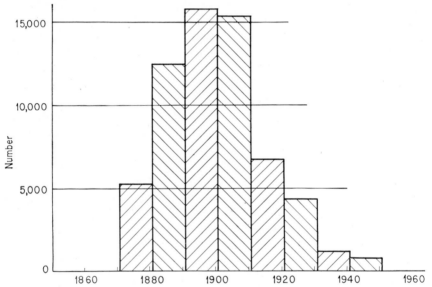

Fig. 15.4   Mineral patents issued in the United States (by decades 1872–1951).

may be seen in the statistics of the claims for mineral patents. The number of mineral claims patented[2] are plotted, by decades, in Figure 15.4. As the West developed after the 1860s, the number of claims patented rose rapidly to a maximum of 16,000 per decade at the turn of the century, and then dropped to a figure of less than 1000 by 1940. In the search for oil, "surface geology, which hit its stride in 1912, was nearly finished in 1924."[3] In the Gulf Coast of Texas and Louisiana, during the period 1924 to 1930, more than 40 salt domes were discovered by the seismic refraction method.[4] Essentially all the salt domes shallow enough for detection

[1] Report of the Advisory Committee on Minerals Research to the National Science Foundation, 1956, p. 3.

[2] Report of the President's Materials Policy Commission, *op. cit.*, vol. V, p. 7.

[3] W. A. Ver Wiebe, *How Oil Is Found*, J. W. Edwards, Publisher, Inc., Ann Arbor, Mich., 1951, p. 235.

[4] Morgan J. Davis, *Geophysics*, vol. 22, p. 225, 1957.

by this method were discovered during these years. (Since petroleum often is trapped against the flanks of salt domes, a salt dome is an important guide in petroleum exploration.) The histories of all successful methods of prospecting show these same characteristics. The methods are energetically employed and the prospectors tend to work themselves out of a job by finding those deposits which they are capable of finding. Thus there is a constant need for research which will develop new exploration tools and more efficient systems of prospecting.

THE GEOPHYSICAL TOOLS

The geophysical methods of searching for minerals are employed under circumstances of relative ignorance about the concealed geological structures under study as a means, less expensive than drilling, for developing significant geological information. The decision to use these methods generally must be made early in a prospecting program, despite many uncertainties concerning the true conditions which will be met. This inevitable element of ignorance about the ground to be explored is unfortunate; for the geophysical tools, like other tools, perform well only under suitable conditions. Success, in fact, will require (1) sufficient contrasts in the physical properties of the pertinent concealed structures and (2) favorable geometrical relationships, such as a target of size sufficiently large in relation to its depth below the surface. We shall return to these points later. For the moment, let it be noted that it is relatively easy to specify what the favorable geophysical conditions *are*, but it is always an open question whether conditions in an area selected for search will really meet the requirements. After choosing a supposedly favorable hunting ground, one usually must carry on with little reassurance about the felicity of the choice until a late stage in the venture, when the returns begin to come in. In the long run, successful results from geophysics will depend primarily upon the geological wisdom and imagination used in selecting good prospecting risks and *not*, necessarily, upon detailed knowledge of the geophysical tools. An understanding of the elementary characteristics of the geological prospecting methods will enable one adequately to appreciate the geological conditions which favor successful applications. One of the present aims, therefore, is to provide information concerning the geophysical methods which may be helpful to those who have to decide, usually in the face of rather large uncertainties about the true geological conditions, whether or not to use these tools.

Since the exploration departments of the petroleum industry are well staffed with experts of many types, this chapter is necessarily directed primarily to mining prospecting, where *small* teams of geologists and geophysicists still search for ore. The emphasis will be upon the nature of the methods, in their basic aspects, with little if any comment concerning the instrumentation by which observations are obtained. While the latter subject is of great importance, especially in the economics of geophysical prospecting, it is a highly specialized field. The basic limitations upon the methods which will concern us here, generally, are *not* of an instrumental nature.

15.6   The Two Types of Geophysical Prospecting Methods

Geophysical prospecting methods are of two types: (1) the flux methods, and (2) the wave methods, or seismic methods. In the first category are the methods important in mining prospecting, such as the gravity, magnetic, direct-current, natural potential, and low-frequency electromagnetic methods. The radioactive methods, now so widely used in the search for uranium, may be grouped in the first category, as may the heat-flux methods, which thus far have received little application. In the second category, unfortunately, only one good representative exists, the seismic method. At first sight, high-frequency radio and radar waves perhaps might be expected to form the basis of a second wave method. But the penetration of such waves into the ground is so restricted that they have had little application in prospecting.

Flux Fields.   The essential characteristics of the flux fields used in geophysical prospecting may be appreciated in terms of the analogous properties of the steady streamline flow of a fluid. When, for example, water steadily seeps through a volume of permeable sandstone, each point in the three-dimensional flow pattern is characterized by a *direction* and by a *velocity* of the local flow. As this flow pattern is distorted by changes in the permeability or "conductivity" of the sandstone, so the pattern of other types of flux fields is distorted by changes in the pertinent physical properties of the materials which are traversed. It is to be remembered that the only evidence of a hidden geological structure provided at the surface of the ground by any of the flux-type prospecting methods is the distortion introduced by the structure into the expected, or normal, pattern of the flux field. The form and magnitude of this distorted part of the field are dependent upon the size, shape, and depth of the target structure and upon the physical properties of the target relative to those of the surrounding rock. But the observations on the surface do not lead to unique answers concerning the causal conditions at depth. Many different structures would theoretically be capable of producing the observations. Of these structures, however, it is likely that only a few, perhaps only one, would be compatible with the known geological environment. Sometimes the observations may have a negative value, by denying the validity of a suggested geological hypothesis. Sometimes the combined evidence from several independent geophysical methods may usefully restrict the scope of interpretation. In practice, the interpretation procedure is usually of the cut-and-try type, in which plausible geological hypotheses are tested by computing their associated geophysical response and comparing these with the field observations. This process is continued until the fit is regarded as satisfactory.

The study of the selected area, in detail, by any means obviously stimulates more penetrating analysis of all types of existing information besides encouraging the search for additional evidence. It is sometimes surprising how the making of a geophysical map will promote more careful geological examinations, which succeed in finding important out-crops, in areas thought to be devoid of such evidence. Thus a hidden asset derived from combined geological, geophysical, geochemical, or other studies is the more effective *thinking* stimulated by the various shreds of evidence. The methods, as individual tools, may be relatively ineffec-tive, but the total evidence may inspire sufficient thought to achieve progress.

In the following paragraphs each of the flux methods will be briefly discussed, with special attention to the three main physical factors which determine its success. These are (1) the size and shape of the targets, (2) their depths below the surface in relation to size, and (3) the contrast in the physical properties of the targets and surrounding rocks.

15.7 Gravity Methods

To obtain a concept of the magnitude of the gravitational attractions exerted by bodies of several different sizes and shapes, Figure 15.5 may be consulted. Here vertical cross sections of five different shapes of bodies are shown. Each of the bounding lines (marked 1–5) of these cross sections determines a family whose maximum gravity response is represented by correspondingly numbered straight lines in the upper-right graph. The lines marked 0 represent extreme cases, in which the top surface of the body is tangent to the surface of the ground. The abscissa is the thickness dimension t or the radius a, as the case may be. The three bodies whose cross sections are shown in each diagram are so selected as to produce maximum gravity responses of 1, $\frac{1}{2}$, and $\frac{1}{4}$ milligal, respec-tively. (A gal is an acceleration of 1 cm per sec^2. The mean acceleration of gravity at sea level on the equator is 978.052 gals = 978,052 milligals.) Thus the figure provides a convenient visual comparison of bodies produc-ing equal maximum response. It is supposed, in each case, that the bodies are of uniform density, differing by unity from the density of the homo-geneous country rock. (In the sedimentary structures encountered in oil prospecting, successful gravity work may be done on density contrasts as small as $\frac{1}{4}$. In the case of massive sulfide bodies, or iron ores, density differences as high as about $1\frac{1}{2}$ or more may be encountered.) To obtain the corresponding attractions for other values of the density difference, multiply the ordinates in Figure 15.5 by the value of the density difference.

a = Radius of sphere or cylinder
Δg in milligals
ρ = Density difference = 1
γ = Newton's constant = 6.66×10^{-8} c. g. s.
Dimensions on charts in meters
Z_0 = Depth to center of sphere or cylinder
Z_1, (Z_2) = Depth to top, (bottom) of vertical plate
t = Thickness of frustum, vertical plate, or horizontal plate

Line no.	Frustum of cone θ, degrees	Long horiz. prism β		Thin vertical plate Z_2/Z_1	Sphere a/Z_0	Long cylinder a/Z_0
		Radians	Degrees			
0	90.0	$\pi/2$	90.0	—	1.0	1.0
1	58.5	.751	43.0	4.49	.847	.478
2	40.4	.375	21.5	2.12	.559	.239
3	28.3	.187	10.75	1.45	.423	.113
4	19.9	.094	5.38	1.21	.299	.060
5	14.0	.047	2.69	1.10	.212	.030
6	9.9	.024	1.34	1.05	.150	.015

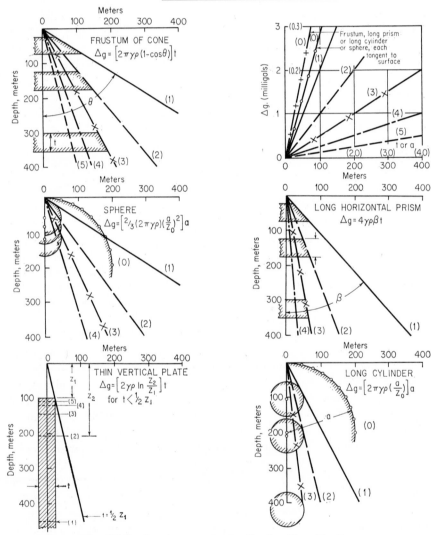

Fig. 15.5 Gravity response for five families of bodies.

The large differences in the equivalent cross sections of the sphere and cylinder are noteworthy. Since in these two cases the attraction is directed to the center or to the axis, respectively, the vertical components of attractions for these cases for points anywhere on the ground's surface, or elsewhere, may readily be computed with the aid of the graphs. Because the attraction of a homogeneous sphere or long cylinder is simply expressed, namely, the same as that of its entire mass concentrated at its center or on its axis, respectively, it is often convenient and satisfactory to estimate the attraction of complex shapes by representing these as an aggregate of a few suitably chosen spheres or cylinders.

Effect of Scale. An important general feature of gravity prospecting is illustrated by Figure 15.5. This is the linear increase in the intensity of the attraction at corresponding points, when the geometric scale is uniformly increased. Thus by a corresponding shift of the decimal point in the abscissa and ordinates, as indicated by the second scales, the linear graphs in Figure 15.5 conveniently serve for bodies of any size. Other things being equal, the large-scale structures encountered in petroleum prospecting, where distances are measured in thousands, or tens of thousands, of feet, are much more amenable to detection by the gravimeter than are small ore bodies, whose dimensions are measured in tens or hundreds of feet.

When the linear scale of a gravity survey is sufficiently small, the torsion balance, now rendered essentially obsolete by the gravimeter, provides superior instrumental sensitivity. The values of the gradients of gravity, i.e., the quantities measured by a torsion balance, remain the same at homologous points when the geometric scale is uniformly changed. Thus when observations need to be taken at spacings as small as 100 ft or less, as in underground surveys in mines, a torsion balance sensitivity of 1 Eotvos unit (10^{-9} cgs) is equivalent to a gravimeter sensitivity of 3 microgals. Perhaps faster, improved forms of the torsion balance will sometime be developed for small-scale applications.

The Important Elevation Corrections. The elevation corrections in gravity work are important, both because they may be large and because the cost of obtaining these corrections is frequently the major cost of the gravity work.

The change in gravity associated with increase in the elevation of the station consists of a part due to the presence of additional material underfoot, known as the *Bouguer correction*, and a decrease due to the increased distance from the center of the earth, known as the *free-air correction*. The Bouguer correction may be obtained from Figure 15.5, frustum of cone, i.e., for $\theta = 90$ deg

$$\Delta g = 2\pi\gamma\rho t \tag{15.1}$$

This graph represents the attraction of a uniform layer of unit density and of unlimited lateral extent as a function of its thickness t. When t represents the elevation change, and a suitable factor for the density of the ground is introduced, the graph represents the Bouguer correction; thus when $\rho = 1.8$, the Bouguer correction is -0.075 milligal per m. The associated free-air correction is $+0.309$ milligal per m; thus the net correction is $+0.234$ milligal per m of station elevation above base level. (For stations below base level, the sign of the correction is reversed.) In some gravity surveys, observational precisions corresponding to standard errors as small as 0.02 milligal are attained. Since (when $\rho = 1.8$) a 0.02-milligal change in gravity is caused by an elevation change of 0.28 ft, the need for accurate elevation determinations in such cases is clear.

Local Density Variations. Variations in the density of soils and rocks are a hidden source of significant local fluctuations in gravity readings. As an example, let us estimate the gravity anomaly produced by a long-buried channel, or valley, in bedrock of density 2.6, filled with soil of density 1.8. Referring to curve 2 in Figure 15.5, it will be seen that a long depression in bedrock, 20 m deep, subtending the half cone angle 21.5 deg produces a negative gravity anomaly of 0.16 milligal. Such examples warn that concealed variations in the bedrock topography can be responsible for gravity anomalies resembling both in form and magnitude those produced by ore bodies. Thus a positive gravity anomaly, coincident with an indication of high electrical conductivity, might be produced either by a massive sulfide body or by an elevated ridge in bedrock associated with a conducting graphitic horizon. When several different interpretations of geophysical results are geologically tenable, drilling of holes to get rock samples may be much preferable to doing additional geophysical tests of uncertain significance.

15.8 Fundamental Concepts of the Three Conductivity Flux Methods

Because of their basic similarities, it is convenient to discuss together the d-c method, the magnetic method, and the low-frequency electromagnetic method. In each of these, changes in a "conducting" property of the rocks at depth alter in a similar manner the established flow pattern of an impressed flux field. In rocks, the range of the electrical conductivity, or its inverse, the electrical resistivity, is enormous; massive sulfide ores have electrical resistivities as low as 0.001 ohm-meter, whereas igneous rocks may have values as high as 100,000 ohm-meters or more. In the magnetic method, on the contrary, the corresponding "conductivity" property (permeability) of rocks varies only a little. Of the two electrical methods mentioned, the d-c method is the simpler and is better suited to provide elementary illustrations over the wide range of the conductivity parameter.

Elementary Properties of Flux Fields.   The steady streamline flow of a fluid such as water, in permeable materials, may serve as a model for visualizing the elementary behavior of the geophysical flux fields. Darcy's law, relating the local fluid velocity to the product of the net pressure gradient and the permeability, is precisely the same as Ohm's law equating the electrical current density to the product of the potential gradient and the electrical conductivity. (Net pressure gradient as used here excludes that part of the vertical pressure gradient $\partial p/\partial z$ which is balanced by the gravitational force per unit volume.) The analogy between streamline incompressible fluid flow and the corresponding d-c flow model is exact. Since fluid-flow patterns have a tangible property which seems to aid their intuitive visualization, and because many

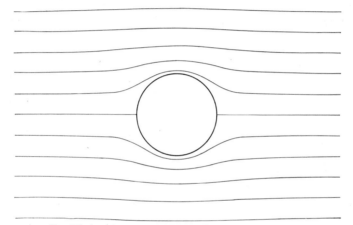

Fig.15.6   Flow pattern around impervious sphere.

diagrams depicting fluid flow are available in the textbooks on hydro-dynamics, it is often convenient to associate geophysical flux problems with their fluid-flow equivalents. Some pertinent general properties of such patterns are the following:

Conservation of Flux.   An elementary characteristic of the flux methods under consideration, including the gravity method, is the so-called "conservative" property of their flux fields. Consider, for example, the motion of an ideal incompressible fluid. Since the fluid is incompressible, there is no net transport of material across any closed surface not enclosing a source or sink; the quantity of fluid entering the region internal to the closed surface, at each instant, is equal to the quantity leaving the region. The flux field is therefore said to be "conservative" and the velocity vector $\mathbf{V}$ is characterized as "divergenceless," written div $\mathbf{V} = 0$. Similarly, in the d-c prospecting method, the current vector $\mathbf{i}$ is divergenceless; and in the magnetic method and electromagnetic method, the magnetic induction $\mathbf{B}$ is conserved, div $\mathbf{B} = 0$.

Accordingly, a geological target being sought by any of these three conductivity methods merely redistributes the flux in its neighborhood. The conservation of the total flow and its redistribution by a "foreign body" may be illustrated quantitatively by the case of the sphere, the long circular cylinder, and the long flat strip, each impervious and

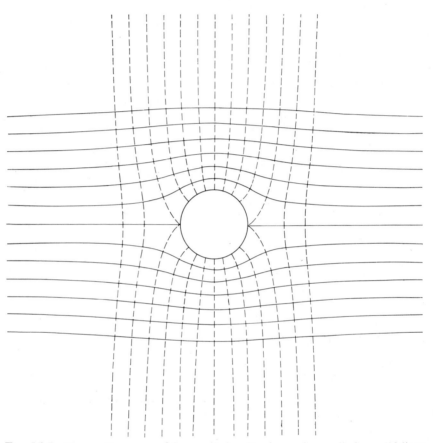

Fig. 15.7   Flow pattern around long cylinder. For impervious cylinder, solid lines represent streamlines; dotted lines, equipressure lines; and vice versa for the cylinder of infinite conductivity.

immersed in a uniform source field. The flow patterns for these cases may be seen in Figures 15.6 to 15.8. Here the radius of the sphere or cylinder, or the half-width of the plate, is denoted by a, and distances in the reference plane from the axis of the cylinder or plate or from the center of the sphere are denoted by y. When y is less than a, the point is within the impervious body, and the *change* in velocity obviously is v_0; thus $\Delta v/v_0 = -1$. Outside these bodies ($y > a$), in the central plane normal

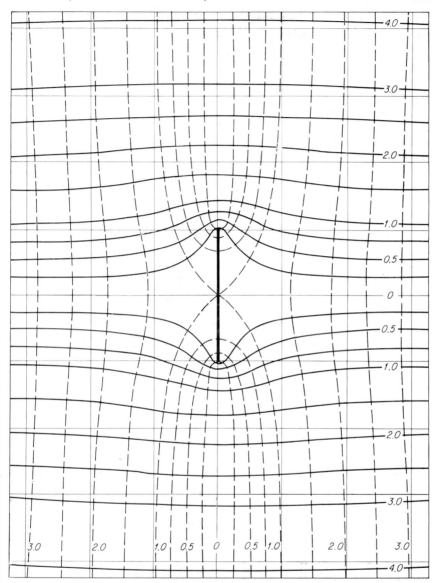

Fig. 15.8 Flow pattern around long flat plate. For impervious plate, solid lines represent streamlines; dotted lines, equipressure lines. For conducting plate, dotted lines represent streamlines; solid lines are lines of equal pressure.

to the flow direction, the respective relative velocity increments $\Delta v/v_0$ are known to be the following:

Sphere:
$$\frac{\Delta v}{v_0} = \frac{\tfrac{1}{2}a^3}{y^3}$$

Cylinder:
$$\frac{\Delta v}{v_0} = \frac{a^2}{y^2}$$

Plate:[1]
$$\frac{\Delta v}{v_0} = \left(1 - \frac{a^2}{y^2}\right)^{-\tfrac{1}{2}} - 1$$

It is clear from the graphs of these formulas in Figure 15.9 how rapidly the anomalous velocity diminishes with distance from the target surface or

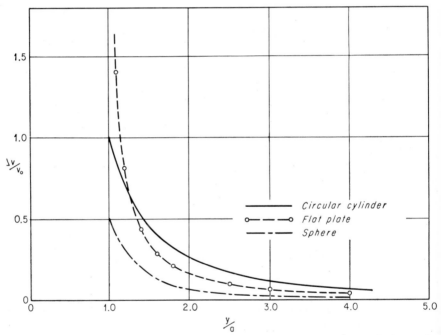

Fig. 15.9   Decrease of flow velocity in central plane for case of sphere, cylinder, and plate. Relative change of flux intensity $\Delta v/v_0$ produced by sphere, circular cylinder, and flat plate. Radius of sphere and cylinder $= a$. Half width of plate $= a$. $\Delta v/v_0$ in central plane, normal to flow direction.

edge. At one radius from the target edge, the respective relative increments are (1) $6\tfrac{1}{4}$ per cent, (2) 25 per cent, (3) $15\tfrac{1}{2}$ per cent; at two radii (1) 2 per cent, (2) 11 per cent, and (3) 6 per cent. It is readily verified that each of the three formulas above is consistent with the requirement of conservation of total flux. For example, in the case of the sphere, the

[1] C. H. Lees, *Proc. Roy. Soc.* (*London*), ser. A, vol. 91, p. 442, 1914.

total excess flux across the exterior central plane $a < y$ is

$$A_s = \int_a^\infty \Delta v\, 2\pi y\, dy = \tfrac{1}{2}a^3 v_0 \int_a^\infty 2\pi y^{-2}\, dy = \pi a^2 v_0 \qquad (15.2)$$

which is the same as the deficiency $\pi a^2 v_0$ across the interior plane $y < a$.

Compared with the circular cylinder, the flat plate produces a larger anomalous flux density at small distances but smaller anomalies at distances y/a greater than about 1.27. In both cases, as may readily be confirmed, the areas under the curves are the same,

$$A_c = \int_a^\infty \Delta v\, dy = v_0 a$$

The deficiency of flux $-v_0 a$ within the body is restored over the exterior plane. Thus a more streamlined section diminishes the local anomaly, but slightly *increases* the more distant response in such a way that the integral A_c above is maintained constant.

The general requirement that the surface integrals of anomalous flux over the infinite exterior plane be equal, and opposite, to a corresponding integral over the finite interior plane is perhaps the key to an intuitive appreciation of the limited range of these conductivity methods. A very small anomalous flux per unit area, integrated over the large external area, suffices to balance that diverted to, or from, the small interior cross section. In the flux methods the maximum range of detection y is always expressible in terms of the value of a dimensionless ratio y/a, where a is a characteristic dimension of the target.

A Simple Reciprocal Relationship. In the case of long "two-dimensional bodies" of any uniform cross section but *not* for three-dimensional bodies, a simple relationship exists between the flow patterns produced for the two extreme conductivity values 0 and ∞. This may be illustrated for the case of the circular cylinder (Figure 15.7) and the flat plate (Figure 15.8). The solid lines in each of these figures represent streamlines of flux, when the body is regarded as impervious, $\sigma_i = 0$. Associated with these flow lines is an orthogonal pattern, shown dotted, which represents lines of equipressure or of equipotential. If now the conductivity of the cylinder or plate is taken to be infinite, instead of zero, the dotted lines will represent the streamlines and the solid lines, the associated equipressure lines. In general, for any shape of cross section, a solution obtained for either of the conditions $\sigma_i = 0$ or $\sigma_i = \infty$ also provides, by such an interchange, the solution for the other condition.

Detectability Independent of Strength of Source Field. The detectability of a target by a conductivity-flux method depends essentially upon the distortion of streamlines of flow or upon the relative changes in flux intensity associated with such distortions. Other conditions being constant, the *relative* change in the flux intensity produced by a "foreign body" and the form of the associated streamline pattern are independent of the intensity of the source field. It follows that the detectability of concealed targets is theoretically independent of the power or intensity of the source. In practice, all that is needed is a source of sufficient power to enable accurate measurements of the relative intensities, or flux patterns. Increasing the power of a source may be useful in extending the acreage in the vicinity of the source which is within the range of satisfactory measurements, but it does *not* improve the significance of readings which are already well above the level of intensity for satisfactory measurement.

Joint Influence of Shape and Conductivity.   The influence of the shape of the conducting target and of its orientation with respect to the source field may be illustrated with simple examples. It is surprising how large such effects may be. For the more complicated geometrical situations generally encountered in nature, the associated response patterns are best revealed from studies with scale models. Model studies are often very illuminating and provide the only satisfactory way for ascertaining the geophysical patterns associated with the complex geometrical configurations presented by nature.

Qualitatively, it is obvious that flat insulating targets produce maximum anomalies when aligned normal to the flow direction and little effect when edge on. Conversely, a highly conducting body produces maximum effect when its long dimension coincides with the direction of flow and little influence when oriented normal to the flow. Quantitatively the response as a function of shape and conductivity variables may be illustrated by considering the ellipsoid of revolution, as its shape is changed from a flat disk to a long needle.

Consider, then, an ellipsoid of semiaxes a and c (the axis of revolution), having uniform conductivity σ_i, and surrounded by a medium of conductivity σ_0. Let the source field have uniform intensity E_0 directed parallel to the axis of revolution. The behavior of homogeneous conductors of ellipsoidal shape in uniform impressed fields is well known. The total field within the ellipsoid is also uniform; furthermore, it is unchanged in direction whenever the ellipsoid is aligned with an axis parallel to the source field. In geophysical prospecting, one is especially interested in the intensity of the target's field at large distances, near the limits of detectability. The field of the uniform ellipsoid at large distances is dipolar and of an intensity proportional to the volume of the ellipsoid times its polarization per unit volume I. The *value* of I is a *direct measure* of the *intensity* of *response*, at distant points, per *unit volume* of the *ellipsoidal target*. The polarization intensity depends on the conductivity ratio and a shape factor N in the following way:

$$I = E_0(\sigma_i\sigma_0^{-1} - 1)[4\pi + N(\sigma_i\sigma_0^{-1} - 1)]^{-1} \qquad (15.3)$$

The "depolarization" factor N depends only on the fineness ratio c/a. It is a maximum 4π when c/a is zero, has the value $4\pi/3$ for the sphere, and decreases to zero as c/a becomes large.

Values of I are listed in Table 15.1 for a range of values of σ_i/σ_0 and c/a. The high negative values of I obtained when $(\sigma_0 - \sigma_i)\sigma_0^{-1} = -1$ and c/a is small are illusory; the volume of the disk vanishes for small c/a, but its moment $M = IV$ approaches a finite value $2a^3/3\pi$, which is about 0.4 that of a nonconducting sphere of the same radius. In Figure 15.10, plots of I versus c/a are shown for a few positive and negative values

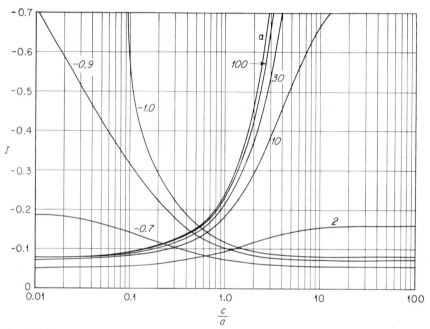

Fig. 15.10 Plots of polarization intensity I versus fineness ratio c/a for several values of the relative conductivity.

of the relative conductivity difference $(\sigma_i - \sigma_0)\sigma_0^{-1}$. As both c/a and σ_i/σ_0 become large, the value of I increases rapidly. When c/a is fixed, I approaches the asymptotic value $(\sigma_i - \sigma_0)(4\pi\sigma_0)^{-1}$ as σ_i/σ_0 is increased. Since conductivity ratios in excess of 1000 occur in geophysical prospecting, the high values of I which then can result are noteworthy.

Discussion of Shape and Conductivity Effects, D-C Method.   In the d-c prospecting method, as has been mentioned, very large values of the conductivity ratio are encountered. Long bodies of high relative conductivity offer excellent opportunities for detection, when the excitation field has a large component along the long dimension of the conductor. Since the source current is necessarily parallel to the ground's surface, at the surface, the most favorable conditions occur when a long conductor lies approximately parallel to the ground's surface, say when the pitch is less than 30 deg.

Maps of the resultant current-flow patterns for bodies of several different shapes, in a uniform flow field, have been shown in Figures 15.6 to 15.8. For the case of the perfectly insulating sphere, the value of the polarization I is -0.119; for the perfectly conducting sphere, $I = +0.238$, i.e., double the previous figure; and for the thin insulating disk of thickness ratio $c/a = 0.1$, $I = -0.572$ (see Table 15.1 or Figure 15.10). For long

Table 15.1 Value of Polarization I for Ellipsoids of Revolution in Terms of Fineness Ratio c/a and Ratio of Conductivities $\sigma_i \sigma_0^{-1}$

$$I = E_0(\sigma_i \sigma_0^{-1} - 1)[4\pi + N(\sigma_i \sigma_0^{-1} - 1)]^{-1}, \ E_0 = 1$$
$$N = \text{depolarization factor (last column lists } N^{-1})$$

c/a \ $\sigma_i\sigma_0^{-1}-1$	-1.0	-0.96	-0.9	-0.7	2	10	30	100	1000	∞
0	....	-1.908	-0.719	-0.185	0.0530	0.072	0.078	0.079	0.079	0.0796
0.1	-0.572	-0.440	-0.318	-0.140	0.0585	0.083	0.089	0.091	0.092	0.0924
0.5	-0.167	-0.1536	-0.136	-0.088	0.0776	0.127	0.141	0.15	0.151	0.1512
1.0	-0.119	-0.1123	-0.103	-0.0728	0.0954	0.184	0.216	0.23	0.238	0.2389
2.0	-0.096	-0.0916	-0.0849	-0.0634	0.1182	0.291	0.375	0.43	0.456	0.4600
5.0	-0.084	-0.0807	-0.0754	-0.0580	0.1432	0.5105	0.891	1.21	1.40	1.4244
10.	-0.081	-0.0778	-0.0729	-0.0565	0.1530	0.661	1.485	2.63	3.74	3.9231
20.	-0.080	-0.0769	-0.0720	-0.0559	0.1570	0.746	1.986	4.75	10.27	11.7774
40.	-0.080	-0.0765	-0.0717	-0.0558	0.1584	0.779	2.244	6.57	25.33	37.5603
100.	-0.080	-0.0764	-0.0716	-0.0557	0.1590	0.792	2.358	7.63	55.65	185.4144
200	-0.080	-0.0764	-0.0716	-0.0557	0.1592	0.794	2.376	7.86	70.57	624.6795
500.	-0.080	-0.0764	-0.0716	-0.0557	0.1592	0.794	2.385	7.94	77.72	3318.361
∞	-0.080	-0.0764	-0.0716	-0.0557	0.1592	0.796	2.387	7.96	79.6	∞

For $c < a$, $N = 4\pi e^{-2}[1 - e^{-1}(1 - e^2)^{\frac{1}{2}} \sin^{-1} e]$, $e = (1 - c^2/a^2)^{\frac{1}{2}}$

For $c > a$, $N = 4\pi(1 - e^{-2})\left(1 - \frac{1}{2}e^{-1}\ln\frac{1+e}{1-e}\right)$, $e = (1 - a^2/c^2)^{\frac{1}{2}}$

prolate ellipsoids of high conductivity, far higher values of the polarization result. For example, when $c/a = 20$ and $\sigma_i \sigma_0^{-1} = 1000$, the polarization value is 10.3, or $43\frac{1}{2}$ fold that for the infinitely conducting sphere. If such a sphere is regarded to be detectable, on the basis of only a 10 per cent change in the flux intensity, at a distance of 2.15 radii from its center, then the above prolate ellipsoid, of equal volume, would be detectable, on the basis of an inverse cube law, at the distance $2.15a_s(43.5)^{\frac{1}{3}} = 7.58a_s$, where a_s is the radius of the sphere of the same volume. Since the semiaxis c of this ellipsoid is $7.38a_s$, the indicated range of detection is $1.03c$. Despite the great differences in shape, these two ranges $2.15a_s$ and $1.03c$ are comparable when measured in terms of the respective major dimensions of the two bodies. This result is in crude conformity with a common rule for the approximate limit of detectability in d-c methods. Namely, the depth of overburden should be less than about half the pertinent characteristic dimension of the target, i.e., the diameter of sphere, width of long flat plate, diameter of a long cylinder oriented normal to the excitation field, length of a long conductor parallel to the excitation field.

Clearly bodies of high conductivity with upper portions extending for long distances nearly parallel to the surface present the really favorable opportunities for d-c methods. By the same token, the presence of buried valleys in bedrock, or other linear conducting features, constitutes a chief and important hazard to the interpretation of d-c results in terms of conducting ore. The conductivity contrasts between overburden and bedrock are often as great as those between ore and country rock.

15.9   Chief Applications of D-C Methods

Three chief applications for the d-c prospecting are the following:

Resistivity Logging of Oil Wells.   By far the most important use of d-c methods is the resistivity logging of oil wells, introduced by the Schlumberger group about 30 years ago. Resistivity well logs, in combination with other types of well logs, greatly facilitate identification of corresponding horizons pierced by drill holes; in addition they may be diagnostic of porosity and salinity conditions in the wall rock of the hole. In the petroleum industry, the electrical logging of drill holes has become almost universal practice. In mining, the use of electrical logging is sporadic, but is usually easily accomplished, when the holes are shallow, as an activity auxiliary to other geophysical work. Resistivity logs provide a valuable systematic record of the electrical resistivity *in situ* of the rocks or ore penetrated by the hole.

Tracing of Ore Pierced by a Drill Hole.   When conducting ore is pierced by a drill hole, or exposed in mine workings, an opportunity exists for introducing electric current directly to the ore. The pertinent electrical quantity here is the *ratio* of conductivity of ore to that of the host rock. Since the host rock is usually a fairly effective insulator, a moderate value of the conductivity of the ore usually suffices to provide a favorably high value of this ratio. Current introduced directly even to a small peripheral stringer of conducting ore will tend to raise the ore body to a uniform high potential, with high gradients of potential in the surrounding rock. Thus when the conducting body is large, a strong electrical anomaly will extend over a correspondingly large region, which may enable the general trend of the ore body to be clearly recognized at the ground's surface. Furthermore, when neighboring drill holes exist, and are accessible, the profiles of potential observable in such holes may be significant and informative. Since the ore body itself acts as the source of the flux field, the limitations upon range of detection are far less severe than those previously discussed. Applications of this method have been described in the literature.[1]

Measurement of Conductivity and Thickness of Surface Soils. Direct-current electrical methods are commonly used for the routine measurement of the electrical resistivity of soils or rocks *in situ*. They are also employed for determining the approximate thickness of overburden and the depth to the water table in porous rocks or in soils. Successful application of this technique requires that the layers be reasonably homogeneous and of relatively constant thickness, over lateral distances of five to six times their thickness. The two- or three-layer cases are those most commonly investigated in the field.[2]

Knowledge of variations in the conductivity and thickness of surface soils is frequently valuable as an aid to the interpretation of other electrical methods. For example, in the special application mentioned in the preceding paragraph, it may be important to determine whether an electrical anomaly mapped on the surface is explicable by a change in the thickness, or the conductivity, or both, of the surface soils, rather than by the potential existence of conducting ore at depth. The study of surface conditions by d-c electrical methods may provide definitive evidence for distinguishing these two possibilities.

15.10   Magnetic Methods

In the magnetic method, two types of magnetization are to be distinguished. (1) The so-called "soft" type is precisely analogous to the polarization I produced in a conductor, which was discussed in connection with the d-c method. This type would disappear if the earth's magnetic field could be "turned off"; in direction and magnitude, it is consistent with the notion that the present earth's magnetic field is maintaining the magnetization. (2) The second type is the remanent variety, like that of a permanent magnet, which may have an intensity, or direction, or both, quite different from that which would be caused in a soft magnetic material by the present earth's field. Remanent magnetization sometimes has a direction nearly the reverse of that of the present terrestrial field. Reversed directions of magnetization are in fact likely when ilmenite is associated with magnetite in proportions greater than 25 per cent.[3] The

---

[1] H. V. McMurry and A. D. Hoagland, "Three-dimensional Applied Potential Studies at Austinville, Virginia," *Bull. Geol. Soc. Am.*, vol. 67, pp. 683–696, 1956; and L. B. Slichter, *Mining Congr. J.*, vol. 33, pp. 47–51, 1947.

[2] See W. W. Wetzel and H. V. McMurry, "A Set of Curves to Assist in the Interpretation of the Three Layer Resistivity Problem," *Geophysics*, vol. 2, no. 4, 1937.

[3] J. R. Balsley and A. F. Buddington, "Correlation of Reverse Remanent Magnetism and Negative Anomalies with Certain Minerals," *J. Geomagnetism & Geoelectricity*, vol. 6, no. 4, pp. 176–181, 1954.

possible presence of remanent magnetization of unknown direction and intensity adds an extra element of uncertainty to the interpretation of magnetic surveys. In the following discussions, it will be assumed that the magnetization is "soft." Since magnetite is by far the most abundant magnetic mineral, and also possesses a magnetic susceptibility tenfold higher than that of other natural minerals, magnetic prospecting is almost equivalent to "magnetite" prospecting.

In contrast to the electrical method, the magnetic method is characterized by the *small* range for its pertinent conductivity ratio $\mu_i\mu_0^{-1}$. The ratio of magnetic permeabilities $\mu_i\mu_0^{-1}$ varies between unity, for nonmagnetic rocks, to a value of only about 3 or 4 for the case of ores rich in magnetite, containing, say, 50 per cent magnetite. When $\mu_i\mu_0^{-1} = 3$, the saturation value of the magnetization for infinitely long bodies, and for unit impressed field, is 0.16 [see Equation (15.1)]. For a relatively short body, with $c/a = 2$, and $\mu_i\mu_0^{-1} = 3$, the induced magnetization is 0.12, only 25 per cent below that for the infinitely long body. For the vast majority of rocks, specifically, those containing less than 10 per cent of magnetite, the value of $\mu_i\mu_0^{-1}$ will lie between 1 and 1.35. Thus even when N in the denominator of Equation (15.3) has its maximum value 4π, the shape-dependent variable N $(\mu_i\mu_0^{-1} - 1)$ is small relative to the additive constant 4π. In other words the magnetization intensity is *essentially independent* of the *shape* of the *body* but is proportional simply to the product of the strength of the source field and the relative permeability difference $(\mu_i - \mu_0)\mu_0^{-1}$. The fact that *shape effects* and interaction effects between neighboring bodies are almost always negligible in magnetic prospecting greatly simplifies the theoretical procedures for interpretation. The same simple process which is used in gravity computations is valid for computing the resultant magnetic field. That is, the contributions of the individual volume elements are merely *added*, perhaps by the aid of charts, or sometimes by forming suitable "volume integrals." This elementary similarity in the computation of the gravity and magnetic fields may be expressed by the following formula, attributed to Poisson:

$$\Delta H_s = (\gamma\rho)^{-1} I_x \frac{\partial g_s}{\partial x} \tag{15.4}$$

Here g_s is the component of gravitational attraction in the direction s exerted by a volume element of density ρ; γ is Newton's constant, 6.66×10^{-8} cgs; and ΔH_s is the component of the magnetic field in the s direction, caused by the component of magnetization I_x of the specified volume element. More generally, the above relation may be written

$$\Delta H_s = (\gamma\rho)^{-1} \left(I_x \frac{\partial g_s}{\partial x} + I_y \frac{\partial g_s}{\partial y} + I_z \frac{\partial g_s}{\partial z} \right) \tag{15.5}$$

High Sensitivity of Magnetic Method, and Chief Applications.
The magnetic method is one of the few geophysical methods responsive
to very minor percentage differences in the mineral content of rocks.
(The radioactive methods and soil-chemistry methods are examples of
other highly sensitive exploration tools, responsive to very small changes
in the content of a pertinent mineral.) A difference of only 0.01 per cent
in the magnetite content of large contiguous rock masses would theoretically produce a change of 7 gamma in the vertical intensity of the earth's
magnetic field. (1 gamma $= 10^{-5}$ oersted. The mean intensity of the
earth's magnetic field varies from 31,300 gamma at the magnetic equator
to 62,600 gamma at the magnetic poles.) In air-borne surveys, it is
feasible to measure changes of only 1 gamma. Since magnetite is so
universally present in rocks, at least in the minor amounts needed for
detection by sensitive magnetometers, significant structural conditions
which are associated with minor systematic changes in magnetite content
are often revealed in magnetic surveys. The regional strike, local changes
in strike, "grain" of the country, concealed intrusives, dikes, folds,
faults, and variations in depth to the igneous basement rocks are examples
of such structural features.

The speed and economy of aerial mapping with geophysical instruments, and by aerial photography, has made feasible the reconnaissance
of large regions the examination of which would otherwise be intolerably
expensive.

15.11   Electromagnetic Methods

Electromagnetic prospecting methods commonly employ a continuous
oscillatory source field, of frequency between 300 and 4000 cycles per sec.
We shall be concerned with the response of conducting targets to such
steady-state "e-m" excitation fields, but *not* in the equipment with which
such fields are produced or measured. It will be assumed that the oscillatory magnetic field is uniform in the neighborhood of the target and that
the effective conductivity of the country rock at the frequency used is
essentially zero. In electromagnetic prospecting it is convenient to
classify conducting targets in the following three ways: (1) those of very
high effective electrical conductivity, (2) those of moderate conductivity,
and (3) those of low conductivity. The significance of these distinctions
will become evident upon consideration of the following simple example.
Let a circular ring of radius a_1, formed by a thin wire of radius α_1 and
conductivity σ_1, be introduced into a source field $B_0 \cos \omega t$, with the plane
of the ring normal to the flux vector B_0. The oscillatory source field induces
the Faraday voltage $\pi a_1{}^2 B_0 \omega \sin \omega t$ in the ring; and in accordance with
simple theory the associated current I is

$$I = -\pi a^2 B_0 \omega (R^2 + \omega^2 L^2)^{-\frac{1}{2}} \cos (\omega t + \delta) \tag{15.6}$$

where
$$\cos \delta = \frac{\omega L}{R} = p^2 \tag{15.7}$$

The resistance R of the ring is $2a_1 \alpha_1^{-2} \sigma_1^{-2}$, and the self-inductance is of the form $L = \mu_0 a F$, where F is a known numerical factor dependent on the ratio a_1/α_1 and μ_0 is the permeability of free space. Hence, referring to Equation (15.7)

$$p_1^2 = F \alpha_1^2 (\tfrac{1}{2} \omega \mu_0 \sigma_1) \tag{15.8}$$

At points far from the ring in relation to its radius, the secondary field associated with the induced current I is of dipolar type, with radial and transverse components B_r and B_θ, respectively, of magnitude

$$B_r = \tfrac{1}{2} \mu_0 a^2 I r^{-3} \cos \theta \qquad B_\theta = \tfrac{1}{4} \mu_0 a^2 I r^{-3} \sin \theta \tag{15.9}$$

where r denotes the radial distance from the center of the ring and θ the angle between r and the direction of the impressed field (when $t = 0$). It is the secondary field due to the induced current in the conducting body, such as the ring considered here, which is measured in electromagnetic prospecting. Using Equations (15.6) and (15.8), the factor $\mu_0 a^2 I$ may be written

$$\mu_0 a^2 I = -\pi F^{-1} B_0 a_1 \cos \delta_1 (\cos \delta_1 \cos \omega t - \sin \delta_1 \sin \omega t) \tag{15.10}$$

Thus the induced current is expressed by the sum of two terms, in quadrature, whose relative amplitudes are determined only by the value of p_1^2. When p_1^2 is *small*, i.e., the resistance is *large* relative to ωL, the second term overrides. This term represents a field lagging 90 deg behind the source field, in time phase, and is called the "resistive" or "out-of-phase" component of the response. For small values of p_1^2, the amplitude of the out-of-phase component increases linearly with p_1^2, reaches a maximum, when $p_1^2 = 1$, in this case, and diminishes to zero as p_1^2 becomes large.

The other term in Equation (15.10) represents a field whose direction on the axis of the coil is *opposite* to that of the source field. This field lags the source field by 180 deg and is called the "in-phase" or "inductive" component of the response. Its intensity increases as p_1^4 for small p_1^2. On the positive axis ($\theta = 0$) when a/r is small and p_1^2 is large, the secondary field approaches the asymptotic value $B_r = -(\pi/2) F^{-1} a^3 r^{-3} B_0 \cos \omega t$. These features of the response of a simple circular ring are characteristic of the e-m response of conducting bodies in general. It is, indeed, instructive to compare the response characteristics of some simple shapes for which exact solutions are available. Such comparisons are provided by the circular ring, thin spherical shell,[1] solid sphere,[2] and long circular cylinder.[3] In Figure 15.11, the resistive components Y of the response dipole moments for these bodies are plotted against the respective inductive components X. The latter have been normalized to the value unity for large values of the conductivity parameter p_i^2. Using the ordinate scale to the right, the corresponding values of p_i are also graphed

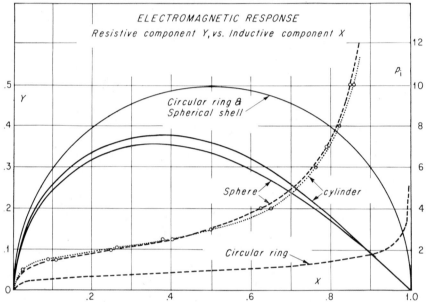

Fig. 15.11   Resistive component of electromagnetic response versus inductive component.

(dotted curves) as functions of X. The respective parameters p_i^2 for these several shapes are defined as follows:

Ring: $p_1^2 = F\alpha_1^2(\tfrac{1}{2}\omega\mu_0\sigma)$
Spherical shell: $p_2^2 = \tfrac{2}{3}\gamma_2 a_2(\tfrac{1}{2}\omega\mu_0\sigma)$
Sphere: $p_3^2 = a_3^2(\tfrac{1}{2}\omega\mu_0\sigma)$
Cylinder: $p_4^2 = 2a_4^2(\tfrac{1}{2}\omega\mu_0\sigma)$

Here α_1 denotes the radius of the wire cross section and γ_2 the thickness of the spherical shell. In Figure 15.12, the two components Y_3 and X_3 of the response dipole moment for the sphere are plotted against p_3^2; and

[1] L. B. Slichter, "Electromagnetic Model Response of Conducting Spheres," in *Geophysical Prospecting*, American Institute of Mining and Metallurgical Engineers, 1932, pp. 443–459.

[2] *Ibid.*

[3] J. R. Wait, "The Cylindrical Ore Body in the Presence of a Cable Carrying an Oscillating Current," *Geophysics*, vol. 17, pp. 378–386, 1952.

similarly, the components Y_4 and X_4 of the dipole moment for the long circular cylinder are plotted against $p_4{}^2$. In Figure 15.13 the respective values of p_i for the sphere and cylinder are plotted against the ratio X/Y.

Discussion.   *Nonuniqueness of Response.*   For the ring and spherical shell, the graphs Y vs. X in Figure 15.11 are semicircular and *identical*.

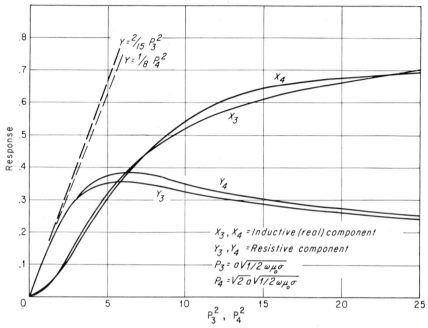

Fig. 15.12   Resistive and inductive dipole moments of sphere and cylinder plotted against $p_i{}^2$.

It may be shown that the conditions for equality of the dipole moments of the ring and spherical shell are the following:

$$p_1 = p_2 \quad \text{and} \quad \frac{\pi}{2} F^{-1} a_1{}^3 = a_2{}^3$$

In practice, these may readily be satisfied, subject also to the auxiliary requirements that the ratios α_1/a_1 and γ_2/a_2 both be small. Thus at large distances from these bodies, the response fields may be identical for all choices of excitation frequency, and it would be impossible to distinguish the two target types by the e-m measurements. This is an example of a general feature, previously noted, of the interpretation problem for the flux methods; that is, the interpretations are generally nonunique. Many different causal structures may produce the same observed flux pattern at the surface.

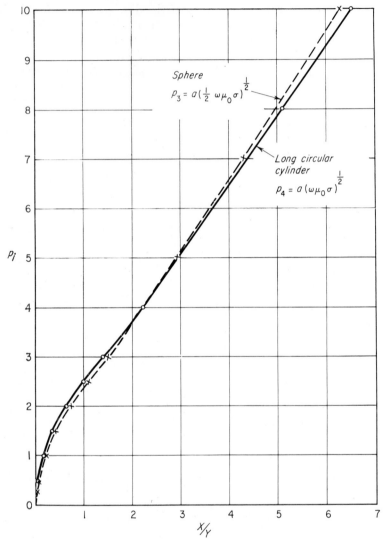

Fig. 15.13 Comparison of p_i for sphere and cylinder, as functions of X/Y. Dimensionless conductivity parameter p_i for sphere and cylinder in terms of ratio of in-phase to out-of-phase components of response.

Ratio X to Y Diagnostic of Conductivity Parameter, Rather than Shape.
In the case of the solid sphere and long cylinder (see Figure 15.11) the respective response curves Y vs. X and p vs. X are remarkably alike, departing from one another by less than 10 per cent. The similarity in the response characteristics of these two extremely different shapes is further illustrated in the graphs of Figure 15.12, and even more strikingly

in Figure 15.13 in which p_3 and p_4 are plotted against the ratio X/Y. These two graphs are nearly identical. The field geophysical maps, in plan, will usually easily distinguish between a long conducting structure or a nearly equidimensional object, like a sphere. Thus the appropriate definition of p_i may be chosen, the corresponding value of p_i determined for the observed X/Y ratio, and thence also the conductivity factor $a^2\sigma$. Here the implied assumption that the country rock possesses essentially zero effective conductivity at the operating frequency is critical. In practice, the validity of this assumption may easily be tested by noting whether the values of the ratio Y/X observed over neighboring normal ground are indeed very small.

Because the respective values of p_i as functions of X/Y differ so little for these two bodies of extremely different shapes, it is suggested that, when the resistivity of the surrounding ground is high, the ratio X/Y is diagnostic of the *size* and *conductivity* of a conducting body and is *little dependent upon its shape.*

The E-M Conductivity Requirement for Ores. In the formulas of type $p^2 = L^2(\omega\mu\sigma)$ expressing the effective conductivity of a body in an e-m field, the factor μ varies but little in rocks; thus at a given angular frequency ω the response characteristics are determined by the product $L^2\sigma$ of the *square* of a characteristic length L expressing the size of the body and its specific conductivity σ. In respect to its *effective* conductivity, a large body may easily make up in *size* what it may lack in specific conductivity. Because of their large dimensions, topographic features of moderate conductivity formed of wet soils, clays, or the dry alkaline soils common in arid country may have values of $L^2\sigma$ as great or greater than those characterizing small conducting ore bodies. Furthermore, the electrical conductivity of the environment varies widely from region to region, even for rock types apparently the same. For instance, some limestones in Colorado have twenty times the electrical conductivity of apparently similar limestones in Virginia. Hence caution is needed in appraising the electrical characteristics of an unfamiliar region. Field tests in the area may result in improvements in the efficiency of an e-m exploration program, through selection of more effective operating frequencies or a better size for the volume of ground effectively being sampled by each e-m observation. Alternatively, critical field tests may lead to an early decision to abandon an unjustifiable e-m project. The effects of topographic and other large-scale features may be reduced by using a smaller separation distance between the e-m source and receiver. In this way the relative response of small conductors near the surface is increased, but at a sacrifice in the ability to find large ore bodies at depth.

The interplay of the size and conductivity factors relating to conducting ore bodies and to their geologic environment is so complex that no general specification of the geological requirements for successful use of e-m methods seems possible. It may be noted, however, that almost all the published ore finds with e-m methods have been massive sulfide bodies, at depths less than 500 ft, and almost always less than 100 ft.

Response for Small or Large Effective Conductivity.   It will be noted that the out-of-phase component Y for the sphere and cylinder (see Figures 15.11 and 15.12) is nearly linear in p^2 when p^2 is less than 2 and overrides the in-phase component. This linear portion of the Y response curves may easily be computed for bodies of simple symmetry. Such shapes include the sphere and circular disk and all bodies possessing symmetry about an axis parallel to the direction of the source field. Also included are long two-dimensional bodies, with axis normal to the impressed field and possessing a plane of symmetry parallel to the source field, or possessing two orthogonal planes of symmetry (such as the long cylinder of elliptical section) with neither plane of symmetry necessarily parallel to the direction of the source field. When p^2 is small, the induced secondary field is relatively small, and interaction effects between induced currents (self-inductance effects) are negligible. Application of Faraday's law of induction provides the value of the electric vector due to the component of the source field parallel to the plane of symmetry as a function of distance from this plane. The associated current distribution then follows from Ohm's law. In this way the linear portions of the curves shown in Figure 15.12 were computed as a check upon the exact results.

At the other extreme, when p^2 is very large, the conducting body (in free air) behaves as an impervious obstacle in the streamline flow field of an incompressible fluid. (Examples of such flow fields have been shown in Figures 15.6 to 15.8.) Thus for either small or large p^2, simple solutions are sometimes available for e-m problems which are useful in bracketing the more intricate general solutions obtained for intermediate values of p^2.

Applications of Out-of-phase Component.   In a preceding paragraph, it was noted that the ratio X/Y of the in-phase and out-of-phase response components serves to determine, under suitable conditions, the effective conductivity parameters p^2 for the case of the sphere and the cylinder. These parameters, as defined, were seen to be almost the *same* function of X/Y. Under the same conditions, it will be noted (see Figure 15.12) that use of the out-of-phase component alone also suffices to determine the conductance quantity $a^2\sigma$ almost independently of considerations of shape. That is, at the frequency f_m for which Y attains its maximum, the value of p_i^2 is about 6 or 7, in either case; and one of the two following relationships holds, to an approximation determined of course by the degree to which the field conditions approach the assumed ideal,

$$p_3^2 = \sigma_3 a_3^2 (\mu_0 2\pi f_m) = 6\tfrac{1}{2} \qquad \text{(for a long body)}$$
$$p_4^2 = \sigma_4 a_4^2 (\tfrac{1}{2}\mu_0 2\pi f_m) = 6 \qquad \text{(for a short ``spherical body'')}$$

Thus, in either case the value of the product of the cross section πa^2 and the conductivity, i.e., the conductance, may be estimated by determining the approximate frequency at which the out-of-phase component is a maximum. The use of the out-of-phase component has proved to be especially important in air-borne e-m prospecting systems.[1] In such surveys, it is customary to mount a source coil in the airplane and to pick up the signal by receiver coils mounted in a so-called "bird" or "bomb" towed below and behind the plane by a cable. The orientation and position of the towed bird vary with respect to the plane, with consequent change in the source field intensity, i.e., with change in the *in-phase* intensity. However, an *out-of-phase* component having significant intensity at the source frequency can be produced *only by a semiconducting body*, regardless of the orientation or position of the receiving coils. Thus by separately observing the two components, and in essence using only the out-of-phase component, false indications due to misalignments of the towed coil are eliminated. Furthermore by making observations of the out-of-phase component at two or more frequencies, an approximate determination of the frequency for maximum Y is feasible. Thus the associated value of the conductance $\pi a^2 \sigma$ may also be estimated; and in this way geologic structures of low conductance, such as some topographic features, may be separated from those, such as massive sulfide bodies, having high conductance.

Important Case—Long Thin Conductors near the Surface. The previous discussions have been limited to e-m problems for two media, in particular to the case of an electrical conductor embedded in an insulator. It was noted that the response field of the long circular cylinder of high electrical conductivity diminishes with distance as a^2/r^2. On the basis of this inverse square law, the cylinder would produce very small effects indeed when a/r is small. In the field, a long pipe of conducting ore which parallels the surface throughout distances larger than its depth of burial appears to resemble the case of a long insulated circular cylinder. Fortunately, field experience indicates that such long conducting stringers of relatively small cross section can be detected at far greater distances than those computed for the case of the insulated cylinder. An explanation of this favorable result is suggested by the following laboratory model experiment.

Let the homogeneous ground or host rock be represented, with correct electrodynamic similitude, by the salt water in an e-m model tank. Just above the water level, suspend in the air a long bare wire of high conductivity, but insulated from the ground. When this wire is subjected to a transverse e-m field, no appreciable secondary field is observed at distances large relative to its radius, in conformity with the simple theory. However, if the wire is lowered slightly, beneath the surface of the

[1] Aeromagnetic Surveys, Ltd., Toronto, Canada.

conducting water, a large secondary field is produced by currents induced in the wire. The explanation of this large increase appears to be the following. The source field in the water below the wire induces secondary currents around the conducting paths formed by the wire and the large volume of water below it. In the corresponding region above the wire, the conducting medium is restricted in size by the air-water boundary; the return paths above the wire have relatively small total cross section and relatively high resistance. In the wire, the currents associated with the upper and lower paths have opposite direction, but those from below override, because of the low resistance of these paths. It is therefore a paradox of practical significance that a finite conductivity value for the ground, which reduces the conductivity contrast *below* that for the extreme case, can lead to an e-m response much larger than that attained for the infinite conductivity ratio.

Electromagnetic Signals of Natural Origin. The earth's magnetic field, which is regarded as essentially steady for purposes of magnetic prospecting, is actually in a state of very small random oscillation. Measurable values of energy in the small oscillatory portion of the magnetic field are observed, over a wide range of frequencies, even at stations so remote from man-made currents as to receive almost no artificially produced magnetic disturbances. In the frequency band useful in e-m prospecting, natural fluctuations set a limit on the sensitivity of e-m equipment, and thus control the rational design of such apparatus.[1] It has been suggested that techniques for observing the natural oscillations of the magnetic field may eventually be developed to an efficiency which will permit these natural oscillations to be substituted for artificial sources in e-m prospecting. The distant natural sources would provide a locally uniform field, which is the advantage associated with using the earth's magnetic field in magnetic prospecting. Furthermore, one might conveniently select any frequency or frequencies which seem appropriate for the particular problem at hand.

Chief Applications. The e-m method ranks second to the magnetic method in volume of use in mining prospecting (but in respect to *expenditures*, the seismic method seems recently to have surpassed the e-m method in mining).[2] Its use is rapidly increasing, both on the ground and in the air. Air-borne e-m methods have been introduced since World War II, in Canada and the United States, by H. Lundberg, McPhar Geophysics, Ltd., the International Nickel Co. of Canada, Aeromagnetic Surveys, Ltd., and the Newmont Mining Corp. in cooperation with Aeroservice, Inc. The present chief use of e-m methods in mining is the

[1] L. B. Slichter, "Geophysics Applied to Prospecting for Ores," *Economic Geology, Fiftieth Anniversary Volume*, pp. 951–968, 1955.

[2] H. G. Patricks, *Geophysics*, vol. 22, p. 118, 1957.

search for highly conducting massive sulfide ores. The problem of obtaining satisfactory electrical indications from disseminated sulfide ores, or from other disseminations of metallic conducting particles, is much more difficult. This important problem has been receiving increasing study in recent years.

15.12 Seismic Prospecting

During the first six months of 1956, seismic prospecting accounted for 82 per cent of the crew months of geophysical prospecting for oil,[1] and in terms of moneys expended, seismic prospecting probably represents 95 to 98 per cent of the cost of all geophysical work. Because of the wealth of published material about seismic techniques,[2] this report will be brief.

The seismic-reflection method is distinguished by the amazing amount of detailed structural information it provides, throughout the large thickness of a sedimentary column. In petroleum prospecting, the physical properties of the sedimentary rocks are of a most fortunate character for purposes of reflection seismology. In them, transmission of the elastic energy occurs with little loss; and from almost all depths minor but significant variations in the amount of reflected energy are received which possibly are diagnostic of minor discontinuities and of marker horizons which are guides to structure. The smallness of the wave amplitudes reflected at any depth level is fortunate since this means that sufficient energy is transmitted to enable the effective exploration of the deeper horizons. The seismic-reflection method is unique in its ability to provide detailed information throughout large volumes, at great depth.

The recent introduction of magnetic-tape recording in reflection seismology has provided a more flexible and convenient means for examining and extracting the information contained in the seismic records. Magnetically stored information, here as in the case of high-speed automatic computers, is well suited as an input for modern electronic systems for processing and analyzing data. Needed corrections may automatically be introduced; groups of multiple pickup recordings may be suitably combined; the effects of introducing changes in the frequency passbands, or frequency characteristics, may conveniently be studied. All such operations are facilitated by the magnetic recording of seismic-reflection data.

The picking of events on the records in accordance with the personal judgments of interpreters, and the plotting of such events on cross sections, is tedious, and, also, the process of selection may eliminate important

[1] *Ibid*, p. 105.

[2] C. H. Dix, *Seismic Prospecting for Oil*, Harper & Brothers, New York, 1952; M. Ewing and F. Press, "Seismic Prospecting," in *Encyclopedia of Physics*, vol. 47, Springer-Verlag, Berlin, Vienna, 1956; also "Geophysics."

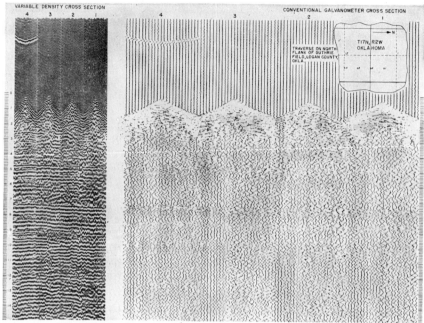

Fig. 15.14 Seismic cross section. (*Seismographic Service Co.*)

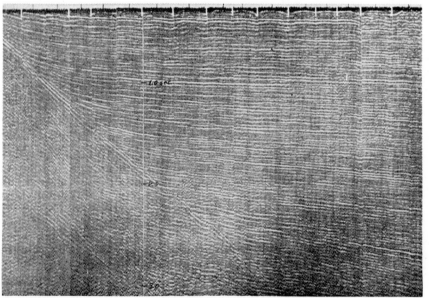

Fig. 15.15 Seismic cross section. (*Gulf Research and Development Co. Reproduced by permission of the editor of Geophysics.*)

information from future consideration. Progress is being made in the presentation of seismic observations in forms which retain the full content of the observational information and enable this information to be conveniently visualized. In the variable-density methods, the conventional wavy trace of a galvanometer recording is replaced by a straight line of variable photographic density. Thus a series of traces from a line of closely spaced seismic stations may be placed in juxtaposition with time axes vertically downward to form a composite which closely resembles a line etching and has the appearance of a geologic cross section. Examples of such seismic cross sections are presented in Figures 15.14 and 15.15. To the right, in Figure 15.14, a series of seismic records of the conventional wavy form is shown, with time axes downward. To the left, the corresponding variable-density plot is shown. In Figure 15.15, which is also a variable-density seismic cross section, the steep dips in the structure, in the left part of the figure, are due to the approach to the flank of a salt dome. As E. M. Palmer[1] remarks, this method of presentation "compresses the great mass of information of a seismic traverse into a compact relationship which retains all detail originally recorded, and displays this information at a glance."

15.13   Geochemical Prospecting Methods

Traces of ore ranging in size from small particles to large ore boulders may be transported many miles from the parent body by the action of glacial ice or water. These signs of ore are distributed in the vicinity of their source in patterns determined by the post-ore geologic history of the local area and have long formed clues encouraging to prospectors. The systematic panning of alluvium to trace placer gold and the careful mapping of ore boulders in glacial drift (especially in Sweden) in efforts to locate concealed ore bodies are examples of the use of such clues. In the last twenty years, the potential of this ancient prospecting tool has been greatly extended by studies in Scandinavia, the Soviet Union, and North America.[2] The expanding capabilities of the method are primarily due to the introduction of rapid, cheap methods for analyzing field samples for very minor amounts of the ore metals and to an increasing understanding of the significance in prospecting of the faint dispersion patterns observable with the new techniques. The methods employed by the U.S. Geological Survey[3] enable determinations of zinc, nickel, copper,

[1] E. M. Palmer, *Geophysics*, vol. 22, p. 308, 1957.

[2] H. E. Hawkes, "Geochemical Prospecting for Ores," in *Applied Sedimentation* (P. D. Trask, ed.), John Wiley & Sons, Inc., New York, 1950, pp. 537–555.

[3] H. W. Lakin, H. Almond, and F. N. Ward, "Compilation of Field Methods Used by the U.S. Geological Survey in Geochemical Prospecting, 1952," *U.S. Geol. Survey, Circ.* 161, 1952.

cobalt, molybdenum, lead, silver, or tungsten at a rate of 25 to 30 samples per man-day, in concentrations equal to, or less than, their average content in igneous rocks. These methods are at a disadvantage in active or old mining camps, because of contamination from dumps, dust, smelter fumes, and water-deposited sediments, but should have their greatest application in virgin areas.

Because of the sensitivity of these newer techniques for geochemical prospecting, dispersion patterns generated by ore bodies may be recognized over large areas, sometimes many miles "downstream" from their source. Brief mention of the development of the geochemical prospecting method is included in this discussion of the geophysical methods because the two methods have similar functions in the strategy of search for concealed ore. Both types of methods may provide clues which can eliminate large areas of apparently barren ground at a difficult early stage of the prospecting program.

15.14 Analysis of Prospecting Plans and Expectations

Since World War II, business management has been discovering many new applications for the methods of "systems engineering" or "operational research." In that subject the aim is to bring quantitative methods into the analysis of the efficiency of a complex system for the purpose of maximizing the economy of the operation as a whole. The business of finding hidden mineral deposits is growing more expensive as more knowledge develops and more complicated methods for prospecting are introduced. It is becoming more and more worthwhile to improve the over-all efficiency of the exploration business. In the present section, applications in prospecting of methods of systems engineering will be considered. The process of searching for concealed deposits consists of a succession of studies by which ground of high potential value is distinguished from large areas of unmineralized ground. In considering this process of concentrating values, it is of interest to note (1) the average natural abundance of minerals in rocks of the crust, (2) the degree to which these must be concentrated to make ore under present mining economics, and (3) the average productivity in mineral wealth of some large, richly endowed geological provinces.

The Natural Abundance and Required Concentration Factors for Some Economic Minerals. Occurrences of ores of the important metals, or the existence of an oil field, are rare phenomena and generally represent a concentration by factors of several hundred to several thousand above the normal levels of abundance. In Table 15.2 the average content in igneous rocks of 10 important metals is listed (column 2) together with the respective concentration factors needed to make ore.[1]

[1] M. Fleischer, "The Abundance and Distribution of the Chemical Elements in the Earth's Crust," *J. Chem. Educ.*, vol. 31, pp. 446–455, 1954.

In column 5 appears a list of numbers which are remarkable for their uniformity. These numbers are the products of the price per pound (as of August, 1956) times the percentage metal content of workable ores. These figures therefore represent the value in cents of the metal contained in 1 lb of ore. The fact that these figures are so similar indicates that the price of these metals is to a significant degree the cost of processing the tonnage of rock from which the metal must be separated. No large differences, representing variations in the difficulty of finding the ores or in costs of separation, seem to be present. On the basis of these figures,

Table 15.2

	Work-able, %	Abun-dance, %	Concen-tration factor	Price per pound, cents	(1) × (4)	Parts per million in sea water
	(1)*	(2)*	(3)*	(4)†	(5)	(6)‡
Iron........	30	4.7	6	3 (pig iron)	90	0.01
Copper.....	1.0	0.007	140	40	40	0.003
Nickel......	1.5	0.008	190	64½	96.7	0.0005
Manganese..	25	0.10	250	6⅓	158.	0.002
Tin.........	1.0	0.004	250	98½	98.5	0.003
Zinc........	8	0.013	620	13½	108	0.01
Lead........	5	0.0016	2500	16	90	0.003
Silver.......	0.05	1 × 10⁻⁵	5000	1,323	66	0.003
Gold........	0.001	5 × 10⁻⁷	2000	51,042	50	0.000004
Platinum....	0.001	5 × 10⁻⁷	2000	153,100	155	Present in marine organisms

* After M. Fleischer, "The Abundance and Distribution of the Chemical Elements in the Earth's Crust," *J. Chem. Educ.*, vol. 31, pp. 446–455, 1954.

† As of August, 1956.

‡ Most probable values—personal communication, Dr. E. D. Goldberg, Scripps Institute of Oceanography.

the price of copper and of gold is exceptionally low; the value of the metal in a pound of gold or copper ore is about half the value in a pound of iron, lead, zinc, nickel, or tin ore. For all these metals, except iron, very large initial concentration factors, between 100 and 5000, are needed to produce workable ores. The uniformity of these ore values per pound is the more remarkable because the grades of the ores listed vary ten-thousand-fold.

The concentration factors required to produce an oil field are comparable to those needed to make gold or silver ore. L. G. Weeks,[1] in an estimate of world petroleum reserves, has suggested "that a large, highly developed region with an average spread of basin and oil occurrence

[1] L. G. Weeks, "Concerning Estimates of Potential Oil Reserves," *Bull. Am. Assoc. Petrol. Geologists*, vol. 34, pt. 2, pp. 1947–1953, 1950.

conditions, such as that of the United States, is approximately representative of the average situation throughout the world." From this, and other considerations, he estimates that about 50,000 bbl of oil per cubic mile of sediments may be produced on the average under present recovery practices and economics. If 40 per cent of the oil is recovered, the average amount of oil present per cubic mile is 125,000 bbl, or 526,000 cu ft of oil. Assuming a porosity of 16 per cent, the associated volume of oil sands per cubic mile (147.2×10^9 cu ft) of sediments is 3.29 million cu ft. It follows that producing oil sands form on the average 1 part in 45,000 of the volume of the average sedimentary rocks. This ratio, then, is the a priori chance that a randomly chosen volume of sedimentary rock, of adequate size, will be an oil field. The smallness of this ratio and, in the case of metals, the large values of the concentration factors required indicate how great are the odds against success in prospecting by pure chance. Economical means for greatly multiplying the natural chances for success obviously are essential.

Average Base Land Values in Mineralized Provinces. A first consideration in selecting land for prospecting is the probable mineral value of the region and the degree of reliability with which this value can be estimated. In the case of petroleum, Week's estimates indicate that average sedimentary rocks carry fairly high values. At a price of $3 per barrel, a square mile of sediments 1 mile thick will produce, on average, about $150,000 worth of oil. It is well known that the petroleum industry has been successful in exploiting such mineral values and in discovering many of those rare regions, comprising only 2 thousandths of 1 per cent of the total volume of the sedimentary rocks, which are oil fields.

In the case of mining, the following two examples are illustrative of districts for which some of the average initial mineral values are known with a fair degree of reliability. The first relates to an area of 650 sq miles in the lead-zinc region of southwest Wisconsin. In this area, the production of lead between 1789 and 1955 is estimated to have been 590,000 short tons, and of zinc, for the years 1859 to 1955, 1,110,000 short tons.[1] At $0.06 a pound for lead and $0.05 for zinc, this represents an average production of $280,000 per square mile. Allowing for future discoveries and production, the metal values are probably as high as $400,000 to $600,000 per square mile. The ore bodies occur at depths of only a few hundred feet, and the costs of exploration by the churn drill have been low. Aided by low drilling costs and the high metal values per square mile, exploration has been successfully carried on for years, almost solely by use of the drill with no significant applications of the newer prospecting tools. Methods for

[1] These data are supplied by courtesy of Thomas Mullen, of the U.S. Geological Survey, and John Hague, of the New Jersey Zinc Co.

determining the most economical spacing of drill holes in such prospecting problems have recently been discussed.[1]

The following case, discussed by T. B. Nolan[2] presents, in contrast, a very complex prospecting problem. In the Basin and Range Province, in an area within 200 miles of Hoover Dam, there are 285 known mineral districts which have yielded a production of gold, silver, copper, lead, and zinc in excess of a billion dollars. This production is distributed essentially uniformly over this large area of 125,000 sq miles, and it is therefore to be expected that other large portions of this same geologic province will be equally productive. "It seemed reasonable to conclude . . . that in very large areas, all within the same geologic province, a roughly constant amount of ore material has been introduced per unit area."[3] Since between one-half to two-thirds of the area of potentially productive rocks is concealed by younger unproductive rocks and gravel-filled valleys, one may estimate (allowing for some future production from known mining districts) that the total value of the area in these metals only is about 3 billion dollars, or an average of $24,000 per square mile. As an estimate of total mineral values this figure is obviously much too low, for it takes no account of other economic minerals present, of nonmetal deposits, potash, fluorspar, borax, construction materials, water, etc.

Of these 285 known mineral districts, however, only 45 have produced in excess of 1 million dollars, and only 11 in excess of 10 million. The 45 have accounted for about 97 per cent of the dollar production, the 11 for probably over 80 per cent. Of the districts 123 produced less than $10,000 apiece. Whereas the old-timers may have been rewarded by discovering a $10,000 deposit, the modern problem clearly is the search at high probable cost for a few rich districts sparsely distributed in a very large area. In the 10-million-dollar-plus category, only one district per 11,000 sq miles has thus far been discovered and proved; in the 1-million-dollar-plus category, one per 2800 sq miles. How can such large areas be searched for blind ore with expectations of profit? The key to success in such a venture is the cheap coverage provided by the airplane, as a carrier of cameras and of geophysical instruments. Of course many auxiliary studies and procedures are also essential, but without the lift provided by the speed and economy of flight, the process of search would be intolerably expensive.

The Stages in the Search Process.   The plan of search of such large areas is customarily a stepwise process, in which land of probable

---

[1] L. B. Slichter, "Geophysics Applied to Prospecting for Ores," *Economic Geology, Fiftieth Anniversary Volume*, pp. 887–915, 1955.

[2] T. B. Nolan, "The Search for New Mining Districts," *Econ. Geol.*, vol. 45, pp. 601–608, 1950.

[3] *Ibid.*

lower mineral value is discarded, by stages. For example, let us suppose that the initial area chosen for prospecting is 10,000 sq miles, possessing an average value of $25,000 per square mile. Four stages of prospecting will be assumed: (1) geological studies, (2) air-borne magnetic work, (3) ground electromagnetic work, (4) drilling to prove ore.

For the first stage, it will be assumed that excellent background information, provided by governmental agencies, is available in the form of geologic and topographic maps on a scale at least 1 to 62,500, so that the composition, structure, and distribution of the rocks are generally known. Unfortunately this basic information is still very deficient in many major metalliferous districts of this country. Government geologists estimate that 1500 to 2000 fifteen min quadrangles in those areas ought to be mapped and studied geologically.

Through additional geological studies in the field, and of the literature, let us assume that it is decided to discard three-quarters of the area, and that the retained quarter is estimated to have a unit value twice the previous average. The cost of this supplementary geological survey is, let us say, $200,000.

During the next stage, the retained area is surveyed by air with magnetic instruments, and aerial photographs are made, at a total cost of $80 per square mile. As a result, one-fifth of the area surveyed by air is retained and now estimated to have $2\frac{1}{2}$ times its previous average value.

In the third stage, e-m work and other investigations are conducted on the ground, at a total cost of $400 per square mile. As a result, the land is again fractionated, retaining conducting areas and other preferred zones, totaling only 5 per cent of the initial area for this stage. The unit value of the retained land is now expected to be eightfold its previous average.

In the fourth and final stage, the expensive operation of drilling is decided upon, over the area determined above. The cost figure for test drilling only is $25,000 per square mile, and we shall assume, with luck, that 2 per cent of the ground tested will yield commercial ore and be valued at fortyfold the previous average.

Clearly the true sequence of events has been highly simplified and idealized in the telling. Despite all the simplifications, however, it certainly is not at once apparent whether we are winning or losing in the venture, as described. One must examine the arithmetic carefully to see whether the postulated conditions lead to wealth or ruin. In an actual case, the complexities would obviously be many times greater than can be indicated here, and the need of more thorough analysis of the risks and costs is correspondingly greater. To give the answer in the case of the simple example assumed above, the arithmetic shows that the value V of the discovered ore, in A_0 sq miles of value v_0 per sq mile, would be

$$V = (\alpha_1\alpha_2\alpha_3\alpha_4)(m_1m_2m_3m_4)v_0A_0 = \$20,000,000$$

and the cost of the survey,

$$C = (c_0 + \alpha_1 c_1 + \alpha_1 \alpha_2 c_2 + \alpha_1 \alpha_2 \alpha_3 c_3)A_0 + C_0 = \$1,525,000$$

where the symbols α_1, α_2, . . . represent the fractional area retained in each stage; m_1, m_2, . . . , the factors by which unit values of the retained land are multiplied at each stage; and c_1, c_2, . . . , the respective unit costs of exploration. C_0 represents an overhead cost, here taken to be $300,000, which is independent of the size of the area surveyed. The prospecting profit ratio in this case is agreeably large, about 13.

The tentative process outlined above will, of course, need to be compared with alternative systems for prospecting the ground. For example, suppose that an air-borne e-m survey of the entire region, at a cost of $100 per square mile, is substituted for the first two stages. The air-borne e-m survey is expected to eliminate 99 per cent of the area, and the retained 1 per cent is estimated to have twenty-five times its original unit value, i.e., $\alpha_2 = 0.01$, $m_2 = 25$. In the next stage, in which ground e-m work and other ground investigations are conducted, 90 per cent of the remaining ground is eliminated, and the retained 10 per cent is judged to have five times its original unit value, i.e., $\alpha_3 = 0.1$, $m_3 = 5$. The next stage is the drilling stage, for which the constants are the same as those of the first example. The two examples may be compared in tabular form, as follows:

Example 1

Stage	α_i	m_i	c_i
0	. . . .	. . . .	20
1	0.25	2.0	80
2	0.20	2.5	400
3	0.05	8.0	25,000
4	0.02	40.0	

Overhead, C_0. . . . . $ 300,000
Estimated values discovered. 20,000,000
Total prospecting cost. . . 1,525,000
Profit ratio. 13.1

Example 2

Stage	α_i	m_i	c_i
0			100
1	. . . .	. . .	100
2	0.01	25	400
3	0.10	5	25,000
4	0.02	40	

Overhead, C_0. . . . . $ 300,000
Estimated values discovered. 25,000,000
Total prospecting cost. . . 1,590,000
Profit ratio. 15.7

In final performance the two examples do not differ greatly. But in judging their relative merits, one should give weight to the ability of e-m methods positively to identify conductors. In both cases the commitment in prospecting costs is heavy, the uncertainties in the estimates are large, and the risks clearly are great. The validity of such estimates of discovery values obviously depends entirely upon the reliability of the average mineral value v_0 and the values for the separation factors α_i and m_i.

Optimum Intensity of Search. In all field work relative to prospecting, decisions must repeatedly be made concerning the desirable density of the field observations. If these are too closely spaced, waste is incurred by duplicating information provided at neighboring observation points; and if too sparsely spaced, valuable information may be missed. Because of the high expense of drilling, it is especially worth while to examine the question of the spacing of drill holes, with the purpose of maximizing the yield in information per unit of drilling cost. For some cases, this kind of problem has been discussed quantitatively and optimum spacings have been determined.[1] In the search for randomly distributed targets by the drill, it appears that the *shape* of the target is of relatively little influence in determining the optimum hole spacing. This spacing is determined primarily by the size of target and by the cost factors which are associated with the prospecting. These costs of course are specific to the district, but under assumptions appropriate to some mining areas, it was found[2] that maximum profit ratios occurred when the hole spacing was about 1 to 1½ times the square root of the area of the target. Under the assumed conditions, maximum profit ratios were obtained when the hole spacing was so large that only one-quarter of the ore present would be discovered.

15.15   Need for Quantitative Studies

There is great need of improving the science of prospecting and of reducing the high cost of finding concealed minerals. To learn what is really going on when field evidence from geology, geophysics, and geochemistry is used to make important prospecting plans and decisions, a large cooperative effort among mining people will apparently be required. The statistics of prospecting experience need to be pooled, compiled, and analyzed, and those aspects identified which are capable of quantitative evaluation and formulation. Although judgments based upon the long experience of experts will continue to be the final basis of prospecting decisions, it seems desirable to fortify such judgments whenever feasible by quantitative considerations. Numerical values invite criticism and comparisons. They facilitate the communication of information and, thus, the building of prospecting technology for the future.

To many, the attempt to assign numbers and formulas to prospecting processes must seem artificial, unrealistic, and unduly speculative. An educated guess by a competent expert might well give a truer evaluation of the end result. The author is fully conscious of the force of such an opinion. The justification of efforts to introduce more *numbers* resides in the history of science. In the long term, the growth of technology is inevitably from the qualitative to the quantitative.

---

[1] L. B. Slichter, "Geophysics Applied to Prospecting for Ores," *Economic Geology, Fiftieth Anniversary Volume*, pp. 887–915, 1955.

[2] *Ibid.*

16

Fossil Fuels—Reserves, Use, and Prospects

CHARLES A. SCARLOTT

MANAGER, TECHNICAL INFORMATION SERVICES
STANFORD RESEARCH INSTITUTE

16.1 Introduction

The words written and spoken about our energy reserves are mounting out of all proportion to the rate of information accumulation. This situation arises out of a growing realization that we—the United States and the world—are inexorably headed toward a fuels problem. The corners of this problem can be blunted if certain things are done now. One approach is to increase the general awareness of the facts about fuels, and that is the purpose of this chapter.

The figures presented here are not new; all have been taken from other sources. But it is hoped that they, and more particularly the pictures they create and the concepts that accompany them, will give a basis for a better understanding of our energy balance and budgets.

The energy scene is dominated by two facts concerning people: their growing numbers and their growing taste for the things energy can do. Every consideration about the energy future must hold these two statistical facts in sharp outline. There is no greater folly than to measure our present Btu bank account in terms of present withdrawals. The answers come out dead wrong—and unfortunately on the lulling side.

We are living amid an explosion—a population explosion. The human race has, for a variety of reasons, including improved sanitation, better control of disease, nationalistic pride, and religious creed, begun to take seriously the admonition, "Go thou and populate the earth."

The earth now has about 2.5 billion people. Population is expected to reach 6 to 8 billion in another century. Furthermore, not only is population increasing, but also the rate of population increase is rising. The curve is bending upward.

413

What is true for the world as a whole is especially true for the United States. The United States population in 1900 was about 76 million, and by mid-century the count stood at 151 million. Various estimates place the number in 1975 at 228 million, with 300 million crowding the 49 states in 2000 and about 375 million by 2050. Every year the increase is the equivalent to the population of a city of the size of Chicago or Philadelphia.

The story is compounded by the energy-consumption rate. During the past century the world increase of energy utilization has averaged about 2.2 per cent per year compounded. Now it is about 3 per cent. The rate in the United States has been above the world average, or about 5.4 per cent per year compounded.[1]

The energy input per capita per year in the United States during the first decade of the nineteenth century was about 38,000 hp-hr. By 1850 it had risen to about 40,000 and by 1900 to nearly 60,000. In 1950 the total energy supply (input) per person in the United States amounted to 90,000 hp-hr, and only 5 years later it was 92,000 hp-hr.

As the total energy use per person has risen, the origins of the energy have changed. The demand on some sources has risen sharply; the use of other sources has declined in percentage. At the turn of the present century, coal accounted for nearly 90 per cent of the energy (not counting wood, which is indeterminate), and of this about 18 per cent came from anthracite. By 1955, coal supplied less than 30 per cent, with all but approximately 2 per cent coming from bituminous and lignite. The big change has, of course, come in oil and gas. Oil in 1900 supplied slightly less than 5 per cent of the total energy, but today the figure is about 41 per cent. The corresponding figures for natural gas are 3 per cent and 25 per cent. Interestingly, although water-power development has grown about sixfold since 1900, the proportion of the energy burden carried by hydroelectric developments has scarcely changed (1900, 3.2 per cent; 1955, 3.8 per cent). Water power will probably never carry a larger percentage of the total.

Changes are occurring in the end uses of energy, but these are more difficult to catalogue because only for recent years are good figures available. The most recent year for which satisfactory use totals are given is 1947; relationships have changed but slightly since then. At that time 27.6 per cent of the total United States energy consumption was accounted for by the manufacturing industries, with iron and steel taking a third of that figure. This area of use represented almost no percentage change in 20 years. The energy required by the nation's transportation systems declined slightly in the period between 1929 and 1947 from 33.4 to 30.7

[1] P. C. Putnam, *Energy in the Future*, D. Van Nostrand Company, Inc., Princeton, N.J., 1953, pp. 70, 96, and 220.

per cent. Most of the remainder was used for domestic and commercial purposes and is rising slightly, from 31.2 per cent in 1929 to 33.6 per cent of the total. Most of the latter (or nearly 30 per cent of the total) is used for space heating of homes, offices, and other buildings. With air conditioning on the ascendancy, the amount of energy spent on human bodily comfort will probably increase.

Looking to the future, there is no discernible justification for believing that the per person energy consumption, either in the world or in the United States, will less than double in the next 25 years. Even conservative estimates present us with a fivefold increase in total energy use by the year 2000. Estimates of the ratio of total energy consumption in 2050 to that in 1950 cover a range from a minimum of 10 to as much as 100. C. C. Furnas,[1] Chancellor of the University of Buffalo, using various assumptions and two routes of estimation, arrives at a figure of $22\frac{1}{2}$ as the factor by which total energy utilization will increase in the next century.

The point is, it really does not matter how optimistic or pessimistic one is about the energy demands. The fuels picture comes out pretty much the same in any case. Whatever the term of years, measured against present rate of use, one assigns to the residual recoverable fossil fuels, the lifetime for fossil fuels becomes shockingly brief when future increases in use rate are considered. Fortunately, nuclear fuels will help ease the burden, but for many reasons, nuclear energy cannot do the whole job.

Whatever the approach, two conclusions emerge. We must, in the relatively near future, develop all energy sources. Also we should make the best use of the remaining stored fuels. In particular, each should be used for the most appropriate application, not indiscriminately as a source of Btu's.

A general discussion of each fossil fuel, its reserves, distribution, and use, is therefore in order. A suitable starting point is coal, which towers above all others in magnitude of reserves.

16.2   Coal

The total amount of coal underlying the surface of the earth is astronomical. One authority[2] has estimated the earth's original endowment of coal as 5767 billion tons, although this figure is anything but firm. Of this, less than 100 billion tons has been mined to date.

---

[1] C. C. Furnas, "Energy Resources of the Future," a paper presented before the meeting of the Division of Industrial and Engineering Chemistry, American Chemical Society, New York, Sept. 14, 1954.

[2] *Bituminous Coal Annual,* Bituminous Coal Institute, Washington, D.C., 1953, p. 37.

The earth has an enormous aggregate amount of coal, but its distribution is far from uniform. Inexplicably, about 95 per cent of the world's known coal lies in the Northern Hemispheres—a far larger proportion than can be accounted for by either relative land area or completeness of exploration.

On a continental basis, Asia (including the Soviet Union in both Asia and Europe) and North America possess slightly more than four-fifths of the world's coal in roughly equal amounts (Asia about 44 per cent, North America about 39 per cent). Europe has most of the remaining coal (less than 13 per cent), which leaves for Africa a scant 4 per cent, for Australasia barely 1 per cent, and for South America still less. To be sure, many parts of the world have not been explored.

In the family of nations, the United States is coal rich. Originally it contained more than a third (35 per cent) of the estimated original gross. By comparison, England, which we think of as a great coal nation, now has only one-twentieth as much, or less than 50 billion recoverable tons.[1]

It is misleading to treat all coals alike. Coals vary in "rank," as they are classified, from anthracite, through the low- and high-volatile bituminous and subbituminous, to the lignites—even, if you wish, including peat at the end of the line as coal in the making. Bituminous is by far the most abundant. It accounts for slightly more than one-half of the world's coal. Subbituminous and lignite together comprise most of the remainder, or about 40 per cent; approximately 7 per cent is anthracite or "hard coal." A comparison of coals, peat, and wood on the basis of heat content is given in Table 16.1.

Table 16.1   Heat Value of Solid Fuels

Fuel	Btu per pound (dry)
Anthracite	13,350
Low-volatile bituminous	14,260–14,650
High-volatile bituminous	13,630–14,854
Subbituminous	9,520–11,860
Lignite	6,980–7,350
Peat	1,500–1,885
Wood	7,600–8,025

SOURCE: American Petroleum Institute, *Petroleum Facts and Figures*, 11th ed., p. 306.

The United States is outstandingly blessed with coal, not only in total amount but also as to quality and availability. Approximately one acre out of seven, on the average, is underlain with coal. Out of 48 states,

---

[1] E. Ayres and C. A. Scarlott, *Energy Sources—Wealth of the World*, McGraw-Hill Book Company, Inc., New York, 1952.

35 are known to have some coal. Coal lies beneath the surface of more than two-thirds of Illinois and West Virginia.[1]

On a rank basis the distribution of coal is less uniform. Only about one-third of the total coal lies east of the Mississippi River, but 60 per cent of the bituminous and essentially all the anthracite is found there. On the other hand, the two-thirds of the total coal lying west of the Mississippi River includes almost all the subbituminous and lignite. The vast, essentially untouched deposits of lignite lie mostly in North

Fig. 16.1   One of nature's greatest gifts. Taken near Pittsburgh, Pennsylvania, this picture shows the richest vein of any mineral in the world. This bituminous vein is thick, homogeneous, horizontal, and not deeply buried. Unfortunately, this type of occurrence, being the easiest and cheapest to mine, is disappearing. (*Photograph by Pittsburgh Consolidation Coal Co.*)

Dakota, with a much smaller amount in Montana and a little in Texas. Subbituminous reserves are principally in Montana and Wyoming, with smaller amounts in New Mexico and Washington. These are remote from the present large fuel-consuming industries of the east. The low-rank coals do not ship well. They tend to break up on exposure to the air and to give trouble from spontaneous combustion if held long in storage. The western coals are, however, well suited to the production of liquid fuels, which may have great portent for these regions as the crude-oil reserves become more critical.

United States Coal Reserves.   Estimates of coal reserves have long been surrounded with confusion. The one consistent thing about periodic reviews of reserves is that each new estimate gives a smaller figure, which

[1] "Coal Resources of the United States," *U.S. Geol. Survey, Circ.* 293, Oct. 1, 1953.

is exactly contrary to the annual quotations of liquid and gas reserves. The statement, frequently expressed only a decade ago, that we have coal to last two or three thousand years is now definitely known to need severe qualification. Such numbers still occasionally show up in print and add to the energy-supply confusion. The unjustified complacency they engender is hard to dispel.

There are good reasons for the steady decline in estimates of recoverable coal. Early figures of necessity were based on scanty or, in some cases, it seems, no information. For lack of better data, some early estimators counted the whole of a county as coal bearing if it showed any coal at all. Also, our present notion of how much of the coal in the ground will be recovered is based on a more realistic view of economic and social factors and on a more conservative estimate as to what should be considered as deposits of recoverable coal.

The U.S. Geological Survey summarizes the history of total coal-reserve estimation as follows:[1]

The first considered estimate . . . was prepared by M. R. Campbell of the Geological Survey, and published at various times in the period prior to 1928. For more than 20 years this estimated reserve served as the principal reference on our national coal reserves and was republished, with only minor modification, by other individuals and organizations. Campbell's generalized estimate was necessarily based on many assumptions concerning the thickness and lateral extent of coal beds in areas for which little geological data were then available. The estimate included all coal in the ground in beds more than 14 inches thick under less than 3000 feet of overburden, without attempting to distinguish between reserves of thick easily accessible coal and reserves of thin, deeply buried coal.

The figure commonly quoted for the total United States original coal reserves was 3000 to 3500 billion tons. The total coal mined (not counting "losses," much of which consists of coal necessarily left underground) has amounted to about 32 billion tons.

The Geological Survey, several years ago, began the monumental task of making a comprehensive reappraisal of the nation's coal resources. The state-by-state study classifies the coal in considerable detail according to thickness of beds, thickness of overburden, and relative abundance of reliable information available.

The first progress report of this resurvey was published in December, 1950. Because the totals for the states completed by the time of this report showed substantial reductions, the total reserves of remaining recoverable coal were given provisionally as 1.3 trillion tons, compared

[1] *Ibid.*

with the Campbell figure of 1.5 trillion (assuming 50 per cent loss in mining).

The second progress report[1] was released October 1, 1953. The new total, still provisional, is given as 0.95 trillion tons. This figure includes coals of three categories: measured reserves in beds 28 in. or more thick and not deeper than 1000 ft below the surface; indicated reserves in beds also 28 in. or more thick but less than 2000 ft deep; and inferred reserves, reserves in thin beds, and reserves 2000 to 3000 ft below the surface. All these are classed in the present accounting as recoverable, although obviously not all at present-day costs.

The report also contains this interesting statement: "As new estimates are prepared for the remaining states a further reduction of the total reserve figure is in prospect, though the reserves still will be large." The figures produced in the 1953 report are summarized in Table 16.2. The final figures are being awaited with much interest.

Table 16.2 Coal Reserves and Production in the United States
(In millions of short tons)

Coal	Estimated original reserves	Production and losses to 1953	Recoverable reserves, January, 1953*
Bituminous	1,093,740	44,283	524,729
Subbituminous	373,806	872	186,467
Lignite	463,616	260	231,678
Anthracite and semianthracite	24,132	10,140	6,996
Total	1,955,294	55,555	949,870

* Assuming 50 per cent recovery.
SOURCE: *U.S. Geol. Survey, Circ.* 293, Oct. 1, 1953.

A further insight into our coal future is given by the statement that, for the states whose survey had been completed and which contain an estimated two-fifths of the total and are considered as typical of the United States as a whole, "5 per cent of the total is measured reserves in beds 28 in. or more thick, and less than 1000 ft below the surface; and 20 per cent is indicated reserves within the same limit of thickness and less than 2000 ft below the surface. The remaining 75 per cent is inferred reserves, reserves in thin beds, and reserves 2000 to 3000 ft below the surface."

It is especially significant that virtually all coal now being produced comes from that first 5 per cent. Mines in the United States are seldom more than 1000 ft deep. It is interesting to observe that the *average* depth of coal mines in Great Britain is greater than 1000 ft. Also, whereas many

[1] *Ibid.*

English coal veins are pitched steeply, the bituminous coal beds in the United States now being mined are more gently pitched.

The Geological Survey, in arriving at a total of just under a trillion tons as recoverable coal, assumes that only one-half the coal in a mine is realized. Unfortunately, experience supports this lamentably low figure of recovery. A survey in 1950–1952 of 11 counties in Pennsylvania, Kentucky, and West Virginia gave a weighted average recovery of 54 per cent. The range was from 46 to 62 per cent. The factors responsible for this one-half recovery are many, few of which are susceptible to improvement.

The reserves of coal that can be recovered by stripping have not been well appraised. While they are important, they are a small part of the total. Montana and North Dakota probably have larger reserves of strippable coal than any other states.

Stripping coal has lately risen rapidly in importance. In 1920, strip mining accounted for only 1.5 per cent of the total coal produced. However the proportion began to rise rather rapidly about fifteen years ago. It grew to approximately one-fourth of the total coal production a decade ago and has since remained approximately constant. The rise in surface-produced coal can be accounted for by the remarkable development of earth-moving machinery.

Coal production in the United States has had its ups and downs. The total produced to date amounts to about 32.2 billion tons, of which about half has been produced in the last 20 years. (This does not count mining "losses," which includes coal that for technical reasons must be left in the ground.) Coal mining before 1800 was insignificant but then began to grow rapidly, and until World War I it frequently doubled each decade. In 1900, total coal production amounted to 269 million tons, and by the outset of the World War I output had risen to 508 million tons. An early peak was reached in 1918 with 678 million tons, which was not again exceeded until during World War II (1944) when production touched 683 million tons. The all-time production peak is 688 million tons, mined in 1947. Since then production has declined rather steadily. In 1954 it amounted to 394 million tons, but rose in 1955 to 470 million tons. Since about 1920, coal mining has been beset by the rapid rise in favor of oil and gas, by economic depressions, and by mine shutdowns.

Coal production is not facing a permanent slump. Quite to the contrary, coal production can be counted on to rise again and to pass far beyond previous all-time peaks. It is probable that the low point of 1954 will not be touched again for many decades.

The reasons for this belief are compelling. Energy demand is curving upward at an ever steeper rate. Also, in another decade the ability to produce the luxury fuels, oil and gas, will be significantly behind demand.

Even assuming rapid application of nuclear fission to power production, the crude-oil deficit will force utilization of both oil shale and conversion of coal to liquid.

Fig. 16.2   About one-fourth of the coal produced in the United States comes from surface mines. Behemoths like this, that can scoop 60 cu yd at a bite, make possible high-volume, low-cost production. (*Photograph by Pittsburgh Consolidation Coal Co.*)

The situation was well summed up by Eugene Ayres,[1] whose professional career has been spent in the oil business:

all signs now seem to point toward an almost explosive expansion in the United States consumption of coal. . . . By 1958 I believe that demand should be about 600 million tons; 1960—640 million; 1965—900 million; 1970—1200 million. Reasons for such a rapid rise are: (1) the rates at which electric power demands are increasing; (2) inadequate potential capacity of hydro power; (3) expected

[1] *Bituminous Coal Annual*, Bituminous Coal Institute, Washington, D.C., 1953, p. 10.

peaks of production of natural petroleum and natural gas around 1965; (4) expected peak of production of world petroleum between 1985 and 2000; (5) expected high rates of domestic and world demands for liquid fuel.

I believe that by 1960 we shall be unable to import all the oil we need because of the competitive need of the rest of the world. By 1970 we shall want to import

Fig. 16.3   The by-product coke oven is one of the all-time greatest resource-conservation devices. Vast amounts of hydrocarbon chemicals once lost in the beehive-oven method of producing metallurgical coke are now caught and form the raw materials of many major chemical products. (*Photograph by Kopper Co.*)

4.5 billion barrels, while the world shortage will be nearly 4 billion. And by 1980 we (and the world) will have around 7 billion barrels per annum less than we need.

Because of these conditions of shortage, the price of petroleum will be high enough to justify the conversion of coal to liquid fuel. No residual fuel oil will then be sold except that required for ship bunkers. Some liquid fuel will be produced from oil shale but only a minor part of what we shall need.

16.3 Petroleum

Petroleum presents strong contrasts to coal. Each year-end quotation of total reserves is larger than the one before. This pleasant fact, however, gives small comfort against the realization that, in the aggregate, petroleum reserves are pitifully small in terms of years of supply. Taken the world over, the estimated ultimate recovery of crude oil is believed to be but 2 to 3 per cent as much as coal, on a heat basis. And the picture at

Table 16.3 Estimated Proved World Crude-oil Reserves, January, 1956

Area	Million barrels	Per cent of world total
North America, total.............	34,123	18.03
United States.................	30,012	15.86
Canada......................	2,208	1.17
Mexico......................	1,900	1.00
South America, total.............	13,612	7.97
Venezuela....................	12,000	6.91
Colombia....................	580	0.36
Western Europe.................	825	0.43
Eastern Europe, total............	11,244	5.94
Russia......................	10,000	5.28
Romania....................	600	0.32
Africa.......................	169	0.09
Middle East, total..............	126,271	66.72
Saudi Arabia.................	37,000	19.55
Kuwait......................	40,000	21.13
Iran........................	27,000	14.27
Iraq........................	20,000	10.57
Far East, total.................	3,025	1.60
Indonesia....................	2,300	1.22
Total world reserves.............	189,269	100

SOURCE: American Petroleum Institute, *Petroleum Facts and Figures*, 12th ed., p. 348.

home is no better. From an energy standpoint we have thirty to fifty times as much recoverable coal as oil, whereas we are presently using these two fuels at comparable rates.

The world proved reserves of crude oil were estimated as of January, 1955, to be 189 billion bbl (of 42 U.S. gallons), as listed in Table 16.3. (One ton of bituminous coal is roughly equivalent to 4 bbl of oil.) The United States rates well, with a little more than a fifth of the world total. But for each barrel in the United States, the Middle East has more than two. The United States and the Middle East together have the lion's share of the world's liquid-fuel heritage—four-fifths of the total. Most of the remainder is accounted for by Venezuela and Russia, in almost equal

Fig. 16.4   The search for oil continues at an accelerating rate and is leading to areas where operations are more difficult. Thus far, oil geologists have been amazingly successful in finding new fields. Unfortunately, the average size of find is decreasing. (*Photograph by Gulf Oil Corp.*)

proportions. As with coal, only a tiny fraction of the liquid reserves lie south of the equator.

In the catalogue of states, Table 16.4, Texas is preeminent. It has more than all others combined. Texas and its neighboring states, Oklahoma and

Table 16.4   Estimated Proved Reserves of Crude Oil in the United States, January, 1956

State	Million barrels	Per cent of United States total
Texas...................	14,933	50.2
California................	3,801	13.1
Louisiana.................	3,255	10.0
Oklahoma.................	2,016	6.6
Wyoming.................	1,374	4.4
Kansas...................	998	3.3
New Mexico..............	819	2.7
All other.................	2,816	9.8
United States total..........	30,012	1C0

SOURCE: American Gas Association, *Gas Facts*, p. 158, 1956.

Louisiana, have two-thirds of the aggregate. In listings for individual states, California is second only to Texas and has about an eighth of the total.

Every year the proved reserves of crude oil grow bigger, in spite of ever-increasing production. In 1921 the reserves were listed as about 5 billion bbl. By the end of 1925 the reserve quotations had risen to 6.5 billion, by 1930 to 10.5 billion, 1935 to 16 billion, 1940 to 20 billion, 1945 to 21 billion, 1950 to 25.3 billion, and at the end of 1955 to 30.1 billion bbl. Meanwhile during this 33-year period a total of 42 billion bbl was consumed—some eight times more than the known reserves in 1921.

This mounting reserve has caused much confusion, considerable complacency, and gives excuse in some quarters for calling those predicting an early end to crude oil nothing less than alarmists.

Crude-oil reserves are counted on a different and more conservative basis than those of coal. They are an estimation of the quantity of petroleum that we can reasonably expect to produce from known wells by present methods. Obviously there will be future discoveries, but these are not counted in proved reserves. Improvements in technology also will increase the total to be recovered from existing fields, but the reserve figures do not anticipate that.

The sum of oil eventually produced in the United States will considerably exceed the present proved-reserve figure. How much more is open to disagreement. The most pessimistic figure for total future crude production is about 20 billion bbl more than present proved reserve, or about 50 billion bbl in all our future. The guesses—and they cannot be much more than that—range from that number up to about 70 or 80 billion beyond the 30 we presently count as proved reserves. Perhaps as good a figure to take as any is the 83 billion bbl as the gross future production estimated in 1950 by George R. Hopkins of the National Resources Board.[1]

The temptation is to take some figure, being as pessimistic or optimistic as you like, and divide it by the present annual production to obtain a number that suggests how many years of oil sufficiency remain. One such approach would be to divide Hopkins' figure of 83 minus the 11 billion bbl of crude oil produced since he made his estimate in 1950 by 2.5, the going rate of crude-oil production, and come up with 1984 as the year the United States oil wells will run dry. Such temptation should be restrained, however. The date so obtained is meaningless. Even the so-called pessimists recognize that a hundred years from now oil will be flowing from wells in this country, although it will have dwindled to a comparative trickle.

A judgment of whether or not the charge of short-sighted pessimism against the "alarmists" will persist requires a look at several factors:

[1] G. R. Hopkins, "A Projection of Oil Discovery, 1949–1965," *J. Petrol. Technol.*, June, 1950, p. 6.

present and future rates of production, imports, rates of discovery, and improvements in recovery techniques.

In 1955 the United States produced 2.48 billion bbl of crude oil. This is nearly forty times the 0.063 billion bbl produced in 1900. With the exception of the years 1930, 1949, and 1950 the rise in crude-oil production has been uninterrupted. Crude-oil production will probably reach 2.7 billion bbl by 1965.

In considering liquid-fuel reserves the liquids resulting from natural-gas production should be added to those for crude oil. Oil in a finely divided and gaseous state is separated from the gas to form natural-gas liquids. With the rise in natural-gas production, these have become an increasing factor in liquid-fuel totals. They have risen from 157 million bbl in 1949 to 264 million in 1955. The proved reserves of natural-gas liquids in January, 1955, were 5.24 billion bbl, which raises the liquid-fuel reserve total almost to 35 billion.

The combined crude-oil and natural-gas liquid production of 2.75 billion bbl in 1955 is not synonomous with consumption. The United States is currently importing about 15 per cent of its liquid-fuel needs. The United States changed from a liquid-fuel export nation to an importer in 1947. Imports have risen every year since, both in percentage and in absolute amount. It is not likely that the demand for liquid fuel in the United States will ever again be met by the wells within its borders. With the demand for liquid fuel climbing at least four times faster in the less-developed nations than here, the day when the United States can no longer buy oil abroad cheaply is not distant, probably no more than a decade hence. We can expect the cry heard in some quarters against imports to diminish to a whisper in a short while. The justification even now is difficult to discern.

How much oil we have, or how much we use, is comparatively unimportant. The issue of first concern is when will the demand begin to painfully outrun ability to produce. Already the United States is experiencing a mild deficit, one that is easily made up in the buyers' world market at no economic disadvantage. However, this comfortable situation is not a stable one. The disparity between the rather steeply rising curve of world use and the production curve with slower rise will begin to be felt in the next few years. Unfortunately the severity of competition will become marked about the time the peak of production of petroleum is reached in the United States.

Disagreement as to the peak of production does not involve whether it will happen or not, but how soon. Even on this point the spread of opinion is not so great as might be expected. The authority previously quoted, Eugene Ayres, sets forth cogent reasons why the peak of United States liquid-fuel production can be expected to arrive about 1965. He gives 1970 as the outside date, assuming even the most favorable combination of events of discovery and demand. By the same logic, he sets the date for the peak of world production as about 1975 or 1980. After those peaks are reached, production will start its slow but inevitable decline. Meanwhile, demand for liquid fuel almost certainly will continue to grow both here and abroad. Thus, before or about the same time as the United States peak of production is reached, oil in the world market will carry increasingly higher price tags. No longer will the question be whether we should import crude oil, but whether we can afford its price.

Unlike many of our mineral reserves, we cannot increase the rate of oil production at will. With coal and metals, more mines can be opened or production of going pits increased. But, with oil it is not a case of opening valves wider. There is a certain optimum rate for flow from a well. It can be increased temporarily but at the cost of lessened total recovery.

Percentage of recovery of oil originally in the ground has been much improved. It is still lamentably low. For the older fields (and for most part the larger ones), even with application of improved techniques such as water flooding or gas repressuring, for every barrel delivered to the pipeline more than one barrel is left in the ground, probably forever. In isolated cases—where production management has been good, the geology particularly favorable, or where fields are young, as in Canada, and can benefit from advanced production know-how from the outset—recoveries up to 80 per cent are expected. On the whole, recoveries vary from a fifth to two-thirds, 40 to 45 per cent being average. The reasons are several: technical, legal, and avariciousness. Francher,[1] after a careful study of the Texas fields, has concluded that about 43 per cent of the original oil will be brought to the surface. Torrey[2] estimates that for the whole United States the original oil content of known commercial reserves amounted to 272 billion bbl. Of this, 105 billion has been recovered or remains to be produced by primary and secondary methods, leaving behind as unattainable by present known methods 167 billion. Thus for every hundred barrels in the ground, we bring out 43, leave 57.

In all fairness to the technologists it should be pointed out that roughly one-fourth of the oil in the rocks is required for the oil to flow at all. There is no present known method of getting this oil. Thus if, in a particular case, one-half of the oil has been recovered by primary methods, only another fourth can possibly be recovered by the most effective secondary recovery methods. Moreover the most effective methods are not always

[1] T. V. Moore, "Production and Recoverable Oil Reserves," American Petroleum Institute, San Francisco, Calif., Nov. 16, 1955.

[2] *Ibid.*

practical; they are expensive and even when they can be successfully applied, economics sometimes rules against them.

Oil geologists have a happy but disconcerting way of confounding the oil-discovery prophets. Is there not a chance that they may discover oil in such floods that fears of early peaks of production may be allayed? A chance, yes. But all present evidence relating to discovery points to the contrary. As G. R. Hopkins puts it,[1] "despite a continually expanding wildcat program, fewer and fewer large fields are being found. More and more 'discoveries' are being made, it is true, but many of them are not large enough to name."

This points up the fact that the newspaper headlines are often misleading. Accounts of new fields need to be read against a background of some total production numbers. For example, the accounts of the discoveries of the Williston Basin of North Dakota, while important and highly welcome, undoubtedly are interpreted by the public as larger than they are. The total reserves of recoverable crude oil of North Dakota, as of January, 1955, are given as 134 million bbl—equivalent to about 18 days of liquid-fuel consumption in the United States. The recent finds in western Canada are of unquestioned major importance. The proved Canadian reserves of both crude oil and natural-gas liquids summed up in 1954 to 4.6 billion bbl, which would meet United States requirements for about 16 months. In both cases, more oil than these numbers indicate will undoubtedly be found and produced, but not in such amounts as to change significantly the total liquid-fuel picture.

The search for oil continues at an accelerating pace. More wells, both wildcat (i.e., in areas not previously explored) and exploratory (i.e., in areas known to possess oil), are being drilled. But on the average they are deeper (and much more costly) and, in general, the discoveries are smaller in size. The average depth of well increased from 3547 ft in 1947 to 4069 ft in 1953, or about 15 per cent in 7 years.

In 1947 a total of 6775 wells was drilled. For each successful hole, four were dry. In 1953, of the 13,313 drilled, 10,637 were dry, and 2680 were producers. The percentage of success has remained substantially constant. The cost of exploration, however, has more than doubled in 7 years. The average drilling cost per barrel added to the reserves was, in 1947, $1.22; in 1953, $2.67.[2] The average addition to the crude-oil reserves for each successful well brought in declined from 1.35 million bbl in 1947 to 1.23 million in 1953. The proportion of new fields discovered that were better than 10 million bbl declined significantly in the comparative years 1947 and 1953. In 1947, four fields larger than 50 million bbl were discovered; in 1953, none. As a general statement, since 1940 the number of new fields

[1] G. R. Hopkins, *loc. cit.*

[2] American Petroleum Institute, *Petroleum Facts and Figures*, vol. 11, p. 86.

found yearly has been fairly constant, but the average size of field is less. The number of 10-million-bbl fields has markedly decreased; the million-barrel fields have increased. And it must be remembered that, to keep abreast of demand, oil geologists must discover about nine 1-million-bbl wells every day.

The specter of a major oil deficit in another decade is real. That it will be dispelled by a burst of discovery is indeed a slim prospect.

16.4 Natural Gas

Natural gas is a continental fuel. Unlike coal and oil it cannot be stored readily. Its use is limited to those areas which can be economically reached by pipeline, the only practical mode for its transportation. Natural gas, technically, can be converted to liquid fuel. However one plant built to do this has been abandoned, with great financial loss. The reserves of natural gas are not sufficiently extensive and the costs in Btu's and dollars are too great to justify it. Conversion of natural gas to liquid on any sizable scale is unlikely.

Thus, world gas reserves are important to the United States only indirectly, to the extent that reserves abroad affect the world energy situation. In any case, estimates of world reserves are not reliable, much less so than for crude oil.

At home we can do much better. The figure for proved reserves in January, 1956, totaled 223.7 trillion cu ft, with production, including that used for repressuring, amounting to 10.98 trillion. As with crude oil, discoveries of natural gas each year outrun use, even though consumption has doubled, on the average, every decade since 1900. Reserves and use since 1920 are shown in Table 16.5.

Table 16.5 United States Reserves and Consumption of Natural Gas
(In trillions of cubic feet)

Year	Proved reserves at end of year	Marketed production*
1920	. . .	795
1925	. . .	1,170
1930	. . .	1,940
1935	65	1,969
1940	85	2,734
1945	148	4,042
1950	186	6,282
1955	224	8,743

* Does not include losses and waste, which run about 10 per cent of marketed production.

SOURCE: American Gas Association, *Gas Facts.*

Something like 130 trillion cu ft of natural gas is believed to have been produced since 1900, but the figures are not known with precision. In the years before pipelines were available, vast quantities of gas were wasted by flaring and large amounts were used for carbon-black production for which accurate records were not kept. Ultimate total future production will probably not exceed 600 trillion cu ft, or something like 50 years of current rate of production. Production in 1965 is likely to be about 12 trillion cu ft per year. And if the potential 1975 rates of demand are applied to these reserve figures, the result is nothing short of alarming. It is believed that most United States wells producing gas alone have been discovered. Future increases in natural-gas reserve are likely to be associated with discoveries of new oil wells, unless experience with offshore drilling should prove the contrary.

In grand summary the United States inventories of the three presently used fossil fuels, on the basis of present quoted figures of recoverable reserves, stand this way: coal, $20,500 \times 10^{15}$ Btu; crude oil, 225×10^{15} Btu; natural gas, 202×10^{15} Btu. Or, percentagewise, coal nearly 98 and oil and gas about one each.

Large finds of natural gas have been made in Canada in recent years, mostly as a by-product of the search for oil. Most of the reserves and present production are in western Canada, although the older wells are in Ontario. Canadian reserves at the end of 1954 were given as about 16 trillion cu ft (or about one-fifteenth of the United States reserves) and increasing at the rate of $1\frac{1}{2}$ to 2 trillion cu ft yearly. Production in 1954 amounted to 0.121 trillion cu ft.

16.5 Miscellaneous Sources

Oil Shale. From all that has been said about the underground mountains of oil shale in the Colorado plateau, the feeling has been created that when crude oil begins to be depleted we can fall back indefinitely on shale oil. That prospect should not be regarded with equanimity for it is not true. The reserves are not limitless, and oil is not to be had simply for the retorting.

Definite quantitative values of either oil-shale or shale-oil resources are almost meaningless. The extent of oil shale is only hazily known. And because of their variability as to structure, accessibility, and oil content, and considering the present state of shale-oil technology, what should be counted as reserves is open to much question.

Some generalities can be made. The United States and Brazil are believed to possess virtually all (about 98 per cent) of the world oil shale, with the United States holdings being a little larger, in the ratio 55 to 43. A rough estimate, that could be quite wide of the mark, places the recoverable oil from United States shale as 365 billion bbl. Although this is ten times the present liquid-fuel (crude plus natural-gas liquid) reserves, it still is only about a tenth the Btu equivalent of the trillion tons of estimated reserves of coal.

Oil can be produced from shale. The Bureau of Mines at its experimental plant at Rifle, Colorado, has amply and capably demonstrated

Fig. 16.5 The Bureau of Mines, with its development work extending over several decades at Rifle, Colorado, laid the technical foundation for the eventual and inevitable exploitation of oil shales. Above and behind the gas-combustion retorting plant is seen the typical oil-shale formation exposed in recent geologic times by erosion. (*Photograph by U.S. Bureau of Mines.*)

this. Yields run from 10 to 60 gal per ton of shale, with 30 a fair average. Furthermore, using high-grade shale and Bureau retorting methods, the cost is not enough more than the cost of liquid fuel produced from crude oil to be frightening. It is a virtual certainty that billions of barrels of oil will be produced from shale and that a start will be made on a commercial scale in the next few years. It is equally certain that we had better do so, or face a serious deficit of liquid fuel.

Recovery of oil from shale is not easy. Oil from shale contains more undesirable constituents than are found in crude oil. One of the "impurities," incidentally, is uranium which is contained in small quantities in some shale oils. The quality of shale oil varies considerably even in a given shale bed. Bodies of oil shale vary considerably as to both dimensions and slope. Oil from shale has an objectionable and persistent odor.

Nature in her seemingly perverse way has arranged that much of our fossil-fuel reserves lie in regions of scant water supply. It is true of the large deposits of lower-rank coals. It is also the case for oil shale. This will present recovery problems.

Then there is the matter of ash. For each barrel of oil produced, there remains nearly a ton and a half of waste to be disposed of. And when production reaches large numbers, this will not be easy. You cannot idly dismiss a few hundred billion tons of anything, including spent shale. It has been estimated that, if all the rich shale of Colorado were retorted, enough waste would be left over to cover the state to a depth of 10 ft.

Tar Sands.   Much of what has been said about oil shale can also be said about tar sands. They are more variable in structure than are the oil shales, and less is known about their extent. Also, they are more difficult to process for their bitumen content.

For the most part, the United States can forget about tar sands. What little the United States has, so far as is known, is in Utah and California. And from none of it can fuel be extracted by known methods. Venezuela has considerable deposits of tar sands, but they are as intractable as those in this country.

Extremely large deposits of tar sands occur in northern Alberta. A rough estimate gives 750 million tons of bituminous sand, with a potential fuel recovery of 90 million tons equivalent to about 500 million bbl.[1] (United States crude-oil production in 1953 was 2400 million bbl.) Attempts were made to establish tar-sand plants for processing the Athabaska sands during World War II to alleviate the fuel shortage. None was successful; none survived. Periodically since then efforts are made to develop these sands. So far the score is pretty close to zero, although it is likely that eventually a workable process will be devised and plants established.

Unlike shale oil, hydrocarbons cannot be separated from the sand by simple distillation. The bitumen and sand is not a simple mixture. The bitumen resides as a film around each sand particle. The most practical separation means seems to be hot water and solvents.

[1] S. C. Ellis and A. A. Swennerton, "Bituminous Sands of Northern Alberta," Mines Branch of the Department of Mines of Canada, October, 1936.

In any case, total reserves are small, and because of separation difficulties, tar sands will have little total influence on the energy situation.

Peat. Peat is technically not entitled to be included in a consideration of fossil fuels. It is a contemporary fuel, in the sense that most deposits are of recent origin, on the geologic time scale. In fact, peat bogs are growing at measurable rates. A Roman road of the first century A.D. was found beneath a peat bog. From the age of the road and depth of the bed, the rate of accumulation is estimated to have been 4 in. every century, assuming that peat formation began soon after the road was built.[1] In general, peat accumulates in an active swamp at the rate of about 10 ft in 2500 years.

Many nations have sizable amounts of peat. A figure of 136 billion tons has been quoted as the world total, but there is a lot of guessing behind this figure. On a Btu basis, this represents the equivalent of about 70 billion tons of coal. Russia appears to have the most, with an estimated 60 per cent of the world total. Ireland, Scotland, Denmark, Canada, and the United States have large peat bogs. Even in the British Isles, where peat "winning" has been an industry for many decades, the full extent of peat bogs is not accurately known. In Ireland, peat is the principal fuel. Denmark, hard pressed for fuel during World War II, produced nearly 50 million tons of peat.

Peat occurs in beds up to 50 ft deep. In the harvesting process, a system of drainage ditches is built to allow the surplus water to run off. The sod is then cut, nowadays, by a machine that provides a slab several inches thick and something more than a foot square. These slabs, which are about 90 per cent water, are stacked and allowed to air-dry until the moisture content drops considerably. They are then fuel-dried further to about 15 per cent moisture, whereupon they can be burned as a low-grade coal, giving about one-half as much heat as coal of the same weight. Peat could be made the basis of liquid-fuel production, but is less desirable for the purpose than any of the coals.

Minnesota has about three-fifths of the United States peat reserves. Estimates place Minnesota peat at 6835 million tons, if reduced to 30 per cent moisture content, lying in beds more than 5 ft thick. This is equivalent to about 3500 million tons of good coal, or about 0.3 per cent of the United States recoverable coal.

16.6 Liquid Fuel

Summing up the available fuels as so many Btu's does not tell the whole story. Other considerations forbid such simplification. One is the matter of fuel form.

---

[1] Ayres and Scarlott, *op. cit.* p. 77.

We have become strongly addicted to liquid fuel. The convenience of its handling and transportation and the simplification of storage are enormously powerful factors in our growing dependence on the liquid variety. Oil is, of course, the basis for all transportation—water, land, or air. A large part of domestic heating is carried by oil, as is much of the electric-power production. We have been so won by the convenience of liquid fuel that it is difficult to visualize a return to solid fuel, even for those uses which can burn either, such as locomotives. It appears probable, when the supply of crude begins to fall considerably short of demand, that we will turn to methods of extracting oil from shale or producing it synthetically from coal, even though the cost will be greater. And it will be greater, but the cost of liquid fuel is bound to increase anyway.

Certainly if the conversion is from solid to liquid, the cost in Btu's will be considerable, i.e., the life of our recoverable coal will be shortened accordingly. By either of the two known basic methods of converting coal to oil—gas synthesis and hydrogenation—slightly less than half the Btu's in the solid show up in the final liquid product. The price of the conversion is about one-half the original energy, even with detail improvements and the employment of all economical heat traps. Possibly the most needed of all technical developments, not only for fuel conversion, but also for hundreds of heat-producing operations, is a low-cost means of capturing, storing, and using low-level heat.

Both gas-synthesis and hydrogenation processes have operated successfully, if not economically, many times on a production scale. The Nazis, to meet their desperate need for liquid fuel, produced thousands of tons of liquid fuel from brown coal, similar to lignite, via gas synthesis. The Bureau of Mines and Pittsburgh Consolidation Coal Company have improved on a German technique and amply demonstrated its technical feasibility.

Basically the process requires burning coal with insufficient air to produce carbon monoxide and hydrogen, which is synthesis gas. This gas is then reacted with steam in the presence of a catalyst (cobalt in Germany, iron in the United States) to produce a gas from which a wide variety of hydrocarbons ranging from gasoline to heavy waxes can be condensed. To some extent, the proportions are controllable. The gas-synthesis process is continuous and is conducted at modest pressures and temperatures.

In hydrogenation, powdered coal is mixed with tar from a previous run, one or a combination of several possible catalysts added—all subjected to hydrogen under high pressure and heat. The result is a variety of liquid hydrocarbons, a heavy tar that is reused, and waste. The process entails pressures of several thousand pounds per square inch. The amount of steel required for a hydrogenation plant is high.

Improvements in both gas synthesis and hydrogenation are likely. Which process will be used cannot now be said. Each has its proponents. The products of the two differ somewhat; so perhaps each process will find its way into full-scale use as the shadow of an oil deficit lengthens. Possibly a better answer is to convert only a part of the coal to liquid, leaving a desirable solid fuel for electric-power generation.

There is also the possibility of burning the coal *in situ*, bringing to the surface a synthesis gas that can be burned or converted to liquid fuel. This is theoretically possible. The evidence from the meager work done to date with underground gasification of coal leads to the belief that this technique will be limited, at best, to thin veins of favorably situated coal that cannot be mined by conventional methods. Because the synthesis gas produced by underground burning has a low Btu content (90 to 120 Btu per cu ft when air is the injection gas), the distance between production and conversion to liquid or other use will be short.

16.7 Energy Utilization

An adequate discussion of energy use could not be contained in anything less than a large volume. It will not be attempted here. The discussion of this section will to a large extent not apply to the straight-forward major uses of energy, such as electric-power production, transportation, and comfort heating, but to some less-conspicuous energy matters. Several of the uses, or aspects of uses, to be discussed are individually small in their proportional consumption of energy, but taken together they play a part in the rising energy use per capita.

Coke for Steel.   The large amount of coal required in the manufacture of steel affects our fossil-fuel supplies. To produce 1 ton of steel requires the coke from about 1.35 tons of coal. Coke is best produced from medium-volatile bituminous coal.[1] Coke that is equally satisfactory, however, can often be produced by blending two different ranks of coal. Generally a blend consisting of one-sixth to one-third low-volatile bituminous coal and the remainder high-volatile bituminous coal makes a satisfactory charging stock for coke ovens.

The original reserves of recoverable low-volatile bituminous coal are given in the 1953 U.S. Geological Survey progress report as 20.2 billion tons, of which three-fourths was in West Virginia and Pennsylvania. Even at the start of mining, these high-quality coals comprised only about one per cent of the total. And, it is for these coals that mining has been and is most extensive. The remaining reserves of coal of this rank are small and are being rapidly depleted. In the words of the Geological Survey:

---

[1] "Coal Resources of the United States," *U.S. Geol. Survey, Circ.* 293, Oct. 1, 1953, pp. 16–18.

The areas containing low-volatile bituminous coal . . . are rapidly being mined out, and the remaining reserves of this coal are now much less than one per cent of the total coal remaining in the United States, of which no more than half can be regarded as recoverable. With only a limited supply of low-volatile bituminous coal available, it is apparent that coking operations and metallurgical processes soon must be adjusted to permit increasing use of lower-rank coal, of which larger reserves still remain.

Of the low-volatile bituminous coal now being mined, only about one-fourth is used in the manufacture of coke. The remainder is simply burned for its heat content, a function other coals would serve just as well. The view that posterity will take of this practice is not pleasant to contemplate.

The Automobile.   Automobile manufacturers point with pride to the improvements that have been made in gasoline-engine efficiency. This is true—so far as it goes. The modern automobile engine is a tribute to the mechanical skills and accumulated experience of its designers. It is a more efficient engine, measured from gas tank to crankshaft, than its predecessors of two decades ago. Much of this comes about by the steady rise in compression ratio, which in turn has been made possible by the developments in refining of high-octane fuel. But, the rise in engine efficiency does not necessarily mean any lighter drain on our liquid-fuel reserves. The gross take of the average engine per mile is, in fact, probably less than it used to be. The gain in engine efficiency, however, is spent for other purposes—mostly in the interest of greater comfort, more effortless driving, and more pleasant riding. Cars are heavier. In the first place, the modern automobile engine demands fuels of an octane rating that, before the war, was superior to that supplied even to aircraft engines. And this is not achieved without a price in Btu's. To produce 100-octane motor fuel requires about one-third more crude oil than 80 octane.[1] And the dollar cost of doing so is startling. At present prices, the investment the oil industry must make to raise the octane number by two points is about one billion dollars.[2]

Although the automobile engines have become more efficient as converters of chemical to mechanical energy, a smaller proportion of the Btu's in the gas tank is used to move the car along the highway. The disposition of energy in a typical modern car is somewhat as follows.[3] To move a particular car at 60 mph requires 27 hp. Two-thirds of this, or 18 hp, is spent in overcoming wind resistance or drag. The remaining third is charged to chassis resistance (tires, bearings, rear axle, springs,

[1] A. T. Colwell, "Effect of Wartime Fuel Development upon the Postwar Automobile," paper presented before the Society of Automotive Engineers, Cleveland, Ohio, Nov. 10, 1943.

[2] Eugene Ayres, "An Impression of Automobile Engine Research," not published.

[3] A private communication from an automobile manufacturer.

shock absorber, propeller shaft, and seals). An essential auxiliary, the radiator fan, takes 2 hp more. The electrical system, to supply ignition power, the several dozen lamps, the radio and power to roll the windows up and down, adds another $\frac{1}{2}$ hp. Operation of the automatic transmission requires $2\frac{1}{2}$ hp, and the pump for automatic steering, 1 hp. If air conditioning is added, 4 hp must be provided for the compressor and fan, making a total of 37 hp.

The energy chargeable to the tires also is more than is generally realized. The large low-pressure tires, while they add much to passenger comfort, absorb much energy as they deform to provide traction and to mattress the road's rough spots.

A little-considered factor is the energy in the carbon black required for the tires. In 1952, about one billion pounds of carbon black was consumed in tire manufacturing. That same year, cars and trucks burned 40 billion gal of motor fuel. Considering conversion losses, 5 to 10 per cent as much energy goes into the carbon black in the tires as into the gas tank. Not long ago, carbon black was made by a very wasteful process from natural gas. Fortunately, now most of it is made much more efficiently from petroleum.

Chemical Fuels.   The coming of rockets and other space vehicles has brought a new fuel technology. It is the field of high-energy fuels, sometimes referred to improperly as exotic fuels or chemical fuels. Their principal reason for being is to secure higher rates of energy release for a given mass or volume, or in the case of high-altitude rockets, propulsion systems independent of oxygen supply. Already many of these high-energy fuels have been formulated and more are to come. Many are remarkable, almost fantastic, in heat-release capabilities.

These high-energy fuels are, of course, not new primary sources of fuel. On the contrary, they are manufactured fuels. A great deal more energy from conventional sources is used in their preparation than they contain. From a fuel standpoint they can be justified only because of the special function they serve.

Metallic Ores.   We are witnessing a major, and energy-significant, shift in the source of iron. The deposits of soft red ore that have for decades been scooped by immense shovels from the gigantic open pits of the Mesabi Range in Minnesota, and used with little or no enriching treatment, are nearing their end. The steel industry is already in transition to using a concentrate won from flint-hard rock called taconite. Much of this taconite is so hard that it defies the toughest bits. The holes for the dynamite cannot be drilled. They are formed in the rock by jets of flame of 4500°F, moving 6000 fps, created by burning kerosene and oxygen under pressure. The boulder-size taconite rocks are then crushed and milled to the size of face powder and the iron particles separated magnetically. By heat and the addition of carbon, i.e., fuel, the concentrate is finally re-formed into manageable lumps. Each of these steps consumes large amounts of energy.

A ton of direct-shipping ore scooped from the dwindling Mesabi pits without any enrichment and ready for shipment to the blast furnaces represents an energy investment of less than 5 kwhr per ton. Taconite concentrate of equivalent iron content contains about 75 kwhr of electric energy plus the fuel used in processing. The total energy content for blast-furnace feed from taconite comes to something like thirty-five times more than for the ores concentrated and softened by nature in the past several million years.

Many other minerals display this same pattern of rising energy use, copper, for example. A few decades ago ore containing less than several per cent copper was ignored as worthless. The spoil banks of some old mines are richer in copper than some mines now being worked. Big open pits are operating on rock containing about 18 lb of copper per ton. This is possible, of course, because of the facility with which mountains of material can be handled by energy-consuming machinery.

The light metals, aluminum, magnesium, and more recently titanium, are taking larger places in the industrial economy. Each of these metals comes only with a high-energy investment, an investment established by nature, not by lack of man's ingenuity. The energy used in manufacturing aluminum is about ten times that for steel; it is more for magnesium than for aluminum; and it is more for titanium than for magnesium.

Synthetic Rubber.   Other newcomers in our industrial economy are more subtle in their impositions on the energy supply. World War II forced the Western world to an independence of the hevea tree for rubber. Under the pressure of necessity, chemists learned how to produce it synthetically, using ingredients that have their origin in fossil fuels. Thus, in making rubber instead of growing it, another burden has been shifted from the sunshine of today to the sunshine of past millenniums.

Consumption of synthetic rubber in the United States is now running about two-thirds of a million tons annually. To produce this much synthetic rubber requires nearly a half million tons of petroleum products. Although no one begrudges synthetic rubber, except possibly the rubber-tree plantation owners and workers, it does represent—in the United States alone—about 100 million gal of petroleum per year that we do not have to drive trains, airplanes, and automobiles, to build roads, or to heat homes.

Latex-base paints have rocketed to great popularity. Even these, in their small way, have energy implications. In 1954, the people of America spread nearly 50 million gal of latex paint. To make this paint required about 10,000 tons, or nearly 3 million gal, of raw material that came from oil wells. Insignificant in the national total, yes. But it combines with many similar little-observed developments to add to the burden on stored fuels.

Man-made Fibers. Another tree has figured in the shift from the energy of today's sunshine to that of paleozoic times. This is the mulberry

Fig. 16.6 This modern "rubber tree" in Akron has its "roots" in Texas oil wells. (*Photograph by Goodyear Tire & Rubber Co.*)

tree, the traditional origin of silk, long cherished by women for the feeling of luxury it gave to stockings and other garments. The silkworm has been largely displaced by the mechanical spinneret that continuously and uniformly extrudes that fabulous filament known as nylon. The 300 million lb of nylon currently produced yearly comes not from the ceaseless mastication of leaves by the silkworm but from prosaic lumps of coal or smelly crude oil. Gracing each nylon-encased feminine leg is at least 750 Btu of energy in raw material alone.

The ladies wear out about 600 million pairs of nylons each year. If all the raw materials for hose and other nylon products were to come from coal (some is now derived from petroleum and farm wastes), the annual production of nylon would require several million tons of coal.

Fig. 16.7   The origin of these shiny strands of man-made fibers destined for automobile tires is the oil or gas well, the coal mine, or farm waste. (*Photograph by E. I. du Pont de Nemours & Co.*)

Nylon was but the first of a large family of man-made fibers having their origin in fossil fuels instead of growing things. Dacron, Orlon, Dynel, Acrilan, and others have become familiar household textile names. Production of these man-made fibers in the United States (excluding the rayons and acetates, which originate in animal or plant fibers) amounts to about 200,000 tons annually and is increasing.

Plastics.   In every bathroom and kitchen is something new—the squeezable bottle. This flexible, unbreakable bottle, made of polyethylene, has captured our fancy and much of the market for cosmetic containers and other uses. It is only one of the new developments in plastics that is based almost entirely on crude oil and natural gas. In 1957, the United States consumed over 100,000 tons of polyethylene, which called for some 100 million gal of petroleum products.

At the automobile shows and occasionally on the highways we have admired the sleek lines of the plastic-bodied sports car. We fondly envision the day when a dented fender in a new car is less of a tragedy. However, we may not have thought, and quite possibly should not think, of the

Fig. 16.8 In the rapidly growing petrochemical industry, crude oil is looked to as a source of hydrocarbons, not Btu's. (*Photograph by Richfield Oil Co.*)

Fiberglas plastic body in terms of the oil bank account. Just suppose, however, that the day arrives when a significant number of the automobiles have them. Each hundred thousand plastic-bodied cars will mean about 3 million fewer gallons of fuel with which to run them.

Detergents. For centuries man has freed his clothes of soil with soap made from animal grease or tallow from vegetable oils. The last decade, however, has seen this time-honored practice upset by the development of detergents. These have had phenomenal acceptance. Starting from almost nothing in 1944, United States production of detergents has grown to about a million tons per year. As a consequence, tallow is on the technologically unemployed list to the extent of about one billion pounds yearly, with the figure still rising. It hardly need be stated that chemicals originating in petroleum products are used in making detergents.

More Roads.　Other trends also qualify as new or increased users of energy. Seldom are they thought of in terms of their energy implication.

Consider the proposed program for an enormously expanded road-building program. The request is for an additional 25 billion dollars of Federal money to be spent over the next 10 years. This sum would combine with other Federal road-building funds and those provided by state, county, and city governments to make a total of 100 billion dollars.

With the daily mounting congestion on the highway, most of us are prone to say that this new order of magnitude of road building comes not

Fig. 16.9　The automobile is one reason liquid fuel is not just a luxury, but a necessity to our way of life. The amount of gasoline consumed per vehicle has risen steadily, from 350 gal per year in 1920 to 725 in 1950. (*Photograph by Chrysler Corporation.*)

a bit too soon. It is interesting, however, to measure the cost in terms of energy as well as dollars.

From past experience, and averaged over the country as a whole, we can expect that, in the execution of a 100-billion-dollar road program, the earth-moving and road-building machinery and other equipment will consume the stupendous total of 15 billion gal of gasoline, oil, and grease. This is at the rate of 1.5 billion gal per year, which is to be compared with the total present United States annual consumption of motor fuel of 50 billion gal.

Also to build that 100 billion dollars worth of roads we must order up to 1250 million bbl of cement and 30 billion tons of bituminous aggregates. To manufacture these 1250 million bbl of cement will require 30 billion kwhr of electrical energy and the equivalent of 9 billion gal of petroleum in direct heat energy.

This road-building program does not, of course, represent either all or the end of the job. It is recognized as simply an attempt to catch up with the needs of that voracious, energy-consuming machine, the automobile. After 1965 even larger expenditures of dollars, and energy, will be called for.

These several facets of our expanding economy that have little suspected influence on the energy situation are by no means all. They are only illustrative. Each by itself is small when measured against the total direct energy consumption. They are presented here not as disquieting evidence of pending energy shortage, but to help complete the picture of our future energy requirements.

16.8 Conclusion

Today fossil fuels are plentiful in the United States. They are cheap. In the scale of history, man's appreciation of their services has been sudden. On them man has fashioned a standard of living undreamed of even as recently as when this nation was founded. But with use rising at a sky-rocket rate we are becoming increasingly aware of the exhaustible nature of the supplies. The statements of fuel plenty for thousands of years are fallacious and misleading. Stored fuels are sufficient, however, to give us the interval in which to learn how to serve ourselves from other sources—fission, fusion, or solar. The closer one examines the fossil-fuel situation, the more urgent appears the need to get on with that learning process.

17

Solar, Wind, and Water-power Resources

FREDERICK A. BROOKS

PROFESSOR OF AGRICULTURAL ENGINEERING
UNIVERSITY OF CALIFORNIA, DAVIS

17.1 Introduction

Increasing attention is being given to the inexhaustible energies that men must rely on when the rising costs of fossil fuels finally justify the rather high capital costs of systems for collecting diffused natural energy from wind and sunshine. These energies, though inexhaustible, have inherent practical limits that should not be forgotten. Tidal power is very dependable, but is seen to be a minor resource. Geothermal heat (in use at a few places), ocean-wave energy, and ocean-current energy seem to have relatively small usable potentials, so will not be treated here.

The continually renewed energy in flowing water and air depends directly on solar radiation converted to heat at the earth's surface. The three major power resources, hydro, wind, and direct solar, vary greatly with season and weather cycle. Water power has the advantage of being concentrated in rivers, and further, can be stored, reducing the arrival variability of hydro energy to a banked reserve with manageable rate of use. Because of these advantages, water power is already well established in competition with fuel energy. Using it in combination with solar- and wind-power plants seems to offer considerable promise in increased "firm" power.

Wind power has been used for many centuries, and wind–electric power network installations seem to be feasible in Scotland and other windy locations. In spite of its relatively low potential, wind power may get significant development before direct solar power does because it is not competitive for land area.

Construction of tidal plants is so expensive that it seems questionable whether this very dependable resource will come into use before large-scale development of wind power.

444

So far there has been almost no use of solar energy for power, but there are regions where solar-power plants are now feasible because of local high costs of fuel. The Southwestern United States, where sunshine is most dependable, appears *not* to be favorable for early development of solar energy as power, because, according to Hobson,[1] fuel costs are low there and absorber costs are high. Development of solar power is to be expected first in other areas—mostly in those parts of Africa, Asia, and Australia where there are a high number of sunshine days, fuel is scarce, and construction costs are moderate. Probably the most desirable system would "tie in" solar power with hydro- or fuel-power plants. However, this is not vital for firm power from the part-time sunshine. The usual method for obtaining continuous output utilizes enclosed thermal storage, but there are large possibilities in energy storage in the open—in shallow ponds such as that planned for the low-temperature-difference power plant at Abidjan, Africa, operated in conjunction with cold deep-ocean water.

All potential power resources must be compared with prospective development of nuclear energy for nonmilitary use. This could be done rather specifically if two economic factors could be generalized for all power resources: (1) the variation of unit installation costs per kilowatt, ranging from the very large power plant to the personal-use generator, such as from the 2500-kw wind turbine to the 2-kw farm wind-electric generator; and (2) the useful load factor (kilowatthours per kilowatt) which depends not only on demand for fuel and nuclear power but also on weather for solar, wind, and hydro power. Since these relationships are not yet known for either nuclear- or solar-power resources, it seems most useful to compare power resources by discussing their apparent feasibilities relative to the present use of power.

The total annual consumption of all commercial forms of energy and the present annual use of three continuing forms of energy—hydro, wood fuel, and agricultural wastes—are shown in Table 17.1, with their distributions by broad geographical areas. Ayres and Scarlott[2] show that the useful energy obtained averages only 22 per cent of the energy input, and they give the total energy input of the United States in 1947 as 9.3×10^{12} kwhr. Similarly for the whole world, Putnam's[3] figure for total energy *input* in 1947 is $93,000 \times 10^{12}$ Btu (27.3×10^{12} kwhr). Table 17.1

[1] J. E. Hobson, "Economics of Solar Energy," *Proceedings of the World Symposium on Applied Solar Energy*, Phoenix, Arizona, Stanford Research Institute, Menlo Park, Calif., 1955.

[2] E. Ayres and C. A. Scarlott, *Energy Sources—The Wealth of the World*, McGraw-Hill Book Company, Inc., New York, 1952, p. 153.

[3] P. C. Putnam, *Energy in the Future*, D. Van Nostrand Company, Inc., Princeton, N.J., 1953.

does not include two other forms of renewable energy now in limited use: wind power and geothermal heat.

It might be noted with relation to electric production that the total production in the United States (including industrial, mine, and railway electric power plants), as reported by the Edison Electrical Institute, [1] in 1954

Table 17.1   Energy, Use and Production

Area	Approx population, 1955, millions[1]	Total commercial energy,* 1955, 10⁶ kwhr/year[2]	Energy use per capita,* 1955, kwhr/year[3]	Total electrical production, 1955, 10⁶ kwhr/year[4]	Total hydro production, 1953, 10⁶ kwhr/year[5]	Wood fuel approx input, 1953, 10⁶ kwhr/year[6]	Agricultural wastes approx equiv input, 1953, 10⁶ kwhr/year[7]
North America, ex. United States	76	253,000	3,330	90,500	62,300	62,000†	104,000
United States	165	2,270,000	13,750	629,000	110,000	274,000	240,000
South America	125	115,000	933	28,400	....	....	175,000
Africa	223	95,700	433	25,100	1,900	....	300,000
Europe, ex. Soviet Union	409	1,320,000‡	4,200‡	476,000	141,000	134,000	590,000
Soviet Union	200	736,000	3,770	170,000	19,200	....	300,000
Asia, ex. Soviet Union	1,481	304,000§	367§	97,300	47,400	132,000	3,570,000
Oceania	14.6	69,500	4,770	23,400	5,040	22,000†	20,000
World	2,691	5,710,000	2,150	1,540,000	387,000¶	624,000†	5,300,000

* These figures represent net useful energy (energy input times efficiency). They exclude wood fuel, agricultural wastes, and peat for lack of adequate data. Estimates for wood fuel and agricultural wastes are given, however, in the last two columns of this table.

† Incomplete. Putnam estimated the total world wood fuel input for 1947 as 1.26 × 10¹² kwhr.

‡ Figure for Western Europe.

§ Figure for Asia excluding the Soviet Union, China mainland, and North Korea. For China mainland 161,000 × 10⁶ kwhr was used in the year at a rate of 267 kwhr per capita per year.

¶ Excludes South America. The figure for the Soviet Union is from United Nations, *Statistical Yearbook, 1956*, which also lists 23,100 for the Soviet Union for 1955 and 116,000 for the United States for 1955.

sources: [1] United Nations Statistical Office, *Statistical Yearbook, 1956*, New York, 1956, Table 1a.
[2] *Ibid.*, Table 127.
[3] *Ibid.*
[4] *Ibid.*, Table 123.
[5] United Nations Statistical Office, *Statistical Yearbook, 1954*, New York, 1954, Table 120.
[6] F. Brown (ed.), *Statistical Yearbook of World Power Conference, No. 7*, Annual Statistics for 1950–1952, 1953, Lund Humphries & Co. Ltd., London, 1954, Table 8c.
[7] P. C. Putnam, *Energy in the Future*, D. Van Nostrand Company, Inc., Princeton, N.J., 1953, p. 173.

increased 6 per cent over 1953, from 514,169 × 10⁶ to 544,645 × 10⁶ kwhr. It should also be noted in Table 17.1 that Putnam's estimate of energy input from agricultural wastes cannot properly be compared with developed hydropower, because methods of use yield very different efficiencies. Further, the ultimate power potential from farm wastes cannot well be

[1] Edison Electric Institute, "Electric Utility Industry in the U.S.; Statistical Bulletin for 1954," *Edison Elect. Inst. no. 22, Publ. no. 55-2*, May, 1955, p. 13.

estimated for the future, because of the prospect that the value of plant life as food will continue to increase. Putnam shows that, world-wide, wood has for 75 years had decreasing use as a fuel. Also it is of interest to note his 100-year extrapolation for total energy use of all kinds (based on 3 per cent annual gain per capita) which indicates a need for 880×10^{12} kwhr per year.

The commercial nuclear-power plants now being built are additions to large power networks. With increasing fuel prices it is expected that nuclear energy will in the near future be the main source of power for industrial centers. Thus a very large block of energy, made available by nuclear scientists, is being fitted in very opportunely between fossil fuels and the ultimately necessary use of solar energy in the distant future. Although the quantity of essential radioactive ores is limited, conversion of matter to energy is so tremendous that the power industry[1] estimates potential heat from uranium and thorium (at a 1 to 1 breeder ratio) of 1771×10^{18} Btu, or $520,000 \times 10^{12}$ kwhr. If Putnam's 880×10^{12} kwhr per year is assumed to be the future average power demand, total world nuclear-energy resources alone would suffice for about 600 years—unless large quantities are discarded when only partially used, as proposed now to avoid very expensive processing.

It is not claimed that nuclear energy will be the only form of energy used. Nuclear-power plants require very special provisions for successful and safe operation. Even for ship propulsion, nuclear energy seems to need Federal subsidy. It seems incontrovertible that small mobile power units will require portable fuel (unless there is great improvement in storage batteries). Thus the need for nonnuclear power indicates a continued dependence on fossil fuels for at least several more decades. Meanwhile, rising costs as fuels become scarce will spur the development of other power and energy sources. In particular, if small nuclear-power plants prove to be relatively expensive, early development can be expected of natural, continuing energy resources, mainly wind and sunshine. Already direct power from wind is economically feasible at favorable sites, and direct use of solar energy for space heating and water heating is competitive with bottled gas and with domestic electric heating in much of the Southern United States. Use of solar energy for power seems much more remote unless it can be used directly by photoelectric converters or can serve indirectly by generating artificial fuels by the separating of water into hydrogen and oxygen.

In general there are very large inexhaustible natural resources available per unit area of the land surface of the earth. The ultimate natural power resources might be assumed, therefore, to be plentiful considering that

---

[1] Walker L. Cisler, "The Development of Atomic Energy as a Source of Power," *Edison Elec. Inst. Bull.*, vol. 21, no. 7, pp. 287–291, July, 1953.

they impinge on a land area that itself is of limited extent. In other words, high-energy civilization might be limited by nonenergy factors if utilization efficiencies of solar energy are comparable to those now obtained with fuels. Without some restriction on population growth, the reasonable presumption now seems to be that world-wide production of foods and metals and the disposal of wastes will all be inadequate before the end of the nuclear-power age.

The values of all forms of natural power depend, of course, on the cost of the power plants, the distance from centers of power demand, and the dependability of the power resource.

17.2 Ultimate Totals of Natural Energies Reaching the Earth

Because power plants must function at or near the surface of land under a variable atmosphere, only small fractions of total natural-power potential are readily available. All continuing energy forms, however, will probably be used in the future, and it is very fortunate for mankind that solar energy and all resulting power sources seem destined to continue very much as at present for untold millions of years. A comparison is of basic interest, therefore, of the over-all totals of the main continuing power resources. However, there is such a wide spread between total existing energies and the totals available at feasible sites that it seems most useful first to review the existing energies and their rates of generation by nature for the world as a whole.

The primary resource, solar energy, incident on the outside of the atmosphere, amounts to 178×10^{12} kw (for a solar constant of 2.00 cal per sq cm per min) for the whole globe. This amounts to $1,560,000 \times 10^{12}$ kwhr per year. But nearly one-third of this is completely ineffective; much is reflected to space, and large land areas are too cloudy for practical harnessing of solar energy. The greatest effect of solar energy reaching the surface of the earth is evaporation of water, a small part of which leads to hydraulic power. Solar energy is also the basic generator of wind, which theoretically has a larger ultimate power potential than water.

The meteorological thermodynamic engine produces cloud belts and cloudy regions that intercept locally a large fraction of the incident solar energy. To describe the area-wide availability of solar energy, therefore, it is necessary to allow for cloudiness and atmospheric depletion, that is, to know the distribution of average daily insolation per unit of horizontal land area. Houghton[1] furnishes these magnitudes for every 10 deg of latitude in his recomputation of heat balance for the Northern Hemisphere, as shown in Table 17.2. It is seen that the total insolation on land in the Northern Hemisphere is nearly 400×10^{12} kwhr per day. Cloudi-

[1] H. G. Houghton, "On the Annual Heat Balance of the Northern Hemisphere," *J. Meteorol.*, vol. 11, no. 1, pp. 1–9, February, 1954.

ness does not follow exactly the same pattern in the Southern Hemisphere, but in the absence of specific information a fair estimate of total insolation can be made by assuming the same latitude cloudiness on the smaller land area of the Southern Hemisphere. This indicates about 200×10^{12} kwhr per day; so with average cloudiness the whole land surface of the earth receives approximately 600×10^{12} kwhr of solar energy per day. Thus the yearly total for the whole land area is about $216,000 \times 10^{12}$ kwhr per year. Only a small fraction of this incident energy can be used, as will be discussed later.

Table 17.2 Distribution of Area-wide Solar Energy on Horizontal Land Area with Normal Cloudiness

Latitude, deg	Houghton's solar radiation with normal cloud kwhr per sq m per day	Land area,* 10^6 sq km	Insolation on land, 10^{12} kwhr per day
90°N	1.743	0.000	0.00
80	1.720	1.496	2.57
70	1.871	8.442	15.75
60	2.370	13.823	32.77
50	3.220	16.524	53.21
40	4.173	15.643	65.25
30	5.092	15.895	80.90
20	5.253	13.309	69.92
10°N	4.986	10.412	51.90
0–5°N	4.766	4.737	22.57
Total, Northern Hemisphere..................		100.281	394.84
Approx total, Southern Hemisphere............		. . . . . .	(197.)
Approx world total insolation on land.........		. . . . . .	592.

(Approx world total insolation on land = $216,000 \times 10^{12}$ kwhr per year.)
* From Smithsonian Meteorological Table 164.

The ultimate figures for hydropower can be seen in a study by Jacobs[1] on ocean-water evaporation. The total for the Atlantic plus the Pacific north of the equator averages 44.3 in. per year, or $371,842 \times 10^6$ cu m per day. Nearly five-sixths of this is wasted by precipitation back to the oceans, amounting to $303,650 \times 10^6$ cu m per day. The net result is an average transport of $68,200 \times 10^6$ cu m daily, totaling 25×10^{12} cu m per year. This amounts to 6000 cu miles of fresh water delivered annually onto the whole land surface of the Northern Hemisphere. Except for moisture transport across the equator in summer, the above net genera-

[1] W. C. Jacobs, "The Energy Exchange between Sea and Atmosphere and Some of Its Consequences," *Bull. Scripps Inst. Oceanog., Univ. Calif.*, vol. 6, no. 2, pp. 27–122, 1951 (see p. 80).

tion of fresh water represents the ultimate runoff from the total land surface north of the equator. According to Young[1] the world ultimate potential for hydropower is 2300×10^6 kw, or 20×10^{12} kwhr per year maximum.

The latent heat involved (585 cal per g) for the net transport in the hydrologic cycle for the Northern Hemisphere utilizes solar energy at sea at a rate equivalent to 1.93×10^{12} kw. This indicates a world-wide use of about 4×10^{12} kw in nature's process of maintaining the hydrologic cycle from sea to land. More than six times this amount goes into evaporation over the entire surface of the globe, while Egerton[2] estimates the total meteorological vapor-pressure engine at about 60×10^{12} kw. As a system for pumped hydraulic storage it is exceedingly inefficient. The mechanical equivalent of heat of vaporization would lift the water vertically 240 km— about fifty times the height of rain clouds.

Much of the solar energy in the thermodynamic atmospheric engine is in the kinetic energy of atmosphere circulations. For the Northern Hemisphere, Bjerknes and Mintz[3] show 0.7×10^{17} kilojoules in July and 2.4×10^{17} kilojoules in January, neglecting the time variation of the wind. For the whole world this indicates 3.1×10^{17} kilojoules, or 86×10^{12} kwhr. This huge free-wheeling energy is really energy stored in fluid momentum and is a continuing power source only to the extent of its natural rate of regeneration. This regeneration rate, approximated from Mintz's estimate[4] of decay time of about 9 days in winter and 12 in summer, indicates an initial regeneration power of 1.6×10^{12} kw for the whole world, assuming exponential decay to 99 per cent. A much smaller regeneration of wind power is indicated from a partial but more direct estimate in January from a summation by Pisharoty[5] of surface friction in latitude belts 5 deg wide, which leads to a total of 0.22×10^{12} kw for the 33.8 per cent of the earth's surface between $17\frac{1}{2}$ and $77\frac{1}{2}$ deg north latitude. For the land area between these latitude limits, the frictional dissipation in the lowest kilometer of the atmosphere would be 0.136×10^{12} kw (1670 kw per sq km), which is one-fourteenth of the continuing vaporization energy that maintains the hydrologic cycle in the

[1] L. L. Young, "Developed and Potential Water Power of the U.S.A. and Other Countries of the World, December 1954," *U.S. Geol. Survey Circ.* 367, 1955.

[2] A. C. G. Egerton, "Power and Combustion," *Engineering*, vol. 150, pp. 424, 454, 479, Nov. 29, Dec. 5, 13, 1940.

[3] J. Bjerknes and Y. Mintz, "Investigations of the General Circulation of the Atmosphere," University of California, Department of Meteorology, General Circulation Project, U.S. Air Force, Geophysical Research Directorate No. AF 19 (122)-48, Los Angeles Final Report, Mar. 15, 1955. See P. R. Pisharoty, Article XIV, "The Kinetic Energy of the Atmosphere."

[4] *Ibid.*, p. V-3.

[5] *Ibid.*, Table XIV-14.

Northern Hemisphere. Since no comparable figures are available for the Southern Hemisphere, only an approximation can be made. Since the kinetic energy in the atmospheric circulation in the summer is only seven twenty-fourths that for winter, the simultaneous friction-layer dissipation in the Southern Hemisphere might be assumed to be 490 kw per sq km. The total energy dissipation rate over land would thus be about $167,500 \times 10^6$ kw for the Northern Hemisphere in winter and roughly $24,000 \times 10^6$ kw at the same time on land in the Southern Hemisphere. This indicates a world total wind-energy dissipation rate over land of about 0.191×10^{12} kw, which corresponds to a regeneration of 1700×10^{12} kwhr per year. Only a small part of this power is within reach of ground structures.

Tidal power is somewhat like wind power, presuming that the basic consideration is regeneration rate rather than the energy stored in the vast surges of ocean water. Jeffreys[1] estimates the average power in tidal friction to be 1.1×10^{19} ergs per sec, or 1.1×10^9 kw, or 9.6×10^{12} kwhr per year. Again, only a very small fraction is utilizable at the shore lines of the oceans, but this energy type is completely reliable and is independent of weather, excepting only a pile-up in extreme winds. It is interesting, though impractical, to speculate whether very large extraction of tidal power would decrease the tides or merely utilize more of the angular momentum of the earth.

Comparing the four perpetual energies in Table 17.3, it is seen that wind friction is only 1 per cent of the solar energy received on the ground, that hydropower potential is only 1 per cent of wind friction, and that tidal power is less than half the hydropower potential. With the exception of hydropower, only very small fractions of these basic power potentials can be developed for practical use.

Table 17.3 Ultimate Totals of Natural Energies Incident Annually on the Land Area of the World

Solar energy incident on the outside of the atmosphere	$= 1,560,000 \times 10^{12}$ kwhr/year
Average insolation on land area	$= 216,000 \times 10^{12}$ kwhr/year
Wind fractional dissipation on land only, whole world, approx	$= 1,700 \times 10^{12}$ kwhr/year
World's ultimate potential hydropower*	$= 20 \times 10^{12}$ kwhr/year
World's total tidal friction†	$= 9.6 \times 10^{12}$ kwhr/year
World's 1953 total commercial energy use‡	$= 4.5 \times 10^{12}$ kwhr/year

* L. L. Young, "Developed and Potential Water Power in the U.S.A. and Other Countries of the World, December, 1954," *U.S. Geol. Survey, Circ.* 367, 1955.

† H. Jeffreys, *The Earth, Its Origin, History and Physical Condition*, 3d ed., Cambridge University Press, New York, 1952, p. 231.

‡ United Nations Statistical Office, *Statistical Yearbook*, 1956, New York, 1956.

[1] H. Jeffreys, *The Earth, Its Origin, History and Physical Condition*, 3d ed., Cambridge University Press, New York, 1952, p. 231.

17.3 Principal Tidal-power Plans

Although tidal power has much less potential than hydropower, it enjoys the remarkable advantage of being largely independent of weather. Bullard[1] found that favorable sites for tidal power are relatively limited, there being only about 50 in the whole world. These are largely in high-latitude bays that are long arms of the sea and favor high tides. There must also be irregular shore lines with partially enclosed smaller bays that can be closed to trap the high tides without excessive costs.

The Bay of Fundy is probably the most favorable because in some places the range from low to high tide is 50 ft. Here, economic feasibility is very near, and two projects—Canadian and American—have well-developed plans. A start was made at Passamaquoddy, Maine, to construct a two-basin system for continuous power output utilizing an average tidal range of 23 ft to generate 100,000 kw of firm power. Since the extra rise of the spring tides relative to the neap tides, 7 days later, offers extra storage volume besides extra hydraulic head, there is considerable value in using some of the extra rise to provide pumped storage to supplement the lower power available from neap tides. With such auxiliary power the two-basin Passamaquoddy plan could deliver 580×10^6 kwhr per year at a generating cost of 10.5 mils per kwhr in 1941. The alternative one-pool plan for 125,000 kw at Passamaquoddy indicated an unregulated generation of 340×10^6 kwhr per year at a cost of 5.4 mils per kwhr. The American project was abandoned because its cost would be much higher than that of fuel power plants and because of the high transmission cost to centers of large power loads—roughly 300 miles to Boston or Quebec. The distance is comparable with the power line from the Colorado River to Los Angeles, but heavy ice loads are a problem in New England. The Canadian plans are for much larger power plants.

An 800,000-kw system has been designed for the Severn River, in England, for 10 hr per day utilizing a single tidal basin of 25 sq miles. Such a development, producing 2000×10^6 kwhr per hr, would about equal all existing hydroelectric power plants in the United Kingdom. Its feasibility at present, however, has to be judged in comparison with nuclear-power plants rather than in the saving of the coal resources of Great Britain. Several other plans have been published, but no large tidal-power plants have been constructed yet. According to Putnam the world-wide total tidal-power potential amounts at present to about $100,000 \times 10^6$ kwhr per year.

---

[1] E. C. Bullard, "Utilization of Solar Energy," *Engineering*, vol. 174, pp. 607, 645, 679, Nov. 7, 14, 21, 1952.

17.4   Natural Limitations of Hydroelectric Power

The 6000 cu miles of water per year that falls on land in the Northern Hemisphere amounts to an average depth of 19 in. But this precipitation is concentrated largely in coastal and mountain areas. Important exceptions are the heavy rainfall areas in the tropics and southeast Asia. It is to be noted that, although raindrops formed thousands of feet above ground lose most of their potential energy in falling through the air, the upslope effect on condensation causes major precipitation to fall on ground considerably above sea level, thus providing a large, natural recurrent power resource.

To get some idea of the average potential head available for water power, the total annual hydrologic circulation can be related to the $1,415,500 \times 10^3$ hp available[1] with 100 per cent development of all physically feasible sites in North America, Europe, and Asia. This horsepower for mean flow indicates a total production of 12.40×10^{12} hp-hr per year, or 24.56×10^{18} ft-lb per year. The 6000 cu miles per year is 55.1×10^{15} lb per year. Thus the average usable head is about 450 ft, much of this being used in successive power plants on the same river.

In each geographical region the hydrologic cycle—precipitation, evaporation, percolation, and runoff—is very complicated. Surface runoff especially differs with changes in exposure, soil, and cover crop. Therefore, long records of stream-flow measurements are required for evaluating hydropower potentialities. The interpretation of such tabulations by Young[2] shows the ultimate limit for total mean flow for the world to be $3,078,950 \times 10^3$ hp. The potential hydropower listed by Young for ordinary minimum flow ($648,620 \times 10^3$ hp) is about the same as given by Weaver[3] for total potential firm hydropower. Although this potential, firm hydroelectric power is five times as large as all the world's installed hydro capacity, Europe and North America have already developed 69 per cent of their firm hydropower, and undeveloped hydropower in the United States is only one-twentieth the present use of all forms of power. That full development of potential power may be very distant, even in Africa, is seen in the plan, to be discussed later, of a direct ocean low-temperature–difference power plant at Abidjan in preference to a hydroelectric development only 200 miles distant.

Many data on the dependability of stream flow are needed before estimates can be made on the competitive status of hydropower versus steam power, which for short-term analysis is fundamentally a comparison of

---

[1] Young, *op. cit.*

[2] *Ibid.*

[3] John C. Weaver and F. E. Lukermann, *World Resource Statistics: A Geographic Sourcebook*, 2d ed., Burgess Publishing Company, Minneapolis, 1953.

the amortization cost of reservoirs versus the operating cost of fuel. One current example given by Creager[1] shows very clearly the reversal of economic advantage with change in annual capacity use factor. Both steam-power and hydropower plants can be adjusted rather easily to hourly variations in load demand, and either of them can therefore be used as an essential adjunct to direct use of solar energy for power where the latter is inherently limited to the main daytime sunshine hours.

Assuming that hydroelectric power will continue to be an important part of our permanent natural resources, growing opposition to the diversion to water storage of good agricultural land in valley bottoms is certain to increase the capital costs of new hydroelectric installations. The more vital need of flat land for food production would result in groups of smaller reservoirs, dispersed in narrow canyons, which, being more shaded and relatively deeper, would have the compensating advantage of decreased evaporation losses.

Considering further the basic problems of water loss by evaporation, there are maps showing the mean annual evaporation from shallow lakes and reservoirs, but there is still a vigorous controversy over losses from such important areas as Lake Mead and San Francisco Bay. To determine the evaporation from Lake Mead, a large joint research project was undertaken by the U.S. Department of the Interior (Geological Survey and Bureau of Reclamation) and the U.S. Department of Navy, Bureau of Ships, Navy Electronics Laboratory,[2] with assistance from the U.S. Department of Commerce, Weather Bureau, focusing on measurements at a model reservoir, Lake Hefner, near Oklahoma City. This project also included wind-tunnel tests by Cermak[3] on a topographic model at Lake Hefner. It should be noted that the average deviation of plus and minus 25 per cent in full-scale measurements cited is not an indication of serious error but rather a demonstration of the inability of spot measurements to indicate accurately whole-lake evaporation rates. In other words, considerable natural local variabilities are to be expected. In electronic terms, the outdoor "noise level" is inherently very high but does not obscure the significant signal magnitude. Hence, to determine good mean values it is only necessary to have extensive spreads of observations both in area and in time. Then using these substantial mean magnitudes,

[1] W. P. Creager and J. D. Justin, *Hydroelectric Handbook*, 2d ed., John Wiley & Sons, Inc., New York, 1950, pp. 10 and 271.

[2] U.S. Geological Survey: "Water-loss Investigations, Lake Hefner Studies, Vol. 1, Technical Report; Vol. II, Base Data Report," *U.S. Geol. Survey, Circ.* 229 and *Profess. Paper* 270, 1952 and 1954.

[3] J. E. Cermak and H. J. Koloseus, "Lake Hefner Studies of Wind Structure and Evaporation," Final Report, Part II, *Colorado Agricultural and Mechanical College, Report* 54JEC22; U.S. Navy, Bureau Ships Contract Nobsr-57053, July, 1954, p. 13.

interpretation by logical analytical expressions can lead to highly significant determinations.

17.5 Nature of Wind Power

Power can be obtained directly from wind without an intermediate heat phase, which is essential with fuels, nuclear energy, and most applications of sunshine. Moreover, all the power mankind needs now is in the wind—if it could be put to work. But this natural power is very diffused horizontally and vertically. Even the reversible land-to-sea circulations are of great depth in an engineering sense. And man cannot harness even the concentrated wind power in the jet stream of 50 to 150 miles an hour speeding across the United States 20,000 to 40,000 ft above the ground.

In the meteorological sense, air flow overhead is virtually frictionless. Velocities above 3000 ft developing from steady pressure differences would be almost limitless were it not for the dynamics due to the earth's rotation which turns the direction of free air flow crosswise to the pressure gradient. The resulting air flow near the ground is not directly propelled by pressure difference except in density currents. Instead, the air near the ground is rather loosely dragged along by the overhead wind except when convergences produce a strong blast. Wind-power structures cannot cover all the ground and must be designed to catch the wind in spite of its tendency to deflect upward or around. That this escape tendency is a function of spacing can be seen in the bending of a single tree, exposed on bare ground and subject to great wind loads, while a forest of such trees shows little action because the equivalent level of zero flow has been raised to nearly the top of the tree canopy.

Nocturnal density currents of chilled air flowing downhill are weak, as is the opposite, anabatic, daytime air flow up a warmed slope. These upslope currents are even less manageable than the cold-air drifts because obstructions can serve as additional take-off lines for vertical convections. In moist atmospheres the major escape stacks for surface-heated air are along the ridges, and the updrafts become visible in cumulus clouds forming above the hilltops.

In general, therefore, density currents are not power sources, and windmills, to capture energy from a true wind, must be widely spaced or else located along hilltops, which cause a faster flow definitely related to the configuration of the ridge. Such horizontal spacing on flat land and selected ridge sites means that only a minute fraction of the kinetic energy of the atmospheric circulation is available for wind power. A rough estimate of the availability of wind power can be attempted by using a few arbitrary assumptions. New interpretation[1] of the world-wide distribution of atmospheric circulations makes it possible to generalize on the dis-

[1] Bjerknes and Minz, *op. cit.*

tribution of mean wind as a function of latitude. The trade-wind peaks move 5 to 8 deg latitude from winter to summer, but averaging together the January and July curves, as shown in Figure 17.1, would not obscure the low-velocity belt at the equator. It should be noted that the relatively high velocity at 50 deg south latitude is twice that at 50 deg north latitude, largely because of the strong winds in the South Atlantic and South Indian Oceans. There is very little land area at that southern latitude; so

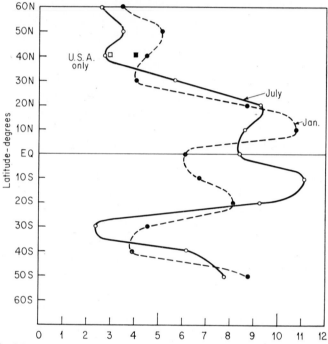

Fig. 17.1   Mean surface wind velocity over the oceans, and two comparable average magnitudes for the United States from 35 to 45° N latitude. (*Scaled from maps by Mintz & Dean, see Bjerknes and Mintz, Art. 1, 1955.*)

the total availability is small, but the wind potential per unit land area there may be highly significant. For the north-latitude belt between 35 and 45 deg the round-the-world mean surface wind matches very closely the average surface wind (10 m aboveground) for the United States reported from 39 airports. These 24-hr mean magnitudes are so low it is clear that special sites are needed for present practical development of wind power, probably on hilltops or shore lines where higher velocities are found. The power output expected on such selected sites can be investigated in great detail, as reported by Putnam,[1] but to estimate total

[1] P. C. Putnam, *Power from the Wind*, D. Van Nostrand Company, Inc., Princeton, N.J., 1948, p. 209.

world-wide wind-power potential, it seems necessary to revert to flat-area mean wind velocities.

The first step is to estimate the wind velocity at the height of the center of a practical large-power windmill (117 ft for the Smith-Putnam turbine). Air velocity is not regularly measured at such a height, but a reasonable adjustment can be made by taking it roughly as about 65 per cent of the gradient wind or 1.2 times the 10-m wind, depending on the data at hand. Then one might determine the average kinetic energy per square mile in a sheet of streaming air having a reasonable working vertical depth (175 ft for Smith-Putnam). Such calculation of potential wind power, however, would not take into account the evasive nature of wind, which, unlike water channeled in a river, is confined only on the bottom surface and is constrained in its detouring around power-catching structures only by the dynamic reaction of the all-surrounding air flow. Thus some practical assumption needs to be made on how many wind hurdles per mile would capture the maximum power from the bottom of a flowing atmosphere.

From experiments on windbreaks it is known that there is about 90 per cent recovery in velocity near the ground at a distance downwind eight to ten times the height of the windbreak. Such spacing of wind-power machines would probably preserve the effectiveness of each, especially since the power structure must be designed for through air flow. Since windmills seem to be the most practical type for generating power, an estimate of the optimum number of these per square mile may lead to a rational figure for the total potential wind power. Such a basis can be almost independent of the size of the windmill because for an agreed ratio of spacing to diameter the number of machines per square mile would vary inversely with the individual propeller-disk area. Hence the total disk area per square mile would be constant, and the only increase in potential power with size would be due to the somewhat greater wind velocity reached by the higher (bigger) propellers. If propeller machines are taken as a standard type, the spacing in the direction of air flow can be shortened as the spacing transversely to wind is increased. Utilizing a simple square pattern with a Smith-Putnam 175-ft propeller turbine every one-fourth mile (seven heights), a density of 16 such machines per square mile would not be an excessive concept for a wind-power farm on a windy plain. This arbitrary deduction implies a rating disk area of, say, 390,000 sq ft per sq mile (14,000 sq m per sq km), regardless of propeller diameter. Contrary to solar-power plants, which necessarily cover large areas of land, such a sprinkling of towers with propeller-swept vertical area only one-seventieth of the horizontal area will not interfere appreciably with normal land use for food productions or industry.

Assuming the same 175-ft-diameter Smith-Putnam[1] design and the same air density (0.075 lb force per cu ft), the air power streaming through the disk area would be $0.120V^3$ kw per machine when the average wind velocity V is in miles per hour. By the above concept the total potential wind power in kilowatts per square mile can be taken as $1.92V^3$. The inherent error of using the cube of the mean velocity instead of integrating in time and space seems to be no larger than the losses involved in restricting operation to moderate velocities for structural safety. Applying this area-wide scheme of estimating potential wind power (see Table 17.4)

Table 17.4   Distribution of Area-wide Wind-power Potential

Lati-tude	Yearly mean velocity, mph		$V^3_{115\,ft}$	Land area 10^6 sq mi	Approx wind potential, kw per 10 deg lat on land
	10 m	115 ft			
60°N	4.29	5.15	136.59	5.34	1,399 $\times$ 10^6 kw
50	4.55	5.46	162.77	6.38	2,004
40	3.84	4.61	97.97	6.04	1,136
30	5.14	6.16	233.74	6.13	2,755
20	8.43	10.11	1033.40	5.14	10,200
10°N	10.25	12.30	1860.87	4.02	14,430
0	7.57	9.10	753.57	3.99	5,775
10°S	9.43	11.31	1446.90	3.64	10,120
20	9.19	11.02	1338.20	3.98	10,230
30	3.70	4.44	87.53	2.79	463
40	5.35	6.42	264.61	0.682	346
50	8.79	10.54	1171.40	0.226	509 $\times$ 10^6 kw
Total	.....	.....	....	.....	59,367 $\times$ 10^6 kw (297 $\times$ 10^{12} kwhr per year at 5000 hr)

indicates a total three times the 2×10^{10} kw Willett estimated for Putnam[1] but makes no allowance for uneconomic regions of low average wind velocity. Contrary to conclusions of others, that wind power has small potential, the above estimate shows a possibility of fifteen times the total hydro potential. The problem of excluding the wind power indicated at velocities too low to be useful is met by an arbitrary assumption that reduces by 40 per cent the available hours per year, namely, to 5000 hr, whereas the theoretically perfectly steady wind would generate 8760 (or 8765.81) kwhr per kw per year. This assumption applies purely to estimates of power availability, not to calculations of efficiency, which

[1] *Ibid.*

would be based on the total energy streaming through the propeller-disk area.

Assessing the practical possibilities of developing a "firm" power output involves a study of the natural variability in wind velocity which is even more complicated than a like study for solar energy. Both have certain threshold values below which it is useless to operate, and both involve persistence of the too-low condition. But wind load, unlike solar-energy loads, can be too great. The hazards of very high velocity, and of icing, may well be the limiting factors of practical structural design. On the other hand, frequent spells of moderate excess wind power can be advantageous if the excess power can be used to conserve fuel or hydraulic power potential in the same power network. A mere 6 per cent speed excess in wind causes nearly a 20 per cent increase in power output. Petterssen[1] based a world-wide study of the variability of daily wind on the number of hours per year that wind exceeded a reasonable design velocity. Knowledge of greater speeds hourly is needed only for safety. Petterssen's units are simply the annual kilowatthours to be expected per kilowatt of capacity installed. His results, as shown in Figure 17.2, indicate that there are areas of low reliability, but also some rather dependable wind belts. Considerable reliability can be expected in higher latitudes, where solar energy would be less dependable.

Court[2] made one of the few studies that utilizes statistical probability to evaluate the incidence and hazards of high winds. He encountered considerable difficulties in using long-time records because most of the stations had been moved at least once and, of course, local surroundings change with time. Nevertheless, the semilog plot of maximum velocity versus years per occurrence reproduced in Figure 17.3 furnishes information essential for economic design on a known risk basis for 20 major locations. Similar studies are needed for all probable sites of wind-power installations.

Finally, icing hazard must be considered both on the wind-power turbine and on the transmission lines. For the latter there is already considerable knowledge because of the existing country-wide network of electric power lines. Unfortunately, maps show that icing hazard is most serious in the areas where one would ordinarily expect wind power to be more dependable than solar power.

In view of natural restrictions on the development of wind power it seems sensible to assume an average operating time of only 2000 hr per year (Petterssen's lowest curve) when one makes an estimate of world-wide potential annual output. Even this low value indicates a world-wide

---

[1] S. Petterssen, Fig. 7, p. 21 in Putnam, *op. cit.*

[2] A. Court, "Wind Extremes as Design Factors," *J. Franklin Inst.*, vol. 256, no. 1, pp. 39–56, July, 1953.

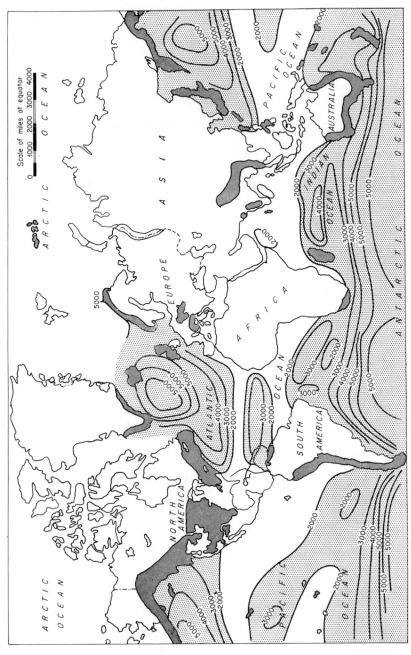

Fig. 17.2 Geographical distribution of potential power from oceanic winds. (*After Petterssen.*)

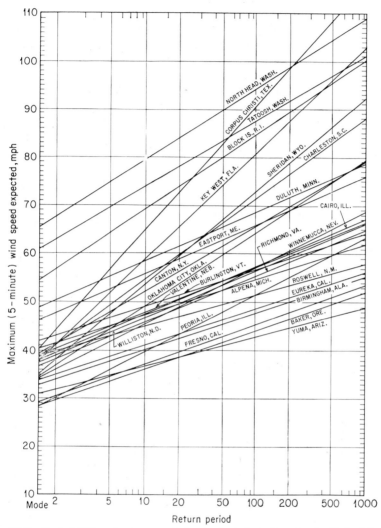

Fig. 17.3 Probabilities of extreme winds at selected stations in the United States.

annual potential wind power of 120×10^{12} kwhr, which is twenty-five times the world's total use of commercial energy in 1953. The essential problem, therefore, in using wind as a natural power resource is the cost of wind-power plants.

The outstanding installation for testing commercial wind power was the Smith-Putnam[1] 1250-kw wind propeller turbine with adjustable-pitch propeller 175 ft in diameter. The location, at 2000 ft on Grandpa's Knob,

[1] Putnam, *loc. cit.*

Vermont, took advantage of a speed-up induced by the shape of the ridge, but the actual average velocity was less than expected. Some simplifications have been found possible; so the cost of generating electric power by wind at favorable locations is now nearly competitive with hydroelectric plants. Putnam presupposes only 50 such sites near industrial centers suitable for group installation, having 50,000 kw each, totaling a practical central station potential of only 2,500,000 kw. It is to be noted that this is only 1/24,000 the available potential as estimated above. It is clear, therefore, that only a minute part of the wind-power potential is considered feasible now and that large use of wind power requiring a multitude of widely dispersed power plants would be developed only if less expensive than direct use of solar energy.

17.6   Characteristics of Solar Energy near the Ground

Eventually the major power resource of the world will be solar energy. It has already provided all the fossil fuels. It currently generates all the hydropower and wind power and by natural photosynthesis provides all the wood, cane, and agricultural wastes used extensively for fuel. The development of this primary power resource needs to be considered, first, in extending the age-long use of solar energy in space heating and, secondly, in using it for power. The sun has been studied intensively by astrophysicists. After eliminating as far as possible the effects of the earth's atmosphere, it has been established that the normal variation in total energy radiated from the sun is only about one per cent. Atmospheric depletion of solar energy, however, is very large, and cloud interference further seriously limits the total energy received at the ground.

Availability of Solar Energy at the Ground. The shadow cast by inclined absorbers covers the amount of ground that would be required by a horizontal surface to receive the same energy input. Not every square meter of land, however, can be used for controlled conversion of solar radiation to heat, even when economic feasibility is disregarded. Sunshine is a necessity for agriculture, and this vital requirement for food production would probably prevent the use of good soil areas for solar absorbers. Much nonagricultural land is unsuitable because of orographic cloudiness and strong winds. Power generators will require heat sinks, which are not available everywhere. Therefore, until competitive use for land is studied with due attention to future needs for direct use of solar energy, a ratio of solar area to whole land must be arbitrarily assumed in order to estimate total availability. For this we have assumed an area equal to one-seventh the total land area, this being ten times the working area ratio previously assumed for wind power. This availability assumption has nothing to do with apparatus efficiency, which is based on energy impinging on the structure itself.

Following the latitudinal distribution of incident solar energy given in Table 17.2, the one-seventh basis for total available potential solar energy for the land area in the Northern Hemisphere indicates 56×10^{12} kwhr per day. If the same energy distribution per latitude is assumed for the Southern Hemisphere, the total potential there for the smaller land area would be 28×10^{12} kwhr per day. Thus the daily solar potential for the whole land area of the world can be taken roughly as 85×10^{12} kwhr. The total magnitude per year would be $31,000 \times 10^{12}$ kwhr, which is one-fiftieth of the solar energy incident on the outside of the atmosphere. About 20 days of available solar energy, therefore, would equal the presently estimated nuclear-energy resources. More significant is the indication that available solar energy is only about thirty-five times Putnam's lower estimate of power demand 100 years hence.

Not all this potential solar energy is available at useful temperature levels, and there is inherently a considerable loss by reflection from any covering surface, especially at large angles of incidence. Moreover, inclining the absorber shades the effective surface from early morning and late afternoon sunshine in the summer.

Following the previous concepts that disallow very low energy rates, the threshold of useful solar-energy input needs to be estimated. This depends on two factors: (1) how high the useful temperature is above the ambient air temperature and (2) the rate of heat loss from the absorber assembly at the useful temperature. Hottel[1] calls this the critical heat rate, below which heat collection should not be attempted. Heywood[2] simply confines all ratings to the middle 8 hr of the day. This simplification rejects nearly 20 per cent of the incident energy in May; so it seems reasonable to make a 25 per cent reduction in the estimate of available solar power on a horizontal surface simply for the geometric effects of the continual change in angle of incidence of the sun's rays and the necessity of obtaining a useful temperature rise. This further reduces the world-wide estimate of available solar energy to about $24,000 \times 10^{12}$ kwhr per year.

Table 17.5 then gives the approximate standing in availability of the four perpetual-energy resources, except that the figures for hydropower and tidal power are for feasible potential, which if applied to the wind, would hardly touch its full potential. The total energy demand estimated by Putnam for A.D. 2050, that is, 880×10^{12} kwhr per year, is three times the estimated total potential wind power; so it is very clear that there

---

[1] H. C. Hottel and A. Whillier, "Evaluation of Flat-plate Solar-collector Performance," Conference on Solar Energy—the Scientific Basis, Stanford Research Institute and University of Arizona, Tucson, Ariz., Oct. 31, 1955.

[2] H. Heywood, "Solar Energy, Past, Present, and Future Applications," *Engineering*, vol. 176, pp. 377–380, 409–411, Sept. 18, 25, 1953.

must be great development of solar power before the limited store of nuclear energy is used up. There need be no fear, however, of ultimate power shortage, for the forecast demand is less than 4 per cent of a rather conservatively calculated availability of solar energy on the ground, which is a continuing annual resource not depleted by use.

Table 17.5 Approximate Total Available Potentials of Three Forms of Energy on Land Area of the World and the Practical Potential for Tidal Power

Total solar energy on $\frac{1}{7}$ the land area, and less 25%	$\cong$ 24,000 × 10¹² kwhr/year
Total available wind power (at 2000 hr/year)	$\cong$ 120 × 10¹² kwhr/year
Total hydropower potential*	$\cong$ 20.0 × 10¹² kwhr/year
Total feasible tidal power†	$\cong$ 0.10 × 10¹² kwhr/year
Forecast of energy need in A.D. 2050 at 3% increase per capita†	$\cong$ 880 × 10¹² kwhr/year

* L. L. Young, "Developed and Potential Water Power in the U.S.A. and Other Countries of the World, December, 1954," *U.S. Geol. Survey, Circ.* 367, 1955.

† P. C. Putnam, *Energy in the Future*, D. Van Nostrand Company, Inc., Princeton, N.J., 1953.

The Solar Spectrum before and after Depletion in a Cloudless Atmosphere. Water vapor has strong spectral absorption bands, largely in the longer-wave part of the solar spectrum; haze and dust particles cause depletion by scattering, mainly in the short-wave part of the solar spectrum. Furthermore, photochemical reactions depend on irradiations at certain wave-number frequencies.

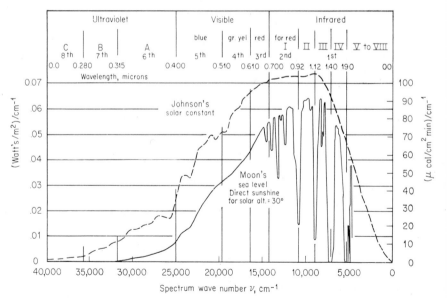

Fig. 17.4 Spectrums of the solar constant and of direct-beam sunshine at sea level. (*Plotted from Johnson and from Moon.*)

Figure 17.4 shows the spectral distribution of energy per unit wave number in direct-beam sunshine outside the earth's atmosphere as given by Johnson.[1] Also shown is the spectrum after depletion in an optical air path of 2 atm (sun's altitude 30°) as recommended by Moon[2] and adopted by the American Society of Heating and Air Conditioning Engineers. It is to be noted that, although the spectrum is arranged with longer wavelengths to the right, the abscissa scale is in units of wave number to represent frequency instead of wavelength.

This presentation is advantageous in that the energies of quanta are proportional to wave number, and all photochemical reactions, including eye response, are quantum reactions. Putting the abscissa in units of wave number makes the shape of absorption lines symmetrical and expands the spectrum in the short-wave region, where more detail is of interest. It changes the position of "peak" intensity from about 0.5 to 1.1μ, however, and this shows that parts of the spectrum of the sun must be considered not by respective intensities per wavelength or wave number (which differ for characteristic absorption lines), but as energy segments between finite wave number or corresponding wavelength boundaries. Eleven standardized segments are shown and their respective energy fractions given in Table 17.6. The segments recommended by the Dutch Committee on Plant Irradiation[3] are as follows:

First band: greater than 1.000 micron. No specific effects of this radiation are known. It is acceptable that this radiation, as far as it is absorbed by the plant, is transformed into heat without interference of biochemical processes.

Second band: 1.000 to 0.700* micron. This is the region of specific elongating effect on plants. Although the spectral region of elongating effect does not coincide precisely with the limits of this band, one may provisionally accept that the radiant flux in this band is an adequate measure of the elongating activity of the radiation.

Third band: 0.700* to 0.610 micron. This is almost the spectral region of the strongest absorption of chlorophyll and of the strongest photosynthetic activity in the red region. In many cases it also shows the strongest photoperiodic activity.

Fourth band: 0.610 to 0.510 micron. This is a spectral region of low photosynthetic effectiveness in the green and of weak formative activity.

Fifth band: 0.510 to 0.400 micron. This is virtually the region of strong chlorophyll absorption and absorption by yellow pigments. It is also a region of strong photosynthetic activity in the blue-violet and of strong formative effects.

[1] F. S. Johnson, "The Solar Constant," *J. Meteorol.*, vol. 11, no. 6, pp. 431–439, December, 1954.

[2] Parry Moon, "Proposed Standard Solar-radiation Curves for Engineering Use," *J. Franklin Inst.*, vol. 230, no. 5, pp. 583–617, November, 1940.

[3] E. C. Wassink, Dutch Committee on Plant Irradiation, "Specification of Radiant Flux and Radiant Flux Density in Irradiation of Plants with Artificial Light," *J. Hort. Sci.*, vol. 28, pp. 177–184, July, 1953.

* Now being considered in place of 0.72.

Table 17.6   Energy Distribution in the Solar Spectrum

Spectral region			Energy in spectral regions			
Regions	Bands and windows*	Interval boundaries		Johnson's solar constant outside atmosphere		Moon's recommended sea-level direct-beam sunshine, sun's altitude = 30° $(m = 2)$
		Wave-length, microns	Wave num-ber, cm^{-1}	Cum. %	Cal/ sq cm/ min per interval	Cal/ sq cm/ min per interval	Watts/ sq m per interval
Uultraviolet.......	....	0.0	∞				
(C)............	8th	......	......	0.51	0.010	0.000	0.
		0.280	35,713				
(B)............	7th	......	......	1.97	0.029	0.000	0.
		0.315	31,746				
(A)...........	6th	......	......	9.03	0.141	0.028	20.
		0.400	25,000				
Visible (blue).....	5th	......	......	24.9	0.318	0.155	108.
		0.510	19,608				
(green yellow)...	4th	......	......	38.4	0.270	0.169	118.
		0.610	16,393				
(red)..........	3d	......	......	48.8	0.208	0.147	102.
		0.700†	14,286				
Far red..........	I	......	......	66.5	0.354	0.249	174.
		0.92	10,870				
Infrared..........	II	......	......	76.7	0.204	0.138	96.
		1.12	8,929				
	III	......	......	85.5	0.176	0.092	64.
		1.40	7,143				
	IV	......	......	93.02	0.150	0.070	49.
		1.9	5,263				
	V to VIII	......	......	100.00	0.140	0.013	9.
		∞	0.0				
Total..........	....	......	....	......	2.000	1.061	740.

* Tait Elder and John Strong, "The Infrared Transmission of Atmospheric Windows," *J. Franklin Inst.*, vol. 255, no. 3, pp. 189–208, March, 1953.

† Being considered now by Dutch Committee on Plant Irradiation instead of 0.720.

Such energy segments should be used for determining photochemical efficiencies when comparing systems that use artificial light with those that use sunlight. The infrared windows I to VIII from Elder and Strong[1] are bounded by strong water-vapor absorption centers.

Direct-beam Sunshine and Diffuse Solar Radiation. The energies in specified spectrum segments (excepting ultraviolet) retain systematic proportionality to each other, whatever the degree of depletion. Rather good knowledge, therefore, of the energy distribution in direct-beam sunshine near the ground can be obtained from simple whole-spectrum energy measurements. The accuracy is further improved if the relative effects of haze particles and of water vapor can be known approximately, as is possible on cloudless days, even without filters, if the quality of the atmosphere does not change.

Consider Moon's monochromatic expression for atmospheric transmission to direct-beam sunshine:

$$\tau_\lambda = [(\tau_{p\lambda})^{p/1013}(\tau_{w\lambda})^{w/20}(\tau_{d\lambda})^{d/800}]m \qquad (17.1)$$

where $\tau_{p\lambda}$ = spectral transmission factor associated with scattering by a dry atmosphere at 1013 mb pressure and with sun at zenith

$\tau_{w\lambda}$ = spectral transmission factor associated with water vapor, for 20 mm of precipitable water directly above the observer

$\tau_{d\lambda}$ = spectral transmission factor associated with haze dust, for 800 particles per cubic centimeter at the level of the observer, and with sun at zenith

p = barometric pressure, mb

w = depth of precipitable water, mm

m = optical air path ($m = \sec \theta$, where θ = zenith angle of sun, $m = 1$ for sun at zenith)

Elder and Strong[2] have found that absorption over all wavelengths in the atmospheric "windows" between strong absorption lines (see Figure 17.4, segments II, III, IV) can be well represented by an average exponential. In other words, the proper monochromatic expression needs only slight distortion to represent the integrated effect over a considerable band of frequencies. The essential problem, therefore, is arbitrarily to convert Equation (17.1) from the monochromatic into an empirical three-factor expression fitting the spectrum as a *whole*. Using the integration of Moon's monochromatic study as a model, supra exponents were found that result in the formula:

---

[1] Tait Elder and John Strong, "The Infrared Transmission of Atmospheric Windows," *J. Franklin Inst.*, vol. 255, no. 3, pp. 189–208, March, 1953.

[2] *Ibid.*

$$\frac{I}{420/r_v{}^2} = (T_pT_wT_d) = (0.915^{(pm/1013)0.75})(0.84^{(wm/20)0.6})(0.92^{(dm)0.9}) \quad (17.2a)$$

which reduces to the exponential

$$\frac{I}{420/r_v{}^2} = \exp - 0.089^{(pm/1013)0.75} - 0.174^{(wm/20)0.6} - 0.083^{(dm)0.9} \quad (17.2b)$$

where I is the incident normal solar radiation at the ground, in Btu/hr/ft^2; $r_v{}^2$ is the seasonal sun's distance factor; the T's are whole-spectrum transmission factors, and the other symbols are as defined for Equation (17.1), except that d is now considered an empirical measure of dust in the whole depth of the atmosphere. The expression gives results in close agreement with a study by Moon, as shown in Table 17.7. Figure 17.5 is a two-part alignment chart representing Equation (17.2). The left-hand part treats the first two factors T_pT_w as functions of optical air path m and the right-hand part the haze-dust factor T_d. The total transmittance

Table 17.7 Comparison of Three-factor Equation (17.2) with Moon's Calculated Whole-spectrum Transmissivity at Sea Level

Optical path m (1)	Moon's total direct-beam transm. T_{pwd} (2)	Dry-air transm. $p = 1013$ mb T_p (3)	Water-vapor transm. $w = 20$ mm T_w (4)	Haze-dust transm. $d = 1.05$ T_d (5)	Total transm. Eq. (17.2) $T_pT_wT_d$ (6)	Difference (6) − (2) (7)
0	1.0000	1.000	1.000	1.000	1.0000	0.0
1	0.7019	0.915	0.840	0.917	0.7045	+0.0026
2	0.5596	0.861	0.768	0.850	0.5620	+0.0024
3	0.4595	0.817	0.714	0.791	0.4613	+0.0018
4	0.3849	0.778	0.670	0.738	0.3847	−0.0002
5	0.3250	0.743	0.633	0.690	0.3244	−0.0006

The T's are whole-spectrum transmissivities, whereas the τ's of Equation (17.1) refer to transmissivity at a wavelength λ.

is thus the product of the transmittances found in the two graphs, and this is the intercept on the central (logarithmic scale) of the line connecting the two.

Although direct-beam sunshine is the major useful solar radiation, the brightness of the whole sky adds a significant fraction. This fraction in cloudless skies naturally comes from the radiation scattered by dry air and haze aerosols but is usually evaluated relative to direct radiation received on a horizontal surface. The radiation from the cloudless sky is about one-fifth that of direct sunshine at noon. It is easily measured by shading a recording pyrheliometer from direct-beam sunshine.

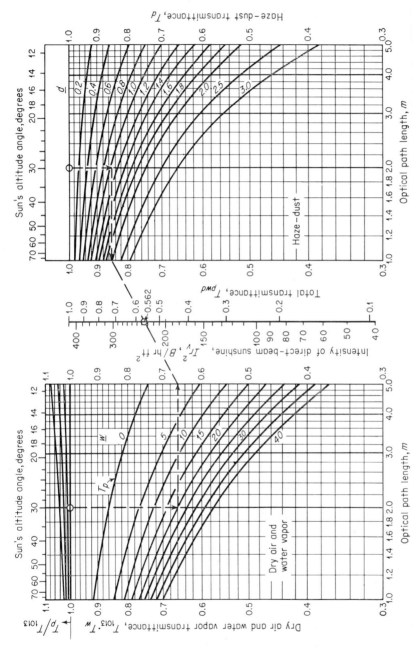

Fig. 17.5 Calculation chart for direct-beam sunshine intensity. (*University of California, Department of Agricultural Engineering, Davis, Feb. 19, 1957.*)

469

Direct Use of Solar Energy as Heat.   Solar energy may be utilized as a source of heat or as a source of power. In the typical case both uses require energy collectors and a means of energy storage. The utilization of solar energy for power also requires an energy-conversion device, such as a heat engine which will operate on a temperature difference. The necessity for storage arises because of the intermittent nature of sunshine. If intermittent operation is satisfactory, for example, in pumping water for irrigation, the storage requirement may be eliminated.

The use of solar energy for the economical generation of power is a matter of considerable difficulty, but the use of solar energy for heating offers immediate promise. A major application is to space heating. The United States may be divided into zones of maximum feasibility, engineering feasibility, and minimum feasibility for solar heating as has been done by Siple.[1] Commercial solar hot-water heaters, which represent another application of solar energy, have been available in Florida, Arizona, and California for several decades. A solar cooker consisting of an aluminum reflector, 10 sq ft in area, has been developed in India. The reflected solar energy is concentrated on the blackened bottom of a cooking utensil.

The usual flat-plate collector used for solar heating utilizes a black absorbing surface and a glass covering which is transparent to solar radiation but which reflects the heat radiated from the absorbing plate. Among the substances used for energy storage are water, crushed rock, and glauber salt (in which the heat of fusion is used).

The meteorological factors affecting solar-energy use for heating have not been widely understood and deserve consideration. Meteorologists are primarily interested in daily total solar radiation on a horizontal surface as measured now in 80 or more stations in the United States. The energy received varies greatly with season and cloudiness. Hand[2,3] has prepared a map of the average annual distribution for the past 40 years and annual curves of daily averages by the week for 35 stations.

However, those concerned with buildings, livestock outdoors, seed beds, and plants are more vitally interested in the heat received hourly in *direct-beam* and diffuse irradiation. This is because windows do not face upward, and most animals and plants have shape factors that favor broadside intake of solar radiation. Even in forests it is the direct-beam irradiation on foliage soon after sunrise that starts the daily air warming, and it is the slope of the ground relative to beam radiation that determines

[1] P. A. Siple, "Climatic Considerations of Solar Energy for Space Heating," presented at the Solar Energy Symposium, Massachusetts Institute of Technology, Cambridge, Mass., Aug. 21, 1950.

[2] I. F. Hand, "Weekly Mean Values of Daily Total Solar and Sky Radiation," *U.S. Weather Bur., Tech. Paper No. 11*, 1949.

[3] I. F. Hand, "Distribution of Solar Energy over the United States," *Heating & Ventilating*, vol. 50, p. 73, July, 1953.

to a considerable degree the character of natural vegetation. Roofs have different heat loads for slopes and shadows that vary hourly with sunshine.

Some method should be adopted for presenting hourly solar-energy data that would inherently emphasize the direct-beam aspect. Too often architects specify large glass areas facing west or east, and hand the design to air-conditioning engineers to figure the heating and cooling loads. Very little reconsideration is given to the original design even if it is discovered that the building is subject to an excessive solar-heat load.

A bad example was given an Award of Merit by the American Institute of Architects "for excellent orientation." Possibly the orientation is the best possible for the building as designed, but the excessive solar heating will plague the occupants for the many years it will take tall shade trees to grow. The building has a wide two-story lobby, with the entire east wall in glass. The concrete floor and the "washed-air" conditioning are unable to hold lobby air temperature below 90°F in the morning on clear summer days when the outside air temperature is only in the seventies. Under these conditions the offices facing east are virtually unlivable— 92°F at 8 A.M. Of course, the occupants promptly covered the windows with wrapping paper, but the best solution converted half the glass wall (the fixed portion) into an opaque mirror by applying aluminum foil. This dropped the temperature 10°F relative to identical brown-paper treatment. Glass-fiber drapes seem to have negligible effect, but judging by tests on an 8-ft cubicle, white roller shades could cut the temperature rise to about 30 per cent of that experienced with clear glass.

Many other examples of lack of "feel" for solar energy could be cited; so it is of interest to see how the concept of sky exposure long used by microclimatologists to describe conditions in deep valleys can be formalized to specify the hours of exposure and the maximum intensity of sunshine to be expected at a semienclosed spot. Dr. Pleijel[1] has slightly distorted the radial scale of the conventional monthly polar-coordinate diagram of the sun's daily path to match the vertical angles of a 360-deg camera view of the surroundings. Figure 17.6 shows how vividly this gives the time, duration of exposure, and cumulative heat input of direct-beam sunshine throughout the year in relation to nearby structures. The magnitudes shown in this example on the seven trajectories are the cumulative heat inputs, Kcal per square meter per hour, for the east-west horizontal component of direct-beam sunshine summed from zero at solar noon. With similar charts of the other components of direct-beam radiation and others including diffuse short-wave sky radiation, the building designer or agriculturist can confidently determine for any partly

[1] Gunnar Pleijel, *The Computation of Natural Radiation in Architecture and Town Planning*, Statens nämnd för byggnadsforsknig, Victor Pettersons Bokindustri Aktiebolag, Stockholm, 1954.

shaded spot the maximum and the average solar heat load to be expected in any month. Of course the hourly heat rates vary greatly with cloudiness and with local humidity and air pollution, as discussed previously. With proper control, the direct use of solar energy for heating can be of immediate, practical use over large areas of the world.

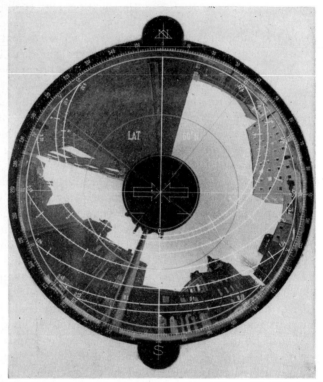

Fig. 17.6   Comparison of polar diagram at sun's position with 360° sky photograph. (*G. Pleijel.*)

Basic Considerations Regarding Solar Power.   Power can be generated from solar energy by utilizing the heat from a collector to raise the temperature of a working material and by operating a heat engine from the temperature difference obtained. The maximum efficiency of heat engines is determined by the temperature difference between the hot source and the cold source. This maximum efficiency, the Carnot cycle efficiency, equals $1 - T_2/T_1$, where T_1 is the temperature of the hot source and T_2 is the temperature of the cold source. The temperatures T_1 and T_2 are measured from absolute zero which is $-273°C$, or $-459°F$. A major problem in solar-machine development is the difficulty of obtaining a high enough T_1 and maintaining a low enough T_2 to give a useful value of efficiency. Parabolic or parabolic-cylindrical mirrors can be used to concentrate solar energy, but the expenses are large. Furthermore, problems of storage and transmission of large amounts of energy appear prohibitive at this time.

The silicon solar battery, which converts solar energy directly to electrical energy without an intermediate heat phase, is a device of great interest. At present, however, it is expensive and limited to special applications. The development of the silicon solar battery was announced in 1954 by D. M. Chapin, G. S. Fuller, and C. L. Pearson of the Bell Telephone Laboratories.[1] An efficiency of 11 per cent has been achieved. This efficiency is to be compared with 1 per cent for thermocouples, less than 0.5 per cent for photogalvanic cells, and 0.6 per cent for selenium photovoltaic cells, three previously known devices for converting solar radiation to electrical power.

The silicon solar battery is based upon action taking place at the junction between p-type silicon and n-type silicon. An n-type semiconductor is obtained by adding a very slight amount of arsenic or phosphorus to pure silicon, and a p-type semiconductor is formed by adding a very slight amount of boron or gallium. The efficiency of 11 per cent is achieved at an operating voltage of 0.45 volt with a power output of about 11 milliwatts per square centimeter.

Effect of Inclination on Fixed-plate Absorbers. Since the efficiency of a solar energy absorber increases as the input intensity per unit area increases, it is advantageous in middle and high latitudes to incline a plate absorber to face the sun as directly as possible for the season of maximum usefulness. Less diffuse radiation is received on a sloped than on a horizontal absorber unless the short-wave reflectivity of the ground in front of the absorber is high. For long-wave radiation loss, inclination will decrease the area of cold-sky "seen" by the absorber. Thus the result will be a little better than indicated by considering solar radiation alone.

For sloped surface in the summer the hour angle from solar noon to zero positive incidence is less than at sunrise and at sunset. In the winter the sun's rays always fall more directly on a sloped absorber than on a horizontal surface. These effects can be calculated and the optimum slope determined for the time of year the most energy is desired: steep slope for maximum in the winter and moderate slope for maximum energy intake in the summer (to drive an air-cooling system). It is usually adequate, however, to determine the best slope from Orendorff's[2] measurements of total direct and diffuse radiation received at 40 deg north latitude in the New York–New Jersey area. The monthly values tabulated

[1] D. M. Chapin, G. S. Fuller, and C. L. Pearson, *J. Appl. Phys.*, pp. 25–76, 1954.

[2] J. H. Orendorff, "Application of Climatic Data to House Design," U.S. Housing and Home Finance Agency, Washington, D.C., January, 1954.

from horizontal to vertical give the family of curves shown in Figure 17.7. The average values rather than clear-sky values are plotted since the solar absorber will also work during some cloudiness, and the best slope for a fixed flat absorber would be somewhat less than the optimum indicated from the cloudless-day observations. Figure 17.7 shows that the optimum slope for an absorber for using solar energy in winter should be nearly 15 deg steeper and for maximum summer utilization about 15 deg flatter than the latitude angle.

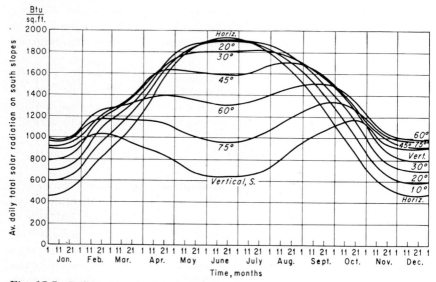

Fig. 17.7   Daily average total solar energy incident on fixed slopes at 40° N latitude in the New York–New Jersey area. (*Plotted from Orendorff tables.*)

Performance of Fixed-plate Absorbers.   The efficiency of a solar absorber depends primarily on the rate of solar radiation entering the exposed cover (or absorbed directly) and on the rate of heat loss from the same receiver surface. During tests in 1935 at Davis, California,[1] there was no local measurement of insolation, but judging now from our mid-November clear-day records, the total short-wave irradiation was probably close to 288 Btu/(hr)(sq ft) at midday on the sloped single-pane thermosiphon pipe absorber. Subtracting the 159 Btu/(hr)(sq ft) useful output and assuming no heat storage in the absorber box at 1 P.M. gives a linear over-all heat-loss coefficient U_L of about 1.95 Btu/(hr)(sq ft)(°F), which is practically the same as the 1.9 for Heywood's single-glass ab-

---

[1] F. A. Brooks, "Use of Solar Energy for Heating Water in California," *Univ. Calif., Coll. Agr. Bull.* 603, 1936.

sorber at 200 Btu/(hr)(sq ft) input. Considerable variation in U_L is to be expected with changes in wind and net thermal radiation.

Tests with the same pipe absorber in September, 1935, showed a useful heat intake of approximately 1000 Btu/(sq ft)(day), with a temperature rise of 53°F with natural thermosiphon circulation. A greater temperature rise is often wanted, and some heat loss occurs in overnight storage, which indicates a need of about 800 Btu/(gal)(day) for an 8-month period in the central valleys of California. The total insolation on the cloudless day of September 23 would have been less than our extreme records of 2140 Btu per day; so the efficiency of the fixed-pipe absorber is close to 50 per cent, which has been confirmed by Heywood and several others for the fixed-position single-glass absorbers in spite of the variability expected with wind. It is to be noted that Ward[1] recommends the same 1 sq ft per gal in Singapore, where the average maximum daily insolation is only 65 per cent of our September cloudless average, and 50 per cent is expected for a duration of 15 days.

The most feasible application of solar energy by means of fixed absorbers seems to be for combined heating and cooling with a heat-pump system. Jordan and Threlkeld[2] showed that, if some of the costs are allocated to space heating in areas of mild winters, the solar air-conditioning system should have lower operating costs than conventional space heating and refrigerating systems and, further, that the decreased first cost expected with mass production of standardized collectors and heat-storage units should make the solar heat-pump system economically feasible in the southern one-third of the United States in the near future.

Engineering design of such systems needs some method of interpreting the daily performance of different types of systems in various kinds of weather. To avoid recalculating throughout for each combination, Hottel and Whillier[3] developed a nondimensional utilizability criterion ϕ based on the statistical frequency of the difference of two ratios: one, the hourly energy totals relative to the long-term average of total hourly horizontal incidence, the other the useful threshold rate relative to the same long-term hourly average. The spread of the hourly ϕ curves increases as the threshold ratio is raised because, for a high-temperature level of operation, only hours of extra-high insolation result in useful collection.

Storage of Intermittent Solar Energy in Ponds. One of the important ways of using solar energy in low-temperature difference power

[1] G. T. Ward, "Performance of a Flat Plate Solar Heat Collector," *Inst. Mech. Engrs. (London)*, September, 1955.

[2] R. C. Jordan and J. L. Threlkeld, "Designs and Economics of Solar Energy Heat Pump Systems," *Heating, Piping, Air Conditioning*, vol. 26, pp. 122–129, February, 1954.

[3] Hottel and Whillier, *op. cit.*

plants is in a reheat cycle, as proposed by Nizery[1] for the Abidjan power plant, using cold sea water from a depth of 1380 ft. Very large rotary vacuum apparatus is involved for a 5000-kw unit, with a housing of 85 ft inside diameter. Only about 5° of the 36°F temperature difference will be used, and reheating of this amount is by solar energy falling on an isolated basin. Partly cloudy skies will not restrict operation of the plant.

An intriguing possibility in pond energy storage is reduction of heat loss by establishing maximum temperature in a layer considerably below the surface. A spectacular natural case reviewed by Bloch[2] has a temperature of 72°F at the surface, of 125°F at 7 ft, and of 72°F again at 46 ft. Such extraordinary temperature differences can persist only with an inflow of relatively fresh water on top and no wind strong enough to generate turbulence. Further, there should be a submerged layer of material that absorbs the short-wave energy transmitted through the water; the natural example of 7 ft may not be optimum. Making intentional use of this nonturbulent barrier to heat loss involves arranging a very quiet withdrawal of water in the hot layer for forced circulation through heat exchanges, or else making the heat exchanger itself the submerged surface of direct absorption of solar energy. Further investigations of this natural phenomenon seem highly desirable.

17.7 Conclusion

There is considerable spread in the estimates of world-wide power use at present, and nearly a 10 to 1 ratio among forecasts of future needs. Losses are very large in transformation of fuels to power, varying with the system used. The consumption of agricultural wastes for heat and power is poorly known. The potentialities of hydropower are the only ones that are relatively well known. Development of that perpetual resource is proceeding in spite of a slight economic advantage of fuel-burning power plants. Unfortunately the total potential hydropower is utterly inadequate for the future. Nuclear power will serve for a long time, but it is a mined resource. Eventually power must be taken from the wind and directly from sunshine. Wind power is in use now, but the concept of potential wind power per square mile needs to be developed: there are questions both of spacing of wind turbines and of threshold power output below which utilization cannot be considered.

[1] André Nizery, "Utilization of the Thermal Potential of the Sea for the Production of Power and Fresh Water," E. D. Howe (ed.), Institute of Engineering Research, University of California, Berkeley, Calif., March, 1954.

[2] M. R. Bloch, "Discussion at Solar Energy Conference," Tucson, Ariz., November, 1955, quoting from A. Defant, "Die Vertikale Verteilung von Temperatur und Salzgehalt im Weltmeere," Z. der Gesellschaft fur Erdkunde zu Berlin, pp. 28–42, Fig. 11, Saltsee von Maros-Torda, Ungarn, 1930.

The problems of optimum spacing and threshold power output apply also to development of solar power for an area. There is also the problem of providing a cold source for generating power from heat. It will probably be difficult in energy-favorable desert regions to maintain a cold source below 80°F. For a 100°F temperature difference the Carnot-cycle efficiency would be less than 20 per cent. Including absorber losses, the overall daily efficiency in converting solar radiation to mechanical or electrical power is likely to be about 10 per cent. The practical available total *power* potential of solar energy is, therefore, only about three or four times the foreseeable ultimate demand. This indicates that the most economical third or more of the total solar-energy potential must be developed by the time nuclear energy becomes limited. Avoiding the natural distribution of clouds over the earth, the ultimate power belts of the world would tend to be in the subtropics—not where the major use of energy is at present. Developing economical solar power plants capable of operating in the partly cloudy regions would therefore be very valuable.

18

Nuclear Energy

CHAUNCEY STARR

VICE PRESIDENT, NORTH AMERICAN AVIATION, INC.

GENERAL MANAGER, ATOMICS INTERNATIONAL DIVISION

18.1 The Need for Nuclear Energy

The development of nuclear energy as a natural resource is stimulated by the fundamental fact that the availability of fossil fuels, coal, oil, and gas, and of hydroelectricity appears to be sufficiently limited that within the next 100 years a serious shortage of energy from these sources will appear. Prediction of the world requirements for energy depends directly upon world economic development, which in turn depends upon such factors as the availability of energy resources, their efficiency of utilization, the technological development of the more undeveloped areas, and so many other interrelated factors that accurate analysis is literally impossible. It is possible, however, to project the trends which have been established for some time and to estimate from these the probable magnitude of future energy requirements. These requirements, of course, need to be compared with the available world resources, and these in turn are also difficult to estimate accurately. In addition to the unknowns associated with the exploration and discovery of new fossil-fuel resources, availability of such fuels is associated with their market price. Resources presently considered marginal for economic reasons will be utilized if the market price justifies their exploitation; such marginal reservoirs of energy are large in extent. In spite of the qualitative nature of such an analysis, however, it is possible to extrapolate the present rate of discovery of new resources and to determine the probable order of magnitude of the total available resources of these conventional fuels. When such estimates are compared with the estimates of world requirements, the serious nature of our energy-resource problem becomes evident.

For roughly the past 100 years the use of primary fuel in the world has grown at a rate of about 2 per cent per year. It is most likely that this usage rate will increase faster than in the past since it appears that

478

the industrialization of any part of the world results in a rapid increase in the per capita utilization of energy. If the world rate of energy consumption increases at 3 per cent per year, the estimated resources of conventional fuels will be close to exhaustion within 100 years. Additionally, there are other factors which tend to intensify this situation; for example, the world output of coal has been increasing at a rate of only $\frac{1}{2}$ per cent per year, which is clearly insufficient to maintain the pace set by the world's needs. Undoubtedly, a continuous increase in the market price of coal would stimulate the marginal mining of this resource, and such a price increase would undoubtedly occur if no other energy source became available.

An additional and vital factor is that there are many forms of energy utilization for which hydrocarbon fuels are at present the only suitable raw materials. One might cite, for example, the airplane or the automobile. Further, hydrocarbon fuels are being used more and more as raw materials for the chemical industry and, in fact, have become an essential resource for other than energy purposes. These specialized applications for which hydrocarbons are best suited will become increasingly important and will further stimulate the development of other energy resources.

With this background picture of future energy requirements, the potential attractiveness of nuclear energy is evident. If available in sufficient quantities, it must become an essential supplement to hydropower and fossil fuels. However, in view of the many decades which must transpire before this problem becomes pressing, one might well inquire as to the necessity for consideration now of nuclear-power development. The answer is associated with the working lifetime of power-generation equipment—what the scientist might call the "time constant" of the problem.

At present, central-station power equipment is expected to serve usefully for at least 30 years. In view of the rapid rate at which power-generation capacity is being added—in the United States capacity doubles every 10 years—nuclear-power stations must be placed in use soon, in order that nuclear fuels may be a significant contributor to power generation decades hence.

The availability of nuclear fuels is clearly a key consideration in such a long-range program. In order to understand the factors involved, it is desirable to consider the physical process of atomic-power generation.

18.2 Nature of Nuclear-energy Process

Atomic energy arises from the splitting or "fission" of certain heavy atoms, such as uranium, by neutrons. In the process of such splitting a considerable amount of energy is released, which can be converted into heat for either explosive or power purposes. The naturally occurring element uranium contains the isotopes U^{235} and U^{238} in the proportion 1 to 140. The U^{238}, which makes up the bulk of the natural element, does not have the characteristic of being easily fissionable, as does U^{235}. However, in a nuclear reactor the neutrons resulting from the fission of the fuel (U^{235}) can convert the U^{238} into the artificial element plutonium (Pu^{239}), which is easily fissionable. In addition, the element thorium (Th^{232}) may similarly be converted in a nuclear reactor to U^{233}, which is also easily fissionable. There exist then three useful fissionable materials:

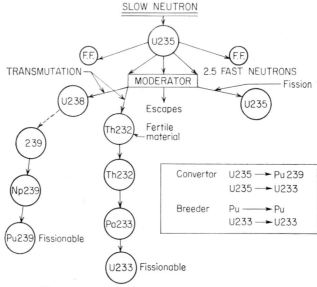

Fig. 18.1   Reaction sequence in nuclear reactor.

U^{235}, derived from natural uranium, and the two manufactured elements Pu^{239} and U^{233}.

Figure 18.1 shows the sequence of phenomena that occur in a nuclear reactor. A "slow" or "thermal" neutron enters a U^{235} nucleus, causing the nucleus to become unstable and to fission. The "fragments" of the nucleus fly out with most of the kinetic energy produced. Gamma radiation and several fast neutrons are also emitted. These latter are slowed down by collisions in a substance called a *moderator*. One of these slowed neutrons strikes another U^{235} nucleus and serves to keep the chain reaction going by fission. The remaining neutrons may leak out of the assembly, or they may be absorbed in U^{238} or thorium, converting these "fertile" materials to Pu^{239} or U^{233}, respectively.

During the operation of the fission-chain reaction, much radiation is emitted. This is illustrated in Figure 18.2. Some radiation is emitted at the time of fission, some later by the radioactive fission fragments. Further, some of the neutrons produced can be absorbed in many ordinary elements to produce radioactive isotopes. This artificial radioactivity has a wide variety of applications, some of which are listed.

The complete fissioning of 1 kg (2.2 lb) of uranium will produce energy equivalent to that produced by 20,000 tons of TNT, or 3300 tons of coal. This is approximately 7.8×10^{10} Btu, or 2.3×10^7 kwhr. The startling

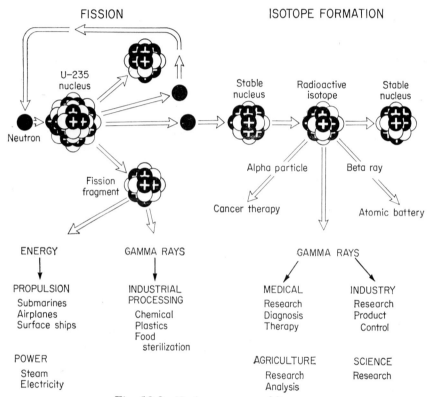

Fig. 18.2 Nuclear energy and its uses.

compactness of nuclear fuels is best illustrated in Figure 18.3, which gives the volumes of various fuels for equivalent energy production. The small volume of nuclear fuels is dramatic, but unfortunately hard to benefit from in practice. The surface area and volume required for heat removal are so large that this engineering factor determines the size of most reactors. Further, the heavy shielding required to protect personnel from the radiation produced further increases the bulk of material associated with the reactor. Nevertheless, the compactness of the fuel can best be illustrated by the fact that to duplicate the output of Hoover Dam an electrical power plant would only fission (or use up) 10 lb of uranium per day.

As a practical matter, it should be emphasized that, because of the existence of so-called "side" reactions (nonuseful absorption of neutrons by uranium), only about 85 per cent of the U^{235} atoms exposed to neutrons will fission. The remainder become nonuseful isotopes.

During the operation of a nuclear reactor containing both a fissionable "fuel," such as U^{235}, and a "fertile" material, such as U^{238}, or thorium, the process of "conversion" takes place. Assume that, for every atom of U^{235} fissioned, x atoms of new fuel (plutonium or U^{233}) are formed by the absorption of neutrons in the fertile material. If utilized in the reactor as fuel, these new atoms are eventually fissioned and produce energy. Assume that each of the new atoms in turn produces y atoms; thus, xy new atoms are formed for each original starting atom. If the process of

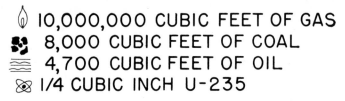

10,000,000 CUBIC FEET OF GAS
8,000 CUBIC FEET OF COAL
4,700 CUBIC FEET OF OIL
1/4 CUBIC INCH U-235

ALL PRODUCE AN EQUAL AMOUNT OF ENERGY

Fig. 18.3   Comparison of energy produced in various forms.

conversion is continued indefinitely, for each atom of original fuel (U^{235}) that is fissioned, the total energy produced comes from

$$1 + x(1 + y + y^2 + \cdots) = 1 + x\,\frac{1}{1 - y}, \text{ where } y < 1$$

fissionable atoms. The conversion process thus multiplies the original energy available in the fuel by manufacturing additional fuel.

Practical conversion ratios (atoms formed per atoms destroyed) for mixtures of U^{235} and U^{238} or thorium may range from 0.7 to somewhat more than 1. Plutonium as a fuel can permit somewhat greater conversion since it produces more neutrons per fission (3) than U^{235} (2.5). Obviously, if the conversion ratio is 1 or greater, the system is self-sustaining and power can be produced indefinitely as long as fertile material (U^{238} or thorium) is supplied. Under such circumstances the initial loading of U^{235} eventually disappears and the sustaining fuel is the artificial element (plutonium or U^{233}) manufactured in the reactor. Such self-sustaining systems are called *breeders*. If the breeding ratio is greater than unity, an excess of fissionable material is produced and can be utilized in other reactors, or stored.

The essential aspect of this short review that is of interest in this discussion is that the "converter" type of reactor not only utilizes the original fuel supplied, but also greatly multiplies the energy available by utilizing the fertile material present. The converter requires a source of fuel, however (either isotope-separation plants or other reactors), to keep it going. As the conversion ratio increases, the self-sustaining "breeder" is reached, and if the breeding ratio is greater than unity, a surplus of fuel is produced.

In evaluating the economics of electrical power produced from atomic-energy plants, it is necessary to consider the complete complex of facilities which are associated with the operation of the nuclear reactor. The natural uranium supply either can be fed into an isotope-separation plant to produce various enrichments of U^{235} or can be fed directly into nuclear reactors for the production of plutonium. Nuclear reactors can be designed to operate on uranium of various enrichments, from natural uranium up to highly purified U^{235}. In such reactors the U^{235} in the process of being fissioned, or "burned," produces both power and neutrons. In the natural or low-enrichment reactors the unseparated U^{238} inevitably captures many of these neutrons and produces plutonium, so that these reactors can have two useful products, power and plutonium. In the highly enriched machines the neutrons may be captured in any fertile material purposely placed in the reactor, as described above.

The natural or low-enrichment uranium reactors depend upon the existence of isotope-separation plants for a reasonable utilization of the U^{235} in our natural resources. For various technical reasons, the breeding ratio for the manufacture of plutonium in such reactors is not sufficiently great to permit a self-sustaining system. In comparison, the high-enrichment breeder reactors require the isotope-separation plants only for their initial charge of fuel. Once started, they supply their own fuel for continued operation and no longer depend on the isotope-separation plants.

18.3 Description of Nuclear Reactors

The essential components of a nuclear-power reactor are the core (or critical assembly), the heat-transfer system, the radiation shielding, and the instrumentation and control system. Figures 18.4 to 18.8 show the sequence of assembly of a typical reactor.

The core consists of the fissionable fuel, the structural materials required to support the fuel, and in "thermal" reactors, a material called the *moderator* whose function it is to slow down the high-velocity fission neutrons to a thermal-energy level at which they are more easily absorbed by the fuel. A "reflector" usually surrounds the core in order to scatter back into the core some of the neutrons which travel or "leak" out. Reactors which have no moderator are called *fast reactors* because of the speed at which the fission neutrons travel. Reactors are also classed as *homogeneous* or *heterogeneous*, depending on whether the fuel and the moderating material are combined in a homogeneous mixture or are arranged as discrete bodies. An example of a homogeneous reactor is the solution type whose core might consist of fuel in the form of a uranium salt dissolved in a moderator such as distilled water. A heterogeneous core might consist of individual metal fuel slugs immersed in a liquid moderator or encased in blocks of a solid moderating material.

The reactor-core assembly contains fissionable material and a moderator of just the proper quantity and dimension to support a continuous-

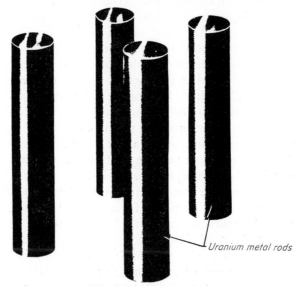

Uranium metal rods

Fig. 18.4 Reactor fuel.

chain nuclear reaction. The core assembly must be such that the fission neutrons produced are of sufficient number to continue the fission process and to provide for the numbers lost from the assembly by leakage or by nonfission absorption. A fraction of the neutrons produced is continually being absorbed by the fuel, which then fissions and produces sufficient neutrons to maintain the neutron numbers in the core.

The fission fragments are ejected from the original uranium atom with extremely high velocities. These fragments collide and rebound from the atoms of the surrounding material, and with each collision they give up some of their kinetic energy to the surrounding material. As the kinetic energy is absorbed by the surrounding atoms, it appears as heat. After their birth the fission fragments are radioactive, and the radioactivity given off continues to result in the production of heat as it is absorbed in

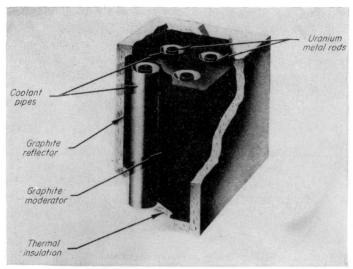

Fig. 18.5 Reactor core assembly.

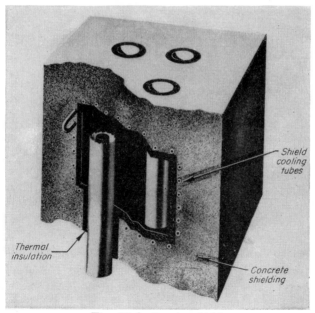

Fig. 18.6 Reactor shield.

the surrounding material. About 83 per cent of the total heat generated is the result of slowing down and stopping the fission fragments, 11 per cent of the heat is that associated with absorbing the radiation from the fission fragments, and the remaining 6 per cent is produced by absorption of the kinetic energy of the neutrons and by the absorption of gamma-ray energy produced at the instant of fission.

The energy represented by the motion of the fission fragments and neutrons and by the radiation released by fission-fragment decay results

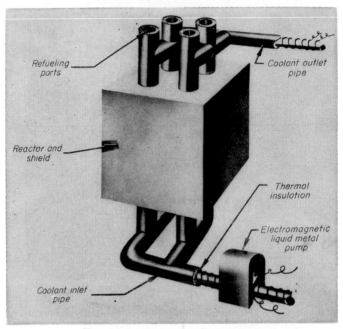

Refueling parts

Coolant outlet pipe

Reactor and shield

Thermal insulation

Electromagnetic liquid metal pump

Coolant inlet pipe

Fig. 18.7   Reactor cooling system.

from the conversion of some of the mass of the original U^{235} nucleus. This conversion from nuclear mass to kinetic energy is indicated by the fact that the sum of the masses of the original U^{235} nucleus and the captured neutron which caused the fission is greater than the masses of the fission fragments and fission neutrons. The difference in mass is equivalent to the energy released. Einstein's theory predicted over 50 years ago that such a process should be possible. It has taken these years to discover the neutron and the fission process and to learn how to apply them in a nuclear reactor.

In order to remove the heat energy produced, a circulating coolant is required. This can be a gas or a liquid. Gases considered in the past include air, carbon dioxide, and helium. Liquids may be water or organic

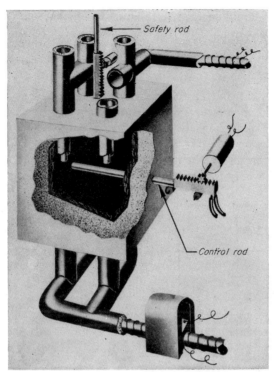

Fig. 18.8 Reactor control system.

Choices to be made in reactor design					
Fuel	Fertile material	Neutron energy	Coolant	Geometry	Moderator
U^{233}	Th	Fast	Gas	Heterogeneous	H_2O
U^{235}	U	Intermediate	Liquid metal	Homogeneous	D_2O
Pu^{239}		Slow	H_2O		Be
			D_2O		BeO
			Hydrocarbons		C
			Etc.		Etc.

Fig. 18.9 Reactor-design variables.

compounds or liquid metals. A table showing the combinations which might be utilized in reactor design is shown in Figure 18.9. Of the hundreds of combinations that can be arranged, only about a dozen are presently feasible, and these are undergoing development in various parts of the world.

Heat extracted from the nuclear reactor by the coolant stream may be used to produce steam, and this steam then produces power by conventional means. This is shown in Figure 18.10. No practical way of producing useful power by direct conversion of nuclear energy to electricity has yet been found. As a result, the nuclear reactor and its coolant system are a replacement for only the boiler portion of the conventional plant.

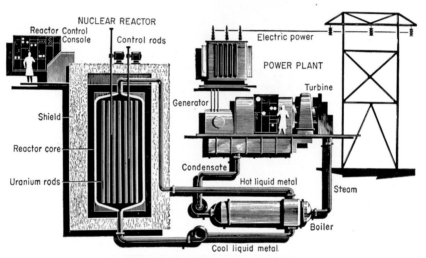

Fig. 18.10 Nuclear-power plant.

In considering the industrial complex of which the nuclear reactor is a part, it is essential to include isotope-separation plants which are utilized to separate U^{235} from natural uranium. U^{235} makes up 0.71 per cent of natural uranium. Many reactors can operate on natural uranium, but many require some enrichment of the U^{235} concentration. Further, uranium fuel must be removed from the reactor and reprocessed before most of the U^{235} content of the fuel has been used up. The depleted fuel is sent to an isotope-separation plant for reenrichment. In the United States, isotope separation is accomplished by a gas-diffusion process. The flow chart for this complex interconnection between the reactor and diffusion plant is shown in Figure 18.11.

In spite of the complex processing cycle that nuclear fuels must undergo, in comparison with fossil fuels, their cost is not excessive. Natural uranium and thorium metal are available from the United States government at about $20 a pound. Uranium enriched in U^{235} to 90 per cent is presently available at $17 per gram of U^{235} contained. At these prices the fuel costs in present nuclear reactors will be about the same as fossil fuels. As reprocessing improves, and as utilization by breeding is further developed, these costs should drop. At present nuclear power is about 1.5 times as costly as conventional power, but considering the infancy of the technology, it will undoubtedly become competitive.

In a nonmilitary economy, power becomes the principal objective, and plutonium manufacture has only an industrial market as an atomic

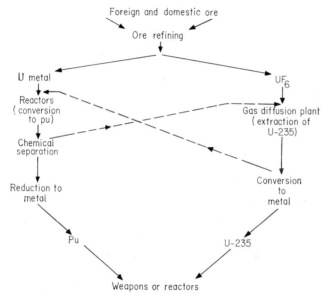

Fig. 18.11   Fuel-processing flow chart.

fuel. For complete utilization of our resources, the very long-term energy requirements would make it desirable to operate the breeder type of plant.

In fact, the existence of atomic-power breeders with a breeding ratio of unity (just self-sustaining) would be sufficient greatly to increase the uranium resources available by raising the permissible price for natural uranium. Consider the price the breeder plant would be willing to pay the miner for expanded ore supplies. Assume, for example, that a cost of 0.3 mil per kilowatthour was permissible for the feed material to a breeder plant. As 1 g of completely utilized natural uranium produces 23,000 kwhr of heat, or roughly 7000 kwhr of electricity, it would be permissible to pay $7000 \times 3 \times 10^{-4} = \$2.10$ per gram. This is $950 per pound and is several magnitudes greater than present costs. A similar case would undoubtedly exist for the thorium reserve.

The situation of the "converter" in the nonmilitary power economy is not unlike that of the self-sustaining breeder, although the converter is not quite as desirable. One can assume that a multiplication of the initial fuel by a factor of 10 or more is reasonable. Let us, for example, assume a multiplication of 14. Then the cost per kilowatthour of the fuel fed to the converter plant would be a factor of 10 greater than that in the breeder, as only one-tenth of the total supply is utilized. But if the price of natural uranium is less than \$95 per pound (one-tenth of the price assumed above), the contribution to the cost of power still does not exceed the 0.3 mil per kilowatthour used in the breeder example. Therefore, when the cost of natural uranium is as low as it undoubtedly is at present, the converter can produce power at costs that may be quite competitive with that from the self-sustaining breeder.

The economically available uranium resources are therefore expendable by large factors as an approach is made to good neutron economy in converters or breeders. This dynamic relationship between our fissionable material resources and the nuclear performance of power reactors is similar to the existent relationship between the availability of hydrocarbon fuels and the thermal efficiency of conventional plants.

18.4 Natural Resources

Before the advent of atomic energy, metallic uranium had little practical value. Uranium ores were mined in Africa, in Canada, and in Colorado primarily to obtain other elements such as radium which occurred with the uranium. Although uranium is generally considered to be rare, it actually makes up about four-parts per million of the earth's crust and is more abundant than such metals as cadmium, mercury, and silver. Its apparent scarcity and high cost are due to the fact that it is usually present in such low concentrations that its extraction is difficult.

Uranium is found in a variety of minerals, the two most important of which are pitchblende and carnotite. Pitchblende is found mostly in Canada and the Belgian Congo; smaller deposits are located in Czechoslovakia. Pitchblende is classed by geologists as a primary mineral, meaning that it was formed by heated solutions coming up from deep within the earth. Its composition varies, but it is essentially an impure uranium oxide. It is by far the richest of the uranium minerals, containing 1 to 10 per cent uranium.

Carnotite is classed as a secondary mineral, which means that it was formed by changes in a primary mineral brought about by weathering, ground waters, and other natural processes. Carnotite has been mined for many years on the Colorado plateau as a source of vanadium, radium, and uranium. It is less valuable than pitchblende, having a uranium concentration of 0.1 to 1 per cent, but is still economically important.

World areas having known deposits are shown in Figure 18.12. The extent of the world's uranium resources is only partially known. Vast portions of the geologically interesting areas of the world are relatively unexplored as yet. Even in those countries where active prospecting has been encouraged, only partial exploration has been accomplished. Nevertheless, it is possible to make judicious guesses based upon the information available.

The richest pitchblende ores (1 to 10 per cent uranium) may exist throughout the world to the extent of 500,000 tons of uranium. The less rich carnotites (0.1 to 1 per cent) are probably available throughout the

Fig. 18.12 World distribution of uranium and thorium.

world to the extent of perhaps 5 million tons of uranium. About ten times as much, 50 million tons, could probably be obtained from marginal sources with concentrations in the range of 0.01 to 0.1 per cent, such as oil shales, phosphate beds, and mine tailings. These sources are presently being partially tapped.

The cost of the uranium, of course, increases in proportion to the decrease in ore concentration. Starting with pitchblendes at roughly $5 a pound for U_3O_8 concentrate, the costs range for carnotites up to roughly $15 a pound, with the bulk of present production averaging about $10 a pound. The cost of uranium from low-concentration sources (0.01 to 0.1 per cent) may range up to $50 a pound, although some lower-cost production can be achieved from these sources as by-product output. For example, 10 million tons of commercial phosphate fertilizer is mined annually in the United States; at 0.01 per cent concentration, 1000 tons of by-product uranium might be produced annually.

A very conservative comparison of the world's economically recoverable nuclear fuels with the fossil fuels is shown in Figure 18.13. This comparison may underestimate the availability of nuclear fuels because of the limited explorations conducted to date.

An interesting study was conducted by Brown, Silver, et al., on the cost of recovering uranium and thorium from ordinary igneous rock granite. Average granite has a uranium concentration of 4 ppm (0.0004

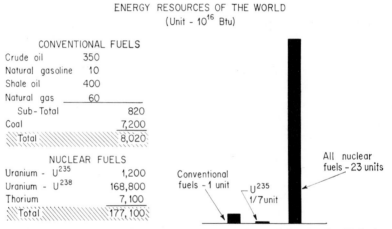

Fig. 18.13   World energy resources in units of 10^{16} Btu. (*J. W. Landis, U.S. Atomic Energy Commission, Conference Paper, AIEE Summer General Meeting, Atlantic City, June,* 1953.)

per cent) and a thorium concentration of 12 ppm (0.0012 per cent). The energy content of these materials, assuming complete fissioning, is equivalent to 50 tons of coal per ton of rock. However, only about one-fifth of the ores is reasonably recoverable, so that in a practical sense, 1 ton of granite is equivalent to about 10 tons of coal.

The cost of production from such rock of the uranium and thorium is, of course, extremely high. Brown and Silver estimated that uranium concentrate from this average granite might range in cost from $270 to $600 a pound and the accompanying thorium from $90 to $200 a pound. Although such costs are a magnitude greater than the costs of ore today, under the special circumstances of complete utilization of uranium and thorium in a reactor system, the above high costs might be acceptable. Under such circumstances the extent of the world's uranium and thorium resources is fantastically increased.

18.5   Thorium in the Atomic-energy Program

Although it is known that thorium is present in the earth's crust in about three times the amount of uranium, few economically workable deposits have been found. The only important thorium ore is monazite sand which has been found in significant amounts in India, Brazil, Africa, the Ural Mountains, and the Scandinavian peninsula. In the United States, small but workable deposits are located in North and South Carolina, Florida, Oregon, Idaho, and California. In the latter two states, gold-dredging operations are potential sources of monazite.

The use of thorium as a nuclear fuel for the production of atomic energy has been an ever-present possibility since the early days of development of the nuclear field. Because thorium is not significantly fissionable, it cannot be used by itself, and so no military requirement for it was ever established. For this reason the original emphasis in atomic-energy work was placed on the utilization of uranium, and in particular the uranium isotope U^{235} which is easily fissionable. However, thorium and U^{238} are both very satisfactory fertile materials and when exposed to neutrons in a nuclear reactor will produce artificial nuclear fuels. As was indicated earlier, U^{238} when exposed to the slow neutrons produced by the fission of U^{235} in a nuclear reactor will absorb some of these slow neutrons and by a process of radioactive decay become Pu^{239}. Similarly, Th^{232} will absorb slow neutrons and by a process of radioactive decay produce the artificial element U^{233}.

Both Pu^{239} and U^{233} are easily fissionable with the slow neutrons which are produced in so-called thermal reactors. However, in this respect they are not of equal value. The result of a capture of a neutron by a fissionable nucleus is sometimes the production of a heavier nucleus and sometimes fission. The three fissionable nuclei U^{233}, U^{235}, and plutonium differ in their characteristics in this regard.

When U^{235} is utilized in a thermal reactor, approximately 2.1 slow neutrons are produced for each neutron absorbed by the U^{235}. When plutonium is used in a thermal reactor, about 2.0 slow neutrons are produced for each neutron absorbed by the plutonium. Finally, when U^{233} is used in a thermal reactor, 2.3 slow neutrons are produced for every neutron absorbed by the U^{233}.

As the slow neutrons produced in the fission process can be absorbed by the fertile material present, either U^{238} or thorium, for the production of new fissionable material, it is evident that the differences in the number of slow neutrons which are available from different nuclear fuels can be significant. In the operation of a nuclear reactor, the number of atoms of fissionable material which are produced for each atom which disappears is called the *conversion ratio*. Because of the above inherent characteristics of the nuclear fuels, the conversion ratio in a thermal reactor for a system which depends on thorium and U^{233} is significantly greater than that which depends on U^{238}, plutonium, and U^{235}. Plutonium does become an advantageous material when utilized in the so-called "fast reactor" or "fast breeder," which is one of the nuclear-power plants presently under development.

In addition to the nuclear advantages of the Th-U^{233} system, there are other physical characteristics which make it desirable. Uranium metal undergoes a phase transition at 1220°F, which at the present time limits its performance to this temperature. In addition, uranium has a complicated crystal structure which is thermodynamically unstable under radiation conditions and may result in considerable distortion of uranium metal during its use. In contrast with this, thorium may be utilized up to temperatures as high as 2000°F because of the absence of phase transitions and because its simple cubic crystal structure does not undergo any serious distortion due to radiation. Because of these characteristics, the thorium-base fuel elements in a reactor could be operated at higher temperatures and thus produce greater power per fuel element and could remain in the nuclear reactor for a longer period of time.

In thermal reactors which utilize slightly enriched uranium or, alternatively, can be fueled with a Th-U^{233} combination, thorium fuels may have a processing advantage. In order to reprocess the slightly enriched uranium fuel, chemical separation of the fission products and by-product plutonium must be performed and, in addition, the depleted uranium will probably require reenrichment by means of a gas-diffusion plant. In the case of the Th-U^{233} fuel only the chemical processing is required since the initial U^{235} required to start this system is directly added in a highly enriched form. Further, the thorium system could become self-sustaining from the point of view of nuclear fuel, because of the improved nuclear properties of U^{233}, whereas such a situation is not likely to be achieved with slightly enriched uranium fuels.

An additional factor which might make the Th-U^{233} system more desirable is that this system produces U^{233} rather than plutonium as a by-product. While both of these materials are alpha emitters and require special handling to prevent human ingestion, the maximum permissible air-borne concentrations are considerably greater for U^{233} than they are for plutonium. For this reason, the cost of handling the Th-U^{233} fuel should be somewhat less than that of handling the slightly enriched uranium fuel.

It may be of interest to examine the relative characteristics of uranium and thorium fuels in a practical atomic-power plant, such as the Sodium Graphite Reactor presently being developed for the Atomic Energy Commission. In this plant, operation with uranium requires an enrichment to 1.8 per cent U^{235} and with thorium it requires 3.7 per cent U^{235}. For the same amount of heat produced, only 0.4 as much weight of thorium metal is required as would be needed with the uranium loading. However, the enrichment to 1.8 per cent of the uranium fuel can be accomplished by partial enrichment of natural uranium in an isotope-separation plant. In contrast with this, the production of highly enriched U^{235} for addition to the thorium fuel requires almost complete isotope separation. For this reason, the inventory of U^{235} is 1.5 times as costly with the thorium-fueled plant as with the uranium-fueled plant.

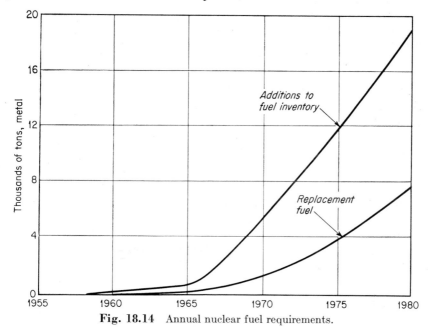

Fig. 18.14   Annual nuclear fuel requirements.

However, because of the higher nuclear conversion ratio and the longer lifetime of the nuclear fuel in the reactor, the operating fuel costs of the thorium-loaded plant should be appreciably less than that of the uranium-loaded plant.

With either the thorium system or the uranium system, the initial start-up of the plant uses U^{235} as the original fissionable material, and both systems require about the same amount initially. For this reason, as long as the rate of start-up of new nuclear-power plants is large compared with the number which have established steady operation, the demands for natural uranium as a feed for the isotope-enrichment process will continue. This is best illustrated by Figure 18.14 which indicates the projected annual requirements of the United States for nuclear fuels for central-station power plants. This projection is based upon a reasonably conservative estimate of the rate of construction and development of these large nuclear plants. As is indicated in the figure, assuming a reasonable rate of acceptance of nuclear-power plants by the power industry, the addition to fuel inventory due to the start-up of new plants is much greater than that required for fuel replacement in steady operating nuclear plants.

It is evident that it will be many decades before the thorium requirement for atomic-power plants approaches the magnitude of the uranium requirement. Further, because of the complexity and uncertainty associated with many of the economic factors which presently appear to put thorium in a favorable light, actual operating experience will be necessary for the evaluation of the economic merit of the thorium fuel system.

18.6   Resources of the United States

For the purposes of this discussion we will assume that 5 million tons of uranium will eventually be available as a resource to the United States at reasonable costs. It can also be assumed that a significant quantity of thorium could be made available, if desired, although very little is known about this subject. If complete fissioning of the above 5 million tons were possible, the total energy released would be about 100,000 trillion kwhr (1 trillion $= 10^{12}$). If only the U^{235} content is fissioned, 720 trillion kwhr would be available—about 600 times the present annual energy requirement of the United States.

In considering the energy problem in the United States, any estimate of the total reserve of conventional fuel resources must recognize that there is a major difference between the economically recoverable fuels and the total geologic reserves. Assuming that economically recoverable coal may be only one-tenth to one-fifth of the geologic reserve, this economically recoverable amount would produce roughly 2500 trillion kwhr of energy. In the case of petroleum, it appears that a potential reserve of over 100 billion bbl may be considered as economically recoverable, and this would produce about 200 trillion kwhr. The estimated reserve for natural gas is about 400 trillion cu ft, and this in turn would produce about 120 trillion kwhr. Figure 18.15 illustrates the relative magnitudes of the energy resources discussed above. It appears that the assumed available uranium resource is about ten times as great as that of coal as a potential energy resource.

The total energy requirement of the United States from 1950 on has been projected in Figure 18.15 on the basis that the present rate of increase of the consumers' energy demand appears to be about 50 per cent in 25 years and that, in addition, energy will be required to convert one type of fuel to another, for example, coal to oil or electricity. This results in roughly doubling every 25 years the total basic energy production rate required to satisfy the projected demand, an increase of 2.8 per cent per year.

The past increases in electrical power capacity in the United States indicate that the rate of electrical power generation has doubled every 15 years, equivalent to a power increase of 4.7 per cent per year. Present rates indicate doubling every 10 years, an increase of 7.2 per cent per year.

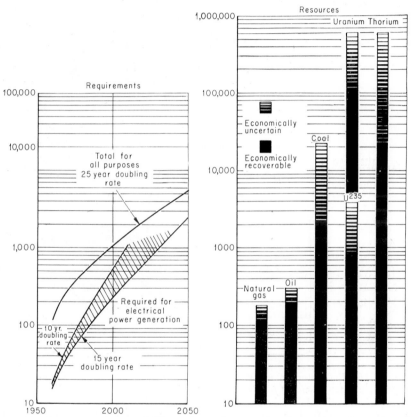

Fig. 18.15   Projected United States thermal energy requirements and resources in units of trillion Kwhr (10^{12} kwhr).

If these rates are projected into the future, it appears that after the next 50 years the above projected total energy requirement and the increase in electrical power output are not compatible; the electrical power requirement exceeds the estimated total energy demand, see Figure 18.15. Without attempting to reconcile this difference in detail, it is not unreasonable to believe that at some future time the increase in the rate of electrical power generation will tend to taper off as a greater fraction of our energy requirement is utilized in the form of electrical power.

The integrated projected requirement from 1950 on is shown in Figure
18.15 for comparison with the estimated reserves. Assuming that the projected total energy requirement and the energy requirement for electrical
power are significant, it appears that the United States has fossil-fuel
reserves (primarily coal) to satisfy the needs for the next 100 years. It
is also evident, however, that in the not too distant future the more

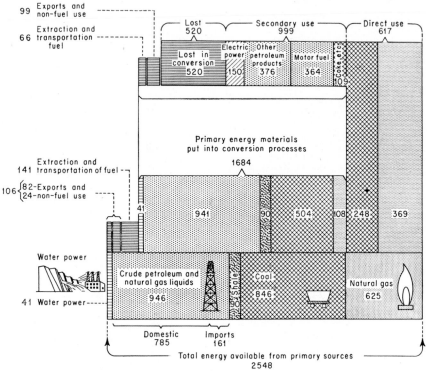

Fig. 18.16 Estimated energy flow in 1975 in millions of short tons of bituminous
coal equivalent. (*Resources for Freedom, vol.* 1, 1952.)

expensive fossil-fuel resources will begin to be tapped, with an associated
increase in cost.

An interesting study of the energy future of the United States was made
by the President's Material Policy Commission in 1952 and reported in
Resources for Freedom. Figure 18.16 which was taken from this report,
shows the hypothetical distribution of energy in the United States in 1975.
This is based upon an assumed 3 per cent per year increase in energy
consumption. It is of interest to note that electrical power is only a small
part of the projected energy demand. This analysis did not include the
availability of nuclear energy, which could contribute to the electrical
and heat requirements. A significant feature of this picture is that the

basic needs for hydrocarbons which cannot be eliminated by nuclear power are likely to be about a third of the total.

If any consideration is given to conserving our fossil fuels for future generations, the need for initiating the extensive use of nuclear power becomes more pressing. In about 50 years it might conceivably be most desirable if the major portion of our electricity and heat for cities was supplied by central-station nuclear-power plants. This would preserve our fossil-fuel resources for mobile power (automobiles, trains, small ships, and airplanes) and raw material for the chemical industry.

It is possible of course that, in addition to the renewable hydrocarbon resources represented by our forests, the synthetic manufacture of hydrocarbons will have been developed. Conversions of this type would inevitably create a new energy demand, but might be necessary to produce the raw materials for our chemical industry. One can only speculate on the nature of a society without fossil fuels available at reasonable cost.

In view of these future problems which may arise if the development of nuclear power is delayed, and considering the long time constant of the power industry, it would appear wise for the United States to pursue the present development of nuclear power as a long-range national program.

19

Economics and Policies of Resource Conservation

S. V. CIRIACY-WANTRUP

PROFESSOR OF AGRICULTURAL ECONOMICS
UNIVERSITY OF CALIFORNIA, BERKELEY

19.1 The Economic Meaning of Resource Conservation

In this country, the word *conservation* when applied to natural resources has become a magic formula in the political process. Its power in rallying support for a public policy or a private interest and in weakening opposition is equaled by few and surpassed by none—except possibly the word *democracy* itself. Political power of this kind is derived from an appeal to emotion rather than to the intellect. Such an appeal suggests that there is a genuine deeply felt public need which finds expression in the word, but also that the meaning of the word is not clearly defined. If an attempt is made here to define the economic meaning of conservation, the intent is not to weaken its emotional appeal but to restrain its abuse in the political process and to increase its usefulness for economic understanding.

Generally, conservation is regarded more as a subject of the natural sciences or the domain of the idealist and the politician than as a vital and theoretically interesting subject of economics. To this, someone might reply that the economic meaning of conservation is of no concern to the conservation movement and that economics as a discipline may well discard the concept conservation and find a more neutral substitute. Such parting of the ways is, of course, feasible but not helpful. Whether they like it or not, the interest of the conservationist and the economist is directed at the same problem, or more precisely, the essential problem of the former looms also large among the problems of the latter. This problem is the concern for the future—the relation of past and present to future use of natural resources. Hence, a semantic bridge between the conservation movement and economics would seem more helpful than strengthening the existing semantic barrier. In the absence of such a bridge, the word

500

conservation will continue to be used for obtaining political support for policy objectives which in their effects upon natural resources are frequently not understood. Conservation has lent support to contradictory objectives such as "breaking of monopoly," "eliminating wastes of competition," "socialization of resources," "private ownership of resources," "birth control to ease population pressure on resources," and "population increase for resource development."

There is fairly general agreement that conservation by itself does not mean nonuse. Conservation in this sense would be meaningless both for nonrenewable or "stock" resources such as oil, coal, and metal ores and for renewable or "flow" resources such as solar and other radiation, precipitation, animals, plants, and scenery. If nonuse were adopted as an objective of conservation policy, the "conserved" portion of the environment would merely be eliminated from the list of resources.

Most definitions of conservation, therefore, are in terms of use. By some, conservation is defined as "continuous," "constant," or "sustained" use; by others, "as the greatest use to the greatest number over the greatest length of time"; and by still others, simply as "wise" use. Such definitions may enhance the emotional appeal of conservation, but they add little to understanding. It is of interest here, however, that these definitions and the many books and papers in which they are presented have one common characteristic. They are concerned with the future use of natural resources —whether the emphasis is on oil and metal ores or on water and wilderness areas. Nearly always, the stimulus for this concern comes from the experience with past and present use.

Economics is concerned with the relations between human wants and the means to satisfy them—especially with the limitations of means. Economics is the study of choosing between alternative courses of action to deal with "scarcity." Such study is based on understanding past choices by individuals and social groups but looks toward the future in order to predict or to plan. Economics has a Janus face. In such an *ex post* and *ex ante* study of choosing, alternatives involving time must be considered. The choice between use of natural resources at different times and the relation between past, present, and future use of natural resources —the concern of the conservation movement—are, therefore, highly significant economic problems. Thus, the concept conservation is tied to a particular aspect of the use of natural resources: its intertemporal distribution. Conservation is concerned with the *when* of use.

More specifically, "conservation" and its logical corollary but economic opposite "depletion" are defined in terms of *changes* in the intertemporal distribution of resource use. Such changes imply comparison of two or more alternative time distributions of resource use, that is, interrelated series of "rates of use" occurring at different "intervals" of time.

A rate of use is the first derivative of cumulative use with respect to time. In order to avoid cumbersome language, the term *use* will be employed here in this sense. Use is measured in physical units, for example, tons, calories, acre-feet, kilowatthours, and man-days.

The term *interval* has a special meaning in time economics. It is defined as that extent of time within which changes of use and of other economic variables can be neglected in the analysis. The actual clock-time extent of an interval may be a day, a week, a month, a year, or a number of years according to the nature of the economic problem to be solved. For example, in the pumping of an oil well, use may be planned by the week or month; in wheat production, the interval is determined by the seasons; in hog production, it is the time required for breeding and fattening; and in forestry, a cutting cycle may extend over decades.

We may compare (*ex post*) actual time distributions of use during different periods of history or in different geographic locations. Or we may compare (*ex ante*) hypothetical time distributions through economic calculation. In either comparison a change from one time distribution to another is called *conservation* if the redistribution is in the direction of the future and *depletion* if the redistribution is in the direction of the present.

The terms *in the direction of the future* and *in the direction of the present* could be defined simply on the basis of the time sequence of increases and decreases of use. This is satisfactory provided that one is interested in a differentiation of conservation and depletion and provided that increases and decreases occur without alternations over all intervals considered, or as a special case, if all changes are of the same sign. These conditions are approximated in most practical applications of the words conservation and depletion. Otherwise, ascertaining the direction of change requires a weighing of each change by time and aggregation. These problems have been explained elsewhere.[1]

Any given time distribution of resource use may be regarded as the result of conservation or depletion and will be called a *state of conservation* in the sense of resulting from or with respect to conservation or depletion. State of conservation is merely a convenient shorthand expression for "a given state in the intertemporal distribution of resource use." An important special case of a state of conservation is the one which may be regarded the economically "best" for an individual resource user or for a social group. This is the *optimum state of conservation*. The optimum state

[1] S. V. Ciriacy-Wantrup, *Resource Conservation, Economics and Policies*, University of California Press, Berkeley, Calif., 1952.

The author acknowledges permission by the University of California Press to make use of this publication in several places in this chapter. However, many significant issues in the economics of conservation could not be treated here. The reader is referred to the book for a more complete statement.

of conservation is an economic maximum that is not necessarily identical with maximum cumulative use.

The above definitions have several advantages. In application they are not contrary to popular terminology, but they are more useful for economic analysis. They are neutral in terms of value judgments. They are not affected by the money veil; that is, changes in the monetary value of use do not affect the definition and measurement of conservation, depletion, and state of conservation. They carry no connotation of efficiency or waste. In the literature, the term *waste* is usually associated with the depletion of flow resources. But conservation of resources also may be wasteful. A few illustrations must suffice here.

Conservation that would try to hold agricultural productivity of a virgin soil with distant markets at the original level or try to restore it to that level may be wasteful in terms of other natural resources (lime, fertilizer, fuel), labor, and equipment. A forester who would hasten the recovery of a cutover forest in a young country through planting instead of waiting for natural revegetation may be wasteful because his efforts may better be directed toward fire protection, improved systems of logging, and the like over a larger forested area. A mine owner who installs expensive permanent equipment in order to increase his recovery rate or to extend the life of his mine may be wasting labor and capital which he could more advantageously employ in alternative enterprises. Under some conditions, depletion of local ground water may enable a community to grow strong enough to import distant surface water, whereas conserving ground water would necessitate limiting economic development.

Apparently, there is an economic criterion for conservation. Somewhere, in conservation, an economically optimum time distribution of use is reached. This distribution was called above the optimum state of conservation. The meaning of waste in resource use must be related to such an optimum. What are the economic issues in making decisions concerning this optimum?

19.2 Conservation Decisions in Private Economics

The economic and social issues in conservation are different in private and in public decisions. We may focus on conservation in private economics first, because most private issues are simpler and because, in a private enterprise economy like that of the United States, both the need and the possibilities for public action are based on an understanding of the objectives of individual resource users and of the way they respond to economic forces, especially those affected by conservation policy.

Such an understanding is required not only for those who make and execute policies. In conservation policy, where continuity is of utmost importance, a continuous public demand for legislation and enforcement is a requirement for action by a democracy. A continuous and articulate demand for conservation policy requires that the electorate become aware of the economic issues involved. Likewise, execution of conservation policy is aided if those immediately concerned, the individual resource users and their political representatives, understand the relations between their own behavior and the interests of the social group.

As stated in section 19.1, conservation and depletion are defined in terms of changes in the intertemporal distribution of use. Decisions concerning such changes may be called, for short, conservation decisions. They are part and parcel of all business planning. Farmers, foresters, mine operators, oil producers, and other resource users plan use for more than one interval. This must be done because use in one interval is related through revenues or costs or both to use in other intervals. This economic necessity for an integrated production plan extending over time and, therefore, the economic significance of conservation decisions may be explained by indicating the types of relations between use in different intervals through revenues or costs.

When we say that use in two intervals is related through revenues or costs, we mean changes of use in one interval will affect revenues or costs in the other. Obviously, in order to measure such effects, use in the other interval must be kept constant. Furthermore, we have to measure the changes in revenues and cost brought about by the last unit of the change in use that is considered. By this we mean, in the terminology of the economist, we have to measure changes in *marginal* revenues and costs. The reason for this requirement is that, at different levels of use, a given change may have quite different effects. For example, up to a certain level of use (in terms of tons of feed harvested or animal units pastured per acre), grazing in one year may not increase the costs of taking the same harvest next year. However, from a certain level onward, an increase of use will require costs for irrigation, fertilization, and other inputs if the harvest next year is to remain unchanged.

We may define relations between use in two intervals as complementary through revenues if an increase of use in one increases marginal revenues in the other; relations are defined as competitive through revenues if a decrease of marginal revenues occurs. Relations are defined as complementary through costs if an increase of use in one interval decreases marginal costs in another; competitiveness through costs prevails if the opposite is true. The relations are called neutral, or use in different intervals independent, if no change in revenues or costs occurs. A parallel set of definitions is used for the relations between different resources through demand and supply, for example, between coal and iron ore (complementary through demand), coal and oil (competitive through demand), silver and copper ores (complementary through supply), and coal and soil (competitive through supply in strip mining).

Relations through revenues depend on market form. Under pure competition, product prices expected in different intervals are identical with marginal revenues. From the standpoint of the individual resource user, prices are given. This is merely a different way of saying that use in one interval does not affect marginal revenues in another. This situation holds for most users of flow resources, for example, agriculture, forestry, grazing, and fisheries. In these instances, therefore, we are concerned largely with relations through costs and can disregard relations through revenues, at least in private economics.

On the other hand, in the utilization of stock resources, market form is frequently characterized by monopolistic conditions of various types. This is true, for example, for metal ores, oil, natural gas, precious stones, and fertilizer materials. Here, the relations through revenues may require an integrated production plan even if relations through costs could be neglected. Monopolistic conditions, therefore, are of considerable significance in the economics and policies of resource conservation. Space does not permit consideration of this problem here.[1]

Competitiveness through costs is implicitly recognized in a large part of the literature on conservation. Such competitiveness is the major reason why conservation can be accomplished through decrease of present use in favor of future use, that is, through "waiting." Actually, however, this relation is frequently not sufficiently realized in business planning. An increase of future costs caused by soil depletion, overgrazing, overcutting, or overpumping is generally taken too lightly. This is due partly to difficulties in evaluating future increase of costs and partly to the laws and customs existing in resource tenure, taxation, and credit. We shall return to these problems later.

Complementarity through costs is a result of what we may call *sunk costs*. They include, first, costs which in short-run instantaneous economic analysis are known as fixed and lumpy. These are the costs of productive factors such as buildings, machinery, trees, and breeding stock which cannot be used economically if such use were confined to any one interval. Sunk costs include, second, some costs which in instantaneous economic analysis (short run or long run) are termed variable. In agriculture, the costs of fertilizer, feed, and labor are sunk over periods of gestation. Considerable costs for labor and materials must be expended to open a mine or to drill a well before production can start. These inputs are potentially useful in obtaining revenues over more than one interval. Additional costs necessary to obtain these revenues may be called *recovery costs*. Sunk costs play a role in maintaining production over time

[1] *Ibid.*, chap. 14.

as do fixed and lumpy costs over a certain range in instantaneous economics. Likewise, recovery costs have economic characteristics similar to that of variable costs of instantaneous economics.

Another cause for complementarity through costs is that it is often difficult for individual resource users to shift to other employment. In terms of opportunity costs, this influence may be regarded as a part of sunk costs; it has the same effects upon maintaining production over time. But indivisibility, immobility, and specialization of the resource user himself differ in their origin and their susceptibility to change from similar conditions affecting other productive factors. In the latter case, these conditions are largely technological, whereas in the former, they are largely institutional. We may now ask: What is the objective of conservation decisions? In other words, what is the optimum state of conservation in private economics?

19.3　The Optimum State of Conservation in Private Economics

The objective of economic decisions is usually formulated as maximization of some expected value or state of economic well-being—variously called "net revenues," "income," "profit," "utility," or "satisfaction."

If the maximization principle is applied to conservation decisions, a flow of net revenues extending over time must be maximized. Net revenues at different intervals are reduced to "present values" through discounting with the prevailing interest rate. The optimum state of conservation is that time distribution of use that maximized the present value of the flow of net revenues.

In economic theory, the optimum state of conservation can be determined in various ways. Revenue and cost functions and the joint-production approach may be employed; or net revenues may be formulated as an integral over a variable period of time and the calculus of variations employed for maximization.[1]

In economic reality, it is usually not practical to calculate many small changes of variables as is theoretically required for maximization. Only a few lumpy changes of irregular magnitude can be considered. The practical objective of conservation decisions is a step-by-step directional (conservation or depletion) change of the existing or some hypothetical distribution toward the optimum. The optimum state of conservation can be approximated only through trial and error. An increment of present net revenues rather than maximum present net revenues is the objective of conservation decisions.

---

[1] S. V. Ciriacy-Wantrup, "Taxation and the Conservation of Resources," *Quart. J. Economics*, vol. 58, no. 2, pp. 157–195, February, 1944. (University of California, College of Agriculture, Giannini Foundation of Agricultural Economics, Paper 110.)

In connection with this more modest objective, the concept of a *conservation practice* is helpful. When resource users make conservation decisions, they usually consider as alternatives whole combinations of interrelated inputs and outputs. Such a combination may be called a conservation practice. Usually, a given conservation practice involves interrelated changes of inputs in more than one interval. The same is true for outputs. For example, in soil conservation, the practice of terracing involves inputs of man-hours and machine-hours for construction, the expenditure of materials for preparing proper outlets, repair and maintenance over the years, variations in size and layouts of fields, changes in methods of cultivating and harvesting, changes in yields, changes in risks, and possible other changes.

Under such conditions, the present total additional value product of the conservation practice is compared with its present additional total costs. Usually, only a small number of alternative conservation practices is calculated. Although no one can accurately determine the optimum state of conservation in this way, save by accident, the modest but practical objective of approximating the optimum step-by-step can be effectively pursued.

Not all questions which can be raised concerning the optimum state of conservation as a concept can be considered here. Two of them, however, deserve at least some mention because they are especially significant for conservation policy. The first question concerns the existence of extramarket values and the second the influence of uncertainty.

There is no need to labor the point that conservation decisions are not solely influenced by positive and negative values which are easily expressed in monetary terms, that is, which are evaluated through and in the market place. The availability of leisure time and good working relations with family members, neighbors, employees, and government officials are common nonmonetary considerations in business planning. Prestige, power, pride in his own achievement, aesthetic appreciation of a well-kept farm or landscape may be as important as monetary rewards. To remain in exclusive control of one's business may be regarded as more essential than to increase pecuniary net revenues. Group-centered motives, such as patriotism and community spirit or envy and vengefulness, may influence conservation decisions.

These values are usually called "intangible" in economic analysis. The implication of this term appears unfortunate. They will be called here *extramarket values*.

For individuals, inclusion of extramarket values in revenues and costs does not prevent approximating the optimum state of conservation. It can be established that individuals are able to compare changes in their state of well-being connected with changes in the combination of extramarket and market goods. They are able to take account of both types of goods in their conservation decisions. The psychological mechanism of these subjective evaluations (for example, whether cardinal or ordinal differentiation of utility is involved) is neither accessible nor relevant for objective evaluation of extramarket goods.

Objective or "administrative" evaluation of extramarket goods can sometimes be accomplished by analogy, that is, by using market values in auxiliary calculations or by employing market criteria, such as equality of supply and demand. Sometimes rates of substitution between extramarket and market goods can be obtained objectively through observation of behavior in situations of choosing, either actual or hypothetical, in questionnaires, for example. Administrative evaluation is of interest for conservation policy.

It is commonly recognized that resource users frequently have only hunches and broad guesses with respect to the economic data necessary for determining the optimum state of conservation. Expectations are uncertain. In more technical language, expectations are not single-valued but appear in the form of a probability distribution. Resource users seldom have exact numerical knowledge of the statistical moments of this distribution. But they have, generally, some notion about the range of possible outcomes and, sometimes, about the most probable outcome. The question arises whether and in what way this situation affects the meaning of the optimum state of conservation.

On one side it can be argued that there is no such influence: resource users employ in their calculations the most probable value of expected net revenues and discount this value for uncertainty, that is, reduce it in proportion to dispersion. Thus, multivalued expectations are treated in production planning as if they were single-valued.

On the other side, it can be pointed out that uncertainty of expectations cannot effectively be taken into account in this way. Without disputing the actual extent of this practice, it has two serious limitations.

1. Discounting is ineffective if the most probable value of net revenues cannot be ascertained. Such situations are common in economic reality because, as just emphasized, expectations frequently consist merely in hunches and vague notions of the range of possible occurrences.

2. Discounting may be an ineffective allowance for uncertainty even if the most probable value of net revenues can be ascertained. This is true if the possibility of a highly unfavorable outcome exists—even though such an outcome may be much less probable than alternative, more favorable outcomes. Discounting the most probable net revenues for the possibility of high negative net revenues (losses) may not lead to decisions that would safeguard the enterprise against bankruptcy if the most unfavorable outcome is actually realized. This threat depends both on the

magnitude of the loss and on the financial strength of the enterprise, which always has definite limits.

A contingency which threatens bankruptcy can be guarded against in various ways, for example, through hedging, pooling, and spreading arrangements or by avoiding commitments which would cause dangerous losses if the most unfavorable outcome should occur, that is, by keeping the production plan flexible. Flexibility is a way of allowing for uncertainty of expectations because most uncertainties increase with distance in time: resource users know that expectations about a certain interval will become less uncertain the nearer this interval is approached in the course of time.

Avoiding the possibility of the most unfavorable outcome involves either definite costs, for example, a risk premium for an insurance policy, or possible losses through flexibility. Losses occur with a more flexible plan, as compared with a less flexible plan that would bring maximum net revenues under the most probable expectation, if the most probable outcome is actually realized or, at least, if the most unfavorable outcome is not realized. Thus, the more flexible plan may not be the optimum plan as defined through maximizing the most probable net revenues. However, these more probable losses through greater flexibility are moderate as compared with the losses through smaller flexibility if the most unfavorable outcome is realized.

In other words, one important objective of conservation decisions is to avoid immoderate possible losses, although of small probability, by accepting the possibility of moderate ones, although the latter are more probable. For our purposes, a loss may be called immoderate if it threatens the continuity of a production plan.

Economic choices between losses of various magnitudes and probabilities exist not only in those special cases in which immoderate losses, in the sense just indicated, are under consideration. Such cases were mentioned, first, because they reveal clearly the insufficiency of taking account of uncertainty through discounting. Much more numerous are cases in which alternatives exist between larger but less probable losses and smaller but more probable ones, although the former need not be immoderate.

It may be concluded that multivalued decision problems are so common in economics that the objectives of conservation decisions are best formulated in a way which takes uncertainty explicitly into account. This can be done, for example, by subjecting the economic optimum to the restriction of avoiding immoderate possible losses or by formulating it as "minimizing maximum possible losses." For conservation policy, such an objective is called here a "safe minimum standard," which will be discussed later.

The preceding discussion of the optimum state of conservation does not by itself explain conservation and depletion in actual situations of resource use. But such a discussion provides the organizing principle by which actual situations may be understood.

The optimum state of conservation is a helpful concept not only for understanding the behavior of resource users on the basis of their objectives. The optimum state of conservation may also be employed as an *ex post* concept without imputing objectives, such as maximization or any other, to resource users. In this sense, observable changes in the state of conservation may be called "toward" and "away" from the optimum in terms of relative economic success (survival) in a given economic environment.

To use an analogy, the concepts "climax type" in ecology and "adaptive peak" in genetics do not explain an actual plant association or the developmental state of a species at a particular time and place; nor do they indicate that static states are realizable or that the system which is being considered is closed. Still they are helpful constructs in understanding the direction of ceaseless change, the resultant of environmental forces which can be observed at a given time and place.

Thus, the optimum state of conservation both as an *ex ante* and as an *ex post* concept is a construct which is helpful as an organizing principle in analyzing the result of economic forces which influence conservation. A study of these forces is the central theme of the economics of conservation.

19.4   Economic Forces Influencing Conservation

An economic study of conservation must explain how a state of conservation and its changes come about. The variables involved in such a study may be called *economic forces*, including the economic effects of social institutions.

An understanding of these forces is necessary for the following four reasons: (1) for explaining the behavior of resource users in the past; (2) for predicting the behavior of resource users under given assumptions with respect to such forces; (3) for understanding the selective processes that operate among a statistical population of resource users and, over time, mold the state of conservation; (4) for designing appropriate conservation policies—economic forces may be obstacles or tools for such policies.

Interest, Income, and Conservation. Among economic forces affecting conservation, interest and related forces are among the most powerful, most consistent, and, from the standpoint of theoretical analysis and practical effects, among the most clear-cut.

Interest rates are used in production planning for making net revenues occurring in different intervals comparable in time. This means that future net revenues that are numerically identical but occur in different intervals are decreased in relation to their distance in time from that interval in which decisions are made. An increase in interest rates means, therefore, a progressive decrease (one that becomes greater with distance) in the present value of future net revenues. The result will be an attempt to change the time distribution of net revenues in the direction of the present. This can be accomplished through redistributing revenues in the direction of the present or through redistributing costs in the direction of the future or through both.

Except for the relatively minor possibilities of reducing storage, revenues are redistributed in this way through redistributing use toward the present.

Costs are redistributed in this way by substituting productive services with shorter periods of gestation for those with longer periods or, in the terminology used above, by reducing sunk costs. This also means a redistribution of rates of use in the direction of the present if the state of technology is assumed to be unchanged. Thus, an increase of interest rates tends to change the time distribution of use in the direction of the present. This means depletion. By the same reasoning, a decrease of interest rates leads to conservation.

The effects of interest rates just discussed are not necessarily dependent on the assumption of economic calculativeness. A rise of interest rates makes relatively more successful not only those resource users who calculatively respond to this change of environment by depleting their resources but also those who for any other reasons or for no particular reason (at random) have a lower state of conservation than others. Thus, over time, selection and imitation would bring about depletion, considering a population of resource users as a whole. Similarly, conservation would be brought about by a fall of interest rates.

Interest rates determined in the market place are relevant for individual resource users if they can easily purchase and sell expected net revenue flows discounted on the basis of such rates. In the terminology of the economist, market interest rates are relevant if the market for the physical, personal, and money "assets" of individual resource users is perfect. In such a market, all individuals can purchase and sell any desired quantities at the prevailing prices.

In economic reality, markets for assets are frequently not perfect. It is often more economical to disinvest in resources through depletion than through sale or borrowing if there are no ready markets in which assets are capitalized or in which funds can be borrowed at interest rates lower than individual "time-preference" rates. Conversely, it may be more economical to invest in resources through conservation than through purchase or lending if there are no ready markets in which assets are capitalized or in which funds can be lent at interest rates higher than individual time-preference rates.

The concept of individual time preference is a marginal one. Time-preference rates, therefore, are affected by the numerical value of net revenues or, better for the present purpose, the level of individual income. Thus, in the economics of conservation, we are greatly interested in the way changes of income levels affect time-preference rates.

A unit of income, a dollar, becomes less and less effective in influencing economic decisions as income increases. In time economics, one must focus on the ratio between the effectiveness (in influencing economic decisions) of the identical amount of income in different intervals. This ratio must also decrease progressively with increasing income levels. This ratio is identical by definition with the rate of time preference. It follows that, in conservation economics, we are interested in those income-changing forces which affect different income levels differently, or in terms borrowed from the economics of taxation which are "regressive" or "progressive" with income, and those forces which do not vary with income during general income changes, as during depressions. The latter forces are called "fixed charges."

If markets for assets and loans are imperfect, a decrease in income levels will increase time preference and lead to depletion; an increase in income levels will lead to conservation. A given change in income levels, however, will have less and less effect on the state of conservation as income increases. In other words, the relations between income levels and conservation decisions are most important in the low-income groups and have more importance during depressions than during booms.

The relations between conservation decisions, interest rates, and income are of special significance for industrially less developed countries. In these, interest rates are high, markets for assets are especially imperfect, incomes are low, and fixed charges on income are increasing through monetization of taxes and substitution of cash rents for share rents.

Uncertainty and Conservation. As we know, allowance for uncertainty can be made through discounting, by keeping the production plan flexible, and through hedging, pooling, and spreading.

The most important uncertainties, namely, those created by changes of technology of consumer demand and of social institutions, increase with time. Uncertainties of nature (drought, pests, hailstorms, fire, floods) increase with time up to a certain limit, for example, within the season. Conversely, resource users know that uncertainty at a certain future date will decrease as this date is approached in the course of time.

Because of these relations between uncertainty and time, changes in the uncertainty discount affect the state of conservation like changes of the time discount: an increase in the uncertainty discount means a progressive decrease in the present value of future net revenues. The result will be an attempt to change the time distribution of net revenues in the direction of the present. Why such an attempt leads to depletion need not be repeated. Conversely, a decrease in the uncertainty discount leads to conservation.

The effects of changes in flexibility are not so simple. First, we may ask how is an increase in flexibility accomplished? Assuming a given command over assets of all kinds, flexibility is largely a problem of keeping liquid funds (cash, government securities) and liquid inventories (finished goods or materials) and of reducing the time over which commitments in durable factors are made. The latter can be accomplished by securing durable factors through short-time leases rather than through long-term leases and through ownership. If durable factors are secured through ownership rather than through lease, flexibility can be increased by giving preference to factors which are less durable. In the terminology used above, periods over which costs are sunk are reduced. What do these changes mean in terms of conservation?

An increase in liquidity does not in itself mean conservation or depletion. On the other hand, a reduction of sunk costs means depletion. Likewise, tendencies to avoid ownership and to shorten leases generally result in depletion, as will be discussed presently. In other words, unless liquidity alone is the method of adaptation, changes of uncertainty, if allowed for through flexibility, tend to change utilization plans in the same direction as if such changes are taken into account through discounting for uncertainty.

Hedging is not very important in the economics of conservation because existing markets for "futures" do not extend far enough in time. Within the narrow limits of its effectiveness, hedging reduces the need for uncertainty discounting and for flexibility and, therefore, encourages conservation.

Through pooling, some uncertainties of nature can be effectively reduced. With pooling, in contrast to spreading discussed below, uncertainties are of the same kind but of random incidence among producers in the same statistical class, that is, operating under similar physical and economic conditions.

The most important condition for pooling is that the membership in the pool be sufficiently large. Since the precision of an average is proportional to the square root of the number of terms it contains, pooling enables the most probable value of expectations to be determined more precisely than is possible for individual members of the pool. As a corollary, the aggregate allowance for uncertainty in the pool is smaller than the aggregate of individual uncertainty allowances without pooling. In other words, the need for uncertainty allowance through discounting and flexibility is reduced, expenditure of sunk costs encouraged; hence, with some exceptions which cannot be discussed here, pooling tends toward conservation.

Some uncertainties are connected with unique nonrecurrent contingencies which affect all producers in the same statistical class, but those in different classes differently. Such uncertainties are connected, for example, with changes of technology and demand and with the discovery of new deposits in the case of stock resources. These uncertainties cannot be reduced through pooling by producers in the same class; often, however, they can be reduced by spreading. This is possible if different branches of a multiple-product firm, different firms, different industries, or different geographical areas are subject to uncertainties of different kinds. Aggregate uncertainty allowance for such a composite of uncertainties can be less than the aggregate allowance for individual kinds of uncertainties because the dispersion of possible around the most probable revenues and costs is less for the composite than for the individual components.

Spreading, like hedging and pooling, reduces the need for uncertainty discount and flexibility. Spreading generally favors conservation. Again, some important exceptions cannot be discussed here.

Prices and Conservation.   We have seen how conservation decisions are affected by changes in two particular prices—time and uncertainty discounts. The effects of these price changes are clear-cut because they have definite relations to time. Time relations of other price changes are more complex.

In order to make conclusive statements about the effects of price changes upon conservation decisions, one would have to know (1) how expected price changes are distributed over time and (2) how interrelations between use in different intervals through revenues and costs are affected, that is, whether a given price change (in a product or a factor) encourages practices that are specifically conserving or specifically depleting. The complexity created by these two requirements can be reduced by making simplifying assumptions. Let us first observe the effect of price changes under the assumption that interrelations between use in different intervals are not affected.

An increase of product prices that is expected to occur at some future interval and to last indefinitely or one that is expected to become greater with time will induce a shift of use in the direction of the future, that is, will encourage conservation. An expected decrease of product prices under corresponding assumptions will lead to depletion. On the other hand, if a current increase of product prices is not expected to last for more than a few intervals, as during a war or the upswing of a business cycle, a shift of use toward those intervals is encouraged. Such a shift means depletion.

With price changes in factors, interrelations through costs cannot be disregarded. Some factors are employed in both conserving and depleting practices. In agriculture, for example, the same labor and equipment can be used for exposing slopes to water erosion and for building terraces. Bulldozers may be used for stopping gullies or for strip mining. For these factors, one can make no general statement about how price changes will affect conservation decisions. Some factors, on the other hand, are conserving under most technological conditions. In agriculture, for example, fertilizer and purchased feed, legume and grass seed are usually, but not always, conserving. Other factors such as mining machinery, the donkey engine in forestry, and hunting equipment are usually, but not necessarily, depleting. In principle, only the production plan and a practice are conserving or depleting.

The absence of hard and fast rules about the effects of price changes upon conservation decisions may cause disappointment. However, emphasis on this absence and on the importance of specific assumptions with respect to the time distribution of price changes and their effects on interrelations between use rates seemed necessary because these assumptions are frequently overlooked.

Price changes of products and of factors have far-reaching effects upon conservation decisions; but to ascertain the direction of these effects (that is, conservation or depletion) and to assess their quantitative significance requires caution. This is especially true if price changes are advocated as a tool of conservation policy.

Property Rights and Conservation. The economic forces discussed thus far—interest, income, uncertainty, and prices—are strongly affected by property rights. But these rights have additional effects on conservation decisions.

Property is a "bundle" of rights to control resource use. This bundle includes the rights an owner surrenders to a tenant when he leases or to a creditor when he borrows and such public rights of control as taxation. The specific influence upon conservation of the three "derived" property institutions will be considered subsequently. Here we will deal in general terms with the broad over-all relations between property rights and conservation. These relations will be discussed under indefiniteness, instability, and imbalance.

Indefiniteness of property rights exists in "fugitive" resources that must be captured through use, such as wildlife, high-seas fisheries, oil, natural gas, and ground water where control of subsurface resources is vested in the surface owner. Definite property rights belong only to those who are in possession. Deferred use is always subject to a great uncertainty: others may capture the resource in the meantime. Hence, every user tries to protect himself against others by acquiring ownership through capture in the fastest possible way; use tends to be concentrated in the least possible number of intervals near the present. Indefiniteness of property rights leads to depletion.

There are effective remedies for the wasteful depletion caused by indefiniteness of property rights: control over resource use may be defined through law and public regulations in such a way that the need for capture disappears. Such definition may vest control in individuals or in collective bodies. Examples are for oil and gas, regulation of well spacing and of proper gas-oil ratio in pumping, and the establishment of unitized pools. Unified control was established over the public range after the Taylor Grazing Act provided the legal and administrative basis. Several ground-water basins have been adjudicated in California, and uncertainty of water tenure is recognized as a major problem of water policy.[1]

Property rights may be well defined but unstable over time. This is another important cause of economic uncertainty and resource depletion. The instability resulting from short leases and from fear of dispossession by creditors will be taken up later. Here, we are concerned with a more widely dispersed type of instability. In periods of political change which threatens a sudden and radical redistribution of property rights, all resource users will hesitate to make investments with deferred yield. In such cases, resource users will adopt a utilization plan that they themselves would regard as wasteful depletion if their property rights were more stable.

Property rights are imbalanced if they lead to such a distribution of revenues and costs among the members of a social group that the individual resource user is not interested in taking into account all revenues and costs that are functionally related to his management. Generally, he will take into account only those revenues which accrue to him and those costs which he is required to pay. Revenues and costs incident on others will not affect his conservation decisions. The difference between the incidence of revenues and costs, on the basis of property rights and their allocation to functionally related use, is of special significance for conservation policy.

Tenancy and Conservation.   Tenancy affects the state of conservation through uncertainty allowance for instability, through incidence of revenues and costs on owner and user, through fixed regressive rents, and through lessening the results of imperfections in the markets for assets.

Uncertainty allowance for instability of tenancy can be reduced through longer lease contracts, through renewal clauses requiring notification in advance about intentions to renew, and through provisions for compensa-

[1] S. V. Ciriacy-Wantrup, "Concepts Used as Economic Criteria for a System of Water Rights," *Land Economics*, vol. 32, no. 4, pp. 295–312, November, 1956. (University of California, College of Agriculture, Giannini Foundation of Agricultural Economics, Paper 154.)

tion if either party refuses to renew without such notice. Longer lease contracts can be made more acceptable to both owner and tenant by sliding-scale cash rents varying with prices instead of the common fixed cash or share rents, by a fair determination of rent, and by clear and detailed setting forth of the rights and duties of both parties to avoid misunderstandings and frictions. Theoretically, if expected revenues and costs functionally related to a tenant's management were incident on him, he would have no reason to alter the utilization plan because he is not the owner. This result can be approached through fuller compensation for deferred revenues and costs at the time of severance of tenancy.

Economic conditions and customs vary so much from region to region that it would not be wise to enact and rigidly enforce detailed regulations about length of leases and compensation. But general rules can be laid down in state land-tenancy acts; and special courts of tenancy arbitration, composed of owners and tenants with an experienced judge as chairman, could be provided to administer them.

The depleting effects of fixity of rents can be avoided if cash rents are expressed as a percentage of net revenues. Such rents are rare, however, because of difficulties in ascertaining all costs. An approximation is a rent variable with gross revenues. The various sliding-scale cash and share rents are of this type. The worst effects of fixity of rents can be avoided by variable payment plans, a surplus over the fixed normal rent being accumulated in periods of high net incomes, and payments being reduced in periods of subnormal production and prices. From the standpoint of conservation, the common fixed share rent is usually, but not always, better than the common fixed cash rent.

If the system of tenancy were sufficiently improved, it would encourage conservation by counteracting the effects of imperfections in the markets for assets. In the absence of such improvement, attempts to transform tenants into owners, as in the Bankhead-Jones Tenant Farmers Purchase Act, tend toward conservation provided that the new owners are set up in economic units and without too great debts. Improvement in tenancy and attempts to increase the proportion of owners do not conflict with each other; both can be pursued at the same time.

Credit and Conservation.   The credit system is related to conservation in much the same way as is tenancy, that is, through uncertainty allowance, through fixed and regressive charges, through lessening imperfections in the markets for assets, and through conservation clauses in the loan contract.

If the owner's equity is small in relation to his creditor's, then ownership does not guarantee tenure. Even if the owner succeeds in fulfilling the loan contract, the creditors may recall the loan before it actually becomes delinquent in order to safeguard their equity. Inability to fulfill a contract and recall of the loan usually happen at a time when refinancing or liquidation of assets through sale is difficult or impossible. The result is bankruptcy and foreclosure. Allowance for this threat results in depletion: the owner may find it advisable to liquidate through depletion as much as possible of the present value of his resources before foreclosure prevents him from saving his equity.

These undesirable effects of the credit system upon the state of conservation may be reduced by institutional arrangements for debt adjustments without foreclosure. Such arrangements may be set up like the special tenancy courts previously suggested or may be combined with them.

Generally, interest and amortization payments are fixed charges which, as we know, tend to discourage conservation under imperfect markets for assets. Furthermore, credit charges tend to be regressive with income; debtors in low-income groups often pay higher interest rates than those with larger incomes because risks are considered greater by lenders and because the cost of administering smaller loans is higher per unit.

The depleting effect of these charges can be reduced by making them vary with income. This may be done by variable payment plans previously suggested in connection with rent payments or by relating interest and amortization payments more directly to the prices or products. A decrease in the amplitude of income fluctuations brought about by making interest and amortization payments flexible not only has favorable effects upon the borrower's utilization plan but is also favorable for the lender: the need for moratoria, refinancing, and foreclosure in periods of depression is reduced, and the purchasing power of interest income is protected in periods of prosperity.

Thus, the undesirable relations between credit and conservation are to some extent avoidable. Further, they are more than balanced by the relations that are economically desirable: a well-functioning credit system reduces the effects (upon the state of conservation) of imperfections in the markets for assets. Such a credit system is an effective aid in conservation.

A not infrequent cause of imperfections in the market for loans is obsolete lending practices such as outdated methods of appraisal, failure to recognize increased stability in developing regions or enterprises and to reduce rates accordingly, and insistence on certain customary types of collateral despite changes in physical and economic institutions. An example of this last situation is frequently encountered on western ranges where the collateral for loans is often livestock and the number grazed is the basis for loan rationing. Lenders, failing to recognize the overgrazing problem, may object to having the number of livestock reduced even though the value of the collateral may be reduced by loss of weight on overgrazed ranges. A change in such practices would eliminate a cause of depletion that is serious both for the borrower and for the lender.

The credit system could encourage conservation by including conservation clauses in the loan contract. Some Federal land banks and some private banks have made proper soil conservation a condition for lending. Similarly, silvicultural practices might be introduced as a part of a public forest credit system.

Taxation and Conservation. Like the other derived property institutions, the tax system has significant but frequently unintended and unrecognized effects upon conservation decisions. Taxation is sometimes an important obstacle for conservation policy. On the other hand, the tax system can be employed more easily and effectively as a tool of conservation policy than can the tenancy or credit system.

Any attempt to make general statements about the effects of taxation upon conservation decisions faces the same difficulties encountered in discussing the effects of prices: when new taxes are levied or existing ones changed (in rates, methods of assessment, modes of payment), one needs to know how interrelations between use in different intervals are affected and how the tax changes are distributed over time.

Taxes are generally not imposed on specifically conserving or depleting factors or products. If they are, conservation will be affected by new or increased taxes in much the same way as by prices.

Variations of taxes over time may be expected because the government has implied or announced that a given change of taxes will be limited in duration or on the basis of extrapolating past experience or because of important present events such as a war or a depression which are known to lead to great changes of fiscal needs. If a given change in taxes is not expected to last over the whole planning period, rates of use tend to be redistributed in such a way that the tax base is increased in those planning intervals in which taxes are more favorable. Conservation or depletion will result according to the time distribution of the tax changes. More usual are situations in which the tax change is expected to last over the whole planning period. In the following discussion of the different types of taxes, we will make the simplifying assumptions that resource users base their plans on this expectation and that interrelations between use are not affected by the change in taxes.

Property taxes are among the most important taxes in resource utilization. Because taxes on personal property are largely evaded, the general property tax has become mostly a tax on physical assets—natural resources, improvements, and equipment. For our purposes, the value of physical assets is assumed to be identical with the sum of discounted future net revenues which these assets are expected to yield. Recurrent (annual) taxes on the present value of resources may, then, be regarded as a special type of taxes on net revenues. In each year in which the tax is paid, net revenues of all future intervals are taxed. The further, therefore, net revenues are distant from the present, the more often they are subject to the tax. This provides an incentive to redistribute net revenues in the direction of the present in order to reduce the number of times they are taxed. Since such redistribution can be accomplished only through redistributing use in the same direction, this means depletion. Property taxes, therefore, affect the utilization plan in much the same way as interest does. Property taxes, in contrast to income and yield taxes, are not automatically adjusted when income changes. Furthermore, properties in a low state of conservation, such as cutover forest land with poor natural vegetation, eroded farm land, and overgrazed ranges, tend to be overassessed relative to other properties. A vicious circle is set in motion: property taxes encourage depletion most on those properties which are already relatively more depleted. This effect is often increased by tax regression.

Sometimes the depleting effects of property taxes are desired by tax authorities in attempts to check speculation in resources withheld from use such as vacant city lots and deposits of minerals under monopolistic conditions. Property taxes, in contrast with income and yield taxes, produce tax receipts immediately and, provided it is economically possible to develop the resource after imposition of the tax, change the time distribution of use in the desired direction.

Income, profit, and yield taxes are taxes on current net revenues and are generally regarded as providing no incentive to change the pretax system of utilization. Aside from certain special problems discussed in the following paragraphs, the common view would be correct in time economics under the assumptions that (1) they are expected to be constant over time, (2) no shifts of productive services into leisure or into less heavily taxed employments take place, and (3) income effects upon individual time preference are disregarded. Under these assumptions, proportional taxes on current net revenues are neutral with respect to the state of conservation.

Somewhat different effects upon conservation result from the fact that the legal definition of income and profits for tax purposes does not coincide with the meaning of net revenues in economic theory. Thus, in agriculture and forestry many expenses for permanent improvements can be charged, for income-tax purposes, to current costs of production, partly in conformity with income-tax laws and partly because segregation of investments from current costs, as required by law, is difficult. At a certain level of income-tax rates, it is economical to evade income taxes by making such investments; for taxpayers can sell their improved properties at a profit and are taxed on the latter only on the basis of their capital gains, a considerably lower tax in the higher-income brackets. Thus, a high income tax in conjunction with a lower capital gains tax may result in conservation.

Yield taxes are superior to most other taxes with respect to economy of administration and accuracy of assessment. Because costs are not taken into account, however, they are inferior to net revenue taxes from the standpoint of ability to pay. They are less flexible than income and profit taxes in periods of income changes caused by factors other than yield.

Estate and inheritance taxes are based on the present value of the estate. But if, as is generally the case, only one payment of these taxes is taken into account, they tax future net revenue only once. Hence, they would be neutral with respect to the state of conservation. However, such taxes may weaken a testator's motives for investment or induce him to disinvest. Under imperfect markets for loans and other productive services, disinvestment may take the form of depletion. The beneficiaries, in turn, are faced with payment of a tax that usually far exceeds current net revenues from the inherited assets. If they have no liquid reserve and if, again, markets for assets are imperfect, they may have to liquidate a portion of the inherited assets through depletion in order to pay the tax. This type of depletion is common in forestry and agriculture.

Direct Tools of Conservation Policy. The economic forces discussed so far may be called "indirect" tools of conservation policy because changes of interest, income, uncertainty, prices, property, tenancy, credit, and taxation are usually brought about with objectives other than changing the state of conservation. In contrast, "direct" tools of conservation policy are employed for conservation. Such direct tools vary in type from government-subsidized conservation education to zoning ordinances, the requirement of specific conservation practices (or the prohibition of depleting ones), and outright public ownership of natural resources.

The need for education in resource conservation has often been stressed and is uncontroversial. It is needed not only for resource users but also for the whole voting public, which is becoming more and more urban and, thus, less in contact with resource problems. It is needed not only in the technology of conservation but also in recognizing when conservation is economically justified. It can help both resource users and the general public understand why conservation policy is necessary.

Important as education is for conservation, however, it is no cure-all. If economic forces stand in the way, results from education alone will be small. Sometimes it is effective only if used in combination with other tools.

Zoning can be successfully applied in the conservation of several natural resources. Forest resources may be protected by zoning against agriculture, grazing, or year-round residence. Important infiltration areas for ground water may be zoned against urban development; as a joint product, flood-control problems may thereby be alleviated in what is sometimes the most economical way. Billboard zoning may be used to protect scenic resources.

Direct public regulation of practices is applied through county and city ordinances, by state and Federal statute, and by special districts. In resource utilization, such special districts are of particular importance. Regulation of practices has gone furthest with water both in social philosophy and in the development of control mechanisms. This is especially true for the semiarid states. Soil-conservation districts have been formed in many states, but regulations have been passed by only a few districts, and enforcement has not been tested in the courts. Some states have not granted these districts regulatory power, and in most states, they do not have taxing power, an important tool for cooperative action. Other resources for which regulation is common are forests, ranges, wildlife, oil, gas, and coal and other mineral resources.

Both zoning and regulation pose the problem of the limits of direct public interference with private enterprise. While they increase economic opportunities for some uses and individuals, they decrease them for others. Such an interference with private utilization plans through use of the police power must, according to the Constitution, be "reasonable" and not "arbitrary." Interpretation of these legal limits is greatly influenced by how much of an economic burden zoning or regulation imposes on private enterprise. The courts have been neither negative nor inflexible in defining a "reasonable" degree of interference. The principle of compensation can sometimes be utilized to expand the economic limits of these tools.

If restrictions are very severe, or if a large compensation is necessary for some time, public ownership may be more effective and cheaper. For example, to protect a watershed for a big city by zoning, most other uses might have to be prohibited. Such areas must be owned by the public or by public utility districts operating under close public control. Exercise of eminent domain contains fewer elements of confiscation than many zoning ordinances and regulations. Public ownership is an important tool of conservation policy.

After reviewing the most important indirect and direct tools of conservation policy, a few words may be said about its objectives.

19.5 Objectives of Conservation Policy

The economic objectives of conservation policy, that is, the optimum state of conservation in social economics, could be determined by criteria similar to those used for the private optimum, provided revenues and costs could be reinterpreted for social accounting in a meaningful way. Several problems are encountered in such a reinterpretation.

First, it may be regarded as axiomatic that all revenues and costs of resource use must be considered in social accounting regardless of who receives or pays them. Usually, only a portion of such social revenues and costs is incident on the resource user who is responsible for them. This problem was discussed under imbalance of property rights. If there are discrepancies between the revenues and costs considered by individual resource users and social revenues and costs, there will be differences between the private and the social optimum in the state of conservation. One objective of conservation policy is to reduce such differences by inducing private conservation decisions to approach the social optimum more closely.

Second, difficulties are created for reinterpreting revenues and costs in social economics by the existence of extramarket values which was also discussed above. For policy decisions, in contrast to private decisions, it is necessary to obtain some objective yardstick for comparing market with extramarket goods.

Third, over time public policy may change the meaning of revenues and cost by changing income distribution, preferences, technology, and social institutions. The economic calculus has validity only under restrictive assumptions with respect to such changes. It can be employed in appraising conservation policies of more limited scope, for example, in appraising a particular project in public resource development. But for policies of broader scope, the restrictive assumptions needed for benefit-cost analysis and for other systematic attempts at a precise quantitative economic appraisal of policy become too burdensome.[1]

Finally, there is the difficulty posed by the existence of uncertainty. The importance of uncertainty for private conservation decisions was emphasized throughout this chapter. But it is even more important in social economics for that important class of flow resources which contain soil, water, plants, animals, and related resources. The flow of these resources is characterized by a "critical zone"; that is, the flow may be decreased by human action until the decrease becomes economically irreversible.

Sometimes such irreversibility is not only economic but also technologic. The decrease in the flow of animal and plant life, for instance, becomes technologically irreversible for a certain species if the flow reaches zero, that is, if the breeding stock is destroyed; or within a species,

[1] S. V. Ciriacy-Wantrup, "Benefit-Cost Analysis and Public Resource Development," *J. Farm Economics*, vol. 37, no. 4, pp. 676–689, November 1955. (University of California, College of Agriculture, Giannini Foundation of Agricultural Economics, Paper 146.)

destruction of a gene system represented by an isolated population (race) is a technologically irreversible loss.

Even if the flow has not reached zero, economic reversibility may be lost if highly complex ecological relations are affected, for example, plant associations and successions on some grasslands and forests. If overdraft of ground water has led to compaction of clay aquifers, restoration of storage capacity becomes economically impossible. Such storage capacity is no less a resource than are good dam sites for surface storage. A decrease in soil productivity can sometimes be reversed relatively cheaply if it results from depletion of plant nutrients, but if deep gullies have been formed which interfere with farm operations, or if all soil has been destroyed through erosion to bedrock or hydraulic mining, the economic reversibility of soil productivity, at least in certain uses, for example, cultivated crops, may have disappeared. Some scenic resources, for example, wilderness areas, may be spoiled irreversibly.

Economic irreversibility is uncertain. It depends on future technology, wants, and social institutions. Furthermore, it is uncertain whether economic irreversibility, if it actually occurs, will lead to what was called above an "immoderate" loss, that is, in social economics, a loss that threatens the survival of a society. This outcome may well have a rather small probability. But according to some serious students of social development, this outcome has actually occurred in the past. Thus, avoiding the possibility of such a loss may well be regarded as an objective of conservation policy.

A decision to avoid the social risk of irreversibility is not dependent on whether or not the losses which threaten are immoderate. As we know avoiding the possibility of immoderate losses is merely a special case of making choices between the possibility of larger but less probable losses and that of smaller but more probable ones. If the more probable losses are small in relation to the less probable ones which may be avoided by accepting the former, the economic choice between the two alternatives would not be difficult. What, then, are these smaller but more probable losses?

They are connected with maintaining a "safe minimum standard of conservation." In the resource class under consideration, a safe minimum standard of conservation is achieved by avoiding the critical zone, that is, those physical conditions, brought about by human action, which would make it uneconomical to halt and reverse depletion. A safe minimum standard of conservation involves losses if its maintenance necessitates costs (either use foregone or positive efforts) and if the contingency guarded against should not actually occur, that is, if depletion should eventually prove not to be economically irreversible. These losses are similar to the costs of flexibility in private economics. The similarity is more than formal: a safe minimum standard of conservation is essentially an increase of flexibility in the continuing development of society.

The costs of maintaining a safe minimum standard are absolutely small if proper action is taken in time and if the proper tools of conservation policy are employed.

In some practical situations, maintenance of a safe minimum standard necessitates that use is foregone. Use in the neighborhood of the critical zone is small and, in the alternative case, that is, if a safe minimum standard were not maintained, would continue only over a small number of intervals. It is well to remember that the safe minimum standard of conservation is far more modest than a theoretical social optimum. Frequently, such a standard corresponds to a state of conservation which is considerably lower than the private optimum. Under these conditions, the great majority of private enterprises will be operating above the safe minimum standard.

In many practical situations, maintenance of a safe minimum standard does not involve any use foregone; rather, it involves a change in the ways (not the quantities) of utilization. These changes may or may not necessitate costs in the sense of positive efforts (inputs) by individuals or by the public or by both. Sometimes a change of social institutions without any inputs is sufficient. Sometimes the costs are only public, for example, if education or a temporary subsidy is the most economical tool of conservation policy. If private costs are increased, for example, as a consequence of regulation by governments or public districts, only a few enterprises may be affected because, as already emphasized, the minimum standard of conservation is a rather modest objective in terms of the private optimum.

Costs of maintaining the safe minimum standard are not only small in absolute amount but very small relative to the loss which is being guarded against, a decrease of flexibility in the continuing development of a society. Costs of maintaining the safe minimum standard of conservation are also very small as compared with generally accepted expenditures of a social group for safeguarding its continuity in other fields. Such fields are, for example, public health and safety and national defense. In these fields, likewise, a safe minimum standard is frequently adopted as an objective of public policy. The reason is the same as in the field of conservation: it is impractical to determine a precise social optimum in the state of public health and safety or national defense because of uncertainty and because of the difficulties of valuating social revenues and costs. On the other hand, it is practical to set up standards which would avoid serious losses—threats to social continuity—in cases of epidemics, internal disorder, and foreign military involvements.

Thus, in the objectives of conservation policy, the emphasis is on minimum standards in resource use rather than on the optimum use, on establishing base levels rather than on locating peaks, and on reducing institutional obstacles to resource development rather than on the "best" development. This approach does not pretend to establish criteria for maximizing social satisfaction. But it offers effective direction signals to conservation policy for pursuing the public interest turn by turn.

20

Natural-resources Research Problems

JOSEPH L. FISHER

ASSOCIATE DIRECTOR
RESOURCES FOR THE FUTURE, INC.

20.1 Introduction

The subject of this chapter is a large one; to present all its various parts in proper perspective is beyond the grasp of one person. Nevertheless, in this final chapter an effort will be made to draw together the various loose ends by directing attention to several persistent and commanding natural-resources research problems. These research problems, research themes might be a better term, do not pertain to any particular resource, or closely related cluster of resources, such as marine resources, soil resources, fossil fuels, or nuclear energy—all of which have been the subjects of previous chapters. Nor will these problems or themes relate exclusively to the physical, economic, or organizational aspects of resources. They will be developed so as to bring out the interrelatedness of resources—interrelatedness among the several disciplines of science, engineering, and social science; interrelatedness between basic and applied research; interrelatedness among research, policy, and action; and ultimately the interrelatedness between resources research and the general welfare. The point of view will be mainly that of the social scientist concerned with how people employ their talents, working time, and natural and technical resources to satisfy their wants as efficiently as possible over a period of time.

Now this is, as has been said, a large order. After a little time has been spent sketching in a background, consideration will be given to the sources of a number of difficulties, which undoubtedly have led to much misunderstanding among the various specialists concerned with resources and which have to be cleared up if research along the general lines indicated is to develop to maximum advantage. Finally, some eight broad research problems, or research themes, will be presented for consideration. It is

527

hoped that these problems or themes will provide a suitable conclusion to this book and will stimulate the reader to want to interrelate and pull together the various subjects previously treated.

Much has been said and written about the resource problem, and it has been given various formulations from Thomas Malthus to Harrison Brown. Essentially the problem is, in homely terms, how to get more and use less. Engineers and economists have long been preoccupied with this seemingly paradoxical problem. The object seems to be to produce more of the products and services from our natural resources, using up as little of them as possible in the process. In the fancier language of the economist, the object is to maximize the flow of utilities (private and social) from natural and other resources over time. Pursuit of this kind of objective has to be reconciled with the requirements of dynamic ecological adjustment among people, their natural resources, their technical and capital resources, and their culture. That is to say, the maximizing of a net flow of utilities must not be pursued in disregard for ecological balances and requirements; otherwise the pursuit can end only in disaster.

The importance of research as the principal means for gaining an understanding of the resource problem and its numerous complexities has been pointed out in preceding chapters. The suggestion is now made that the reader think of the variety of research on resources, not as related to a particular resource such as soil, minerals, or solar energy, but as research into basic data, analysis of that data, technical and economic application, and the formulation of policies and programs.

We seem always to be short of enough reliable basic data and enough skillful analysis of it. This is true of the Los Angeles smog problem. It is equally true regarding the obtaining of fresh water from saline sources, regarding food and other production through photosynthesis, and regarding the production and use of nuclear energy. The need for basic data and their analysis is no less important in the social sciences. We are lacking in basic information about attitudes of people toward their resources, for example. We know very little of a systematic and orderly character about how cities grow outward into surrounding rural areas. We perceive only dimly the play of factors and forces upon the businessmen and the public administrators who make decisions regarding the development and use of natural resources. We are in a bad muddle about how to appraise and compare the net economic returns or benefits of alternative developmental projects.

At the level of technical and economic application, most observers believe that we are relatively well off. Recent statistics gathered by the National Science Foundation indicate that, out of an annual expenditure of about 2 billion dollars by the Federal government for research and development of all kinds, 93 per cent is for what may loosely be called applied research and 7 per cent for basic research. Some 87 per cent of the total Federal research budget is in the physical-engineering field, between 11 and 12 per cent in the life sciences, that is, the biological, medical, and agricultural field. A scant 2 per cent remains for the social sciences, although happily this has been increasing. Both industrial research and government research concerned with military matters have been concentrated at the applied level. It is here that the pay-off is most rapid and visible in terms of profits to industry and military use to the government. There seems to be a growing awareness of the prime importance of substantial and continued effort at the basic research level, but it is an uphill struggle to shift the research emphasis in this direction to any marked extent and to arrange for the training of a larger number of basic researchers.

The final level of research which will be called to your attention is research into policies and programs. This involves the direct organization of data, analysis, and applied knowledge to the understanding and formulation of a public or business policy or program of action. The author's experience has been limited largely to government policy and program, especially in Federal government agencies close to the points of ultimate decision. The need here is especially acute for a disciplined examination of the real alternatives of policy and program so that the consequences of each may be presented accurately. The policy or program problem in such cases is usually set fairly definitely; the skillful policy researcher knows pretty well the political and other parameters of his problem and can proceed to the analysis of the facts and the alternatives. This kind of research is mainly valuable in so far as it furnishes guidance to decision makers. To be really useful for this purpose, it must be exceedingly scrupulous in the way it selects and employs data of a technical, economic, or sociological nature. Especially needed is research into the process by which policies and programs are formulated.

Of the variety of approaches to resource problems, three will be singled out. The first may be called an engineering-economics approach. It is concerned mainly with maximizing, in total and in per capita terms, the output of resource products and services for a given amount of input of raw materials, labor, and other factors of production. Typically, the engineer is concerned with this problem in physical terms within a given process, business firm, or industry. The economist is more concerned with a broader range of alternatives, looking at a number of processes, firms, or industries, or still more broadly at a whole national or world economy.

The second approach is the ecological one. Here the main concern is for living with or adapting to the balance of nature, or the balance between people on the one hand and the natural world on the other. The key word here is balance, whereas in the engineering-economics approach the key word is growth or development. Many of the so-called conservationists take this approach to resource problems. They are concerned lest, through aggressive technological development and economic expansion, we use up or destroy essential resources such as soil or forests.

A third approach, not necessarily contradictory to or exclusive of either of the first two, is taken by those whose aesthetic and ethical beliefs dominate their attitudes toward resources and their actions. This view may be associated with the idea of man as a custodian of resources, who looks upon them perhaps as God-given and feels an intense obligation to pass them on to future generations unmarred in some sense. Or, it may arise out of a system of values which is dominated by a devotion to individual freedom and the right to deal with resources in a highly exploitative manner. Or, it may arise out of a belief in or desire for the aesthetic satisfaction of dealing with resources and the natural environment in certain ways. The common point here is that the approach to resources is an ethical or aesthetic one and not an economic or ecological one and therefore cannot be understood through economic or ecological analysis alone, although it may underlie and influence the other approaches.

Among these approaches there are many interrelations; indeed, it may be contended that the three approaches characterized here can be harmonized. As the engineer looks more widely at the variety of resources which may be used to achieve a given product or service, he begins to approach the business of the economist, especially if he also considers a range of end products and services within which substitutions may be made depending upon relative prices. The economist, if he takes the long view and considers the possible effects of present economic activities upon the yield from a basic resource far into the future, begins to approach the ecologist who is concerned about long-range sustained relationships and balances among people, natural resources, and other elements in man's culture. The engineer, the economist, and the ecologist, as they begin to take more completely into account individual and social welfare in the broad sense, begin to approach resources problems more directly in an ethical way. So long as one is explicit about one's system of value, it is quite possible to reason scientifically within that framework as an engineer, economist, ecologist, or as a combination of all three. But the value systems themselves may be subjected to study in order to find out something about their internal consistency, their relevance to particular social situations, or their implications for the kind of research carried out.

20.2   Sources of Difficulty

The research difficulties considered here are not those concerned with discovering new ore bodies or winning metals from lower-grade ores. The thought is not of the difficulties in determining precisely the chemical composition of a smoggy atmosphere, nor of how to design a nuclear reactor or a solar cooker. Some sources of difficulty will be discussed at an entirely different level. It is because of these difficulties that the several approaches just discussed tend to remain separate and engineers, economists, ecologists, and others have such a hard time understanding one another.

The first source of difficulty lies in the different time horizons of the several specialists who study resource problems. A number of books on the grand theme of the relation between population and resources have been published in recent years in which the attempt is made to look ahead for several centuries and to try to visualize the population-resources equation at that time. To gain some perspective on such a distant period, one has to make assumptions about the rate of change in population, primarily the birth rate, and the rate of change in the availability of resources, primarily through new discoveries and new technology. Historical statistics in accurate form are simply not available upon which to rest projections running so far ahead. The state of things in A.D. 2400 is largely a matter of the imagination. However, this has not prevented speculation, nor should it. But it is a mistake, the author believes, for projections of the more immediate future to be derived from highly uncertain views of a very distant future. The record of long-term forecasts of population and technological advance has not been characterized by accuracy, beginning with Malthus and coming down to more recent estimates.

The forward look of most engineers and economists seldom extends more than 25 years. Frequently it is closer to 5 years or even less. With this kind of time horizon, it is hard to see any serious over-all population-resource problem for this country. The rate of productivity increase in industry and agriculture has been great during recent years, and there is no weight of evidence which would argue that it is likely to slacken in the years immediately ahead. Population has been increasing rather more rapidly during the last ten or fifteen years than previously, and very likely will continue to increase rapidly. Scarcities may appear here and there, and the cost of many resource materials may increase, but the consensus of forecasting is for a continued rise in the levels of living for many years to come. However, it would be a mistake, granting all this for the shorter-term future, to conclude that a century or several centuries from now the population-resources situation will necessarily be that favorable or the outlook that rosy. The difference in time horizon, therefore, continues to be a source of misunderstanding.

A second source of difficulty in approaching resources problems arises out of different space horizons. For example, if the Los Angeles area had no trade relations with the rest of California and the rest of the country, as well as foreign countries, its technical and economic development would have remained primitive. There would be no airplane industry here, the moving-picture industry would have amounted to very little, population would be sparse, orange groves would be few, and there would be no smog problem. Research relating to any one of these developments would have been carried out only to a limited extent and would bear little resemblance to what it is today. Now if the space horizon is extended to include California and the West generally, things appear in quite a different light. Export of petroleum products comes into the picture, the Central Valley development becomes important as a supplier of agricultural products, and the whole complex of technical, economic, and political problems involving use of the Colorado River becomes significant. If the space horizon is still further extended to include the rest of the country and the world, then the heavy migration of people to this area from the middle and eastern parts of the country comes into view, the growth and flowering of the moving-picture industry begin to make sense, the full force of the climatic attractiveness of this part of the country becomes apparent, and the amazingly rapid growth of the airplane and numerous other industries is made possible. Let us pass the question of what this area will look like in some distant period when its locational features have to be viewed against a technical and economic environment which includes other planets. Suffice to say here that this or any other area looks different depending upon the space horizon, and its research problems are likewise different.

A third source of difficulty involves the different institutional frameworks within which natural resources are studied and developed. Technology is included as a part of this framework; for example, the improvement of long-distance transmission of electric power and the long-distance transport of water through aqueducts are of tremendous importance in the kinds of power- and water-using industries and activities which have grown up in Southern California. A different legal framework, for example, in water law, would have altered the way in which the Colorado River has been developed and the degree and manner in which users in Southern California have been able to put that water to work. The technology and economics of agriculture are influenced by the prevailing allegiance to the family-size farm and the 160-acre legal limitation. The remarkably rapid growth in the natural-gas industry has been aided by the industrial and corporate structure which already had evolved in oil and by the large sources of funds which could be tapped to construct a network of pipelines. Political institutions and activities also have a bearing upon the way resources are developed. The formulation and the carrying out of resources research are done within these several institutional frameworks which themselves change over time.

A fourth set of difficulties caused by different analytical approaches to problems has already been mentioned. These frequently give rise to misunderstanding between engineers and economists, though this need not happen. For example, a good deal has been said about the difference between the engineer's and the economist's concept of waste. It is alleged that the engineer tries to arrange the handling and processing of materials so as to minimize the amounts which are not used, more or less regardless of the time, effort, and machinery that may be necessary to cut down on waste. On the other hand, it is alleged that the economist, in his effort to see that more is not spent in preventing waste than the value of the wasted material itself, completely overlooks numerous technical ways of handling waste which are economic. In the author's opinion we are presented here with two straw men; there is no real opposition between a good engineer and a good economist. A good engineer would be just as concerned as the economist that all costs and the full range of factor and product substitutions be taken into account. And the good economist, no less than the engineer, will try to absorb as much relevant information as he can about a variety of technical possibilities for using resources before he applies economic analysis to a resource problem. There is much to be said for the training of a new type of professional who is an engineer-economist; indeed, the demand for people with this kind of training is brisk at the present time.

Finally, a few words will be said about different value systems as a source of difficulty. So as not to go too far afield, the discussion will be limited to differences in formulating and conducting research which may arise out of a value system dominated by a belief in a completely free-enterprise economy and one dominated by a completely state-controlled economy. Actually, of course, the American economy is in between these unrealistic extremes, and always has been. Under the first value system, research directed at understanding the consequences to society of a particular resource use in industry might never be of much direct interest. Instead, research would be concerned more with improving the competitive position of a particular product or firm. Under the second value system, the competitive viability of various economic units would be of distinctly less importance, and one can imagine that research, technical, economic, or sociological, would be directed more toward solving those problems which stood in the way of a continuation of complete control of government. Those few stray individuals motivated by an intense curiosity about the way things and people behave in general might have a hard time of it. In our in-between situation, we find enormous difficulties in setting up our research problems so that the data gathered, the analysis undertaken, and the conclusions reached will, among other things, be instructive as to how business units, government agencies, and other operating units may carry on their activities with just that degree of competitiveness and cooperation that can be supported. The general point is that research is carried out by people who, consciously or unconsciously, have certain beliefs and values and that these usually include more than a simple devotion to finding and understanding facts in a completely objective manner. One runs the risk here of being misunderstood—but enough has been said to make the position plain. It is not meant that capricious or inconsistent beliefs and values should be allowed to take possession in research, rather, that research is more likely to flourish and make sense within a reasonably consistent and orderly value system, one of whose characteristics is a devotion to free inquiry and criticism.

20.3   Research Themes

Having mentioned resource-research problems, the general levels of research which are employed to understand these problems, the variety of approaches that may be made, and finally the sources of a number of difficulties which stand in the way of good understanding among various resource researchers, discussion will now be directed to a number of broad research themes, or lines of research, around which specific technical, economic, and other research may be organized. Emphasis will be given to the development, use, management, and welfare aspects—the social science aspects—and it will be suggested that these aspects frequently make a difference for technical as well as social science research.

Resources in Economic Growth and Stability.   Thus far in its national history this country has experienced remarkable growth. In the words of the Paley Commission:

In the first fifty years of the Twentieth Century, as population doubled and our total national output reached five times the 1900 level, the stream of raw materials increased in volume and value until, in 1950, it was worth two and one-half times as much (in constant dollars) as it was in 1900. In the mixture that made up this stream there were some significant differences, of which the most startling was that whereas our use of forest products actually declined 1 per cent in 1950 compared to 1900, our total consumption of minerals, including fuels, was six times 1900 totals. In 1950 we were taking from the earth two and one-half times more bituminous coal; three times more copper; three and one-half times more iron ore; four times more zinc; twenty-six times more natural gas; thirty times more crude oil; than in the year 1900.

Looking forward from 1950 to 1975, the Paley Commission estimated that demand for minerals as a whole might be 90 per cent higher, for timber products 10 per cent higher, for agricultural products of all kinds 40 per cent, for total energy 100 per cent, for electricity more than 300 per cent, for industrial water 170 per cent. Broadly speaking, a doubling of the gross national product in this 25-year span might require an increase in the total material stream of between 50 and 60 per cent. As services and more highly processed manufactured products become relatively larger parts of the total national production, the rate of increase in the consumption of the raw materials is expected to form a decreasing share of total production, at least for a number of decades ahead. Shifting demands and relative costs, operating within a framework of public policy, will continue to guide the substitution of one resource for another. That resources and raw materials are important to economic growth is obvious, just how important, surprisingly enough, has been perceived only dimly. For example, what difference would it have made to industrial development in this country if at each stage along the way electric power had cost half again as much or twice as much as it actually did? In what particular industry and geographic areas would a difference of any particular amount in the cost of electric power have meant the difference between growth and the absence of it?

The January 1956 Economic Report of the President notes that "we have reached the threshold of a $400 billion economy, and the recent advance has been accomplished without the specious aid of price inflation." It notes further that "the Employment Act has provided sound guidance and serviceable procedures for promoting economic growth and stability." Stability, you will note, is coupled with growth; it is the object of national policy to avoid highly erratic growth with its periods of high unemployment and intense social distress. Some of the resource segments of the economy have been among the most erratic. Prices of metals and other raw materials are subject to wide fluctuations. One of the keys to general business stability may be an understanding of the forces which make for instability in these segments and, based upon this, an understanding of the effectiveness of various private, business, and government policies to promote greater stability. We know all too little, for example, about the possibilities for scheduling resource investments in such a way as to contribute to the offsetting of cyclical ups and downs in business. One desirable policy would be to accelerate certain public and private resource investments whenever the general economy seemed to be taking a downward turn, but to refrain from accelerating those investments which, because they can be launched only a year or two later or because they are inappropriately located or for some other reason, simply will not be of any help. This calls for much better analysis of engineering information regarding the acceleration of construction of resource projects, the kinds of materials and equipment required, and other related information. It also requires the most delicate kind of economic analysis to determine the strategic time for initiating spending upon selected resource projects. We need public works projects and programs selected to meet the particular kind of business recession which may be in view. The vital role of resources and economic growth and stability makes it a grand theme for research, and one on which technical and economic experts may well combine their attention.

Motivation of Individuals and Groups in the Use of Resources. The social sciences, including psychology, are concerned with the understanding of why people behave as they do. When people prepare and consume food, use water for any one of its many purposes, take a drive in their automobile, or visit a public park, their behavior directly involves resources. What lies behind the obvious wastefulness with which people deal with resources? Is it habit, is it to be explained in terms of profit and loss, is it a matter of political impossibility of imposing and enforcing regulations, or does it stem directly from a profligate outlook upon life? Until more is known in the field of motivation of people in the use of resources, we shall not be able to appraise, select, design, and actually put into use in the most intelligent way the variety of resources projects and programs. One particularly enticing line of research here is to try to unravel the varied and complex motives for cooperation among individuals and groups in the resources field. When more is known about the motivations that impel groups and individuals to work together, or to fall at odds, on resource problems, the sum of cooperative efforts might be greater and more productive.

Another intriguing line of investigation is to find out whether people are satisfied that private and public decisions about the use of resources now and in the future conform to their own notion as to the importance of present consumption of resource services and products against deferred consumption of the larger amount. Money markets and rates of interest, as well as business and political administration through which resource decisions are made, may be quite faulty in the way they translate into decisions and actions the desires of individuals regarding present versus future use. But little progress can be made on this question until more is known about what people actually want from their resources and what moves them to act as they do. Those who call for an ethics of resource use or conservation probably will not get far until they know much more about individual motivation without which a workable ethics can hardly be constructed.

Formulation and Evaluation of Resource-development Projects and Programs. Much has been written and said on this topic; possibly it is the most bedeviling practical question now before engineers and social scientists, let alone policy makers and the general public, in the whole field of resources. How can we gain the clearest view of the performance and consequences of various resource projects and programs?

Part of the problem is a technical engineering one, that is, with specific information as to the results which are desired from the project or the program, to design efficient and minimum-cost structures and facilities. Another part of the problem is economic, that is, to guide the selection from among alternative structures, each one technically feasible but offering slightly different results, of that one which provides the greatest net economic benefit. More than that, economics has to guide the selection of a particular structure, for example, yielding a particular result, from numerous other ways in which that or an equivalent result might be obtained; and even beyond that, economics is the discipline through which the allocation of labor and resources is made to achieve a variegated but harmonious economic result upon the widest basis. But the business does not stop with the engineer and the economist. Many of the resource-development projects and programs are now heavily weighted with public interest; consequently, decisions as to project formulation and evaluation have to be reached through political and administrative processes. The whole procedure of project survey, authorization, budgeting, and appropriation, which is the process by means of which Federal projects are decided, illustrates the point. The business and public administrator and the political scientist have to be consulted.

The problem of project formulation and evaluation may be viewed to advantage in two parts. First is the gathering of relevant data and the careful technical and economic analysis of alternative project formulations. Much can be learned from a historical study of similar projects which were constructed in the past and have had a record of performance. Beyond this, projections have to be made into the future in order to gain some insight as to the benefits and costs which will flow from the project over the period of the life of the project. The second part consists of a careful examination of the conditions which have to be met if various individuals, groups, and agencies will be willing to participate in a project in the way that is desired. For example, in the case of the controversial Echo Park dam and reservoir project in the Upper Colorado River Basin, the sheer engineering and economics of it gave only a partial clue as to what actually would be done. Those who wanted to use the Echo Park site for the storage of water for irrigation and for the generation of electric power were pitted against those who were convinced matchless wilderness scenery would be flooded over. Those who favored downstream developments opposed those who would gain more from upstream development. Economy-minded persons criticized the subsidy involved in the project. Local, state, and national political pressures have to be given weight, economic interest groups must be reconciled, and recreational factors have to be taken into account along with electric power and irrigation. Engineering and economic feasibility is only the beginning.

Understanding and Improving the Administration of Resources.
An important part of a more complete understanding of why actions
regarding resources come out as they do involves much deeper research
into the administrative process. To return to the Echo Park, Dinosaur
National Monument example, for several years facts, analyses, political
pressures, and a host of other factors played upon the situation, and the
likely decision outcome swung first for and then against the project.
Should this project ultimately be constructed, and this now appears
unlikely, it is fairly certain that the same factors would play upon
numerous later decisions regarding the administration of the project.
What are the underlying principles of decision and of administrative
structure and process which hold in this and numerous other situations?
By what design of case studies might it be possible to uncover these
principles? What bearing would all this have upon the actual design of
projects and their location and other characteristics? Through an examination of such cases in the resource field, what can be learned about
the general problems of Federal, state, and local relations and about
business-government relations? These are significant questions around
which research can be organized.

Research on Education about Resources.   Although something
may be known in a rough and ready practical way about how actions
regarding resources may be influenced and guided intelligently, not too
much of a systematic nature is available. Until more is understood in
this field, it seems unlikely that the vast amount of wasteful controversy
and misunderstanding can be greatly reduced. This, of course, is especially
true in a democratic system where public decisions ultimately rest upon
the vote and private decisions rest upon the judgment of those business
leaders who are given general support by the nation as a whole. The manner
in which resources are managed and used will not improve except on the
basis of better-informed managers and users. Of particular importance
for research is the requirement of public understanding if support is to be
given to research budgets.   The relatively meager sums going into social
science research point rather clearly to a lack of appreciation of the possible gains from such research, at least as compared to technical research.

How may we come to understand better the education process itself as
it affects resources? This is more than a matter of old-line conservation
education which rests mainly upon the emotional or aesthetic appeal of
saving trees, soil, scenery, or something else for its own sake alone.
Public awareness of resource problems must rest upon knowledge as to
technological trends and possibilities, economic alternatives and costs,
and the possibilities for business and public action. Prompt and effective
translation of research results into a form which the general public can
understand and make the basis of its opinion and action is called for. All

too little is known about how to do this. Resources education would gain in sustained effectiveness if it could be based less upon emotional appeal and preconceptions about how to deal with resources and more upon the objective examination of problems, the careful collection of data, skillful analysis, and attractive presentation. Especially needed is resources education which extends across the boundaries of particular disciplines, the kind being done by the various authors in this book. Research itself can be directed toward finding out how to do this most effectively by careful designing of educational programs and activities and by equally careful evaluation of the results.

Determination of the General Welfare in Regard to Resources. Soil conservation, river-basin development, prices of natural gas, and forest cutting, among other resource matters, are now of general public concern. No longer are these matters left entirely to private initiative and action, although most government interventions are still predicated upon a belief in the superior performance of a fluid business enterprise system. The search for the public interest is a never-ending one. It is important that all resource specialists keep the problem in mind as they perform their various analytical and other services. For example, the engineer will want to examine the projects which he designs in terms of their effects upon the working conditions of those who must man them and upon the health and safety of those who live nearby or use the services and products. What weight shall we give to these aspects of his project? The economist is broadly concerned with the net returns which may be expected to flow from resource programs, both in terms of private business calculation of profit and in terms of social calculations of general benefits and costs. In this latter sense, the broad objective is to maximize the net social benefits of each project or program. Extremely difficult problems arise in the definition and classification of social benefits and costs and the way of valuing them in the future as compared to the present. Those benefits and costs which can reasonably well be stated in dollar terms can be estimated and compared. Numerous other benefits and costs of an indirect and intangible character, frequently of overriding importance, cannot be appraised with complete satisfaction in economic terms but have to be described in other ways and allowed to have an influence over final decisions. Research into these matters so far has been mainly the concern of social scientists. Economics has been referred to as welfare engineering; perhaps engineering might be thought of as technology economics. In any case, the size and impact of many resources activities today are such that their very conception is a matter of direct concern from the general-welfare viewpoint. Each specialist needs the richest understanding of the welfare aspects of his own trade that it is possible for him to have.

Resources Policies and Programs.   A few pages back in discussing the formulation and evaluation of resource-development projects, it was said that the foundation stones were careful analysis of the likely effects of projects, both historically and looking ahead, and an examination of the conditions which various individuals and groups would insist be met before the project could go ahead. On the basis of these two foundation stones, plans and programs for resources development can be erected. Now that multiple-purpose projects and integrated development have become the accepted means for handling resources, the correlated program which usually includes a number of separate projects in a definite time schedule has become of central importance. Research at all levels and in all disciplines has to be arranged to throw light upon the requirements for arriving at programs which are sound in engineering, economic, political, and other terms. The specialists, of course, will work at their particular callings, but the total effect has to be brought together through suitable cooperative processes of research, appraisal, and decision if good projects and programs are to emerge.

This planning and programing function takes place within the framework and under the guidance of private and government policies. For example, in the petroleum industry programs of discovery, exploration, investment, and actual mining take place on the basis of a set of Federal and state laws, administrative rulings, and business policies. Some of these are firmly set in the political and industrial structure, while others are open to considerable modification. Tax-depletion allowances have been allowed in that industry for some thirty or more years, and though leaders in the industry still protect and guard this privilege zealously, it has by now become so much a part of the industry that development programs and activities can be brought forward with considerable confidence that the basic policy is not likely to change.

In other instances, policies are in a very much more fluid state. For instance, the recent Report to the President of the Water Resources Policy Committee recommends that Federal agencies be required, in presenting benefit-cost ratios regarding particular projects, to separate the direct from the indirect benefits and costs and to show only the direct effects in the calculated ratio. This appears to be a somewhat technical economic and accounting matter. Actually it is of utmost importance since it would require the Corps of Engineers, the Bureau of Reclamation, the Forest Service, and other Federal agencies to present their appraisal of projects in such a way that a congressman or anyone else can see plainly the extent to which a project justification rests upon the more indirect and immeasurable kinds of benefits, such as general regional development.

Insufficient research has been mobilized to the understanding of resource policies. What is needed is the most painstaking kind of historical examination of policies relating to energy, minerals, water, and so on so that we may gain an understanding of how we got where we are in these policies. What are the present policies, what are their historical roots, have they performed the way they were intended to perform, what have been their effects, and in what ways are they inconsistent with one another? In an effort to figure out what policies should be looking ahead, it is all too characteristic that researchers fail to look backward to find the lessons in history. Considering the importance of the resource industries in this country, it is surprising that so little is available by way of careful historical research into the origins and effects of policies.

Resources and Regional Development. This chapter will be brought to a close by discussing briefly the importance of resources research for regional development. There is a natural affinity between natural resources and geographical areas. Although their products and services at one or more stages removed may be transported great distances, natural resources themselves tend to be fixed in terms of space location. As the country has grown in population, industry, and means of transportation, the groupings of resources in relatively large regions have emerged as an increasingly significant matter for research, planning, and development. The engineering of resources is now on a large, frequently regional scale, for example, in the Central Valley, the Upper Colorado River Valley, the oil fields of the Southwest, and the land drainage areas in the Mississippi Delta. The economics of resources development likewise have to be considered on a regional basis, and there is intense interest, for example, in the cost of additional water in central Arizona and the basin-wide account for the Columbia River development in the Pacific Northwest. Administrative forms and arrangements have been created which reflect the regional grouping of resources. Interstate compacts have been worked out for the Colorado River Basin, soil-conservation districts now cover much of the country, cooperative sustained-yield forest areas have been worked out in a few instances, and in the Tennessee River Basin a decentralized regional authority created by Federal legislation has been operating for more than twenty years. And in minerals exploration a revolution is going on with the use of new techniques and instruments, many of them air-borne, forcing us to think of this subject in terms of minerals reconnaissance over large areas. The articulation of these matters so that they make sense from a regional standpoint is of increasing concern, and beyond this the problems of interregional flows and relationships, both technical and economic, have to be considered.

Each of the research themes which has been discussed in this chapter, mainly in terms of the national economy or in terms of particular projects and programs, has its regional counterpart. Thus, the role of resources in the economic growth and stability of regions is a subject upon which we have very little data, not much analysis, and therefore meager understanding. The motivation of individuals and groups in the use of resources may vary significantly from region to region. Easterners have little appreciation for the problems of irrigation farming or of disposal and use of public lands, and this no doubt makes their political and economic behavior significantly different from that of Westerners. And so with each of the other research themes here presented.

Looking at resources development from a regional point of view offers definite advantages which are largely lost if resources are considered only in nationwide terms or in particular project and program terms. People live in particular areas and tend to identify themselves with the potentialities and problems of that area. Resource development comes alive in regional terms and does not get lost or submerged in massive national trends which are revealed chiefly in statistical terms. Confining attention to particular projects is unsatisfactory since most people are aware of and affected by a variety of resources projects and programs which impinge upon them and the place where they live. The regional approach has a further advantage in that interrelations can be studied to good advantage on this basis and given direct reflection in the policies and programs which are worked out. It may be hoped that interdisciplinary research will come to a fruition in studying resources and regional development and will be linked more directly to the process of improving policies, programs, and administration. It is hard to find another field in which such prospects are so promising and so exciting.

Bibliography

Many of the following references were used in the preparation of *Natural Resources*, while others are included as supplemental sources of information.

Allen, Shirley W.: *Conserving Natural Resources*, 2d ed., McGraw-Hill Book Company, Inc., New York, 1959.

Allen, Durward L.: *Our Wildlife Legacy*, Funk & Wagnalls Company, New York, 1954.

Ayres, Eugene, and Charles A. Scarlott: *Energy Sources—The Wealth of the World*, McGraw-Hill Book Company, Inc., New York, 1952.

Brown, F. (ed.): *Statistical Yearbook of World Power Conference, No. 7*, Annual Statistics for 1950–1952, 1953, Lund Humphries & Co., Ltd., London, 1954.

Brown, Harrison: *The Challenge of Man's Future*, The Viking Press, Inc., New York, 1954.

———, James Bonner, and John Weir: *The Next Hundred Years*, The Viking Press, Inc., New York, 1957.

Callison, Charles H. (ed.): *America's Natural Resources*, The Ronald Press Company, New York, 1957.

Ciriacy-Wantrup, S. V.: *Resource Conservation: Economics and Policies*, University of California Press, Berkeley, Calif., 1952.

Clawson, Marion: *Statistics on Outdoor Recreation*, Resources for the Future, Inc., Washington, D.C., 1958.

Colman, E. A.: *Vegetation and Watershed Management*, The Ronald Press Company, New York, 1953.

Conservation Foundation: *Resource Training for Business, Industry, Government*, New York, 1958.

Coyle, David Cushman: *Conservation: An American Story of Conflict and Accomplishment*, Rutgers University Press, New Brunswick, N.J., 1957.

Dana, Samuel Trask, and Myron Krueger: *California Lands, Ownership, Use, and Management*, American Forestry Association, Washington, D.C., 1958.

Dasmann, Raymond F.: *Environmental Conservation*, John Wiley & Sons, Inc., New York, 1959.

Dewhurst, J. Frederic, and Associates: *America's Needs and Resources: A New Survey*, The Twentieth Century Fund, Inc., New York, 1955.

Franck, James, and Walter E. Loomis (eds.): *Photosynthesis in Plants*, Iowa State College Press, Ames, Iowa, 1949.

543

Geneva Presentation Volumes, presented by the United States at the Second International Conference on the Peaceful Uses of Atomic Energy, Geneva, September, 1958, Addison-Wesley Publishing Company, Reading, Mass., 1958.

Graham, Edward H.: *Natural Principles of Land Use*, Oxford University Press, New York, 1944.

Gulhati, N. D.: *Irrigation in the World: A Global Review*, International Commission on Irrigation and Drainage, New Delhi, India, 1955.

Gustafson, A. F., C. H. Guise, W. J. Hamilton, Jr., and H. Ries: *Conservation in the United States*, 3d ed., Comstock Publishing Associates, Inc., Ithaca, N.Y.

Haden-Guest, Stephen, John K. Wright, and Eileen M. Teclaff (eds.): *A World Geography of Forest Resources*, The Ronald Press Company, New York, 1956.

Hatt, Paul K. (ed.): *World Population and Future Resources*, American Book Company, New York, 1952.

Higbee, Edward: *American Agriculture, Geography, Resources, Conservation*, John Wiley & Sons, Inc., New York, 1958.

Huxley, Julian: "Man's Challenge: The Use of the Earth," *Horizon*, pp. 48–55, September, 1958.

Jarrett, Henry (ed.): *Perspectives on Conservation*, Johns Hopkins Press, Baltimore, 1958.

Jeffreys, H.: *The Earth: Its Origin, History and Physical Condition*, 3d ed., Cambridge University Press, New York, 1952.

Kellogg, Charles E.: *The Soils That Support Us*, The Macmillan Company, New York, 1941.

Kimble, George H. T., and Dorothy Good (eds.): *Geography of the Northland*, The American Geographical Society and John Wiley & Sons, Inc., New York, 1955.

Krutilla, John V., and Otto Eckstein: *Multiple Purpose River Development*, Johns Hopkins Press, Baltimore, 1958.

Leopold, Aldo: *Sand County Almanac and Sketches Here and There*, Oxford University Press, New York, 1949 (includes sections on conservation, wildlife, wilderness, and a land ethic).

Malin, James C.: *The Grassland of North America*, J. C. Malin, Lawrence, Kansas, 1947.

Meinzer, Oscar E. (ed.): *Hydrology*, McGraw-Hill Book Company, Inc., New York, 1942 (third impression, Dover Publications, New York, 1949).

Ordway, Samuel H.: *Resources and the American Dream*, The Ronald Press Company, New York, 1953.

———: *Prosperity beyond Tomorrow*, The Ronald Press Company, New York, 1955.

Osborn, Fairfield: *The Limits of the Earth*, Little, Brown & Company, Boston, 1953.

Parson, Ruben L.: *Conserving American Resources*, Prentice-Hall, Inc., Englewood Cliffs, N.J., 1956.

Petterssen, Sverre: *Weather Analysis and Forecasting*, 2d ed., vols. 1, 2, McGraw-Hill Book Company, Inc., New York, 1956.

Political and Economic Planning, *World Population and Resources*, George Allen & Unwin, Ltd., London, 1955.

President's Materials Policy Commission, William S. Paley, Chairman: *Resources for Freedom*, vols. I-V, Government Printing Office, Washington, D.C., 1952.

President's Water Resources Policy Commission: *A Water Policy for the American People*, vols. 1–3, Government Printing Office, Washington, D.C., 1950.

Putnam, Palmer C.: *Energy in the Future*, D. Van Nostrand Company, Inc., Princeton, N.J., 1953.

Rabinowitch, Eugene I.: *Photosynthesis and Related Processes*, Interscience Publishers, Inc., New York, vol. I, 1945; vol. II, part 1, 1951; vol. II, part 2, 1956.

Resources for the Future, Inc.: *The Nation Looks at Its Resources*, Report of the Mid-Century Conference on Resources for the Future, Dec. 2–4, 1953, Washington, D.C., 1954.

Saunderson, Mart H.: *Western Land and Water Use*, University of Oklahoma Press, Norman, Okla., 1950.

Schulz, William: *Conservation Law and Administration*, The Ronald Press Company, New York, 1953.

Sears, Paul B.: *Deserts on the March*, rev. ed., University of Oklahoma Press, Norman, Okla., 1947.

————: "Science and Natural Resources," *American Scientist*, vol. 44, pp. 341–346, October, 1956.

Smith, Guy-Harold (ed.): *Conservation of Natural Resources*, 2d ed., John Wiley & Sons, Inc., New York, 1958.

Stallings, J. H.: *Soil Conservation*, Prentice-Hall, Inc., Englewood Cliffs, N.J., 1957.

Stanford Research Institute: *Proceedings of the World Symposium on Applied Solar Energy*, Phoenix, Arizona, Nov. 1–5, 1955, Menlo Park, Calif., 1956.

Terrien, J., G. Truffaut, and J. Carles: *Light, Vegetation, and Chlorophyll*, Hutchinson & Co. (Publishers), Ltd., London, 1957.

Thomas, Harold E.: *The Conservation of Ground Water*, McGraw-Hill Book Company, Inc., New York, 1951.

Thomas, William L. (ed.): *Man's Role in Changing the Face of the Earth*, University of Chicago Press, Chicago, 1956.

Trewartha, Glenn T.: *An Introduction to Climate*, McGraw-Hill Book Company, Inc., New York, 1954.

United Nations: *Proceedings of the International Conference on the Peaceful Uses of Atomic Energy*, Geneva, Aug. 8–20, 1955, vols. 1–16, New York, 1956.

United Nations Department of Economic Affairs: *Proceedings of the United Nations Scientific Conference on the Conservation and Utilization of Resources*, Aug. 17–Sept. 6, 1949, vols. I–VIII, New York, 1950.

United Nations Food and Agriculture Organization: *The State of Food and Agriculture: Review of a Decade and Outlook*, Rome, 1955.

United Nations Statistical Office: *Statistical Yearbook*, New York, Yearly.

U.S. Department of Agriculture: *Climate and Man*, 1941 Yearbook of Agriculture, Washington, D.C., 1941.

————: *Trees:* 1949 Yearbook of Agriculture, Washington, D.C., 1949.

————: *Water*, 1955 Yearbook of Agriculture, Washington, D.C., 1955.

————: *Soil*, 1957 Yearbook of Agriculture, Washington, D.C., 1957.

————: *Land*, 1958 Yearbook of Agriculture, Washington, D.C., 1958

U.S. Forest Service: *Timber Resource Review*, Washington, D.C., 1955.

———: *Timber Resources for America's Future*, Washington, D.C., 1958.

U.S. House of Representatives, Interior and Insular Affairs Committee, *The Physical and Economic Foundation of Natural Resources*, vols. I–IV, Government Printing Office, Washington, D.C., 1952.

Van Dersal, William: *The American Land: Its History and Uses*, Oxford University Press, New York, 1946.

Vogt, William: *Road to Survival*, William Sloane Associates, New York, 1948.

Walford, Lionel A.: *Living Resources of the Sea*, The Ronald Press Company, New York, 1958.

Whitaker, J. Russell, and Edward A. Ackerman: *American Resources*, Harcourt, Brace and Company, Inc., New York, 1951.

White, Gilbert F. (ed.): *The Future of Arid Lands*, American Association for the Advancement of Science, Washington, D.C., 1956.

Woytinsky, W. S., and E. S. Woytinsky: *World Population and Production*, The Twentieth Century Fund, Inc., New York, 1953.

Zimmerman, Erich W.: *World Resources and Industries*, Harper & Brothers, New York, 1951.

Name Index

547

Subject Index

551